ENCYCLOPEDIA
SCIENCE
SUPPLEMENT
A Modern Science Anthology for the Family

1980

ISBN 0-7172-1510-5
Library of Congress Catalog Card Number: 64-7603

CONTENTS

ASTRONOMY & SPACE SCIENCE

BEHAVIORAL SCIENCES

BIOLOGY

COMPUTERS & MATHEMATICS

EARTH SCIENCE

ENERGY

THE ENVIRONMENT

HEALTH & DISEASE

MAN & HIS WORLD

PHYSICAL SCIENCES

TECHNOLOGY

WILDLIFE

STAFF

EDITORIAL

HERBERT KONDO	Editor-in-Chief
LANSING WAGNER	Editor
BARBARA TCHABOVSKY	Editor
SUE ANN HAFFNER	Production Editor
JACQUELINE ROZSA	Copy Editor
SUZANNE SCHUTZ	Proofreader
JILL SCHULER	Indexer
SUSAN DEROMEDI	Assistant Indexer

ART

PATRICIA BYERS	Art Director
FRANK H. SENYK	Art Consultant
DEDE GRACE	Photo Researcher
PATRICIA ZIMMERMAN	Photo Researcher

GROLIER INCORPORATED

HOWARD B. GRAHAM	Senior Vice-President—Publishing
WALLACE S. MURRAY	Vice-President—Editorial Director

CONTRIBUTORS

LAWRENCE K. ALTMAN, M.D., *Medical reporter, The New York Times*
REVIEW OF THE YEAR: HEALTH & DISEASE

ISAAC ASIMOV, *Associate Professor of Biochemistry, Boston University School of Medicine; well-known science writer, author of more than 200 books*
IS ANYBODY OUT THERE?

ROMAINE BAMFORD, *Free-lance writer*
VOICE ANALYZERS
INTERFERON

H. ARTHUR BANKOFF, *Assistant Professor of Anthropology, Brooklyn College*
co-author REVIEW OF THE YEAR:
MAN & HIS WORLD

DOROTHY BEHLEN, *Free-lance writer*
HOMEMADE HEAT

HAL BOWSER, *Senior Editor, Saturday Review; free-lance writer and amateur microscopist*
MICROSCOPY AS A HOBBY

JANE E. BRODY, *Free-lance writer*
FOODS THAT BLOCK CANCER
OBESITY

MICHAEL H. BROWN, *Reporter for The Niagara Falls Gazette*
LOVE CANAL, U.S.A.

PETER D. CAPEN, *Free-lance writer and underwater photographer*
WHY ARE FISH SO COLORFUL?

MARY CARPENTER, *Assistant Editor, Science Digest*
EARTHWATCH

LOUIS S. CLAPPER, *Director of Conservation, National Wildlife Federation*
REVIEW OF THE YEAR: THE ENVIRONMENT

CONSTANCE TABER COLBY, *Free-lance writer; author of "Skunk in the House"*
SKUNKS

ROBERT C. COWEN, *Natural Science Editor, CHRISTIAN SCIENCE MONITOR*
HURRICANES

RICHARD DEGRAAF, *Research Wildlife Biologist, U.S. Forest Service*
THE ECOLOGY OF DEAD TREES

EDWARD EDELSON, *Free-lance writer*
FUSION RESEARCH

CLAUDE A. FRAZIER, M.D., *Physician; author of "Insect Allergy"*
BUGS THAT BITE AND STING

JAMES GANNON, *Free-lance writer and television news producer*
ACID RAIN UPDATE

ROBERT GORMAN, *Free-lance writer*
MAINTENANCE-FREE BATTERIES

TIMOTHY GREEN, *Free-lance writer*
TRYING THE IRON AGE

JOEL GREENBERG, *Behavioral Sciences Editor, Science News*
SLEEP AND THE ELDERLY
REVIEW OF THE YEAR: BEHAVIORAL SCIENCES

KATHERINE HARAMUNDANIS, *Research Associate, Smithsonian Astrophysical Observatory; co-author, "Introduction to Astronomy"*
REVIEW OF THE YEAR: ASTRONOMY

EARL T. HAYES, *Energy consultant; formerly Chief Scientist, U.S. Bureau of Mines*
THE ENERGY PICTURE: 1985 TO 2000

HUGH F. HENRY, *Head, Department of Physics, DePauw University*
co-author REVIEW OF THE YEAR: PHYSICAL SCIENCES

WILLIAM H. JORDAN, JR., *Entomologist; author of "Windowsill Ecology"*
BIOLOGICAL CONTROL OF INSECTS

CAROL KAHN, *Free-lance science writer*
SLOW VIRUSES

RICHARD A. KERR, *Research News, Science*
TSUNAMI !

CHARLES T. KOWAL, *Associate Scientist, California Institute of Technology; discoverer of many objects in skies*
A SURPRISE IN THE SOLAR SYSTEM

H. E. LANDSBERG, *Former Director of Environmental Data Service, U.S. National Oceanic and Atmospheric Administration; Professor Emeritus, Department of Meteorology, University of Maryland*
YOU AND THE WEATHER

SARAH LAZAROFF, *Free-lance science writer*
ALBERT EINSTEIN

BENEDICT A. LEERBURGER, *Free-lance science writer*
THE ACCIDENT AT THREE MILE ISLAND

BARBARA LOBRON, *Former editor, Camera 35; free-lance photographer*
THE SCIENCE OF PHOTOGRAPHY

MYRON S. MALKIN, *Director of Space Shuttle Program, NASA*
THE SPACE SHUTTLE

WILLIAM H. MATTHEWS III, *Regent's Professor of Geology, Lamar University; Director of Education, American Geological Institute*
REVIEW OF THE YEAR: EARTH SCIENCES

BARBARA MCDOWELL, *Free-lance writer*
THE 1978 NOBEL PRIZES IN PHYSICS AND CHEMISTRY

MARTIN MCLAUGHLIN, *Senior Fellow, Overseas Development Council*
co-author REVIEW OF THE YEAR: MAN & HIS WORLD

JULIE ANN MILLER, *Life Sciences Editor, Science News*
REVIEW OF THE YEAR: BIOLOGY

NORMAN MYERS, *Roving editor, International Wildlife*
WILDLIFE IN CHINA

ROBERTA NAVICKIS, *Free-lance writer*
BIOMASS

BARRY NEWMAN, *Staff reporter, The Wall Street Journal*
THE GREENING OF JAVA

KENNETH S. NORRIS, *Author of "The Porpoise Watcher"; Professor of Natural History, University of California at Santa Cruz; Chairman of Environmental Studies Board at University of California at Santa Cruz*
co-author THE TUNA/PORPOISE PROBLEM

DAMON OLSZOWY, *New York Botanical Gardens, Bronx, New York*
CLONING

SHIRLEY A. POMPONI, *Research Associate, University of Miami's Rosentiel School of Marine and Atmospheric Science*
SPONGES

KAREN PRYOR, *Biologist and former porpoise trainer; author of "Lads Before the World"; researcher, National Marine Fisheries Service*
co-author THE TUNA/PORPOISE PROBLEM

JANET RALOFF, *Policy/Technology Editor, Science News*
REVIEW OF THE YEAR: ENERGY

COVER: Stained sponge spicules. Spiny calcium and silicate crystals are found throughout the skeleton of sponges. They present a great variety of shape, and they vary in size from 0.01 millimeter to 40 centimeters. The ones shown here are the microscopic variety. Large spicules are the chief supporting framework of the sponge. The classification of sponges has been based chiefly on the composition and shape of spicules.

Top: sun in eclipse on February 26, 1979, the last solar eclipse to be seen in the 20th century in mainland North America. Bottom: moving from left to right, exposures were made every seven minutes.

Wide World

Wide World

ASTRONOMY & SPACE SCIENCE

ASTRONOMY
AND SPACE SCIENCE
REVIEW OF THE YEAR

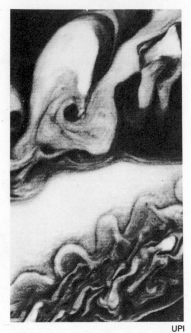

UPI

This photo of a section of Jupiter was taken by Voyager 1, which was 4,800,000 kilometers away from the planet at the time. It shows part of the Great Red Spot in the center. The smallest details are about 88 kilometers across.

The thin sulfur cloud around Jupiter and its moon Io appears to come from Io. The sulfur emission is concentrated in a huge half-doughnut more than 1,000,000,-000 kilometers across in orbit around Jupiter itself. (R_J stands for radius of Jupiter.)

C. Pilcher/drawn by V. Zinser

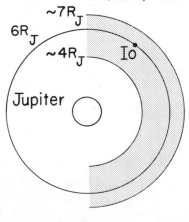

The Solar System. A four-day magnetic storm on the sun culminated on April 28, 1978 with an extraordinarily intense solar flare, some 350 times more intense than usual flares. Both the flare and the magnetic storm caused serious disruption of radio communications on earth.

The laser reflectors and seismographs left on the moon by the Apollo astronauts are being put to use. French scientists Odile Calame and J. Derral Mulholland of the Center for Geodynamical and Astronomical Studies and Research in Grasse, France, used lasers to study resonances in the moon's motion and now think that they know what caused an explosion seen on the moon some eight hundred years ago. The explosion, they believe, was caused by an impact that created the crater Giordano Bruno and whose effects can still be seen today. ■ Meanwhile Gary V. Latham of the University of Texas Marine Science Institute in Galveston, Texas, has studied seismic data from the moon and reports that the core of the moon is probably 170 to 360 kilometers in diameter. ■ Seismographs have also recorded almost 2,000 meteoritic impacts on the moon, heavily concentrated in and around the month of May, and a large number of both deep and shallow moonquakes.

There were also important findings about the planets during 1978. Some of the most surprising were revealed by Soviet and U.S. probes to Venus and are discussed in the article "The Venus Probe," which begins on page 6.

Space probes also added to our knowledge of Mars and Jupiter. Using photographs from Voyager 1, Laurence A. Soderblom of the Geological Survey identified blue wisps along faults in Io's crust. The wisps may be a kind of blue snow condensed from escaping hot gases. ■ An analysis of Pioneer photographs has revealed more details about four of Jupiter's moons. Io has a radius of 1,840 kilometers and a density of 3.41 grams per cubic centimeter; Europa, a radius of 1,552 kilometers and a density of 3.06 grams per cubic centimeter; Ganymede, a radius of 2,650 kilometers and a density of 1.90 grams per cubic centimeter; and Callistro, a radius of 2,420 kilometers and a density of 1.81 grams per cubic centimeter. ■ News about Jupiter itself was revealed when Carl Pilcher and Jeff Morgan of the University of Hawaii mapped the ionized sulfur surrounding Jupiter and found that it is concentrated along the Jovian magnetic equator and extends out to a distance equal to eight times the radius of Jupiter. Io, the Jovian satellite that occasionally gives off radio emissions, travels right through the sulfur cloud.

Uranus may have up to nine rings——so says Eric Persson of the Hale Observatories, adding to the surprising 1977 discovery that Uranus, like Saturn, is a ringed planet. ■ One of the most exciting discoveries of the year was the accidental discovery of a possible moon for Pluto. Pluto is so distant that photos of it are difficult to interpret, but James W. Christy of the U.S. Naval Observatory in Washington, D.C. reported the discovery of a satellite about 20,000 kilometers away from the planet. He established that the moon revolves around Pluto once every 6 days, 9 hours, and 17 minutes. This period is the same as the time it takes Pluto to rotate on its axis, so that the satellite is always over the same point on the surface of Pluto. This report renewed speculation about Pluto itself, some of which is discussed in the article "Pluto" which starts on page 27.

Another moon was also reported——this one for an asteroid. Edward Bowell of the Lowell Observatory in Arizona reported that the small asteroid 532 Herculina may be accompanied by a small moon. ■ Observations of the passage of the asteroid Pallas as it cut off light from the star SAO 85009 revealed that Pallas, the second largest known asteroid, is somewhat larger than previously thought and is shaped like a squashed football.

Our Galaxy——the Milky Way. Donald B. Hall and colleagues at Kitt Peak National Observatory have found a new-born star in the Orion nebula in our galaxy. They suggest that the object is only 1,000 to 2,000 years old.

A perplexing X-ray source has been observed by T. Matilsky and J. La Sala of Rutgers University and J. Jessen of the Massachusetts Institute of Technology. In the usual model of X-ray sources, two stellar objects rotate around each other. One, an ordinary star, gives off matter that forms an X-ray emitting disk around the other object, a very dense neutron star or black hole. In this model, the X-ray source is eclipsed every 3.5 days as the two objects orbit each other——and herein lies the problem with the new discovery. The X-ray source fluctuates every 97 minutes and thus does not fit the model.

The Universe. Two possible black holes have been reported. Using data obtained from radio telescopes in Massachusetts, West Virginia, and California, A. C. S. Redhead, M. H. Cohen, and R. D. Blandford of the California Institute of Technology suggest that the nucleus of radio galaxy NGC 6251 is a black hole with a mass about 100 times that of the sun. ■ Peter J. Young and colleagues at the Hale Observatories, Jet Propulsion Laboratory, Kitt Peak National Observatory, and the University of Victoria in British Columbia, Canada, also suggest that the nucleus of galaxy M87 (NGC 4486) may be a black hole with a mass 3,000,000,000 times that of the sun.

Quasars have long presented a problem to astronomers. Are they close, astronomically speaking, or far away? Allan Stockton of the University of Hawaii has now provided strong evidence that they are as distant as galaxies. If this is true, astronomers studying quasar characteristics conclude that they must be traveling at near the speed of light.

And finally, the age-old question: is the universe closed or open? An analysis, by Melville P. Ulmer and colleagues at Northwestern University and at the U.S. Naval Research Laboratory, of X-ray observations by the HEAO-1 satellite, reveal gas in the region between galaxy clusters Abell 399 and 401. If gas such as this occurs between all galaxies, then there is enough mass in the universe for it to be closed——expanding now, but falling back later.

Katherine Haramundanis

Terry Matilsky

The SAS-1 Explorer was sent into orbit to detect X rays from celestial objects. (Model of satellite shown here.)

This 47-meter telescope listens to signals from deep space. It is the largest equatorially mounted radio telescope in the world and is located at the National Radio Astronomy Observatory in Green Bank, West Virginia.

NSF Photo

Space Sciences.

Space Sciences. In 1978 and early 1979 there were important advances in both manned and unmanned space flight. The Soviet Union led the way in manned space flights, setting new records for human endurance in the weightlessness of earth orbital flight, while the United States had a somewhat frustrating period, preparing for its next venture in manned space flight, the space shuttle. The United States had spectacular success with its unmanned space probes to Venus and Jupiter, however. The Soviet Union also met success with its probe to Venus.

Manned space flight. All of the Soviet-manned space activity centered on its 19-ton space station, Salyut 6, which was rocketed into orbit on September 29, 1977. The crew of Soyuz 26, Yuri Romanenko and Georgi M. Grechko, were launched December 1, 1977 and occupied the Salyut 6 station until they returned to earth on March 16, 1978, setting a then-record time of 96 days in space. During their stay in Salyut, they were joined by two other crews for brief periods and were also resupplied by an unmanned Soviet Progress spacecraft. The Soyuz 27 crew, Vladimir Ozhanibekov and Oleg Makarov, spent six days there in January 1978. The Soyuz 28 crew, Aleksei A. Gubarov and Vladimir Remek, spent eight days in Salyut in March. Remek, a Czech, was the first man in space from a country other than the United States or the Soviet Union.

The crew of Soviet *Soyuz-29* spaceship: Commander Vladimir Kovalenok (seated) with Flight Engineer Alexander Ivanchenkov. They set a new time-in-space record of 140 days.

On June 15, 1978 Soyuz 29 went into orbit carrying Vladimir Kovalenek and Alexander Ivanchenkov. They linked up with the Salyut and stayed in space until November 2—setting a new record of 140 days. (The longest U.S. endurance record is 84 days, set by a Skylab crew in 1974.) As in the previous long-duration flight, the Soyuz 29 cosmonauts were visited by other crews. There was Soyuz 30: Pyetr Klimuk and Miroslaw Hermaszewski, a Polish cosmonaut, for eight days in July. And there was Soyuz 31: Bykovskiy and the first East German cosmonaut, Jahn, for eight days in August and September. On August 2, while the Soyuz 29 cosmonauts were in the Salyut space station, the Soviet Union surpassed the United States as the most experienced nation in manned space flight. The U.S. record had been 937 astronaut days in space.

The Skylab Space Station has been off its orbit for many months, and much effort has been spent in attempting to bring it back to earth as safely as possible. This is an overhead view taken from the Skylab Command and Service Module.

The United States did not have any manned space-flights during 1978—it hasn't had any since 1975—but expects to be sending astronauts back into space in late 1979 or 1980. These astronauts will be testing the new space shuttle, a vehicle that will be launched like a rocket, flown in orbit like a spacecraft, and steered back to a runway landing like a glider. The first of these reusable craft, named Columbia, was delivered to the U.S. manned-space launch center at Cape Canaveral, Florida, in March 1979. A succession of problems with the main engines and the thermal protection system have, however, cast doubt on when the first orbital test flight will take place.

Planetary probes. The U.S. spacecraft Pioneer Venus 1 and 2 arrived in the vicinity of Venus in early December 1978. Designed to study the atmosphere and weather of Venus, they radar-mapped the planet and took hundreds of photographs and scientific measurements. ■ The Soviet spacecraft Venera 11 and 12 reached Venus later in December. Venera 12 deployed a probe that descended to the surface of Venus on December 19. Venera 11 did likewise on December 25. The probes survived the planet's intense heat to transmit data for 110 minutes and 95 minutes, respectively. There were no pictures, however—whether by design or by failure is not known. For a discussion of the findings about Venus, see the article "The Venus Probe" on page 6.

In early March 1979 the U.S. craft Voyager 1 had a rendezvous with Jupiter and several of its satellites. The 815-kilogram craft returned hundreds of television photographs of the planet's turbulent atmosphere and made several surprising discoveries. In the biggest surprise, Io, one of Jupiter's moons, was found to be alive and churning with volcanic activity. Voyager also returned the first detailed photographs of the other major Jovian moons—Europa, Ganymede, and Callistro. For a summary of the Jupiter findings, see the article "Jupiter" on page 8.

Other unmanned spacecraft. In addition to the space probes to Venus and Jupiter, both the United States and the Soviet Union also launched many other unmanned spacecraft.

The Soviet Union had a total of 88 launchings in 1978. One of these was Cosmos 1,000, launched April 1, 1978 to monitor Soviet ship movements worldwide. The Cosmos series, begun in 1962, is not a single type of spacecraft but a designation for nearly every unmanned satellite, military and civilian, sent into orbit by the Soviets. ■ Cosmos 954, an ocean reconnaissance vehicle with a nuclear reactor, disintegrated and fell over northern Canada in February 1978. No one is known to have been hurt.

The United States had 32 unmanned launchings, both civilian and military, during the year. The International Sun-Earth Explorer 3 was launched in August 1978 and placed into a giant "halo orbit" above earth, where it circles a libration point, a point in space where the opposing gravitational forces of two large bodies—the sun and the earth, in this case—are exactly counterbalanced. The spacecraft is monitoring sun spots, solar flares, and the solar wind before the effects of these solar phenomena can reach earth and have a possible effect on earth weather and communications.

On November 13, 1978, High-Energy-Astronomy Observatory 2, also known as the Einstein Observatory, was launched to study some of the most intriguing mysteries of the universe—pulsars, quasars, exploding galaxies, and black holes. The observatory has detected the brightest, most distant, and most powerful objects yet observed to emit X rays: quasars estimated to be more than 10,000,000,000 light years from earth. (A light year is a measure of distance used in astronomy. It is the distance that light travels in one year, or approximately 9,600,000,000,000 kilometers.)

Spacecraft to study earth from an orbital perspective were also launched. On March 5, 1978 Landsat 3 was launched to study and map earth resources with remote sensors and a two-camera vidicon system. ■ Seasat, launched June 24, 1978, to demonstrate remote-sensing techniques for global monitoring of the oceans, operated successfully for 105 days and then suddenly went dead, victim of a massive short circuit. It, nevertheless, sent back valuable data on ocean surface winds, currents, wave heights, and ocean topography. ■ Other earth-oriented spacecraft launched in 1978 included the Heat-Capacity-Mapping Mission, designed to measure day and night temperature differences on the earth's surface; a new Tiros weather satellite; and Nimbus-G, the first pollution monitoring satellite.

John Noble Wilford

UPI

In January 1978 the Soviet *Cosmos* 954, a nuclear powered satellite, plunged into Canada's Northwest Territories at Yellowknife. In this photo members of the Canadian search team check a fellow worker for radioactive contamination.

The Space Shuttle Orbiter *Columbia* is lowered by a massive facility, which is used to mount or remove shuttle orbiters onto or from 747 carrier aircraft. The 747's will be used for lifting off the *Columbia* and other orbiters in the future.

NASA

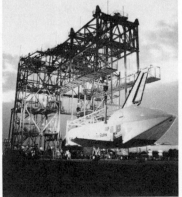

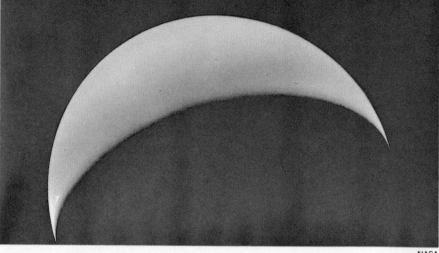

NASA

THE VENUS PROBE

by Barbara Tchabovsky

THE first photos were disappointing. But by the time the U.S. Pioneer probes completed their observations of Venus in late 1978 and early 1979, scientists had a new picture of Venus, and some new theories about the formation of the solar system.

Pioneer Venus 1, was launched on May 20, 1978. In December 1978 it settled into an elliptical orbit around Venus, coming to within 150 kilometers of the planet's surface once every 24 hours. For eight months it took photographs and measurements. It analyzed the atmosphere, captured infrared and ultraviolet images of the cloud cover, and mapped the surface by radar.

Pioneer Venus 2, nicknamed Multiprobe, launched August 8, 1978, had a brief but dramatic mission. In November it separated into five parts. Four probes plunged into widely separated regions of the Venusian atmosphere to measure its temperature and other weather conditions. The fifth, measured the chemical composition of the atmosphere before burning up.

LIKE PLANET EARTH

Venus is the planet most similar to earth in size, mass, density, and distance from the sun. Only slightly smaller than earth, Venus has a diameter of 12,000,000 kilometers. Its mass is 0.81 times that of earth, its density very similar, and its distance from the sun, 108,000,000 kilometers, nearly three-fourths earth's distance from the sun.

Preliminary mapping of the surface of Venus reveals a surface similar to earth's and smoother than the surfaces of Mars or the moon. Mapping reveals a mountain higher than Everest, possible volcanic peaks, and a rift valley five kilometers deep, 280 kilometers wide, and 1,440 kilometers long.

The sister planets differ in many ways. Venus rotates on its axis very slowly, much more slowly than earth or any other planet. It takes 243.1 earth days to complete one turn. The atmospheric pressure is 100 times that of earth's. The planet also lacks liquid water. Learning about Venusian weather will, scientists hope, provide clues to understanding earth's much more complex weather.

A RUNAWAY GREENHOUSE

The surface temperature of Venus at about 455° Celsius is hot enough to melt lead. The reason for the high surface temperature is not, however, what you might think. It is not because the planet is closer to the sun than earth and receives about twice as much of the sun's energy. Venus is cloud covered, and these clouds reflect back about 75 per cent of the sunlight falling on them. Therefore, the total amount of solar energy reaching the surface of Venus is very close to the amount that reaches our surface.

Why, then, the hellish temperatures? The atmosphere of Venus is made up of about 97 per cent carbon dioxide (only 1 per cent for earth). Carbon dioxide gas acts like the glass or plastic roof of a greenhouse. It allows solar radiation to penetrate the atmosphere but blocks its reradiation into space as heat. This "greenhouse effect" on Venus has been known for some time, but scientists were still left wondering, "Why so very, very, hot?"

THREE CLOUD LAYERS

Venus' clouds that are visible from earth begin about 70 kilometers above the planet's surface and extend downward for about 20 kilometers. The clouds occur in three distinct layers and contain oxygen, water vapor, sulfur dioxide, sulfuric acid, and probably some elemental sulfur. The temperature of the top two thin layers ranges from 13° to 20° Celsius. The temperature of the bottom layer, the densest and only layer opaque enough to be like earth's clouds, is about 202° Celsius.

Beneath these cloud layers, there is a pre-cloud layer. And below that there is haze, which extends down to about 30 kilometers above the planet's surface. Below the haze the visibility is still poor. Because of the dense carbon-dioxide atmosphere the surface illumination is gloomy and reddish. Light scattering produces distorted images.

Atmospheric circulation distributes solar heating evenly over the whole planet. Dr. Verner Soumi of the University of Wisconsin theorizes that warm air rises at the equator (as on the earth), cools as it expands, and then flows toward the poles, sinking into a "polar hole," and heating as it compresses. The finding that cloud tops in the polar regions were some 10 Celsius degrees warmer than cloud tops at the equator substantiates this theory. The cloud tops circle the planet at 360 kilometers per hour.

THE BIGGEST SURPRISE

Pioneer Venus 2 found that there is several hundred times more primordial argon and neon on Venus than on earth. This surprise finding has shaken many long-held theories about the formation of the solar system and the inner planets in particular.

Until now most theories proposed that the sun and planets formed at about the same time. The planets formed from a gas cloud that surrounded the sun. The young, fiery sun was believed to have pulled away the lighter gases like argon and neon from the

NASA

A composite photo of the five-probe Multiprobe, with its launching silo and Venus in the background. The probes measured Venus' atmosphere's content and temperature.

inner planets. This would have left these gases in greater concentrations in the outer-planet region.

But Venus appears to have more, not less, primordial argon and neon than earth. And Mars had earlier been found to have less of these gases than expected. These findings may mean that the gas cloud that formed the solar system was evenly heated. In that condition, gravity would cause the lighter gases to concentrate toward the center. The gases could then have been absorbed by dust grains. As the dust consolidated into rock, the gases became trapped in the rocky masses, which form the inner planets. All this may have happened before the sun even heated up.

Scientists hope to find at least some answers posed by Venus as they complete their analysis of the first good look at earth's nearest planetary neighbor □

SELECTED READINGS

"Oceans, glaciers, and mists: role of water" by R. Goody. *Natural History,* October 1978.

"Scientists begin processing, analyzing Venus data" by B. Elson. *Aviation Week,* January 1, 1979.

"Watching the inner planets" by R. Burnham. *Astronomy,* December 1978.

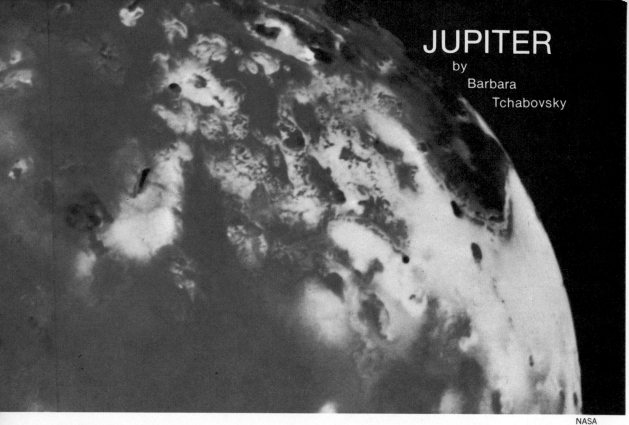

JUPITER

by
Barbara
Tchabovsky

NASA

Io is Jupiter's largest moon. It is about the size of Earth's moon and has active volcanoes, which are spewing lava over the surface.

A SOLAR system within the solar system. That's how scientists are describing Jupiter and its family of satellites as they study the findings of the U.S. space probe Voyager 1. The probe moved to within 278,000 kilometers of the planet on March 5, 1979, and examined four of Jupiter's 13 moons. They hope that the Jovian model may provide clues as to how the entire solar system formed.

ALMOST A STAR

Jupiter is often described as a star that didn't quite make it. It is an enormous, largely gaseous, ball, bigger than all the other planets combined. Its diameter is more than ten times that of earth, and its mass 318 times larger.

Approximately 779,000,000 kilometers from the sun, Jupiter radiates two-and-one-half times more heat than it receives from the sun. Scientists think that Jupiter's excess heat is heat stored from the time when the planet coalesced from the solar nebula, some 4,600,-000,000 years ago. These facts suggest that at one time Jupiter had star potential, but it may have lacked the necessary mass.

A HUGE BALL OF GAS

Jupiter is composed mostly of hydrogen, plus some helium. There is no solid surface. The planet is thought to have a small, solid core and around that a mantle, 65,000 kilometers thick, of molten hydrogen. Water droplets form a cloud layer surrounding the planet. Above that a cloud layer of frozen ammonia forms what we see in photos.

In addition to hydrogen and helium, the atmosphere of Jupiter contains ammonia, methane, water, and acetylene. The first three compounds were present on the early earth. From them amino acids and ultimately primitive life forms are thought to have developed. For this reason, their presence on Jupiter is extremely interesting to scientists.

SWIRLS, EDDIES, STORMS

The Jovian atmosphere has a series of light zones and darker belts girdling the planet from the equator to the poles. There is continuous, tumultuous activity. The best-known atmospheric event is the Great Red Spot. This eyelike spot is anchored in Jupiter's southern hemisphere. It is thought to be a centuries-old, hurricanelike storm the size of the Pacific Ocean. Clouds along its edge move at about 325 to 400 kilometers an hour, but the center appears calm.

Smaller storms, white oval clouds, bright spots, halos, and thunderheadlike plumes move about the planet. They appear to move in a direction opposite to that of the general circulation, which is clockwise in the southern hemisphere and counterclockwise in the northern hemisphere.

Voyager 1 found that a huge doughnut-shaped cloud of charged particles surrounds Jupiter. This cloud glows like earth's auroras, and is composed of sulfur particles.

AND A RING

Voyager found that Jupiter has a ring like that of Saturn. Jupiter's ring is about 55,000 kilometers outside the planet's upper clouds and well within the orbit of the innermost satellite, Amalthea. At least 15,000 kilometers wide but perhaps only about 27 kilometers deep, the ring is sparsely populated with dark rocky debris. The debris probably consists of fragments left when Jupiter formed. Or it could be the remains of a satellite that was broken apart when it wandered too close to Jupiter's intense gravitational pull.

A LARGE FAMILY

Like the sun, Jupiter has a large family—13, possibly 14, satellites—four of which are planet-sized. In both the solar system and the Jovian system, the density of the family members decreases outward as the spacing of their orbits increases. The inner members are rocky, and the outer members liquid or gaseous. Let's take a Voyager look at some of the Jovian "planets."

IO—THE EARTH OF THE JOVIAN SYSTEM

About the size of earth's moon, Io is a rocky body, dry and dense, with a red, yellow, orange, and white surface. It is thought to contain a variety of salts and to be the source of the sodium found in a cloud surrounding it as well as of the sulfur particles that surrounds Jupiter. It has an extremely harsh environment and is constantly bombarded by radiation.

UPI

In this photograph of Jupiter the Great Red Spot appears as an orange-brown oval in the upper left quadrant. To its right and down somewhat the moon Io can be seen against the planet's disk.

Scientists expected to find numerous craters formed by meteorite impact on Io. Instead, they found a body largely unscarred by craters but with dry, salty plains, dome-shaped features, long cliffs, mesas, channels, mountains, and depressions. And most interesting, they found volcanoes—young volcanoes.

Photographs taken when Voyager 1 passed within 21,000 kilometers of the surface revealed one especially large volcanic mountain. It rises about 1.5 kilometers above the surrounding terrain and has an irregularly shaped 50-kilometer wide crater. Smaller volcanoes were also found.

The presence of young volcanoes on Io helps explain why impact craters are missing. Intense heat and lava flows have changed the surface of Io by smoothing out the surface. Volcanoes also explain the salt deposits. Volcanic processes concentrate minerals in water solution, but when the volcanoes erupt, the water evaporates, leaving the minerals as salts. The somewhat surprising find of young volcanoes on Io was topped when Voyager photographed a volcano actually erupting.

Voyager 1 was 9,200,000 kilometers from Jupiter when it made this photo. The Great Red Spot is a long-lasting gaseous feature of the Jovian atmosphere.

UPI

None of the Jovian satellites is known to have an atmosphere. Io also has some unique and unexplained features: a large, white doughnut feature, a Grand Canyon-sized wiggly worm hole, a large dimple, and clusters of bright plumes.

EUROPA, GANYMEDE, AND CALLISTRO

Slightly smaller than Io, Europa, Jupiter's third moon, probably consists mostly of rock. Voyager, passing within 735,000 kilometers of it, photographed a pale brownish surface with dark streaks, some quite long and wide. The surface is probably uniformly covered with ice. The streaks could be fault lines, which could indicate past earthquakes.

Ganymede, the largest of Jupiter's satellites and even larger than Mercury, and the slightly smaller Callistro are strikingly similar. Each can be described as a planet-sized drop of water with a mud or rocky core and a crust of ice. Both are heavily cratered.

Ganymede appeared dark brown and gray, like dirty ice, when Voyager passed within 115,000 kilometers of it. Bright spots may indicate fresh ice, and grooves in the ice crust could indicate crustal movement.

A white-speckled, bronze Callistro, some 1,500,000 kilometers from Jupiter, is more heavily cratered than Ganymede. When Voyager passed within 125,000 kilometers, it photographed "lots and lots and lots of craters, almost shoulder to shoulder." The craters are rather shallow. One scientist theorized that the fluid surface smooths itself out after impact.

SO MUCH—AND MORE TO COME

The wealth of data gathered by Voyager 1, a tiny fraction of which we have glimpsed, plus the information gathered by Voyager 2's study of Jupiter in July 1979, will take years to analyze completely. By then the miniature solar system may well have provided clues to two perplexing questions: how was the solar system formed, and how did life arise? □

SELECTED READINGS

"Nature's turbulent test tube" by Robert Jastrow. *The New York Times Magazine,* April 1, 1979.

"Voyager Approaches Jupiter." *Astronomy,* April 1979.

"Jupiter's World." *Science News,* March 10, 1979.

A BIG DOUBT ON SOLAR THEORIES

by James S. Trefil

THE author of *Ecclesiastes* may have been right when he said there is no new thing under the sun, but during recent years scientists have learned that there may be something new, after all, going on inside the sun. The story has all of the elements of a classical scientific mystery.

First, experimenters find a totally unexpected result. After an initial period of disbelief, other scientists try to come up with explanations. As time goes by, the explanations become more and more bizarre until the whole thing looks very confused. In the classical story, of course, someone comes on stage at this point with the correct answer and everything is resolved beautifully. In our story, the person hasn't yet come on the scene, so all we'll be able to do is report on the confusion.

SUN'S DRIVING FORCE

In a sense our story begins when early people looked in awe at the sun. They improvised stories to explain the regular rising and setting of the sun, often thinking of the sun as a flaming chariot being drawn across the sky. Later, with the invention of the telescope, people discovered that the surface of the sun is a turbulent place, with storms and eruptions spouting thousands of kilometers into space. Until recently, the source of all of this fierce energy—the driving force behind the sun—was a mystery.

During the nineteenth century, scientists calculated how long an object as big as the sun would burn if it were made of coal or gasoline and invariably concluded that if the sun were simply burning, it would never have lasted long enough for life to develop

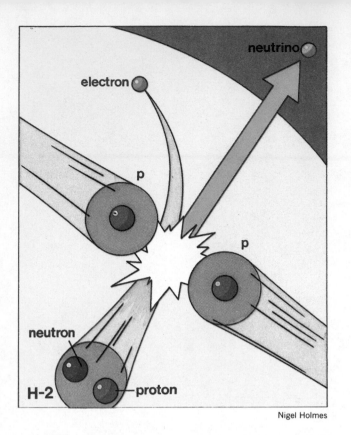

In the sun's core, where the temperature is about 15,000,000° Celsius, protons (hydrogen nuclei) smash into each other forming deuterium nuclei (helium nuclei) and emit an electron and a neutrino.

Nigel Holmes

on the earth. In the twentieth century, however, we have discovered a far more potent form of energy in the nucleus of the atom.

When atomic nuclei (nuclei is the plural of nucleus) combine with each other to form larger nuclei—a process we call fusion—some of the mass of the original nuclei is converted into energy. It is converted according to Einstein's famous formula $E = mc^2$, where E = energy, m = mass, and c = the velocity of light. The energy released by this fusion process has been demonstrated here on earth in the hydrogen bomb. A more attractive aspect of fusion is seen in the attempts of scientists to control it as an energy source. By now, many steps in the solar fusion process have been duplicated in accelerators here on earth, and scientists have created extremely hot, electrically charged concentrations of gases, called plasmas, whose temperatures approach that of the sun. A controlled fusion reaction, however, is still somewhat in the future.

A GIGANTIC REACTOR

From a purely scientific point of view, the first important application of the principle of fusion was in the understanding it gave us of the sun. According to our present ideas of how the sun and other stars work, the light and energy which we see streaming out of the surface of the sun are produced in a gigantic fusion "reactor" deep inside the sun's core. Here, where the temperature exceeds 15,000,-000° Celsius, the nuclei of hydrogen atoms, called protons, are combined in nuclear processes to form helium nuclei, giving off energy in the process. It is this energy, pushing outward from the center of the sun, that keeps the sun from collapsing on itself like a spent balloon under the force of its own tremendous gravity. It is also this energy which, when it reaches the sun's surface, travels to the earth where, as light and heat, it is the ultimate source of life.

NO EASY TRIP FOR LIGHT

While scientists understood the principles of fusion, no one had ever been able to look into a star and actually see the process going on. All that had been seen of stars was the surface. To understand the importance of this statement, let's think a little about what happens to light given off by the fusion process in the center of the star. When light tries to leave the center of the sun, it does not find the going particularly easy. It has to travel more than 640,000 kilometers through mate-

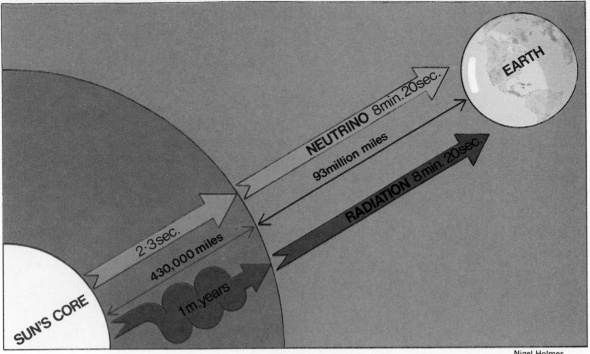

Nigel Holmes

Neutrinos and radiation (photons) take the same amount of time to get from the surface of the sun to the earth. But the light we see today may have taken a million years to get from the sun's core to its surface. Neutrinos take 2.3 seconds to make the same trip.

rial that is, at least near the center, about 100 times as dense as water. When we think of the difficulty that light has in penetrating to the bottom of the ocean (a mere three kilometers or so down), we can understand that light coming from the center of the sun will not reach the surface without incident.

There are a number of things that can happen to the light on its way out to the surface. It can collide with atoms and be scattered from its course or even turned back. It can be absorbed and reemitted in a number of ways, over and over again, by the matter that makes up the bulk of the sun. In fact, when all of this is taken into account, it turns out that the light that is coming from the surface of the sun right now actually left the center of the sun more than 1,000,000 years ago.

To use a sports analogy, the process by which light (and other energy) percolates from the fusion reaction in the sun's core to the outside is more like the progress of a running back in football being knocked around by tacklers than it is like the straight-line motion of a sprinter. Thus, anything we see when we look at the sun tells us only about the solar surface, and not the core.

TO SEE THE SUN'S CORE

This situation is at once gratifying and disturbing. It's gratifying to scientists because it allows them to use their knowledge of the laws of physics to construct a picture of the solar interior without being able to see it. It is disturbing because there is always that nagging doubt that somehow we are missing something. And so astronomers began to think about experiments that might allow us to "see" the core of the sun.

Just as nuclear physics solved the riddle of the sun's energy source, it provided an answer to this problem as well. By 1930 Austro-American physicist Wolfgang Pauli had proposed the existence of a new subatomic particle, one with no electric charge. Enrico Fermi, the man who later built the world's first nuclear reactor in Chicago, Illinois, christened the new particle the neutrino ("little neutral one") and figured out that it gave off radiation in the forms of beta particles. Scientists felt such a particle ought to exist because in some nuclear reactions there seemed to be more energy going in than was observed coming out. If there were a new particle that was difficult to detect, then it

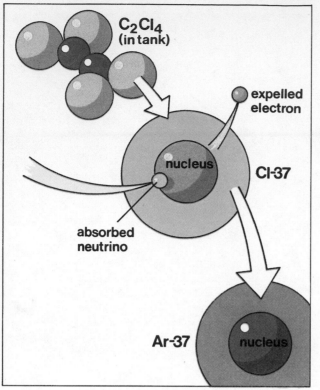

C_2Cl_4
(in tank)

expelled
electron

nucleus

Cl-37

absorbed
neutrino

Ar-37   nucleus

When a neutrino reaches the earth, it could hit a chlorine atom (Cl-37) in a molecule of cleaning fluid (C_2Cl_4). The chlorine atom would absorb the neutrino, expel an electron, and become argon-37.

Nigel Holmes

could carry away the excess energy without being seen. Then physicists would not have to give up the law of conservation of energy, a long-held "dogma" that states that while energy can be transformed, it cannot be created or destroyed.

Now when we say that we "detect" a particle, we don't mean that we actually see it—particles are much too small for that. What we mean is that we see some effect of the particle's presence. For example, the particle may collide with an atom and knock off some electrons, or it may split a nucleus as it passes. We can only detect a particle if it interacts with matter in some ways. So when we say that the neutrino is hard to detect we are really saying that it does not interact very much with ordinary matter. In fact, according to classical theory the interaction of neutrinos with ordinary matter is so weak that a neutrino could pass through a block of lead that stretched from here to the nearest star without disturbing any of the atoms in its path. Small wonder, then, that the particle wasn't detected until 1956, after a 26-year search.

NEUTRINOS OFFER "VIEW"

Two properties of neutrinos suggest them as a tool of solar research. The first is

that they are given off in nuclear reactions, including the fusion going on in the sun. The second is that unlike the particles of ordinary light that undergo innumerable changes just getting to the sun's surface, neutrinos can go from the core to the outer surface of the sun and then come across 150,000,000 kilometers of space to the earth without any change at all. Thus, if we could somehow detect the neutrinos coming from the sun, we would be able to "see" into the sun's core for the first time.

HARD TO DETECT

But of course the very property of neutrinos that makes them so potentially useful as a probe of the sun's interior makes them very difficult to catch in a measuring apparatus on the earth. After all, if we are to know that a neutrino has been somewhere, we have to see some effect of its presence on other matter. If a neutrino can get out of the sun without interacting, it is unlikely to interact in a relatively minuscule experimental setup on the earth.

To get some idea of just how elusive a neutrino is, consider the following fact: right now, as you read this article, neutrinos from the sun are passing through your body at the rate of thousands of millions per second.

This has been going on ever since you were born, and will continue for the rest of your life. It doesn't even matter if it's night, with the entire planet between you and the sun, because neutrinos can pass quite easily through the solid earth. If you think of your body as a neutrino detector, you may ask how often one of them will actually interact with one of your atoms. The answer is about once every ten years.

So the scientist is on the horns of a dilemma: On the one hand, any particle that interacts easily with matter and is therefore easy to detect will never make it out of the sun. On the other hand, the one particle that interacts so little that it can get out of the sun is very difficult to catch when it gets to the earth. Neutrinos can be detected in the laboratory by sending thousands of millions of them down the beam of an accelerator in the hopes that one will hit a target—but one rarely does.

UNIQUE SETUP

In the mid-1960's a group of scientists led by Raymond Davis of Brookhaven National Laboratory on Long Island, New York, and John Bahcall, then of the California Institute of Technology, now at The Institute for Advanced Study in Princeton, New Jersey, began to think seriously about this problem. They realized that the neutrino given off by one of the reactions in the fusion process would have a high probability—at least for a neutrino—of interacting with chlorine atoms, changing them to argon in the process. The argon would be radioactive, and relatively easy to detect. Using this basic fact, they developed an experiment that is truly unique.

The heart of the apparatus is a tank that holds nearly 380,000 liters of perchloroethylene (ordinary cleaning fluid), enough to fill ten railroad tank cars. (At a meeting describ-

Brookhaven National Lab

Raymond Davis of Brookhaven National Laboratory devised this 380,000-liter tank to hold chlorine-cleaning fluid, which is used to detect incoming neutrinos.

ing some early results of the experiment, Bahcall pointed out that this provided a nice escape hatch for the experimenters. If they failed, they could always go into the cleaning business.) If our ideas about how the sun generates its energy are correct, then about once a day a neutrino from the sun should hit a chlorine atom in the cleaning fluid and change it into an argon atom and an extra electron. If we let these reactions go on for three months or so, we would then be able to "detect" the neutrinos by counting the atoms of argon they left behind in the cleaning fluid. The argon atoms would be "visible" because the particular kind of argon produced is radioactive, and thus its presence can be monitored in much the same way that radioactive tracers are detected in medical diagnosis. Even so, finding a needle in a haystack would be simple compared to this task.

Nevertheless, by taking enormous care and by shielding the tank of cleaning fluid by placing it nearly 1,500 meters underground in the Homestake mine in Lead, South Dakota, the experimenters were able to make the experiment work. They were detecting argon that could be produced by neutrinos coming from the sun. They were actually able to "see" into the center of the sun.

Then came the surprise: there were not nearly as many neutrinos as there should have been. Conventional solar theories predicted about one neutrino interaction per day in the cleaning fluid, with one argon atom per day left behind for the detection process. When the apparatus was turned on, however, the results were consistently lower. Instead of a count per day, the experimenters were finding a count every three to five days.

SOMETHING WRONG SOMEWHERE

So the first discovery made with this enormous apparatus was that some of the neutrinos from the sun were not there. Somewhere in the imposing scientific edifice that stood behind the predictions was a flaw. But where?

The first reaction of the scientific community was typical of the reception of a startling new result—most scientists simply ignored it, hoping that a mistake in the experiment would be found and that the whole thing would just go away. As the years went by, however, this became less and less possible. For one thing, the experiment itself was checked and tested. For another, the individual nuclear reactions that are present in the fusion process were measured accurately in laboratories without any surprises turning

Nigel Holmes

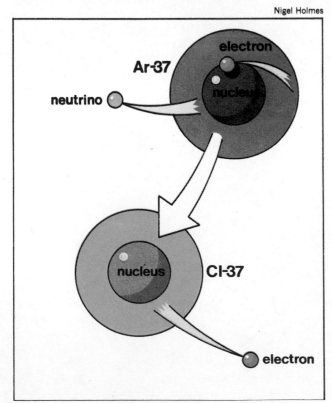

You can't just count argon atoms to find out how many neutrinos hit chlorine atoms. Some argon atoms may spontaneously expel a neutrino and become chlorine (C-37).

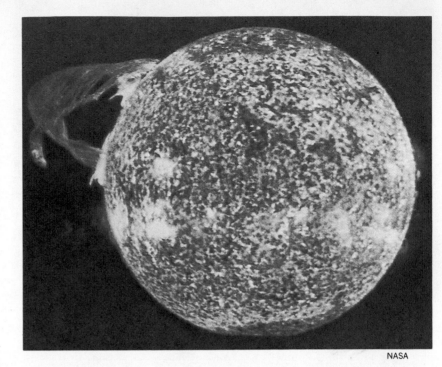

Skylab photo of sun taken by extreme ultraviolet wavelengths shows solar activity. Ionized helium filaments arch from the surface then twist back—a trip of about 587,000 kilometers.

up. Thus, the question of why the neutrinos aren't there has progressed over the last ten years from an interesting but unimportant puzzle to one of the major unsolved scientific problems of our time. There just doesn't seem to be any way around it—something is wrong somewhere.

What that "something" is has become a matter of dispute between scientists in different fields. Astronomers tend to point the finger of blame at physicists, suggesting that either the nuclear processes are not well enough known or that something happens to the neutrinos between the earth and the sun. Physicists, on the other hand, tend to shrug this off and suggest that the astronomers don't really know as much about the sun's structure as they say they do. Even climatologists engaged in the study of the history of the earth's weather get into the act, as we shall see. The general feeling of all of the scientists that I talked to about this problem was that the problem was not with their field, but was somewhere else.

POINTING THE FINGER

Some solutions to the neutrino problem have been proposed. Astronomers have suggested a number of ways that the lack of neutrinos could be blamed on some special features of the sun's history. They say, for example, that comets raining on the sun and depositing a layer of heavy elements in the solar surface could explain the low number of neutrinos detected. Or, some theorize, that the inside of the sun rotates much more rapidly than the outside and that this difference could be responsible for the low neutrino count. In each case, however, other astronomers have been quick to point out that there is no evidence of such effects anywhere among the millions of stars that we can see. Why should the sun be special?

Others have proposed theories which take the solar neutrino evidence at its face value. They say that if the neutrinos tell us that most of the fusion reactions inside the sun have been "switched off," so be it. After all, the light we see from the sun started out from the interior 1,000,000 years ago, while the neutrinos got from there to here in about eight minutes. These theories suggest that in the intervening 1,000,000 years, which is a short time as the life cycle of stars go, something has happened. Perhaps the sun is switched off.

Anything that turns off the fusion reaction will also cause a long-term cooling trend in the sun, and this trend will presumably be reflected in the weather on earth. Yet climatologists who study such things can find no evidence for such a trend. So if the sun is

Another Skylab photo of a solar eruption. The colors represent different intensities of radiation.

NASA

turned off, it must have happened recently.

Other people have suggested that the answer lies in particle physics—that something must happen to the neutrinos between the time they leave the interior of the sun and the time they arrive at the earth. Particle physicists tend to dismiss this, pointing out that neutrinos have been produced for years with no evidence whatever of any funny business going on.

Perhaps the flavor of this mutual finger-pointing between different scientific groups can be captured if I may paraphrase some words of Isaac Asimov to describe my own reactions. "Gentle reader, I am a particle physicist, so if someone tells me that climatologists have missed the single most important trend in the Earth's weather, I will smile. If someone tells me that astronomers don't really know much about the interior of stars, I will grin. If someone tells me that nuclear physicists have mismeasured a reaction by a factor of 100, I will burst into hysterical laughter. But if someone tells me that something happens to those neutrinos between the sun and here, then they've gone too far!"

LOOKING FOR A WAY OUT

Nevertheless, the continued failure of scientists in other fields to come up with a solution has prompted some particle physicists to go beyond a posture of total disbelief and speculate about whether there could be some unexpected property of the neutrino that might provide a way out. They are looking for a new property that would both re-

solve the dilemma of the missing neutrinos and be "safe" in the sense that no experiment done so far could have revealed the new property.

That's where things stand right now. When the absence of solar neutrinos was first announced, scientists felt that there were probably many ways of explaining the result without doing violence to our ideas about the processes that go on in the sun. As time has passed, the options associated with these easy ways out of the dilemma have closed one by one until now it seems that there is no easy way out. The fact that scientists from different fields tend to put the blame on fields outside of their own speciality may tell us something about human nature, but it also tells us something about the magnitude of the problem.

Perhaps the best statement of the attitude of many people was made by Robert Rood, a theoretical astrophysicist at the University of Virginia, who said: "In my own work on this problem I have oscillated between paranoia and complete loss of faith" □

SELECTED READINGS

"Gravity, dust, and solar neutrinos" by John Gribbin. *Astronomy,* January 1978.

"Idea of the neutrino" by L. M. Brown. *Physics Today,* September 1978.

"Our sun" by J. M. Pasachoff. *Astronomy,* January 1978.

"Sun, our star" by K. Frazier, *Science News,* April 22, 1978.

"Sun's missing particles" by J. N. Bahcall. *Natural History,* November 1976.

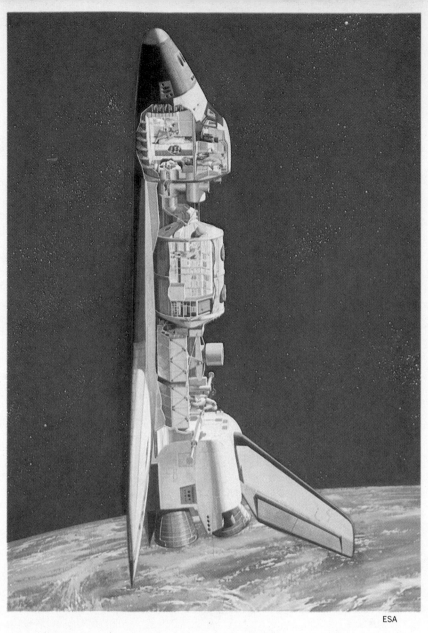

A view of the orbiter, *Columbia*, shows its three main sections. The forward section is a two-level cabin; the upper level is the flight deck, and the lower level the living quarters for crew and scientists. The middle section is a cargo bay, which can be opened up by four enormous cargo hatches. This illustration shows the Spacelab in the cargo bay with the hatches open. In the tail section are *Columbia*'s three main rocket engines.

ESA

THE SPACE SHUTTLE

by Myron S. Malkin

SEVERAL years before the first men landed on the moon in 1969, U.S. scientists were studying ways to benefit from continued space exploration. In order to use space to increase our scientific knowledge and to stimulate development of new techniques and materials that will be useful on earth, space first had to be made accessible. We had succeeded in getting people into space. Now we had to get them there routinely and economically. The space shuttle system is designed to do just that.

Sometime late in 1979, an awkward-looking four-part vehicle will blast into space, and the age of the space shuttle will have begun. The shuttle will eventually carry large payloads into space and return them to be reused. This unlikely looking assembly is

At lift-off, the orbiter is attached to a huge tank of fuel along with two smaller tanks of solid fuel.

what will make full exploitation of space possible, on a routine basis. It is the key to the U.S. future in space.

The four-part vehicle package consists of an orbital spacecraft, which resembles a stubby jetliner and is designed to land like an aircraft when its work in space is completed; a huge, expendable external fuel tank that supplies the propellants to the orbiter's three engines; and two reusable solid rocket boosters that provide the main initial ascent thrust.

LAUNCH, ORBIT, AND RETURN

The four-part package will begin to be disassembled just two minutes into the flight—46 kilometers high and 235 kilometers downrange of the launch site at Cape Canaveral, Florida. The solid rocket boosters, having performed their task, will separate from the sides of the large external tank. Eight small separation rockets in the boosters will push them clear, and the booster rockets will fall toward the sea. At about 6,100 meters chutes will be deployed on each booster to guide them into the sea, nozzle first. Special recovery vessels will pick up the parachutes and tow the boosters to shore for

refurbishment and reuse for as many as twenty times.

The orbiter and propellant tank will continue toward space. Six minutes later (eight minutes after launch) and just short of the altitude at which the craft will be placed in orbit, the orbiter's three rocket engines will shut down, and the external propellant tank will be jettisoned to break up over a remote ocean area 18,500 kilometers downrange. Free of the huge tank, the spacecraft will fire its two orbital maneuvering engines for about 105 seconds to achieve final orbital velocity. Later, another 95-second burn will circularize the orbit at an altitude of about 278 kilometers.

On its first flight the shuttle will have a crew of only two men, a commander and a pilot. Mission duration will be just 54 hours. Like the first flight of any vehicle designed to fly in air or space, this will be essentially a "test hop," and the crew will be acting in the familiar role of test pilots, carefully checking out all the orbiter's systems and equipment. With their mission in space completed, and about half an earth-revolution away from their destination, the spacecraft crew will fire the orbital maneuvering engines again for about two minutes to slow the orbiter for its return to earth.

LANDING

Half an hour after the de-orbit burn, at an altitude of about 150 kilometers, the crew will begin to feel the drag of the thin top layer of the earth's atmosphere. At that moment the most critical and demanding part of the flight will begin. The orbiter must transform itself from a spacecraft into an aircraft while decelerating from its orbital speed of almost 7,700 meters per second to 98 meters per second for landing. The following maneuvers take place for a landing in 30 minutes.

Using control thrusters, the crew will angle the nose of the spacecraft up so that it pushes into the thickening blanket of air with an angle of attack of about 40°. Air friction will heat its underside to temperatures over 1,000° Celsius, and ionization of the surrounding atmosphere will black out communication with the ground. At an altitude of about 93 kilometers the atmosphere will be-

The two solid fuel tanks drop off in two minutes. The main tank holds the liquid hydrogen and liquid oxygen for *Columbia*'s three main engines. The empty tank is to drop away when no longer needed.

come sufficiently dense to permit use of the aerodynamic controls, and the orbiter will become a glider. About 48 kilometers from earth, the nose will be pushed down to reduce the angle of attack to about 14°. At 24,-400 meters, final approach will begin about 92 kilometers from the lake bed runway at Edwards Air Force Base in California's Mojave Desert.

The last few minutes of the flight would cause considerable anxiety to the average aircraft pilot. The orbiter, its rocket fuel expended in the rise to orbit and its orbital maneuvering thrusters useless in the earth's dense atmosphere, will become a glider. It will be an 84-metric-ton glider, diving for the runway at a 22°, nose-down attitude, and an airspeed of some 158 meters per second. At 520 meters, the pilot will begin to flatten the glide to only 1.5°, slow the orbiter, and settle it toward a landing. At 90 meters the landing gear will go down, and seconds later the tires will touch down. All this will take just 30 busy minutes out of the silent weightlessness of space.

An observer watching the launch from the viewing area at the Kennedy Space Center, at Cape Canaveral, or witnessing the landing of the orbiter on the dry lake bed at Edwards Air Force Base would find the flame and thunder of launch and the dramatic dive from space to earth exciting and memorable. But even then an observer could not gain an accurate impression of the size, the power, or the technological sophistication of the space-shuttle system.

THE ORBITER

The orbiter, which is named the *Columbia,* itself is the heart of the space-shuttle system, and all other elements exist for its support. It is roughly the size of a DC-9, with a dry empty weight of about 75,000 kilograms, but bulkier and more complex than the most modern aircraft. Its cargo bay is an unobstructed cylindrical compartment 4.6 meters in diameter and 18.3 meters long, with top-opening payload bay doors extending its full length. It is capable of delivering 29,484 kilograms to a due-east orbit.

The orbiter's three rocket engines, fueled by liquid oxygen and liquid hydrogen, are the most advanced ever built. They are the first large liquid-fuel rocket engines designed for reuse and are intended to power 55 flights before major overhaul. Each engine is controlled through dual redundant computers that monitor performance and automatically either correct any problems that may arise or safely shut down the engine if this becomes necessary.

SHIRT SLEEVE COMFORT

In the cabin in the orbiter's forward section, sea-level pressure and an atmosphere of 22 per cent oxygen and 78 per cent nitrogen almost exactly duplicate normal conditions on earth. This enables the crew to live and work in shirt-sleeve comfort.

The upper section of the cabin is the flight deck from which the orbiter is controlled and the payloads handled. It resembles the cabin of a jetliner, with commander

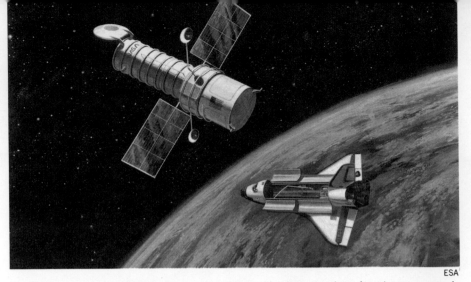

An artist's concept that shows how the orbiter will release and push out some experimental hardware from the payload compartment.

and pilot in the conventional pilot/copilot arrangement. Behind the two pilots are additional stations for a mission specialist and a payload specialist.

The cabin's lower deck has seating for three more crewmen (six more in an emergency such as a rescue mission), a galley, dining area, bunks, a personal-hygiene facility for both men and women, and an airlock that permits space-suited crew members to leave the cabin for in-space activities in the vicinity of the orbiter.

The orbiter's crew and cargo are shielded from the extreme heat generated during launch and reentry by a unique and complex thermal protection system, the first ever developed for repeated use on a spacecraft.

SELF SUFFICIENT

Electrical power for the orbiter and its payloads is provided by three fuel cells, using liquid hydrogen and liquid oxygen, stored in three sets of containers near absolute zero in temperature. The basic system generates about 1,530 kilowatt hours of energy. If more power is required, additional fuel kits can be added, each of which provides fuel for about 840 kilowatt hours. All the water required by the orbiter's crew is produced as a by-product during the chemical conversion of hydrogen and oxygen in the fuel cells to obtain electrical power.

Special electronic systems provide guidance and navigation, flight control, communications, instrumentation, data processing, and electrical power distribution. Flight control uses four digital computers doing simultaneous computations. These computers receive inputs from sources such as the inertial measurement unit, rate gyros, and accelerometers and generate instructions to control surfaces, thrusters, or other units. Each computer compares its computations to that of the other computers, and each sends its commands to the appropriate actuator. If one of the computers finds that the sum of its critical commands does not agree with the other three computers, it removes itself from operation. Or the others, also noting a lack of agreement, will disregard it.

The communications system consists of two different frequency systems. One will be used for communication with the existing ground systems and later with relay satellites. The other will perform radar and high-data rate-communications functions. As a radar it will locate, track, and deliver the data required to bring about rapid and accurate rendezvous with other space vehicles at any time. As a communications system it will provide reliable, high-quality transmission and reception with ground stations by means of two relay satellites. The data-relay satellites are scheduled to be available by 1981.

The Canadian government has underwritten the development of a remote manipulator system for payload handling in space and is supplying one system to the U.S. National Aeronautics and Space Administration (NASA). Subsequent systems will be purchased by the United States from Canada.

Fred Haise, at right, and C. Gordon Fullerton, to his right made a test flight in the *Enterprise*.

PROPELLANT TANK

While the orbiter is the operational heart of the space-shuttle system, the external tank is the structural heart of the system from launch to just short of orbit. The orbiter rides on its back, and the two solid rocket boosters are mounted on its sides.

A large hydrogen tank, a smaller oxygen tank, and an intertank are joined together to form the external tank—a large propellant storage container 46.8 meters tall and with a diameter of 8.4 meters.

The oxygen tank is the forward portion of the container, and, when loaded, contains 600,566 kilograms of liquid oxygen. The liquid-hydrogen tank is larger and holds 102,-514 kilograms of liquid hydrogen. The intertank joins the two propellant tanks and provides a protective compartment between them for the housing of essential instruments. The outer surface of the external tank is thermally protected with spray-on foam insulation.

BOOSTERS

The final element of the launch package of the space shuttle is the pair of solid rocket boosters, whose combined average thrust of over 23,000,000 newtons complements the orbiter's main engines to provide initial ascent power. Each booster is 45.5 meters long, with a diameter of 3.7 meters and houses the largest solid rocket motor ever flown, with about 498,960 kilograms of solid propellant.

SPACELAB

Two additional elements will complete the Space Transportation System, together with launch, landing, tracking, and ground turn-around facilities. These are Spacelab and Upper Stages. Spacelab is a manned scientific laboratory designed to fit in the orbiter's cargo bay. There are several types of Upper Stages to insert payloads in high-energy earth orbits or for planetary exploration.

Spacelab will be reusable, launching and landing with the orbiter as many as 50 times during a ten-year period. It can be configured as a pressurized module, where as many as four scientists and engineers can work in the same kind of shirt-sleeve environment as in the orbiter cabin, or as an instrument-carrying pallet, or as both together. Instruments on the pallet can be controlled from a payload specialist's station on the orbiter's flight deck or from the pressurized module. Crew movement between the orbiter and the Spacelab will be by an airlock and pressurized tunnel.

The laboratory and the segments of the pallet will carry experimental equipment such as furnaces, microscopes, centrifuges, incubators, photographic apparatus, telescopes, antennas, radars, and sensors as well as computers, tape recorders, and checkout consoles as necessary for the various missions.

The crew of the Spacelab will be scientists and engineers who will operate the experiments. They will have on board the necessary computing facilities for a first interpretation of the results obtained and, being "on the spot," can modify the experiments in progress and take corrective action in the event of malfunction.

Spacelab is a $500,000,000 contribution

The main tank is about 52 meters long by 10 meters wide and is made of aluminum and insulated with spray-on foam.

to the Space Transportation System by ten European nations, under the auspices of the European Space Agency. This international group is designing, equipping, and supplying the first Spacelab flight set. Subsequent units will be purchased by the United States from them. Ground and flight operational procedures are being developed by NASA.

UPPER STAGES

The Upper Stages have been developed to boost payloads to altitudes higher than the 1,170 kilometer-altitude the orbiter can attain with its limited propellant. Many missions will involve placing satellites in an orbit 35,680 kilometers high, which allows the satellite to stay always over one spot on earth. Interplanetary launches are also envisioned.

The Inertial Upper Stage, the largest, in the standard version will be 4.6 meters long, 2.7 meters in diameter, and will weigh 15,000 kilograms. It will be remotely controlled either from the orbiter or a ground station. Two other smaller stages, called Spinning Solid Upper Stages, will also be produced.

WHAT CAN IT DO?

We have learned what the space shuttle is. But what exactly can it *do?* And in what ways can it do those things sufficiently better than they are currently done to justify the expense of the program?

Although the nominal mission will be seven days with a crew of four, by adding consumables and equipment, a mission can be extended to more than 20 days and a crew of seven. The system is designed around a standard mission that can place a 29,500-kilogram payload into a 280-kilometer circular orbit due east or 14,500 kilogram into the same orbital altitude at 98° (retrograde) inclination, and return up to 14,500 kilograms to the landing site at the Kennedy Space Center in Florida or to the Vandenberg Air Force Base in California. In the event of an aborted mission, the full load can be returned and landed—an extremely important capability given high priority by payload designers.

There will be no dead time between missions. The end of one mission is actually the beginning of the next, since ground turnaround operations are a key element of each flight. The goal for turnaround is 160 hours from landing to relaunch.

While in space the shuttle will be able to perform a wide variety of tasks. It is sufficiently flexible and versatile to respond to policy changes, take advantage of technological discoveries, and generally operate on an ad hoc basis when that becomes desirable. With its first remote manipulator system, the shuttle will give us the ability for the first time to service and refurbish satellites in space, to refuel them, and to retrieve them for repair and reuse. The orbiter will be able to deliver two or more satellites to the same or different orbits on the same launch, start interplanetary spacecraft on their journeys after a final check of all systems in space, and operate space laboratories in earth orbit. It will eventually provide the capability of assembling a variety of large structures in space, such as antennas, antenna platforms, and orbiting power stations.

As just one illustration of the value of the shuttle's new capabilities, the Space Telescope, which astronomers have been planning since the early 1960's, will become a reality in the mid-1980's. In-orbit maintenance from the shuttle and recovery for ground-based refurbishment will permit a lifetime of 15 to 20 years for the Space Telescope. In increasing the volume of space available to astronomers and making possible observations away from the interfering effects of the earth's atmosphere, the Space Telescope is expected to be an exceedingly valuable tool for astronomers.

The advent of the shuttle means that for the first time people will have regular, frequent, routine, economical access to space. The shuttle operations are expected to save enormous amounts of money in launch and payload costs. Savings will derive from the fact that we will no longer be dealing with expendable launch vehicles, their associated systems, and support facilities now in use; from the new ability to deliver multiple payloads to orbit with a single launch and to repair malfunctioning satellites in-orbit or return them to earth; and from the relaxation of design requirements, made possible by the shuttle's large cargo bay, relatively gentle launch conditions, and in-orbit maintenance capability.

TESTING

In order to assure that the space shuttle will operate as it is designed over the full range of anticipated conditions, extensive testing is required—of overall systems as well as subsystems and components of each element of the shuttle vehicle. The approach and landing systems, the propulsion systems, the thermal protection system, and all the specially designed electronic systems will all be tested. The structural integrity of the vehicles and the effects of vibration will also be studied. This testing began in the mid-1970's and will continue until launch time.

The orbital-flight test program will begin late in 1979 with the second orbiter and will consist of six manned flights, all launched from the Kennedy Space Center. The first four flights will carry a crew of two, increasing to four crew members by the sixth flight. The first four landings will be at Edwards AFB and the last two at the Kennedy Space Center.

The purpose of these orbital flight tests

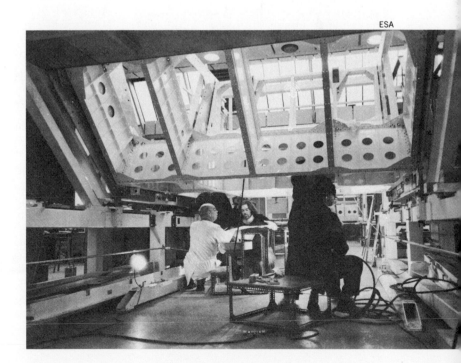

ESA

Engineers and technicians assemble Spacelab, which is a self-contained laboratory and living quarters. It is being produced by the European Space Agency and may be the first load *Columbia* will carry.

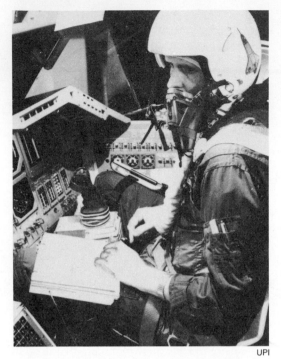

C. Gordon Fullerton, pilot for the Space Shuttle sits in the cockpit of the simulator.

is to verify flightworthiness by demonstrating compatibility among all space shuttle elements—orbiter, external tank, solid rocket boosters, and the main engines. The flights will also verify operational capability and payload compatibility to the maximum extent possible, as well as the compatibility of the ground checkout and launch systems, mission control center, ground flight tracking and data network, space-to-ground data link systems, turnaround operations, and solid rocket booster refurbishment.

After the flight test program is completed in 1980, the Space Transportation System will commence operational flights. The first group of astronauts and mission specialists have already been selected, and they are now in training.

WHAT PACKAGES?

The NASA policy for flying a payload on a space shuttle has been issued. A key part of the policy is that a fixed price—low when compared to the cost on today's launch vehi-

cles—is guaranteed during the early years of shuttle operations.

NASA has also instituted a novel program to fly small self-contained payloads. They must require no shuttle services, such as power or deployment, and are restricted to research and development purposes. They will be flown on a space-available basis, provided they weigh less than 91 kilograms and occupy les than 0.14 cubic meters of space. The price has proved so attractive that this kind of payload has earned the nickname "the getaway special."

During the first 12 years of Space Transportation System operations, NASA plans to fly about 1,000 payloads on the 487 flights now scheduled up to 1992. These will include scientific, defense, commercial, and international payloads.

Spacelab will be flown on 46 per cent of these flights and will carry 464 of the payload experiments. Free-flying satellites, which will also constitute 46 per cent of the payloads carried, will include communications satellites, deep space missions, high altitude explorers, and other research satellites. The remaining payloads will be comprised of spacecraft such as the Space Telescope, Landsat, Seasat, Earth Resources, and meteorological and astronomical observatories. NASA will supply 54 per cent of the payloads, the U.S. Department of Defense 23 per cent, and civilian users 23 per cent.

WILL BECOME ROUTINE

The frequency of shuttle flights will steadily increase throughout the 1980's. Operations are scheduled to begin from Vandenberg Air Force Base in California in 1983. By early 1984 the shuttle will reach its maximum flight rate capability of over 50 launches a year, and its arrivals and departures will have become nearly as routine and as much a part of our national life as passenger airline operations. But it will have changed our lives and the lives of people around the world □

SELECTED READINGS

"Landing the orbiter" by D. Baker. *Space World,* July 1978.

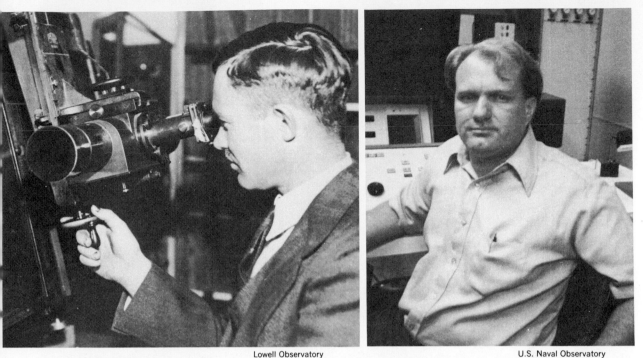

Lowell Observatory · U.S. Naval Observatory

Left: Clyde W. Tombaugh, discoverer of Pluto. Right: James W. Christy, discoverer of Pluto's "moon."

PLUTO

by Ian Ridpath

HOW many major planets are there in the solar system? Most people would say nine, which is the accepted number. Some might say ten, thinking that there could be another undiscovered planet at the outer edge of the solar system. But perhaps the real answer should be eight, for it is becoming increasingly clear that Pluto is not a true planet at all. Certainly, it is too small to have caused the supposed gravitational effects on the motions of Uranus and Neptune, which led to its discovery.

To see what's behind the Pluto mystery, let's go back to the beginning of the twentieth century when astronomers were speculating about the possibility of a ninth planet beyond Neptune. Neptune had been found in 1846. Astronomers had been puzzled by irregularities in the orbit of Uranus and thought that another planet might be responsible. They calculated where such another planet might be found, searched the skies and found Neptune. But Neptune

didn't explain the oddities of the orbit of Uranus and was itself found to have irregularities in its orbit. Was this because of the perturbing effect of yet another unknown planet?

SEARCH FOR NINTH PLANET

Astronomer Percival Lowell certainly thought so, and set about trying to predict the position of this unknown body. So, too, did astronomer William H. Pickering of Harvard, using a different method. But photographic searches in the areas in which astronomers thought such a planet might be found revealed nothing. Eventually, astronomers at Lowell Observatory in Arizona began a thorough search. Shortly after this search started, in 1930, Pluto was discovered by Clyde Tombaugh, an observatory assistant hired for the job. He subsequently shot to fame and eventual success as a professor of astronomy.

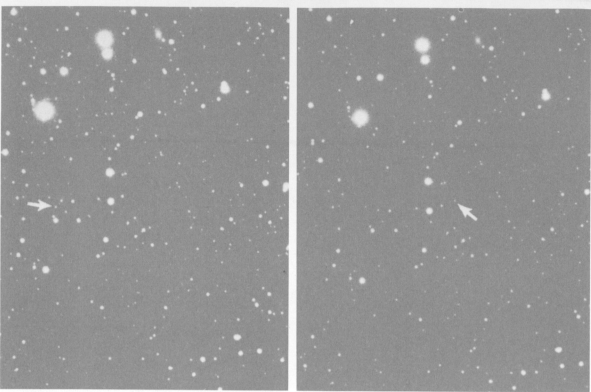

These small sections of the two plates show images of Lowell's mathematically predicted planet, afterward named Pluto. It was identified by Tombaugh as he examined the photos of many night skies.

But Pluto was a disappointing planet. Faint and evidently quite small, it was not the gas giant 6.7 times the mass of earth that had been predicted by Lowell. Tombaugh continued his photographic search, but no other planets were found, even though the search would have permitted discovery of Neptune-like planets up to about seven times Neptune's distance from the sun, or 200 astronomical units. Earth-like planets would have been found out to 100 astronomical units, according to Tombaugh. An astronomical unit is a measure of distance used in astronomy. One astronomical unit is equal to the average distance of the earth from the sun, or approximately 150,000,000 kilometers.

A DISAPPOINTMENT

Here was a paradox: Pluto was evidently not massive enough to have caused the perturbations, or irregularities, in the orbits of Uranus and Neptune, that supposedly led to its discovery. Yet there was no sign of a planet that could cause such perturbations.

Most astronomers now believe the apparent irregularities in the orbits of the outer planets were unreal, caused mostly by errors in observation and by uncertainties in the orbits of Uranus and Neptune, and in star positions against which the planets' motions were measured. The discovery of Pluto seems to have been nothing more than a lucky fluke, a tribute to the thoroughness of the Lowell Observatory search rather than a vindication of any calculations.

To underline this conclusion, every time the size and mass of Pluto were measured, the planet seemed to get smaller and lighter. The best previous values suggested a diameter of 5,900 kilometers and a mass 0.11 that of earth. There were two sources for the diameter estimate: visual observations by University of Arizona astronomer Gerard Kuiper with a 500-centimeter reflecting telescope in 1950, and a near occultation, or blocking out, of a star by Pluto, which placed an upper limit on its size. The mass estimate came from a study of the motion of Neptune, assuming it is still being slightly perturbed by the pull of Pluto.

PLUTO'S MOON

But new observations tell us that the accepted diameter and mass of the planet have to be revised dramatically downward once again. As a result Pluto, the smallest and lightest planet in the solar system, is now known to be even smaller than our own moon. The first part of the new evidence concerns infrared observations, in 1976, which show that Pluto's surface is brighter than had previously been estimated, and thus that its size must be smaller than currently assumed, to account for its dimness. And, most importantly, a satellite of Pluto was discovered in mid-1978. This discovery allows the first accurate calculation of the mass of Pluto.

The satellite was discovered by astronomer James Christy of the U.S. Naval Observatory on photographs taken with the 153-centimeter reflector at the observatory's outstation at Flagstaff, Arizona, as part of a program to refine knowledge of Pluto's 248 year orbit around the sun. Christy noted an elongation of Pluto's image, which was also visible on photographs taken at the observatory in 1965 and 1970, but which had previously been dismissed as faults in the photographic emulsion. A confirming plate taken with the 400-centimeter reflector at Cerro Tololo Inter-American Observatory in Chile also showed the elongation.

There seemed no plausible explanation of the elongation other than that it's caused by a satellite orbiting close to Pluto. So in July 1978, discovery of a moon of Pluto was announced. It is officially termed 1978–P–1, but discoverer Christy named it Charon, after the mythological boatman who ferried souls into the underworld, of which Puto was god.

According to Dr. Robert S. Harrington of the U.S. Naval Observatory, the satellite orbits at about 17,000 kilometers from the center of Pluto. It takes the satellite 6.4 days to orbit Pluto, the same length of time as it takes the planet to spin on its axis. Therefore, Charon must appear to hang always over one point on Pluto.

GAS SNOWBALL

Charon's diameter is estimated from its brightness to be 40 per cent that of Pluto, making it larger in proportion to its parent planet than any other moon in the solar system. But most important of all, a study of its

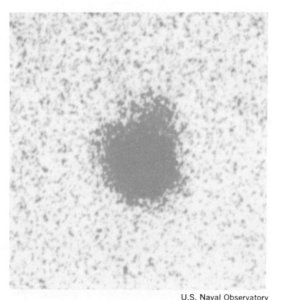

U.S. Naval Observatory
Pluto's satellite shows in this blurred image as a slight elongation of the image of Pluto.

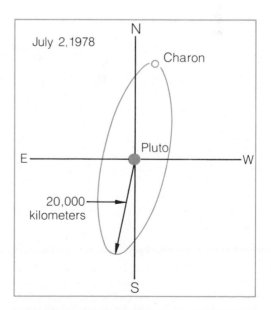

Shown here are the relative sizes of Pluto and Charon and Charon's orbit.

Pluto Facts

This table shows the dramatic changes in our knowledge about Pluto which have taken place in recent years. Estimates of its mass and diameter have declined sharply, while much that was unknown has now been learned. Not so long ago the great mystery of Pluto was its seemingly high density, but we now know that its density is in reality much less than that of earth. Together with the new low figures for its size and mass, this raises the question of whether Pluto has any right to the title ''planet'' at all!

	1960	1975	1978
Diameter (km)	5,900	5,900	2,400
Mass (earth = 1)	0.7(?)	0.11	0.002
Density (gram/centimeter^3; water = 1)	36.8	5.75	1.5
Density (earth = 1)	6.66(?!)	1.04	0.27
Period of rotation	?	6.39 days	6.39 days
Inclination of equatorial plane to plane of orbit	?	?	57°
Effective surface temperature	−230° Celsius	−230° Celsius	−230° Celsius
Atmosphere	?	?	none
Satellites	0	0	1
Orbital period of satellite	—	—	6.39 days

orbit has allowed Harrington to calculate an accurate mass for Pluto: 0.002 that of earth, or 40 times lighter than previously estimated. Combined with a diameter of 2,400 kilometers measured by the infrared observations, Pluto appears to have a density slightly more than that of water. Therefore it can be nothing more than a low density snowball of frozen gases. This is consistent with the infrared observations which did detect plentiful methane frost on its surface.

MOON OF A MOON?

Several of Saturn's satellites are believed to have low densities similar to Pluto's. The similarity of Pluto to the satellites of the outer planets has seemed to add some weight to the supposition that Pluto is an escaped moon of Neptune. This theory, first proposed by Professor Raymond Lyttleton of Cambridge University in England, supposes that Pluto once orbited Neptune every 6.4 days, until it suffered a close encounter with another of Neptune's moons, Triton. During this event, Triton was thrown into its current orbit, which is in the opposite direction from that of the other satellites, and Pluto was ejected to pursue its own course as an independent planet. As a matter of interest, the latest diameter estimates of Triton suggest it is twice the size now measured for Pluto. But how can we account for Pluto's own moon with this theory? No satellite of the solar system is known to have a moon of its own, although there is suspicion that some asteroids may have companion bodies.

INTRUDING TENTH PLANET

A new theory being advanced by Thomas Van Flandern of the U.S. Naval Observatory and Harrington supposes that Pluto is a former satellite of Neptune. When a hypothetical planet nearly collided with Neptune long ago, its satellite system was disrupted, and Pluto was ejected. During the encounter, powerful forces ripped a chunk off Pluto. This chunk is Pluto's moon.

The intruder planet was itself highly perturbed by the encounter with Neptune and was thrown into an orbit far from the sun. The theory supposes it now orbits there, too faint to be seen. Thus, Harrington and Van Flandern have revived the prospect of a tenth planet, but for a different reason than to account for the motions of Uranus and Neptune.

They propose that this extra planet (if it exists) has a mass three or four times that of earth and orbits 50 to 100 astronomical units from the sun. Some years ago, U.S. astronomer Dennis Rawlins and the Englishman Max Hammerton calculated from the motion

Orbits of the outer planets; Pluto's orbit is more eccentric and inclined than the others.

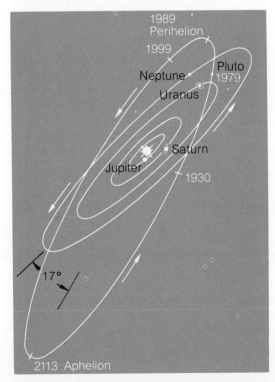

of Neptune that such a body might exist in the direction of the constellations Capricornus, Aquarius, or Pisces. Perhaps, they suggested, it was missed in the Lowell search. If a new search in these areas reveals nothing, then the last hope of a major planet existing beyond Pluto will have evaporated.

OVERRATED FAMILY MEMBER

But should Pluto itself be regarded as a major planet? For one thing, its orbit crosses that of another planet, which no other major planet does. From Jan. 22, 1979 until March 1999, Pluto will come closer to the sun than Neptune, meaning that the solar system temporarily has a "new" outermost planet. Pluto's orbit is in fact reminiscent of Chiron, the minor planet discovered in November 1977 by Charles Kowal at Mt. Palomar, which itself was hailed as the tenth planet before its true diminutive nature became clear.

Chiron spends most of its time out beyond Saturn, but for part of its orbit it crosses Saturn's path to come closer to the sun. Chiron seems to be an icy, low density body similar in nature to the outer moons of Saturn. Does this description sound familiar?

Both Chiron and Pluto may well be examples of the building blocks of the outer planets which were never swept up. Phoebe, the outermost satellite of Saturn, has properties so similar that Phoebe seems almost a twin of Chiron that was captured to become a moon. Is it possible that, instead of being a moon of Neptune that escaped, Pluto is a potential moon that was never captured? And should it, like Chiron, be classified as a mini-planet?

As Pluto moves toward perihelion, its closest approach to the sun, in 1989, astronomers will give increasingly close scrutiny to this controversial—and probably overrated—member of the solar system □

📖 SELECTED READINGS

"Moon believed found for Pluto and for asteroid." *Science News,* July 15, 1978.

"New moons: encounter of serendipitous kind: Plutonian moon and a satellite of asteroid Herculina" by R. A. Kerr. *Science,* August 11, 1978.

"Pluto's satellite." *Sky and Telescope,* September 1978.

Courtesy of Columbia Pictures

Awaiting visitors from space, from *Close Encounters of the Third Kind.*

IS ANYBODY OUT THERE?

by Isaac Asimov

HERE we are, living on a middle-sized planet, circling a middle-sized star we call the sun. That star is part of a galaxy, the Milky Way, that includes some 200,000,000,000 other stars. Beyond our galaxy are 100,000,000,000 other galaxies, each with anywhere from 3,000,000 or 4,000,000 to 3,000,000,000,000 or 4,000,000,000,000 stars. Altogether there may be about 10,000,000,000,000,000,000,000 stars in the universe.

We intelligent beings, *Homo sapiens,* are on a planet circling just one of them. Can we honestly think that nowhere among all those other stars is there another planet carrying intelligent beings? Can we be alone in so large a universe?

And if we're not alone, if we have neighbors, might it not be that some of them are trying to signal us?

HOW TO SIGNAL

Far distant neighbors would have to try to communicate with us with some sort of signal that can cross the vast emptiness of interstellar space. There are, indeed, objects that reach us across interstellar space—for example, charged particles in cosmic rays.

Charged particles, however, aren't suitable for the purpose. Their paths curve in magnetic fields, and every star has a magnetic field. The Milky Way also has an overall magnetic field. Charged particles therefore come looping in on a curved path, and though they end by reaching us from some particular direction, we haven't the faintest idea from that what their original direction of travel was, so that we can't tell where they came from. Such signals would be useless.

Uncharged particles travel in a straight line regardless of magnetic fields. If they are without mass, they travel through vacuum at the speed of light, the maximum velocity, some 300,000 kilometers a second.

There are three kinds of massless, uncharged particles: neutrinos, gravitons, and photons. Neutrinos, which are liberated by the nuclear reactions going on within stars, are almost impossible to detect. Gravitons, which are associated with gravitational fields, are even harder to detect. But photons are easy to detect.

MICROWAVE PHOTONS

Photons are electromagnetic radiation particles. All of them are made up of waves. There are two types of photons that can make their way easily through our atmosphere: the photons associated with waves of visible light, and the photons associated with microwaves, which are about 1,000,000 times longer than those of light.

The signals would be coming from a planet that is circling a star. Every star sends out a great deal of light. If intelligent beings on a planet send out a light signal, the signal might be drowned out in the starlight. On the other hand, ordinary stars are not very rich in microwaves, and a microwave signal sent from a planet would stand out clearly. And if proper instruments are used, microwaves are even easier to detect than light is.

Microwaves come in many wavelengths. Which wavelength should we watch for, and why?

In the early 1940's, a Dutch astronomer calculated that cold hydrogen atoms in deep space sometimes undergo a spontaneous change in configuration that results in the emission of a microwave photon that is 21 centimeters in wavelength. Individual hydrogen atoms undergo the change very rarely, but if there are a great many hydrogen atoms involved, great numbers of photons would be emitted every moment and these could be detected. In 1951 an American physicist did detect these microwave photons, for "empty" space contains a thin scattering of hydrogen atoms that mount up if you consider the tremendous volume of space.

This 21-centimeter wavelength is everywhere, so it is of prime importance in studying the properties of the universe. Any intelligent species would have radio telescopes designed to receive such signals. Therefore, the 21-centimeter wavelength would thus be a natural for deliberate signaling.

If our astronomers ever got a beam of 21-centimeter radiation that contained hardly any other wavelengths, they would become suspicious. If the radiation went on and off, or got stronger and weaker, in a manner that was not entirely regular, and not completely random either, then they would know someone was trying to tell us something.

In this proposed message for intelligences in deep space by Dr. Frank Drake (photo on page 35) black squares are 1's and white squares are 0's. The illustration on the right includes a personlike figure, and the sun and nine planets along the left side. 1's are to be sent out as regular bursts, and 0's are the gaps in between.

Courtesy of Frank Drake

WHERE TO LISTEN

It would be exceedingly expensive and time consuming to try to listen to every star, so we should start with those stars that seem the most likely signalers—stars that have a reasonable chance of possessing a planet inhabited by intelligent beings.

There might be all kinds of life in the universe, but our own form of life is built of the most common elements: hydrogen, oxygen, carbon, and nitrogen. Our form of life has a water background and a backbone of complex carbon compounds. We have, as yet, no evidence that life can exist on a different chemical basis, so we should assume that life elsewhere is fundamentally like our own.

Stars that are considerably more massive than our sun are also considerably brighter and must consume their hydrogen fuel very rapidly to keep from collapsing. Their lifetime is considerably shorter than that of our sun, and probably not long enough to allow the slow processes of planet formation and later evolution of life to develop a highly intelligent species, if life there is fundamentally like our own.

Stars that are considerably less massive than our sun are so dim that a planet would have to circle it at a close distance to be warm enough to possess liquid water on its surface. At such close distances, gravitational effects of the star would slow the planetary rotation and produce temperature extremes during the long day and long night that would not be suitable for life that is fundamentally like our own.

It makes sense, therefore, to concentrate on those stars that are between 0.8 and 1.2 times the mass of the sun.

At least half of the stars in the universe are part of binary systems. It is possible for one or both stars of such a binary system to have planets in stable orbits, but there's less chance of it than in the case of a single star like our sun. Therefore, we ought to concentrate on sunlike single stars.

Naturally, the closer a star is, the less likely it is for its signal to fade with distance—so the stronger the signal, the more likely we are to detect it. Therefore we ought to concentrate on the closest sunlike single stars.

CLOSE SUNLIKE SINGLE STARS

Some of the closest sunlike single stars are sure to be far in the southern skies and invisible from northern latitudes, or, if visible, would always be near the southern horizon. Since the best astronomical equipment we have is concentrated in the northern hemisphere, it makes sense to concentrate on the closest sunlike single stars in the northern sky.

There are three stars, all about 0.8 times the mass of the sun, that seem to fall into this category. They are Epsilon Eridani, which is 10.8 light-years away, Tau Ceti, which is 12.2 light-years away, and Sigma Draconis, which is 18.2 light-years away. A light year is a measure of distance used in astronomy. One light year is the distance light travels in one year, or approximately 9,600,000,000,000 kilometers.

The radio-radar telescope, with its enormous reflector, could be used to receive messages from space.

Cornell University

Senior staff members of the Arecibo Observatory (from left): Harold D. Craft, Jr., Frank D. Drake, and Rolf B. Dyce.

EARLY LISTENING PROJECTS

In 1960 the first real attempt was made to listen to the 21-centimeter wavelength. The attempt was called "Project Ozma." The listening began on April 8, 1960, with absolutely no publicity since the astronomers feared ridicule. It continued for a total of 150 hours through July, and the project then came to an end. The listening concentrated on Epsilon Eridani and Tau Ceti, but nothing was heard. The search was very brief and not very intense.

Since Project Ozma, there have been six or eight other such programs, all at a level that was more modest, in the United States, in Canada, and in the Soviet Union. No signals were picked up.

PROJECT CYCLOPS

In 1971 a group at the U.S. National Aeronautics and Space Administration (NASA) began thinking about something called "Project Cyclops." This would be an array of 1,026 radio telescopes, each 100 meters in diameter. They would be placed in an orderly arrangement and would be steered in unison by a computerized electronic system.

The array would be capable of detecting, from a distance of 100 light-years, the weak radio waves that leak out of equipment on earth. A deliberately emitted message-signal from another civilization could surely be detected at a distance of at least 1,000 light-years. This could make it possible to listen to 1,000,000 different sunlike single stars, and not only two or three very close ones. Such an array of radio telescopes would cost anywhere from $10,000,000,000 to $50,000,000,000.

WHY BOTHER?

Well, suppose we do detect signals from some other civilization. Undoubtedly, they will be more advanced than we because they will have transmitted a detectable signal over far greater distances than we can. If we can interpret what they are saying, we may discover a great deal about the universe that we don't yet know, and that we might not be able to find out by ourselves for many years. We would get a free education, or if not quite free, a priceless one.

Even if we learned one new thing, something that didn't seem very important in itself, it might give us a headstart in a new direction. It would be like looking up one key word in the back of a book of crossword puzzles. It could give us the one clue we need to work out a whole group of words.

Even if we didn't learn anything because we found we couldn't decipher the signals, the effort of deciphering might itself teach us something about communication and help us with our psychological insights here on earth.

The largest radio telescope in the world, the Very Large Array, in New Mexico, consists of 27 antennas spread out over several square kilometers.

ANTIDOTE TO DESPAIR

Even if there was no chance at all of deciphering the message and if we didn't even try, there would be important value just in knowing for certain that out there on a planet circling a certain star was another intelligent species.

• It would mean that we were not alone in the universe, and it might force us to take a new look at the world and at ourselves. We have been so used to thinking of ourselves as lords of the world and as the crown of creation that we have been acting in a dangerously arrogant way. It might do us good to start thinking of ourselves as one of many and as by no means the greatest. For one thing, it might start us to thinking of ourselves as earthlings and encourage us to cooperate.

• It would mean that it was possible for at least one other intelligent species to develop a technology more advanced than our own and to survive. At least one other species would have survived nuclear weapons, overpopulation, pollution, and resource depletion. If they could do it, maybe we could too. It would be a healthy antidote to despair.

MONEY WELL SPENT

Finally, even if we found nothing at all, nothing, it would still be worth it.

• The very attempt to construct the necessary equipment for Project Cyclops might succeed in teaching us a great deal about radio telescopy and would undoubtedly advance the state of the art.

• If we searched the sky with new equipment, new expertise, new delicacy, new persistence, new power, we would surely discover a great many new things about the universe that have nothing to do with advanced civilizations and that don't depend on detecting signals. We can't say what those discoveries would be, or in what direction they would enlighten us, or just how they would prove useful to us. However, knowledge, wisely used, has always been helpful to us in the past and will surely always be helpful to us in the future.

There is every reason, then, to think that the search for extraterrestrial civilizations would be a case of money well spent, however much it would cost □

📖 SELECTED READINGS

"Extraterrestrial intelligence: an observational approach" by B. Murray and others. *Science,* February 3, 1978.

Intelligent Life in the Universe by Carl Sagan and I.S. Shklovskii. Dell, 1968.

"Quest for intelligent life in space is just beginning" by Carl Sagan. *Smithsonian,* May 1978.

We Are Not Alone: The Search for Intelligent Life on Other Worlds by Walter Sullivan. McGraw-Hill, 1966.

World Beyond: A Report on the Search for Life in Space by Ian Ridpath. Harper & Row, 1976.

A relief showing centaurs. The latest solar-system body was named Chiron after a centaur.

A SURPRISE IN THE SOLAR SYSTEM

by Charles T. Kowal

FOR many years, it seemed that all the major features of the solar system were known. There might be other planets beyond Pluto, and there were undoubtedly many thousands of undiscovered asteroids and comets, but we did not expect any major new features or any new types of objects between the known planets. In 1977 two discoveries were made that changed our ideas completely.

In March 1977 rings were discovered around Uranus, and in November, I discovered an object between the orbits of Uranus and Saturn. These discoveries showed us that the solar system is by no means fully explored, and they make us wonder what other surprises may yet be uncovered.

SEARCH FOR DISTANT COMETS

Late in 1976, I began a project called the "Solar System Survey." The original purpose of this program, which is still going on, was to try to discover very distant comets. We normally see comets only when they are rather close to the sun, and everything we know about the distribution of comets is based on this relatively small sample of objects. Yet we know that comets travel out to very great distances, and there must be many that never come close to the sun and thus

that we do not normally see. Therefore, it had to be valuable to find as many distant comets as possible to improve our knowledge of the distribution and origin of all comets.

New photographic materials and techniques had made it possible for us to observe and photograph much fainter and more distant objects than ever before. Done properly, a search for distant comets was bound to turn up other interesting objects, such as unusual asteroids.

The telescope I used for the survey was the 120-centimeter Schmidt telescope—essentially a fast, wide-angle camera—on Palomar Mountain in California. It photographs an area of the sky roughly the size of the bowl of the Big Dipper. The actual photographs are made on 35-centimeter square glass plates. (Ordinary photographic film is not used.)

LOOKING FOR FUZZY OBJECTS

The search technique was fairly simple. I would take photographs of a certain part of the sky on each of two successive nights. I then compared the photographs to see if anything had moved. Actually, each photo showed hundreds of moving objects—the asteroids. There are so many asteroids that most of them have to be ignored. The only

Hale Observatories/Charles T. Kowal

On October 18, 1977, Charles T. Kowal photographed this area of the sky containing the Chiron streak.

objects I studied were those which moved differently from the normal asteroids.

The apparent speed of an object is related to its distance from us. Very distant objects move more slowly, while objects near the earth move faster, making a relatively long streak across the photographic plate. While comets often move at a speed similar to that of normal asteroids, the comets can be distinguished from the asteroids by their fuzzy appearance. So I examined my photographic plates very carefully under a microscope to detect fuzzy objects, or objects moving at unusual speeds.

During the first ten months of my Solar System Survey, I found one not-very-distant comet, and one very unusual asteroid—designated 1977 HB. Most asteroids are confined to a belt between the orbits of Mars and Jupiter, and even the most unusual asteroids pass near this asteroid belt at some point during their revolution about the sun. Asteroid 1977 HB, however, never goes near the asteroid belt. Instead, it travels between the orbits of Venus and Mars. Its average distance from the sun is therefore not very different from the earth's distance. Since this proximity makes asteroid 1977 HB a relatively easy object to reach with a space probe, it may be visited some day,

THE BIG EVENT

The "big event" of the survey came in October 1977. Because of various problems, such as excessive moonlight, I was able to obtain only one pair of plates in that month.

The moonlight was a problem because the 120-centimeter Schmidt telescope is such a "fast" camera that it can not be used while the moon is up—the sky becomes too bright.

The two Survey plates that I managed to obtain were taken on October 18 and 19. Although I examined the plates for conspicuous objects while I was still at the observatory, a detailed examination had to wait until I returned to my office in Pasadena, California. While examining the plates centimeter by centimeter on November 1, suddenly I spotted a very short trail on each of the two plates. It was immediately obvious that some object was moving much more slowly than the asteroids, only slightly faster than the motion of Uranus. It was therefore reasonable to assume that this object was just inside the orbit of Uranus, an assumption that later proved correct.

The only things expected in that part of the Solar System are the comets. Yet this object did not look like a comet, and furthermore, it was much too bright. A normal comet at that distance would have been completely invisible. If this was a comet, it was a huge one. Judging by its brightness, the object was between 150 and 600 kilometers in diameter—a hundred times larger than the nucleus of a typical comet. But if not a comet, what was it?

COMPUTING THE ORBIT

In order to compute the orbit of this object, it was necessary to obtain many more photographs of it. I therefore reported my

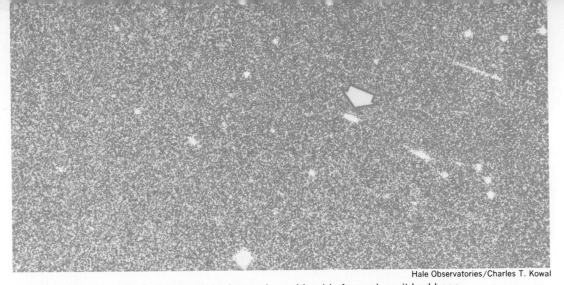

Hale Observatories/Charles T. Kowal

One night later, Kowal's "miniplanet" had moved considerably from where it had been.

find to Brian G. Marsden at the Smithsonian Astrophysical Observatory in Arizona, who runs a clearing-house for new discoveries. He immediately notified other astronomers of my new object, and asked that photographs be taken of it.

Results came in quickly. First, Tom Gehrels, of the University of Arizona, spotted the object on plates he had taken on October 11. Then Richard Green of the California Institute of Technology (Cal Tech), Douglas Richstone, of the University of Pittsburgh, and Tod Boroson, a graduate student at the University of Arizona, all of whom were working together at Palomar, photographed it on November 4. These observations enabled Marsden and James Williams, of Cal Tech's Jet Propulsion Laboratory, to compute a preliminary orbit. These early calculations confirmed that the object was between the orbits of Saturn and Uranus. They also showed that the object's orbit did not resemble the orbits of most comets. It looked more like a planetary orbit. The mystery deepened.

TENTH PLANET?

Meanwhile, the press noticed that something unusual was going on. I started to receive telephone calls from reporters around the United States. Many asked about my discovery of a "tenth planet." I decided to hold a press conference to clarify the situation and prevent sensationalistic reports. With nothing to go on but the preliminary orbit calculations, I was only able to say that the object

was a few hundred kilometers in diameter, that it seemed too small to be a planet, too big to be a comet, and too distant to be an asteroid. For lack of a better term, I called it a "mini-planet." It was already clear that the object was unique, and that it would not fit into any of the current classifications.

Astronomers continued to photograph the object, until, by late November, it became possible to compute a reasonably accurate orbit. Using the improved orbit calculations I was able to find the object on plates I had taken in 1969. These old photographs allowed the calculations to be refined still further. I then found the object on plates taken in 1952. William Liller and Lola Chaisson, of the Center for Astrophysics, then found it on photographic plates made in 1943, 1941, 1936, and, incredibly, 1895. The object had been photographed for more than eighty years before it was discovered.

CHIRON

The time had come to give it a name. Since it was a unique object, I felt that its name should be chosen with great care. Furthermore, I recognize that other objects of the same type might be discovered in the future, so I searched for a well-defined group of mythological characters whose names had not already been used for other objects. I hit upon the Centaurs, those wild creatures who were half man, half horse.

The most important Centaur was Chiron, one of the few of the breed who was well-mannered. He was known for his

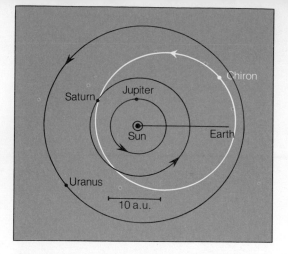

Dots on orbits show locations on January 1, 1977. When Chiron reaches perihelion in 1996, it will be closer to the sun than Saturn. At aphelion it will be close to the orbit of Uranus.

knowledge of astronomy, medicine, and poetry, and had been the teacher of such heroes as Achilles and Aesculapios. Furthermore, he was the son of Saturn and the grandson of Uranus, a pedigree which fit perfectly with the nature of his namesake's orbit. Although the name Chiron had not been used for other objects, this Centaur had already been honored with a place in the sky. Equipped with bow and arrows, Chiron serves as the constellation Sagittarius, the archer.

ECCENTRIC ORBIT

Chiron's orbit, now very accurately determined, is rather eccentric. It takes it from inside the orbit of Saturn to the orbit of Uranus—from 8.5 to 18.9 astronomical units. An astronomical unit is equal to the average distance between the earth and the sun and is about 150,000,000 kilometers.

Chiron takes 50.7 years to complete one revolution around the sun, although this period varies by about two years, because of the gravitational pull of Saturn and Uranus. The orbit of Chiron is inclined only seven degrees to the plane of the ecliptic. Chiron was at the most distant part of its orbit in 1970, and is now moving slowly closer to the sun. It will be closest to the sun in 1996, at which time it will be bright enough to be visible with relatively small telescopes.

In principle, Chiron can come close to both Saturn and Uranus. If it does come close to either of these planets, its orbit may be unstable. That is, someday it may encounter one of these planets and be thrown into a different orbit. But if the orbit is unstable,

why is the object there now? How did it get there? Where did it come from? We just don't know.

Attempts to determine the surface composition of this object have not yet been successful. As Chiron gradually comes nearer, however, it will become bright enough for detailed studies. It should become possible to tell whether the surface of Chiron is made of rock or of ice, or a mixture of the two. This, in turn, will give us some clues about Chiron's origin.

BUT WHAT IS IT?

Chiron is a unique object, and it defies classification. It is too small to be a planet, too distant to have any relation to the asteroids, and too big to be a comet. It also doesn't look like a comet, but we have never seen a comet at such a great distance. The problem of terminology is currently being studied by the International Astronomical Union. At the moment, it seems possible that Chiron will be called a "planetoid" although this word has been synonymous with "asteroid" until now. It is also possible that an entirely new word will be invented. The astronomical community will have to decide. It is also clear that we will have to make more formal definitions of the words "planet" and "asteroid." How big must an object be in order to be called a planet?

So what has Chiron taught us? At the moment, the answer is—nothing. We don't know its past or its future, and we don't know what it is although we will undoubtedly find these things out in the future. For now, one might say that Chiron has only taught us what little we know about the outer solar system. It has not answered questions; it has raised new ones. But after all, we study science because we are intrigued by the universe, and new mysteries can only make the world more fascinating □

SELECTED READINGS

"Does Object Kowal foretell more mysteries?" *Science Digest*, February 1978.

"Kowal discovers a miniplanet." *Astronomy*, February 1978.

"More about Chiron." *Sky and Telescope*, February 1978.

Linda Richards is being helped by a Capuchin monkey, which can do many small chores. The monkey was trained through a project for aiding the handicapped by Tufts—New England Medical Center.

BEHAVIORAL SCIENCES

BEHAVIORAL SCIENCES
REVIEW OF THE YEAR

Drawing courtesy of J. M. Kennedy

Psychologist John M. Kennedy of the University of Toronto is finding that even congenitally blind persons "picture" and can draw things. The drawing is a hand with crossed fingers.

Brain chemistry and behavior. It is becoming increasingly apparent that complex rivers of neurotransmitters—the biochemical signal-carriers between brain cells—are undeniably intertwined with emotional states. In some cases it is believed that the balance of neurotransmitters in the brain dictates a person's behavior; in other cases, a person's behavior is thought to influence neurotransmitter balance. Most often, it appears to be a combination of the two.

The latest results in the burgeoning field of brain research indicate that the neurotransmitters dopamine and norepinephrine, among others, are involved in schizophrenia, depression, and other mental disorders. Autopsy studies reveal that the brains of schizophrenia victims contain about 50 per cent more dopamine than those of non-schizophrenics. Researchers warn, though, that this does not necessarily mean that a dopamine excess causes schizophrenia, but merely that it is associated with it. Other studies, by the U.S. National Institute of Mental Health's Frederick K. Goodwin, suggest that depression—and its opposite, mania—may occur more often in persons whose daily and seasonal sleep-wake cycles are out of phase with the rest of the population. These cycles also appear to be accompanied by curious shifts in the levels of several brain chemicals.

Brain chemicals are also implicated in many other behaviors beyond those in serious psychiatric conditions. In a study of 26 enlisted men in the U.S. Navy—the first study of its kind with human beings—Goodwin reports that "human aggression may have a biological component to it." The psychiatrist found that highly aggressive individuals had uncommonly high levels of the neurochemical norepinephrine, and those who were least aggressive had high levels of serotonin.

Through the use of taught and learned symbols on a computerized keyboard, Sherman and Austin Chimpanzee can accurately request and give 11 foods to one another.

E. Sue Savage-Rumbaugh

Researchers have also found that specific anatomical areas of the brain appear to influence certain behaviors. The overproduction of dopamine in schizophrenics, for example, was found accumulated in the limbic system, that part of the brain thought to mediate emotions. Investigators at Hunter College and Albert Einstein College of Medicine, both in New York City, reported that narcotic addiction may occur in specific brain regions. Diane Avallone of Hunter and Eliot L. Gardner of Einstein found in animal experiments that narcotic tolerance and dependence might be centered in two areas of the brain: the dorsal thalamus of the central brain and the periaqueductal gray matter in the upper brain stem.

Primate studies. A 64-kilogram lowland gorilla named Koko was hailed as the world's first "talking" gorilla during 1978. Under the tutoring of Stanford University graduate student Francine "Penny" Patterson, Koko has learned to communicate using 375 hand signals. She is said to have an IQ equivalent score of between 85 and 95, a score approaching low normal human intelligence. Patterson claims that Koko's successes refute claims that gorillas are not as intelligent as chimpanzees, the first primates taught language.

For their part, chimpanzees also made significant strides in 1978. Reportedly for the first time ever, two chimpanzees at the Yerkes Regional Primate Research Center in Georgia communicated with each other, using symbolic language taught them by humans. The chimps—Sherman and Austin—used a computerized keyboard made up of geometric symbols to ask each other for various meals. The geometric symbols represented specific foods.

Chimps in the wild were also observed doing something humans do—but this was a less encouraging observation. Naturalist Jane Goodall observed chimpanzees in Tanzania exhibiting brutal, gang warfare-type behavior that seemed to parallel behavior in human, premeditated murder.

A parent's grief at the loss of a child can make the familiar world as alien as a distant planet, ringing with echoes of past remembrances.

Sudden Infant Death Syndrome. It is estimated that sudden-infant-death syndrome (SIDS) mysteriously claims the lives of about 10,000 infants a year in the United States alone. Until recently the causes of such deaths almost totally eluded researchers. In the last few years, however, an increasing number of clues have been uncovered. Among the most intriguing is the possibility that sudden infant death is triggered by a subtle "learning disability"—a minor but potentially lethal flaw in the infant's development process. According to Brown University psychologist Lewis P. Lipsitt, a breakdown may occur when the youngster's ability to regain breathing after a breathing stoppage during sleep, fails to evolve normally from a totally biological, protective reflex present at birth, into a "learned, voluntary response" at two to four months of age. Very brief periods of breathing stoppage are considered normal during sleep.

Schizophrenia diagnosis. Ever since the term schizophrenia came into use more than fifty years ago, its use has been a source of constant debate among psychiatrists. The point in question: "What, exactly, is schizophrenia?" The answer to that question has changed somewhat over the years. And today, according to Chicago Medical School psychiatrists Michael Alan Taylor and Richard Abrams, the definition generally accepted throughout the United States leaves more than a little to be desired. In a study of a rural New York State inpatient facility, the researchers determined that hospital doctors diagnosed five times more persons as schizophrenics than truly fit the diagnostic label. Taylor and Abrams say they used diagnostic criteria "more rigourous [and] reliable" than those used by most psychiatrists in the United States. Misdiagnosis, they add, carries the risk of using potentially dangerous drugs on the wrong patients. The researchers call for more stringent diagnostic procedures. The American Psychiatric Association is now in the midst of redefining schizophrenia and several other emotional illnesses for its new diagnostic manual.

Anthony de Casper, of the University of North Carolina, studies a newborn's recognition of sounds. The baby in the photo also has a set of earphones.

Delayed reaction to the holocaust. For its Jewish victims, the Nazi holocaust left a devastating psychological mark. It now appears that some children of holocaust survivors, upon reaching the age of their parents at the time of the holocaust, are undergoing holocaust-related emotional trauma. Sylvia Axelrod of the Long Island Jewish-Hillside Medical Center in New York reported that 80 per cent of the 30 second-generation survivor patients studied at the center's psychiatric facility suffered problems at an age corresponding to that at which their parents were interred in concentration camps. Moreover, the children's difficulties seemed to revolve around fantasies of what their parents did to survive and of their parent's prosecutors.

Joel Greenberg

HYPERACTIVE CHILDREN

by Sharon Sobell

MARK cannot sit still. At school he frequently does not complete his assignments. He often runs around the classroom and disrupts other students with his incessant talking and clowning around. Mark acts impulsively, and he often leaves the room without the teacher's permission. His impatience and frequent temper tantrums make it difficult for him to keep friends. Although he has above-average intelligence, Mark has trouble with his reading and writing, often reversing letters (b=p) and words (cat=tac).

At home, Mark has similar problems. He constantly fights with his younger sister, rides his bicycle recklessly, has difficulty catching a ball, and has trouble sitting through a television program. Because Mark has experienced few successes—academically as well as socially—he has begun to develop a very poor opinion of himself.

IDENTIFYING THE PROBLEM

Mark may be suffering from the hyperkinetic-behavior syndrome, often labeled "minimal brain dysfunction" and commonly referred to as "hyperactivity" or "hyperkinesis." No one knows exactly how many children suffer from this childhood disorder. But an educated guess based on preliminary research findings indicates that approximately 3 to 5 per cent of all school-age children are affected, most of them male.

Although actual diagnosis of the hyperkinetic-behavior syndrome is not simple, hyperactive children typically have several characteristics in common. Hyperactivity is just one of the symptoms. Hyperactive children also tend to behave inappropriately in many situations. They appear unable to control their actions and seem to have much difficulty in learning self-control. Hyperactive

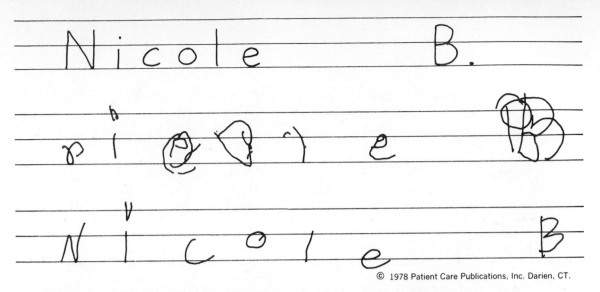

Samples of a hyperactive child's handwriting before and after medication. The top line was written by the teacher; middle line was written before medication; bottom line was written four days after medication began.

children usually have short attention spans and are easily distracted or frustrated. Their behavior is often described as fidgity, restless, impulsive, and quarrelsome. They may have emotional problems and specific learning difficulties.

Some children who are mentally retarded (an IQ of less than 80) or who have major organic disability, such as cerebral palsy, may display similar behavior. But these children do not fall within the diagnostic category of hyperactivity.

Because diagnosing hyperactivity is complex, getting opinions from one or more specialists is frequently desirable. Diagnostic evaluations should include a thorough examination by the child's pediatrician and, in some cases, consultation with a child psychologist, psychiatrist, or neurologist. Careful reports collected from parents, teachers, and school counselors are also helpful in properly identifying the hyperactive child.

WHAT CAUSES HYPERACTIVITY?

The exact origin of the hyperkinetic-behavior syndrome is unknown. No single cause has been established. The disorder has been ascribed by numerous researchers to genetic, biological, physiological, social, and environmental factors.

Although there are many theories about the causes, hard evidence is scarce. For example, there is little evidence to support the theory of brain damage as a major cause.

Since research has shown that the parents of some hyperactive children were themselves hyperactive, it may be that certain children inherit a predisposition for hyperactivity.

Other possible causes cited by various investigators include food additives, radiation leaks from television sets or fluorescent lights, lead poisoning, vitamin deficiencies, and complications of pregnancy, including premature birth. Other investigators attribute hyperkinetic behavior to parent-child relationships or to classroom teaching techniques. Others theorize that the disorder develops only from a combination of certain genetic, environmental, or neurological or biochemical contributors.

Current knowledge about the causes of the hyperkinetic-behavior syndrome emphasizes the need for very thorough diagnostic evaluations before any treatment is undertaken. For example, a child with behavior problems may not be hyperactive. Instead, he may be suffering from poor eyesight or hearing, allergies, improper nutrition, a chaotic home environment, physical diseases, or emotional disorders. There is much disagreement about the causes, prevalence, and treatment of the hyperkinetic-behavior syndrome. The reason for this is that many children are assigned the diagnostic label without proper diagnostic evaluations.

There is really no "cure" for hyperactivity. While research continues to seek an understanding of the underlying causes, treatments have been developed to provide relief of the symptoms. Management of the condition may involve a variety of methods.

TREATMENT BY MEDICATION

If a child has been diagnosed as hyperactive, his doctor may prescribe a "psychoactive" drug. This kind of drug acts primarily to affect mood, thinking processes, and behavior. The most effective medications, to date, are the stimulants. Administered properly, these drugs produce favorable therapeutic results in 70 to 80 per cent of children with hyperactivity.

A commonly held belief is that these drugs have a "paradoxical" effect in children; that is, the drugs stimulate adults and calm children. Recent research has shown that, given equivalent dosages, normal adults and hyperactive children respond in much the same way: they both exhibit improved attention spans and task performance.

With medication, the child is no longer driven by his impulses. Rather, he is more able to control his behavior. As a result, he frequently gets along better with his peers and, therefore, increases his self-esteem. In school his attention and concentration are better. Teachers frequently report that learning performance improves. The effects of medication also make the child more accessible to other forms of treatment such as special-education procedures and counseling.

MONITORING OF DOSAGE

Stimulants are generally safe. But there can be side effects such as insomnia, appetite loss, and, in some cases, irritability, stomachaches, or headaches. These can be controlled by reducing the dosage and changing the time of day the drug is given.

A few fears have been expressed about the long-term use of medication in children. Some parents fear drug taking by their children will lead to dependency or drug abuse in adolescence or adulthood. Others fear the drugs may be toxic. While these fears are understandable, the majority of research studies do not support them. Of course, any type of medication must be used with caution. Children who are taking medications prescribed by a physician should be closely supervised and taught proper respect for the potency of drugs.

Reports that stimulants cause growth suppression are not yet proven. It is prudent for the physician to monitor the height and weight of the child at fairly regular intervals (about twice a year). The physician should also observe the child during "drug-free" periods such as summer vacation. During this time, the physician can reevaluate the child's need to continue medication or determine if dosages should be adjusted.

Stimulants are the physician's first choice of drugs when medicating a child with

the hyperkinetic-behavior syndrome. Suppose a child does not show improved behavior after a week or two, or side effects, such as insomnia, persist. Then other types of medication are sometimes prescribed instead of, or concurrently with, stimulants. These include "major" tranquilizers, "minor" tranquilizers, antidepressants, or antihistamines. Little systematic research has been done with the minor tranquilizers or the antihistamines, and, to date, the usefulness of these drugs is questionable.

The major tranquilizers and antidepressants have been shown to be somewhat helpful, particularly for reducing hyperactive behavior. But they are not as effective as stimulants. Furthermore, the side effects of the major tranquilizers and antidepressants may be more severe than those of stimulants. Also, high dosages tend to reduce a child's ability to learn tasks that require sustained attention. For that reason they should be prescribed and monitored with great care.

TREATMENT BY DIET

A somewhat new and still controversial therapy for hyperactivity includes a special diet advocated by Dr. Ben Feingold. He is an allergist and pediatrician with the Kaiser-Permanente Medical Center of San Francisco. This diet has strong appeal to parents who are unhappy about the use of medication for hyperactivity. It excludes all foods and medicines containing artificial flavorings, colorings, and an ingredient called salicylate (a type of salt) from the child's diet.

Examples of foods eliminated from the child's diet are ice cream, bakery goods, luncheon meats, tea, powdered-drink mixes, and other soft drinks. Some fruits and vegetables that are forbidden are blackberries, grapes, raisins, currants, peaches, strawberries, tomatoes, and cucumbers. Artificially flavored and colored medicines and vitamins are also excluded, as is common aspirin.

Dr. Feingold has reported that, from his clinical experiences, some 30 to 50 per cent of hyperactive children show improvement with this diet. However, it is important to realize that its usefulness for treating hyperactivity is still being studied. Parents are encouraged to consult with their child's doc-

Kaiser-Permanente Medical Center, San Francisco

Dr. Ben Feingold claims success in treating hyperactive children by eliminating artificial food coloring, certain additives, and "junk foods" in general.

tor before the child undertakes such a diet, particularly since it may reduce the intake of certain important vitamins.

TREATMENT BY PSYCHOLOGICAL MEANS

Some parents have found it useful to combine drug treatment for the child with a program such as family counseling or behavior modification. While individual psychotherapy is generally of little benefit to the child, therapy for both the child and his parents can be helpful. By counseling, the therapist may help the parents to understand and deal more effectively with their child's problem.

Also, with the help and guidance of a competent therapist, parents can try one of many behavior-modification techniques in learning to work better with their hyperactive child. Behavior modification typically involves rewarding desirable behavior and ignoring undesirable ones. A few examples follow:

• Tommy's parents have set up a system of "token" rewards to assist him in controlling his behavior. Tommy, when he acts appropriately—by sitting quietly at the dinner table, for example—is rewarded with a token (coin). Tommy works to accumulate these tokens, which are later exchanged for a desired item or activity.

• Bobby's parents have found a way to

deal with his sloppiness, particularly his messy, unkept room. Mom, Dad, and Bobby have established a "contract" (usually a written agreement). All have agreed that if Bobby keeps his room neat for one week he will be given the special privilege of staying up later to watch a well-liked television program. But if Bobby does not clean up his room as he agreed to do, he is made to "overcorrect" his behavior. That is, he not ony cleans up his own room, but also helps his sister and brother straighten up theirs.

• Karen's parents use several techniques to help her control her behavior. First of all, they make sure they always praise her good behavior, especially after she has been punished for being bad and later acts appropriately. They also have used "modeling" techniques whereby they encourage her to imitate the good behavior of her friends and her favorite characters on television and in books.

TREATMENT BY PARENTAL COOPERATION

Because of his behavior, a hyperactive child may be in constant trouble both at home and in school. He may be described as a "bad boy." This label, in turn, leads him to develop a poor self-image. Parents can help a child feel better about himself if they learn effective ways of dealing with his behavior. For example, parents can help a child experience success by assisting him in the completion of a small project such as a puzzle. They can help the child learn to control his impulsiveness by closely supervising his activities.

Setting limits and making and enforcing rules can assist the child in gaining self-control. Overactive behavior may be channeled into sports activities such as wrestling and swimming. To cope with the child's short attention span and inability to complete tasks, they may divide his work into small units and praise him as he finishes each part of the task. Parents can also assist by sharing the child's interests and by helping him with his schoolwork.

In addition to some of the previously mentioned techniques, helping the hyperactive child at school sometimes involves special education and tutoring. Because learning problems may indicate a hyperactive child, it is important that parents, teachers, doctors, and school counselors consult about special education opportunities available within the child's school system.

THE FUTURE AND THE HYPERKINETIC CHILD

Some early studies have shown that overactivity tends to diminish in adolescence. However, the hyperactive adolescent may still be noticeably more restless, impulsive, distractible, and emotionally unstable than his peers. Underachievement, difficulties in focusing attention, and poor self-esteem may remain major problems even into adulthood. And these feelings may increase the vulnerability to delinquency, alcoholism, and mental illness.

Some clinicians believe that the future of the hyperactive child may be determined by whether or not the child receives early treatment. They reason that treatment that helps the child to improve his self-control will strengthen his self-image and reduce the risk of future problems. However, some clinicians believe treatment at any age is useful. An investigation into the effectiveness of treating adolescents and adults is now taking place.

On the other hand, there is some evidence that the flexibility and independence in adult life may be more compatible for the hyperactive individual than the restricted world of childhood. In some cases, hyperactive behaviors, which cause problems during youth, become assets in later life. Followup research has shown that a number of adults who were hyperactive as children are lively, energetic extroverts. And they function very successfully in jobs that allow flexibility and individual freedom and which require endless energy, an outgoing manner, and spontaneity □

SELECTED READINGS

"Childhood hyperactivity: a new look at treatment and causes" by G. Kolata. *Science,* February 3, 1978.

"Food additives and hyperactivity." *Science,* February 3, 1978.

"Hyperactives as teens: problems linger." *Science News,* December 10, 1977.

"Methylphenidate (Ritalin) in hyperkinetic children" by R. Sprague. *Science,* December 23, 1977.

© Ted Spagna

SLEEP AND THE ELDERLY

by Joel Greenberg

ACCORDING to Wilse Webb, a psychologist at the University of Florida, people and certain animals sleep when and as long as they do because at some point in their development that schedule meant the difference between life and death. "All those humanoids who stayed in caves when it was most dangerous and least effective to be out hunting—at night—survived," says Webb. Similarly, sheep, cattle, and goats sleep only two to four hours a day because those who lingered behind the rest of the group faced the prospect of becoming some other animal's dinner.

RISK OF SLEEP

Whether or not it is indeed a by-product of the survival instinct, there is growing indication that sleep may be a crucial mechanism in survival's antithesis—death. Particularly among the elderly, the impact of sleep patterns upon illness and death processes may

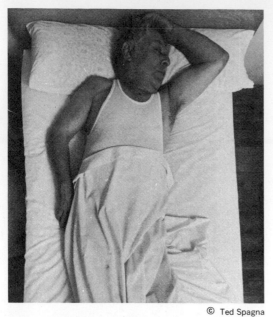

© Ted Spagna

Research on sleep and aging is aimed at trying to discover why sleep becomes a problem with age.

be profound. And although the study of sleep in older persons is just in its infancy, researchers believe there are already indications pointing to such a sleep-illness-death link. "Sleep by its nature is a period of severe risk for the organism," says William C. Dement, director of the sleep research center at Stanford University in California. Dement feels there may even exist a "sudden adult death syndrome" that could be the primary instrument of death in some cases among the elderly.

Such informal, provocative hypotheses kept most participants awake at an early 1978 gathering of sleep researchers at the National Institute on Aging NIA in Bethesda, Maryland. Though the meeting was primarily a brainstorming session designed to lay the groundwork for future studies on sleep and aging, the discussion was based on an expanding, if still preliminary, body of research results.

"So many people in their middle and late years have sleep problems," says NIA Director Robert M. Butler. "Through the study of sleep and sleep pathology there may be some clues about organic brain damage as well as fundamental central nervous-system information in the elderly." A comprehensive review of research thus far points to a number of correlations between sleep patterns and aging.

LONG AND SHORT SLEEP

Some of the most striking data come from an American Cancer Society ACS six-year follow up of more than 1,000,000 people in the United States in the 1960's. Although primarily designed to pinpoint certain antecedents of cancer, the study also yielded a number of previously unrecognized characters of sleep. It showed, for instance, that the elderly—here defined as older than 65—are prone to "short sleep" or to "long sleep." By short sleep we mean four to five hours or less a night. Long sleep is nine to ten hours or more. And throughout the large population sample this held true regardless of other diseases or illnesses that were present, according to Daniel F. Kripke of the Veterans Administration Hospital in San Diego, California.

But what particularly stunned Kripke and others analyzing the data was an 80 per cent increase in mortality among those who slept for extremely long nightly periods over death rates for average and short-length sleepers. Moreover, although only four per cent of all those in the sample who died slept longer or shorter than average, about 75 per cent of deaths associated with long or short sleep occurred in subjects over 65. And even those who slept just one hour more or less than the average 7 to 7.9 hours nightly were more likely to die, according to Kripke.

BODY OF EVIDENCE

Even though the results contain no data on specific causes of death, the strong correlations between death and "pathological sleep"—especially over such a large sample—warrant further examination, the scientists agree. "No question, there's a powerful relationship between how long you report you sleep and mortality," says Allan Rechtschaffen of the University of Chicago department of psychiatry. "The question now is 'why.' We have to look at how illness affects sleep, how sleep affects illness, and how sleep affects recovery from illness." And despite some long-held popular beliefs about bed rest, "We still don't have any evidence that sleep helps recovery from illness," Rechtschaffen says.

Evidence that does exist from the ACS and other studies on sleep and aging, includes:

• Persons who use sleeping pills often were 50 per cent more likely to die within the six-year period of the ACS study. "This does not prove that sleeping pills increase your chances of death," Kripke says. "But it certainly raises the question. We do not know the long-term effects of these drugs," he cautions.

• Persons over 65 average 13 prescriptions a year. The institutionalized elderly are on 6.1 drugs at any one time, according to NIA Director Butler.

• The fear of death among the elderly seems related to sleep problems, Butler says. Forty-five per cent deny death or are extremely anxious about it, but at the same time "there is a great desire to die in one's sleep" rather than while awake, he says.

• Complaints of sleep problems appear to increase with age.

• Increases in heart disease, stroke, cancer, and suicide mortality have all been correlated with patterns of extremely long or short nightly sleep.

• The incidence of waking from sleep during the night increases sharply with age. This is a prominent characteristic among the elderly, even in the "healthy, active, working" women studied by Webb at the University of Florida. While most reported little difficulty in falling asleep initially, 44 per cent of the women described their nightly sleep as "light." A study by Harold Zepelin, a psychologist at Oakland University in Rochester, Michigan, indicates that older people are more easily awakened by external stimuli than young people, especially during the first two thirds of the night. Other studies suggest that stage 4, or "slow wave," sleep declines with age in males.

• Increased numbers of bathroom expeditions to urinate seem to contribute to the high incidence of awakenings, Zepelin says.

• While elderly females show comparatively little of the stage 4, slow-wave decrease which is seen in males, they do exhibit erratic sleep patterns in the REM (rapid eye movement) and third (high electroencephalograph voltage and slow, delta waves) stages of sleep.

• Brain blood flow, particularly in the brain stem and midbrain, appears to increase in pressure in volume during sleep, primarily in the REM stage. Other data suggest that blood flow decreases in stage 2, a relatively low electroencephalograph voltage stage, characterized by intermittent, short sequences of waves.

• A "striking drop" in the levels of brain neurotransmitters norepinephrin and epinephrin was found during REM and stages 3 and 4 in a study of "healthy old men" by Patricia Prinz of the University of Washington in Seattle, Washington. "This is the opposite of what I expected," says Prinz, who also reported "wide swings in heart beat and respiration during REM."

• Snoring also seems to be more widespread among the aged, especially in women. Preliminary data indicate that heavy snoring may be a predictor of hypertension and heart

For many elderly people, dozing throughout the day becomes habitual.

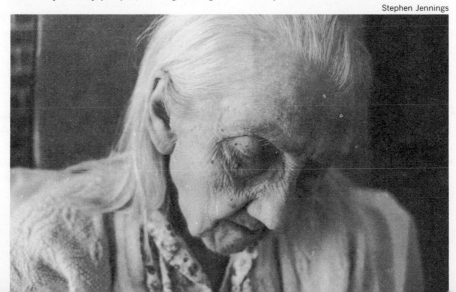

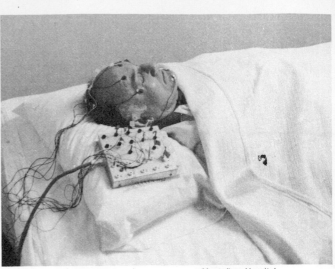

Montefiore Hospital

Dr. Elliot Weitzman of the Sleep-Wake Disorder Center at Montefiore Hospital, New York, monitors an all-night recording of brain waves, chin-muscle tone, eye movements, respiration, and heart rate of a sleeping patient.

disease, and that sleeping pills may contribute to converting snores to more serious problems of sleep apnea, or temporary cessation of breathing.

APNEA

Of all the potential causes of death directly related to sleep, apnea appears the most likely suspect. Also implicated as a cause of sudden infant death, apnea is seen with growing frequency among those older than 65. "Sleep apnea clearly gets worse with age and clearly can be a cause of death by the time a man or woman reaches 65," says Elliot Weitzman, director of the Sleep-Wake Disorders Unit at Montefiore Hospital and Medical Center in New York City. "We've had people referred to us [diagnosed] as presenile dementia that turned out to have severe sleep apnea."

Philipson, who is conducting a variety of metabolic and biological investigations of sleep in the elderly, says that "breathing during sleep may be serving very different functions than when a person is awake ... the control systems—metabolic and behavioral—may be quite different." Arousal from sleep, a frequent occurrence among the elderly, "can have a profound influence on breathing," Philipson says. "We know that the elderly person has less oxygen pressure

and therefore is vulnerable to hypoxemia [deficient blood oxygenation] during sleep." If a person's arousal response is impaired—as studies suggest it may be in the aged—"then they are less apt to wake up" during a threat to respiration, he says. "This can cause severe hypoxia, which could aggravate other medical conditions and maybe [result in] death during sleep," Philipson suggests.

SLEEPING PILLS

Such risks may well be compounded by the wide use of prescription drugs among the elderly, says Dement. "The situation of prescribing drugs to the elderly is abominable," he says. "Hypnotics unquestionably depress respiration—this could be one of the most important points. [Doctors] assume that most of these people will take these drugs for the rest of their lives ... the drugs may actually shorten that life." More than 12,000,000 prescriptions a year are written for flurazepam, a sleeping agent with the brand name of Dalmane. "We have to know whether that drug shortens or prolongs life," says Kripke.

There are other sleep disturbances—insomnia, excessive daytime sleepiness or narcolepsy, seizures, teeth grinding, and circadian, or day-night rhythm fluctuations—that appear more frequently with age. But Webb cautions there is a critical difference between abnormalities and natural changes—not necessarily unhealthy—that simply result from old age. "We don't want to overtreat 'benign insomnia,' " he says, "if it's not affecting the rest of the person's waking life. A person may need some counseling to help cope with it, but that may be all."

NOT SLEEP ATHLETES

Webb views the sleep changes among the aged as "a running down of a process. The change in sleep is akin to not being able to run the 100-yard dash as well as you could before," he says. He terms college-age persons—a group that makes up much of the sleep study volunteer population—"sleep athletes." As people get older, he suggests, "the sleep process becomes a little less athletic than it used to be."

The peak of healthy, deep sleep seems to occur in early adolescence, when "sleep has all the beauty we like to ascribe to it—depth [and] big, slow waves," says Dement. When the youngster awakens, he or she is "totally awake . . . bounding around for 16 hours." From that point on, the sleep structure gradually erodes. "We see a deterioration even from 12 to 16 years old," says Ismet Karacen of the U.S. Veterans Administration Hospital in Houston, Texas.

Still, the conglomeration of study results points to an increase in pathological problems in the elderly beyond the by-products of natural aging. "A perfectly normal pulmonary system can show itself to be dysfunctional in sleep," Webb says. "It is conceivable," he says, that some aspects of sleep might constitute a cause of death, particularly along older persons. "Some people sleep considerably more or less [after 65] than they did at an earlier age," he says. The psychologist, though, says he is not overly concerned about persons who sleep one or even two hours more or less than the seven-and-a-half-hour mean sleep time. It's those who sleep more than 10 and one-half hours or less than four and one-half hours that he terms "pathological—probably due to a biochemical alteration or CNS [central nervous system] disorder."

BIZARRE SCHEDULES

One external factor that might transform a merely eccentric sleeper into a pathological one is a highly structured sleeping schedule such as those used in many nursing homes—where five per cent of all the elderly reside, but 25 per cent die. "Many nursing homes operate on strange schedules, primarily for the convenience of scheduling

Stephen Jennings

Being awakened at a very early hour for breakfast interferes with a patient's usual sleep pattern.

work shifts," Zepelin says. "The patients may get up at 4 or 5 a.m., have breakfast at 6, lunch at 10 and supper at 4 or 5 p.m."

In its preliminary recommendations, the workshop group calls for studies of "bizarre sleep-wake schedules in nursing homes" as part of a wide range of behavioral, biological, metabolic, and epidemiological studies on sleep and aging. "During sleep we may have some of the most dangerous threats to the organism and the brain," says Rechtschaffen. "Poor sleep among the aged may be a sign of the brain's growing failure to react to these challenges."

PREDICTING DEATH?

Dement speculates that one eventually might be able to predict death—and try to prevent it—through sophisticated measurements of cerebral blood flow, cardiac function, metabolism, and other interconnected mechanisms during sleep as well as wakefulness. "[Sleep's] mechanisms are crucially situated in the brain stem," he says.

"Sleep and waking behavior change with age—we have to find out the cause and effect." Dement says. "We know that disturbed sleep can produce a hell on earth" □

📖 SELECTED READINGS

"Biology of aging" by L. Hayflich. *Natural History,* August 1977.
"The science of sleep" by Joan Arehart-Treichel. *Science News,* March 26, 1977.

A very famous bright firstborn was Albert Einstein seen here posed with his sister.

FIRSTBORNS MAY BE BRIGHTER

by Herbert Yahraes

IS there any advantage—or disadvantage—to being the first, second, third, fourth . . . or last child in the family? Put another way, does birth order make any difference?

This question has fascinated hundreds of investigators in the mental health and allied fields and has given rise to many research projects. Generally, the answer has been yes. A child's ordinal position in the family has been reported to be linked to intelligence, achievement, juvenile delinquency, mental illness, success or failure in marriage, and a number of other factors. However, much of this research is now considered to have had no strong scientific merit.

BIRTH ORDER AND SPACING

So far, the most comprehensive study taking into account not only birth order and sex but also the spacing between children is the one carried out by Helen L. Koch of the University of Chicago in the 1950's. It involved the 5- and 6-year-old children of 384 families. Each child had one brother or sister. The children's teachers rated them on a number of behaviors.

Among Koch's findings were the following:

• Birth order interacted most frequently with the factor of sex. When a child and his or her sibling were of the same sex, there were few differences in characteristics that could be attributed to birth order; when they were opposite in sex, there were many differences.

• Firstborns with a sibling of the opposite sex were judged more quarrelsome, jealous, faultfinding, exhibitionistic, and insistent on rights. In the case of second-borns, the trend seemed to be in the opposite direction.

• Boys with a much older brother, as compared with those having a much older sister, received higher average ratings on friendliness to peers, gregariousness, popularity, leadership, kindness, competitiveness, insistence on rights, and cooperativeness.

• Firstborn girls with a brother less than 2 years younger tended to score higher in all the socially positive traits than firstborn boys with a brother. But these girls also had a higher average rating in quarrelsomeness, criticalness, insistence on rights, jealousy, and competitiveness.

• Boys in the groups with the wider spacings—from 2 to 4 years and from 4 to 6 years—were more self-confident, active, aggressive, ambitious, better in sports, less apprehensive socially, and had a wider range of interests. This finding fits in with the hypothesis that when children have been born several years apart, they often have more playmates of their own sex, age, and choosing, and thus are more likely to develop self-confidence in their relations with other children.

• When the spacing was less than 2 years, firstborn girls with brothers insisted more strongly on their rights than firstborn boys with brothers. Boys, on the average, insisted on their rights more strongly than girls only when the age difference was from 2 to 4 years.

THE FIRST RECEIVES THE MOST ATTENTION

Common sense suggests a number of reasons why firstborns might be different from children born later. One is that, for at least a year or two, the parents can and do give them more time and attention. For instance, investigators studying the behavior of mothers while feeding newborn infants have observed that the mothers talk more to firstborn babies, provide more stimulation of other forms, and spend more time with their firstborn babies in activities other than those strictly associated with feeding.

Most parents focus their combined attentions on their firstborn. They talk more to the child and provide it with more stimulations than later-born children.

Studies show that first-borns show the most anxiety and are less likely to participate in dangerous sports such as auto racing.

Gerry Cranham/Photo Researchers

Brian Sutton-Smith, of Teachers College, Columbia University, and B. G. Rosenberg, of Bowling Green State University, Ohio, reviewed the work of several hundred other investigators, conducted studies of their own, and published the results in *The Sibling* (1970). It is the Bible in its field, but some important investigations have been made since it appeared.

The parents of firstborns, in addition to giving them more attention during the earliest years, are less expert about bringing up children than they are likely to be later and may expect too much of the children when they grow up—or possibly too little. Sutton-Smith and Rosenberg report studies indicating that mothers of firstborns do expect more of them and put more pressure on them for achievement both in babyhood and later than do mothers of later-born children. The pattern holds when the mothers of the firstborns have another child: the firstborns continue to be pushed. Perhaps because of the parental pushing, investigators have found that firstborn children tend to show more anxiety than those who come later.

ANXIETY IN THE FIRSTBORN

According to one group of studies reported in *The Sibling,* when college students were confronted with a dangerous or anxiety-arousing situation, the firstborns showed a greater desire than the later-borns to be associated with other people while waiting for the anxiety situation. In psychological parlance, they showed affiliative behavior. It has been theorized that firstborn children learn such behavior early in childhood because every time they are troubled or in pain their mothers rush to give solace; later-born children have to learn to fend for themselves.

Since studies of young children tend to agree that firstborns show the most anxiety, it is possible that the firstborn students in the experiments mentioned above arrived at the laboratory in a more fearful state than the others. In line with this possibility are reports that later-born children are more likely to participate in dangerous sports.

POPULARITY

For one reason or another—possibly related to the way they have exercised responsibility or to their level of anxiety—firstborn are apparently not the most popular with their peers. In one study, more than 1,000 children in grades 3, 4, 5, and 6 chose which classmates they liked most and which they liked least. The most popular turned out to be, in order, youngest children, only children, and the second of two children. Then came the second of more than two children, firstborn children, and, as the least popular, middle children.

Norman Miller and Geoffrey Maruyama, of the University of Southern California, recently studied 1,750 grade school children in Riverside, California, to test the idea that last-born children should be the most popular. The children were asked individually:

Suppose you were picking teams to play ball during recess. Who in your class would you most like to have on your team?

Pretend your teacher is going to let all of the children in your class sit next to his/her best friend. If you had your choice, who would you like to sit next to?

Suppose your teacher told you that you could pick a work partner from anyone in your class. Who would you pick to be your work partner doing school work?

Most often chosen to be teammates and seatmates were last-born children. Then came the middle-born. Last were the firstborn.

A CONTRARY VIEW

A number of birth-order studies were recently analyzed by Carmi Schooler, a social psychologist with the U.S. National Institute of Mental Health, whose early work had contributed to the view that birth order is important. He has since become skeptical.

As an instance of why he thinks most research on this question has produced misleading results, he cites a study of some 600 National Merit Scholarship finalists whose aptitude, to judge from test scores, placed them in the top 0.5 per cent of the general population, or even higher. More of these students had been the firstborn than would have been expected on the basis of chance alone. Similar findings relating birth order and intelligence have often been reported.

Clearly, some element other than chance must have been operating. This element is generally assumed to be something in the interaction between parents and child.

But Schooler believes that this other element is simply the preponderance of firstborn children in the population. As evidence, he cites a study by two English investigators, J. S. Price and E. H. Hare, on some sources of bias in birth-order research. Price and Hare pointed out that in a population where there has been a long-term trend toward a greater number of new families being started each year than in the previous year, there should be more firstborn than last-born individuals—and, indeed, more early-born than later-born people.

The scholarship finalists mentioned above took their test in 1964. If they were 17 at the time, they had been born in 1947—and in that year, 43 per cent of the children born were firstborn. The percentages the year before and the year after were also very high: 40 per cent and 39 per cent respectively. There would have been cause for wonder, then, if the finalists had not included more firstborns.

Sim/Photo Trends

John Travolta is an example of a very popular youngest child of a large family.

Again, a study of high school students who competed in the 1963 Westinghouse Talent Search found that, among those students of high scientific aptitude and also among those of lesser attainment, firstborns appeared to be overrepresented. Considering that all the students had been born in a boom period for new families, the only reasonable comment on this finding must again be: No wonder.

BIRTH ORDER, FAMILY SIZE, AND INTELLECT

Scientists sometimes question other scientists' research because the sample—the number of people investigated—is regarded as too small to be representative. Such criticism can hardly be leveled at a study by Lillian Belmont and Francis A. Marolla of the relationships among birth order, family size, and intelligence.

These investigators, who are research scientists with the New York State Department of Mental Hygiene, had data on almost 400,000 19-year-old men—virtually all the males born in the Netherlands in the period 1944 through 1947. As the basis of comparison, the investigators used the results of an intelligence test known as the Raven Progressive Matrices. This is a nonverbal measure and, therefore, relatively free of cultural and other environmental influences.

No matter what the size of the families, it turned out, the 19-year-olds who had been firstborns got better scores on intelligence

Lastborn children are most often chosen to be seatmates and teammates at school.

Margot Granitsas/Photo Researchers

than the later-borns. Moreover, as birth position fell—from first to second, from second to third, and so on—the scores on the test almost always fell, too. Secondborns scored better than thirdborns, for example, and thirdborns better than fourthborns.

Family size was found to have a similar effect. Within a given birth order, scores on the tests grew worse as the number of children in the family increased. Among the young men who had been born third, for example, those from families with three children scored better than those from families with four, and these in turn scored higher than those from families with five, and so on.

This study included only males. However, H. M. Breland, another student of birth-order effects, reports that the findings are "remarkably similar" to his own, after a study of almost 800,000 young Americans, girls as well as boys, who had applied for National Merit Scholarships.

It is easy to speculate why size of family has some influence on children's intelligence. In general, the more mouths to be fed and bodies to be clothed and sheltered, the less the parental resources—whether measured in money, time, or interest—available, per child, for intellectually stimulating activities.

THE ONLY CHILD IS FIRST AND LAST

The only child gives researchers a problem. Presumably he should rate as high at least as the firstborn of two children. But earlier investigations had shown that this was

not the case, and the findings from the study of the Dutch 19-year-olds bear them out. In this study, the only child rated lower than the firstborn of two children and also lower than the firstborn of three. The Michigan investigators have an answer: An only child is like a lastborn child—in fact, he can be considered to be a lastborn child—in having no one to teach. "If a child does not know how to solve a particular problem," they point out, "he is not likely to ask the youngest; if he is missing a word, it is not the youngest who will supply it; if there is an ambiguity about the rules of a game or a pattern of play, it will not be resolved by the youngest. In short, the lastborn is not a 'teacher' and neither is the only child. It would be quite surprising if the opportunity to perform such a 'teaching' function did not have benefits for intellectual performance."

A major problem in research of the kind reported here is to disentangle the differences that can be attributed to birth order from those attributable to genetic and constitutional forces and from the effects these latter differences have on interactions within the family □

📖 SELECTED READINGS

"Birth order and intellectual development" by D. J. Daves and others, *Science,* June 24, 1977.

"What scholars, stripteasers, and congressmen share: overrepresentation of firstborns; study by Richard Zwergenhaft" by J. Horn. *Psychology Today* May 1976.

John Running

COLD HANDS, WARM HEART

by Richard S. Surwit

MICHAEL JAMES, vice-president of a firm that makes biofeedback instruments, was driving on a cold winter day when he noticed that the heater of his car wasn't working. He had forgotten his gloves and his hands were painfully chilly. While demonstrating the efficiency of his feedback machines, James had learned to raise and lower the temperature of his hands voluntarily. Now, he decided to try to achieve the same control without the machines. He concentrated on relaxing thoughts and on sensations of warmth that he had learned to associate with his demonstrations. Gradually, his hands warmed up.

Behavioral scientists have been studying the relationship between psychological processes and skin temperature for more than 40 years. Research at the Duke University Medical Center in North Carolina and other laboratories demonstrates that various kinds of emotional stimulation will affect skin temperature—and that most people can bring it under conscious control to some extent. Through relaxation, meditation, and other techniques, we can learn to control skin temperature when we are cold or under stress.

USEFUL TECHNIQUE

This knowledge may never be the answer to fuel shortages and lowered thermostats in winter, but it could prove useful for those who are properly trained. An experiment at the U.S. Army Research Institute of Environmental Medicine in Natick, Massachusetts, suggested that it could be helpful in extremely cold climates. One man who was trained to increase his hand temperature was able to prevent frostbite despite bitter cold conditions. The Army never repeated the experiment, but studies in our laboratory—the Behavioral Physiology Laboratory at Duke University—show that the same methods can be applied to treating certain vascular disorders. It seems particularly effective with Raynaud's disease, a side effect of many illnesses. Sufferers from this disorder have cronically cold hands and an inadequate supply of blood to the fingers and toes because the blood vessels in those areas shut down tightly, producing extreme discomfort. We have taught these patients to relieve their symptoms, even in cold environments, with the use of relaxation techniques.

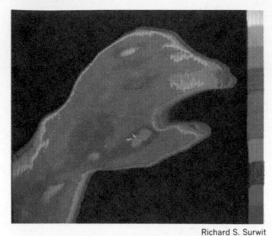

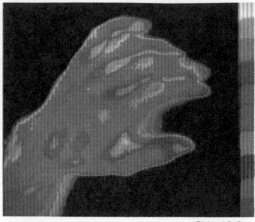

The thermographs above show the hand of a man who is raising his skin temperature by mental con-

centration. The color change from blue to white shows an increase of nine Celsius degrees in ten minutes.

Richard S. Surwit

TWO VARIETIES OF HANDS

Before examining the methods, it's useful to know a few facts about hand temperatures. Hands come in two basic varieties, hot and cold, with only a few in-betweens. Preliminary research suggests that about 40 per cent of the population have hand temperatures about 21° to 24° Celsius, while the rest have temperatures about 33° to 36° Celsius. Within these two categories, average skin temperature in the hands varies with gender and climate.

There are interesting differences between men and women. In winter, both sexes have the same average hand temperature, but women's hands tend to be colder in summer. This agrees with our finding that women report their hands are cold more frequently than do men. Moreover, while the temperature of a man's two hands is usually the same, women show as much as a one- or two-degree difference. The dominant hand is usually warmer. Women are also five times more likely than men to suffer from Raynaud's disease.

EMOTIONS AND SKIN TEMPERATURE

Our emotions, how warm we feel, skin temperature, and inner body temperature are all closely related through the sympathetic nervous system and its control center in the hypothalamus of the brain. The sympathetic nervous system can be activated by either physical or psychological stimulation. In either case, heart rate, blood pressure, and sweat-gland activity increase, while salivation and the blood flow to our hands and feet both decrease.

When this happens, we usually feel cold, but our body is actually conserving heat. Our fingers and toes function as radiators. When we are hot, the blood vessels in the fingers and toes dilate, increasing the circulation in those areas greatly and allowing body heat to escape through the hands. That's why rings feel tighter on hot days; our fingers are engorged with blood as our body rids itself of heat. On cold days, rings slip because the blood vessels in the fingers and toes constrict in order to keep heat from escaping.

The sympathetic nervous system is responsible for the familiar "cold sweat" of nervousness. Overactivity in the system produces cold, sweaty hands and feet by constricting blood vessels and, at the same time, increasing the production of sweat, which cools the skin. On hot days, our sweat contains a substance known as bradykinin that helps keep the vessels dilated to allow them to give off heat, while our skin is cooled by evaporation of sweat.

AN OLD SAYING

The activity of the sympathetic nervous system may explain the old saying, "Cold

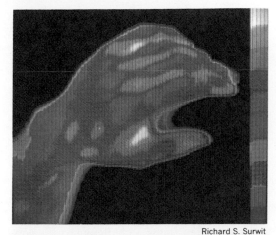

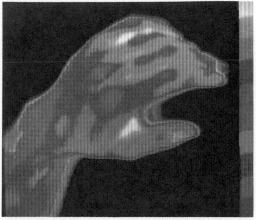

Richard S. Surwit

Our skin temperature and our emotions are closely related through the sympathetic nervous system.

Richard S. Surwit

The system can be activated by psychological stimulation, which is happening above.

hands, warm heart," since the system is a major part of our emotional-response network. When we become emotionally aroused, the sympathetic nervous system stimulates the narrowing of blood vessels that is responsible for cold hands and feet. Thus people with consistently cold hands and feet are likely to be, if anything, more emotionally reactive than people who are always warm.

In a classic 1939 paper, researchers B. Mittelmann and H. G. Wolff showed that emotionally laden material would trigger a decrease in hand temperature. More recent studies by Patrick Boudewyns of the Durham Veterans Hospital and the Duke University Medical Center have provided additional evidence that stress decreases hand temperature. Anxiety, stress, or even the excitement of a novel experience can cause the blood vessels in the hands and the feet to constrict.

The one exception is sexual stimulation, which shows a different pattern. Boudewyns has shown that sexual stimulation at first produces constriction of the vessels in the fingers, as does any novel stimulus. But sexual stimulation itself generates heat in the body. If it continues, the blood vessels in the fingers dilate, to release the heat. Hand temperature continues to rise with continued sexual stimulation, until it levels off at or below internal body temperature. No matter how we feel, the temperature of our hands

and feet can never exceed 37° Celsius, unless we have contracted a fever.

BIOFEEDBACK

Since the late 1960's, researchers have become increasingly interested in bringing these and other "involuntary" psychological responses under control. One technique that has become popular is biofeedback. Although biofeedback has not lived up to all the initial hopes of its proponents, it has been used successfully in the laboratory to control heart rate, blood pressure, sweat gland activity, and peripheral skin temperature. In biofeedback training, a person is shown a moment-to-moment electronic record of his physiological responses—heart rate, for instance—and gradually learns to control them by mental processes that are, as yet, not understood.

One of the most promising clinical applications of voluntary control of "involuntary" responses is the control of hand temperatures. Since 1972, we have been exploring the possibility of regulating skin temperature and blood flow to the hands and feet through biofeedback. Our laboratory subjects watched changes in the temperature of hands and feet on a special meter, which measured differences as minute as a 100th of a degree Celsius.

We found that they could learn to raise and lower temperature and increase or decrease blood flow by this method. But we dis-

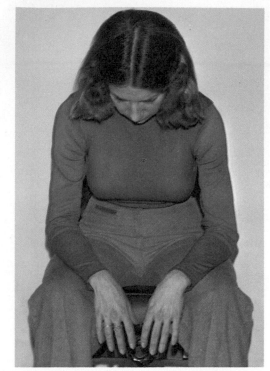

Richard S. Surwit

To warm your hands, sit quietly and repeat, "My hands are warm and heavy. My hands are. . . ."

covered in later studies that complex feedback techniques were not necessary. People can learn to warm their hands by "do-it-yourself" training, a series of mental exercises designed to help them reduce stress at will, by progressive muscle relaxation, and through some forms of meditation.

RELAXATION

We taught lab subjects to raise the temperature of their hands with self-help techniques developed by two German psychiatrists, J. H. Schultz and W. Luthe. In typical instructions adapted from the Schultz-Luthe approach, the person is told to sit in a chair, lean forward with his wrists dangling between and below the knees, and silently recite these words: "I feel quite quiet. My whole body is relaxed and comfortable. My right arm is heavy and warm. My left arm is heavy and warm. My right hand is becoming warmer. My left hand is becoming warmer. Warmth is flowing into my hands.

They are warm. I can feel the warmth flowing down into my right hand. It is warm and relaxed. I can feel the warmth flowing down into my left hand. It is warm and relaxed. My hands are warm and heavy."

Every 15 seconds or so, the subject repeats the last sentence to himself: "My hands are warm and heavy, my hands are warm and heavy. . . ." (Or he can listen to recordings of the words instead of reciting them to himself.)

The secret of voluntary hand-warming is thus the development of a passive, relaxed attitude. In some cases, biofeedback actually makes the process more difficult. For biofeedback often poses a challenge to the subject that, like other stresses, tends to produce a decrease in hand temperature. Passive relaxation techniques do not focus so directly on a specific result, and thus have produced warmer hands more consistently in the course of laboratory experiments.

STILL NEED GLOVES

Of course, voluntary control has its limits. Though the techniques might be useful to people exposed to extreme cold for brief periods and in the treatment of certain diseases, they will never replace gloves for keeping our hands warm. The reasons for this are illustrated by the ending to the story of Michael James, the vice-president of the biofeedback firm who warmed his hands by getting himself to relax. Although James's strategy soon relieved the feelings of cold and stiffness in his hands, he found after a few minutes that he was beginning to shiver. Remember, hands and feet get cold because the blood vessels in them narrow to conserve body heat. When James warmed his hands by relaxing, he dilated the blood vessels in his fingers. As a result, he quickly lost body heat and began to shake uncontrollably □

📖 SELECTED READINGS

"Body's inner voices" by R. Rosenbaum. *New Times,* June 26, 1978.

Stress and the Art of Biofeedback by Barbara Brown. Harper, 1977.

Your Body and Biofeedback at Its Best by Beate Jencks. Nelson-Hall, 1978.

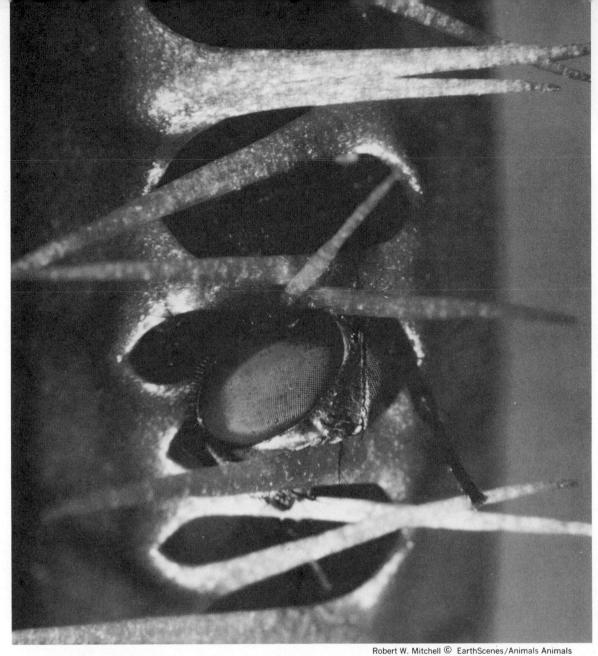

A fly's eye and a leg protrude through the traplike jaws of a Venus's Flytrap leaf, an insect-eating plant. This is the way this plant gets its nitrogen rather than from the nitrogen-poor soil of the Carolina coastal bogs, where it occurs.

BIOLOGY

BIOLOGY
REVIEW OF THE YEAR

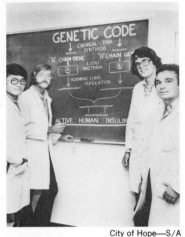

City of Hope—S/A

A group of biologists who chemically synthesized the human gene that commands the production of insulin. This they spliced into a DNA molecule of the *E. coli* bacterium, which then started to produce human insulin.

Cesar Milstein discovered how to make laboratory-grown cells produce a single, useful antibody. He combined antibody-producing cells with cancer cells that reproduce indefinitely in the laboratory. The resulting combination cells produce the antibody.

Science News

Recombinant DNA research. During 1978 human insulin became the first compound important in medical treatment to be produced by recombinant DNA (deoxyribonucleic acid) techniques. In these techniques a cell's hereditary material—genes made of DNA—is cut and spliced to foreign DNA. While it will take several years for the development of large-scale insulin production and even more time for animal and clinical safety tests, the achievement solidified expectations of practical applications for the gene-splicing technology that has developed so rapidly within the last few years. The human insulin production was announced in September 1978 by scientists at the City of Hope Medical Center near Los Angeles, California, and at Genetech, a two-year-old research firm in San Francisco, California. The human-insulin molecule has two chains. Scientists chemically synthesized the gene for each chain and snapped the synthetic genes into rings of natural bacteria DNA. After the new genes functioned to produce insulin chains, researchers isolated the chains from the bacteria and combined them to produce the insulin compound. ■ Earlier, Boston scientists used a different approach to produce rat insulin. They did not synthesize the insulin gene but instead copied it from the rat's DNA. This approach may prove better for producing large compounds since it is less tedious than the chemical synthesis of long genes.

In 1978 biologists for the first time transported a gene between two mammalian cells: a gene from a rabbit was placed into laboratory-grown monkey cells. In other work, a gene was moved from a bacterium into a yeast. In each case, the transported gene functioned to make its protein in its new environment. ■ With a similar technique, plant geneticists used a bacterium to transfer a selected gene into plant cells. This transfer was a major step in the effort to improve crops by direct genetic manipulation. During the year the first maximum safety (P4) facility for recombinant DNA research was opened at Fort Detrick in Frederick, Maryland. The facility has been awaited since the U.S. National Institutes of Health (NIH) issued guidelines for safe recombinant DNA research facilities. However, in December 1978, NIH, responding to the scientific community's conclusion that the likelihood of harm from a DNA-research facility was less than had previously been anticipated, relaxed its safety requirements, so the need for the maximum safety facility lessened. For a discussion of recombinant DNA studies, their promise and possible perils, see the article ''Recombinant DNA,'' which starts on page 66.

Three mice in one. In experimental embryology researchers continued to manipulate early embryos in an attempt to learn more about initial development stages. For several years biologists have manipulated early mouse embryos to produce mosaic animals derived from two embryos, or four parents. In 1978 a mouse with six parents was among the animals made-to-order for biological and medical research (see page 84). In October researchers Clement L. Markert and Robert M. Petters of Yale University published photographs of the first animal to be derived from a combination of three embryos. It is a mouse with a yellow face, black ears, and white stripe around its middle. The researchers took three embryos, each of which had reached the eight-cell stage of development, and placed them together so that the clusters of cells joined to form a single hollow ball. They then transferred the composite embryo to a mouse foster mother in whom it developed. A six-parented mouse, showing characteristics expected from each of the three initial embryos, was born. This mosaic mouse demonstrated that, while most of the cells in an early embryo develop into the tissues that surround the fetus, at least three embryonic cells—in this case, one from each of the three original embryos—are allocated to form the adult animal.

Single antibody production. During 1978 a recently developed technique for producing pure antibodies opened new horizons in identifying and purifying rare biological compounds. The technique, known as the monoclonal-antibody technique, was developed by Cesar Milstein at the British Medical Research Council. When an animal's body reacts to an invading chemical, virus, or bacteria, it produces an assortment of antibodies that bind to different parts of the invader. Milstein discovered how to make laboratory-grown cells produce large quantities of a single, useful antibody. He fused antibody-producing cells with cancer cells that reproduce indefinitely in the laboratory. Each of the resulting "immortal" cells can then grow into a colony of cells—a monoclone—that produces a single antibody. Researchers using this technique have made several important discoveries, among them that the influenza virus must change several of its amino-acid components to create an epidemic. Scientists also used monoclonal-produced antibodies to identify cell-membrane molecules. ■ Hilary Koprowski and collaborators at the Wistar Institute in Philadelphia, Pennsylvania, found a surface molecule specific to a human tumor. Antibodies to that molecule prevented growth of the tumor in mice—an experimental result that has fed hopes of using antibodies therapeutically as agents to destroy specific tumors.

M. P. O'Neill, The Wistar Institute

Research by Hilary Koprowski is pointing the way toward using antibodies as agents to destroy specific tumors. He discovered a surface molecule specific to a human tumor, then he showed that an antibody that attaches to that molecule prevented growth of the same tumor in mice.

Trite, but effective, insect disguise. Lacewing larvae live among, and feed on, aphids, but that lifestyle involves a masquerade. Aphid colonies are often protected by aggressive ant guards, which are rewarded by the sweet fluids aphids secrete. A group of Cornell University scientists, studying how the lacewing larvae get past the ant guards, observed that the larvae, which resemble aphids in overall shape and size, pluck the white wax that coats the aphids and hold the wax flakes on their own backs with hooked bristles. Within 20 minutes they don a complete disguise to fool the ants. Because the flakes bear a striking resemblance to sheep wool, this discovery is a natural illustration of a "wolf in sheep's clothing."

Views into the brain and heart. A new technique that pairs radioactive chemicals and a sensitive screening and computer reconstruction technique is now making possible an *in situ* view into the body's biochemical workings. The technique is known as Positron Emission Tomography and is nicknamed PETT. In humans, PETT has been used to identify brain areas that process visual and tactile information, to pinpoint damage in the brains of stroke victims, and to determine which brain areas exhibit increased activity during an epileptic seizure. PETT has also been used to determine heart damage in cardiac cases and to study blood flow and drug activity. A related procedure has been used in monkeys to determine in more detail which brain areas analyze visual information and which are involved with visual information affecting emotions and actions.

Julie Ann Miller

Positron Emission Tomography is a technique for looking into the body's biochemical workings. The equipment shown here does this by means of radioactive chemicals and a display screen, which is operated by computer-reconstruction techniques.

Oak Ridge Associated Universities, Inc.

RECOMBINANT DNA

by Jenny Tesar

ONE of the most revolutionary scientific achievements is also one of the most controversial. Recombinant DNA—also known as gene splicing—involves combining pieces of genetic material in new and unusual ways. Using this technology, researchers have:

- Created a bacterium that can make human insulin.
- Enabled monkey cells to provide a blood pigment normally made by rabbit cells.
- Isolated bacterial genes that cause diarrhea in humans and livestock.

As the technology is refined and improved, scientists expect to be able to:

- Make major advances in medicine, such as using bacteria as factories for the production of hormones, drugs, and other substances valuable to our health.
- Develop plants that can take nitrogen directly from the air, rather than from expensive fertilizers.
- Create bacteria that will digest oil spills.

At the same time, however, many people, including some scientists, worry that this same technology might lead to:

- Baffling new diseases that wipe out entire human populations.
- New types of bacteria that cause the human body to destroy itself.
- A cancer-like plague spread by a seemingly harmless bacterium.

BITS AND PIECES OF THE GENETIC CODE

Every living cell in every organism contains molecules of the chemical DNA (deoxyribonucleic acid). This chemical acts as a blueprint for the organism. It is the genetic code, telling the cell how to grow, what to do, when to reproduce.

In bacterial cells, in addition to the main DNA molecules, there are smaller loops of DNA. These loops are called plasmids.

Plasmids were discovered in 1952. In the succeeding years, two other important types of cell chemicals were discovered. One of these was restriction enzymes. These are chemicals that cut apart DNA molecules. The other was an enzyme called ligase. This acts as a glue to hold together bits of DNA molecules.

Illustrations by Frank Senyk

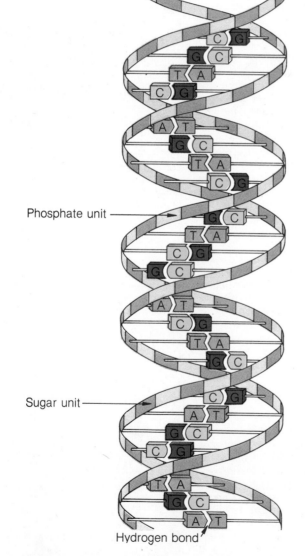

Phosphate unit —

Sugar unit —

Hydrogen bond

DNA molecules have the form of a helical ladder. Molecules represented by A and G are purines, and those represented by T and C are pyrimidines.

CUTTING AND SPLICING GENES

In the early 1970's, Stanley Cohen and his co-workers at Stanford University discovered a comparatively easy way to transfer genes from one kind of an organism to another. They worked with *Escherichia coli* (*E. coli,* for short), a harmless bacterium commonly found in the human intestine. As shown in the drawing, they separated the plasmids from the rest of the *E. coli* cell material. Then they placed the plasmids in a solution with a restriction enzyme, which broke the plasmid loops at specific places.

At the same time, the scientists used other restriction enzymes to separate certain genes from the long DNA molecules of an African clawed toad. The genes were mixed with the open plasmid loops from *E. coli.* Then, with ligase, the toad genes and the *E. coli* plasmids were "glued" together. Thus a completely new type of structure—part bacterial, part toad—was formed. Such a structure has since been named a "plasmid chimera." (The chimera was a mythical animal that was composed of parts from several different organisms.)

The final step was to place the plasmid chimera in a solution containing normal *E. coli* cells. When the solution was warmed, the plasmid chimeras were able to enter the *E. coli* cells and become part of the cells' genetic structure. The toad genes now were part of the bacteria. And when the bacteria reproduced by dividing in half, each of the offspring inherited the toad genes.

The scientists used the same method to enter yeast genes in *E. coli.* And since then, genetic materials from a variety of plants, animals, bacteria, and viruses have been transplanted into bacterial cells.

Bacteria reproduce rapidly. In a 24-hour period, one *E. coli* cell can make a few billion copies of itself. If that cell contains a foreign gene, the gene will be reproduced at the same rate. Hence, there is the possibility of using bacteria as factories.

Once the techniques are perfected, it should be possible to implant the human gene for blood-clotting into a bacterium. Then it would be possible to produce enough of the genetic material to supply the needs of hemophiliacs. As mentioned earlier, the ini-

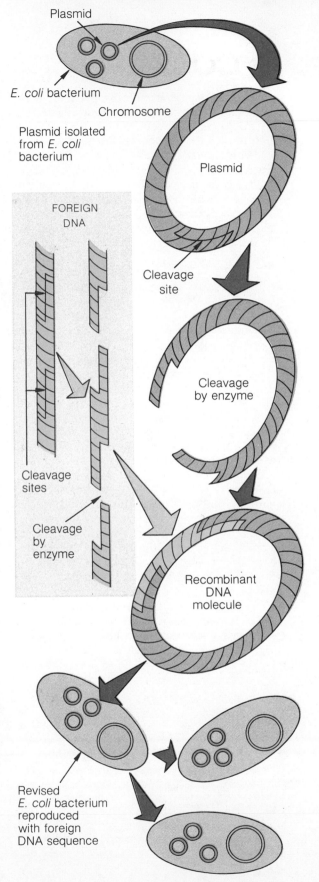

Plasmid

E. coli bacterium

Chromosome

Plasmid isolated from *E. coli* bacterium

Plasmid

FOREIGN DNA

Cleavage site

Cleavage by enzyme

Cleavage sites

Cleavage by enzyme

Recombinant DNA molecule

Revised *E. coli* bacterium reproduced with foreign DNA sequence

tial steps for this process have already been accomplished for insulin, a substance needed by diabetics.

Similarly, genes for the production of hemoglobin in rabbits have been transferred to monkey kidney cells. Kidney cells do not naturally produce hemoglobin, but these cells did so after receiving the rabbit genes. Such experiments can help us understand how genes are regulated and how they express themselves. An understanding of such processes will enable us to understand better how we develop, what makes us healthy, and how diseases attack us.

IMPLICATIONS THAT AROUSE FEARS

A number of scientists believe that recombinant-DNA research should not be done because it interferes with natural evolutionary processes. Famed biochemist Erwin Chargaff asked, "Have we the right to counteract irreversibly the evolutionary wisdom of millions of years . . . ?"

In reply, Stanley Cohen pointed out that ". . . it is this so-called evolutionary wisdom that gave us the gene combinations for bubonic plague, smallpox, yellow fever, typhoid, polio, diabetes, and cancer." Cohen also pointed out that people have been influencing biological evolution for thousands of years—by domesticating animals, cultivating crops, creating hybrids, and so on.

Unfortunately, the results of recombinant DNA are not always predictable. This is particularly true in the so-called "shotgun" experiments. In such an experiment, all of the DNA molecules in the cell of an organism are cut into small segments by enzymes. The segments are separated and each is inserted into a bacterium. As the bacterium reproduces over and over again, the DNA segment is, in effect, mass-produced. This makes it easier to study the segments. David

Hogness of Stanford managed to isolate and identify several dozen fruit-fly genes using this technique.

Since very few genes in any organism have been identified, most DNA fragments used in a shotgun experiment are unknown quantities. Such a fragment might contain genes that cause disease or increase a bacterium's ability to cause disease. Imagine what might happen if the new form of life created as a result of the shotgun experiment was released—either deliberately or accidentally—into the world at large.

GUIDELINES FOR RECOMBINANT RESEARCH

In 1974, as a result of concerns voiced by some scientists, a group of prominent American molecular biologists met to consider the possible implications of recombinant DNA. The biologists drafted a letter, published in leading science magazines in the United States and Great Britain, asking their colleagues not to perform certain experiments. The letter stated, in part:

"There is serious concern that some of these artificial recombinant DNA molecules could prove biologically hazardous. One potential hazard in current experiments derives from the need to use a bacterium like *E. coli* to clone the recombinant DNA molecules and to amplify their number. Strains of *E. coli* commonly reside in the human intestinal tract, and they are capable of exchanging genetic material with other types of bacteria, some of which are pathogenic to man. Thus, new DNA elements introduced into *E. coli* might possibly become widely disseminated among human, bacterial, plant, or animal populations with unpredictable effects."

Paul Berg of Stanford, a leading recombinant-DNA researcher and the person who

National Institutes of Health

This laboratory at the National Institutes of Health meets the requirements for doing P-4 recombinant-DNA research.

chaired the meeting, said afterwards: "I wasn't thinking about the social responsibilities of scientists. . . . We just felt this was a way of telling other people the way we felt about it and asking them to think about it and hold off."

The public, however, viewed the group's action differently. If scientists believed that some research should be banned, then all research in this area must be extremely dangerous. Headlines on newspaper and magazine stories helped feed this impression.

A second, larger meeting was held in February 1975. This meeting, the International Conference on Recombinant DNA Molecules, was attended by about 140 scientists. The consensus was that certain experiments should be conducted only if specific safety precautions were met. The suggested precautions included both physical and biological controls.

Soon thereafter, the U.S. National Institutes of Health (NIH) began to translate the Conference's guidelines into guidelines of its own. These would have to be followed by all researchers whose work was funded, wholly or in part, by grants from NIH. Three levels of biological containment (EK1 through EK3) and four levels of physical containment (P1 through P4) were established.

BIOLOGICAL LEVELS OF DANGER

Biological containment is designed to minimize survival of the organism outside the lab. It limits the chances of a bacterial strain being transmitted from the laboratory host to another host (a person, for example).

Experiments requiring EK1 containment are not considered to present much danger. Such experiments can use ordinary strains of *E. coli*. EK2 containment requires a mutated strain that has a decreased ability to survive in the human intestinal tract. EK3 containment requires a strain that has less than 1 in 100 million chances of surviving outside a laboratory.

EK2 and EK3 strains did not exist at the time that NIH announced its guidelines, but were developed by researchers in 1976. In fact, the EK3 strain was named $x1776$ in honor of the U.S. Bicentennial. This strain of *E. coli* is unable to replicate its DNA except in a carefully controlled laboratory environ-

ment. It also is extremely susceptible to chemicals such as detergents.

RESTRICTIONS ON LABORATORY PROCEDURES

Physical containment is meant to confine organisms to the laboratory. This is achieved through the use of special equipment and by practicing certain laboratory procedures. Specially designed labs provide a secondary means of protection.

P1 containment can be achieved by an ordinary microbiology lab. This is acceptable for experiments involving genetic transfers such as those that can occur naturally between bacteria. These experiments can use only the EK1 strains of bacteria.

P2 containment is only slightly more restrictive. It is required for experiments with bacteria that do not naturally exchange genetic material. In such experiments, the EK2 strain must be used.

P3 containment is required for moderate-risk experiments. Such experiments include those using embryonic tissues from vertebrates or mammalian and bird DNA. The EK2 strain must be used. Researchers must wear sterilized lab clothing and gloves. All air in the laboratory must pass through special filtering systems that remove micro-

A researcher watches a TV screen as he adjusts the controls of a microscope in the sealed-off compartment by means of rubber gloves.

organisms. Special safety cabinets must be used for all equipment and manipulations that produce aerosols.

P4 containment is necessary for high-risk experiments, such as those using animal-virus DNA containing harmful genes. These labs must be separated from the outside environment by air locks. People who work in the labs must shower and change their clothes before leaving the labs.

Prohibited: Six categories of potentially hazardous experiments were prohibited under the NIH guidelines. These included experiments using DNA from disease-causing organisms or genes for very potent toxins, such as diphtheria toxin or snake venom. Also prohibited was the transfer of drug resistance to bacteria and the deliberate release into the environment of any organism containing recombinant DNA.

RESPONSE AND REVISION

The NIH guidelines were not legally binding. Nor were they applicable to work done by groups not receiving NIH funds. However, other government agencies that supported recombinant DNA research soon brought their scientists under the guidelines. This still left research conducted in the private sector, such as that done by pharmaceutical companies, uncontrolled.

Similar guidelines also were set up in Great Britain, France and other countries.

Many people, including many scientists, continued to object to all recombinant DNA work. Congressional groups held hearings and introduced legislation that would have restricted experimentation (none of these bills have been passed). Communities around the United States also expressed concern about recombinant-DNA work being done in laboratories within their borders.

In July 1976 Cambridge, Massachusetts—home of Harvard and the Massachusetts Institute of Technology—called for a moratorium on P3 and P4 research at those universities. The moratorium lasted until February 1977, when the Cambridge city council voted to permit such research but only if conducted under the NIH guidelines. The city council also required a few additional precautions recommended by a committee of Cambridge citizens.

In the past two years, the debate has continued, though on a somewhat reduced scale. There is increasing evidence that recombinant-DNA experiments are not as dangerous as many people originally feared. The imagined horrors have not materialized. Meanwhile, the potential value of the research has become increasingly evident.

On December 15, 1978, Joseph A. Califano, Jr., Secretary of the U.S. Department of Health, Education, and Welfare (of which NIH is a part), announced revised guidelines for recombinant-DNA research. The revisions exempt five categories of experiments from safety restrictions. These were generally classed as low-risk under the initial guidelines, and NIH has since concluded that they presented no known health risks.

Restrictions are eased on other permissible experiments. "The revised guidelines," announced Califano, "assign almost all categories of research physical containment and/or biological containment levels at least one step lower than in the 1976 guidelines. Since the likelihood of harm now appears more remote than was once anticipated, the scientific community has now concluded that this downgrading is appropriate."

NIH continues to ban the six categories of potentially hazardous experiments prohibited by the 1976 guidelines. The new guidelines, however, permit the director of NIH to grant case-by-case exceptions to these prohibitions, provided appropriate safeguards are employed.

Finally, steps were taken to require that research done by private companies would comply with the guidelines. Califano asked the U.S. Food and Drug Administration and the U.S. Environmental Protection Agency to use their regulatory authority to accomplish compliance.

What happens next is anyone's guess, but some people still worry about possible catastrophes □

📖 SELECTED READINGS

"Recombinant DNA: the containment debate" by L. Riesenberg. *Chemistry,* December 1977.

"Recombinant DNA: fact and fiction" by S. Cohen. *Science,* February 18, 1977.

"The Recombinant-DNA debate" by C. Grobstein. *Scientific American,* July 1977.

Larry West

THE ECOLOGY OF DEAD TREES

by Richard M. DeGraaf

WHEN people think about birds and trees, they usually picture the trees with a healthy crown full of leaves and the birds with nests hidden among all that foliage. There are some birds, however, that nest in holes among the branches, and these creatures often require trees or limbs that are dead or dying, not healthy. The birds are called "cavity nesters." They play an important role in the forest as pest control agents. Most of them are insect eaters.

There are about 85 species of cavity nesters among the approximately 800 bird species in the United States, and they have not had an easy time of it lately. Dead and dying trees have been thinned by fire and by chainsaw. To the lumberman, big old trees left standing in the woods represent an almost sinful waste. As a result, standing dead trees, often called "snags," have become rare in some areas—and so have some of the cavity nesting birds that depend on them.

Flickers are cavity nesters that are not choosey about the holes they nest in.

FUSSY BIRDS

A few cavity nesters are extremely fussy. The American ivory-billed woodpecker had such exacting requirements about where it nested that it presumably has ceased to exist. This bird's needs included large tracts of old growth where it nested in dead trees and foraged for insects by scaling off large pieces of bark.

By contrast, some hole nesters can adapt to almost any situation. The common flicker, for example, has been known to nest in burrows and even on the bare ground. On islands off the Massachusetts coast, where there are few large trees, flickers commonly nest in utility poles.

Many cavity nesters depend upon the huge pileated woodpecker for making tree holes.

SOME ENDANGERED

Few other cavity nesters are this adaptable. One large group—the woodpeckers that thrive on tree-killing bark beetles and other forest pests—might disappear if intensive timbering removes all dead trees. The pileated woodpecker, the largest of all surviving woodpeckers in North America, may soon be in trouble for the same reason. Like most cavity nesters, the pileated feeds on insects, specifically carpenter ants, which penetrate upward from the base of a tree into the heartwood, eventually killing it. Somehow, the pileated locates an infested tree and chisels a hole to reach the heart of the ant colony. Oblong excavations, often a whole series up to 50 centimeters in length, are evidence that the pileated has been at work.

The U.S. Forest Service (USFS) recognizes the advantages of having insect-eating woodpeckers and other cavity nesting birds in a forest. Consequently, that agency has adopted a policy to save some trees just for them. But timber interests have continued to complain that the USFS leaves too many good trees standing on federal land. In *The Forest Herald,* a paper published by a lumber company in Oregon, a recent article on snags decried leaving them for wildlife: "Even if all the snags were taken out of the woods that can be taken out, there would still be sufficient nesting places for the ground animals in those snags which have deteriorated so far that they cannot be utilized. As for the standing snags, we are well acquainted with a number of birds who tell us that they don't mind one bit nesting in green trees."

There are three things wrong with this statement:

• Taking all but the most rotted snags means that soon there will be no snags.

• Many birds cannot make holes in hard green trees, much less find food, as they do in dead wood.

• Many cavity nesters need holes but can't make their own in any kind of tree. They require holes that have already been made in snags.

For its part, the USFS is conducting detailed research into the habitat needs of hole nesters. Biologists Evelyn L. Bull of the

Karl H. Maslowski

A barred owl has taken over an old hollow maple snag for its nesting place and perch.

Karl H. Maslowski

An eastern bluebird returns to its hole in a dead tree with an insect treat for its young.

USFS, and E. Charles Meslow of the U.S. Fish and Wildlife Service, found that each pair of pileated woodpeckers in Oregon's Blue Mountains requires at least 130 hectares of land containing about 45 snags and 45 replacement trees. Because it takes about 100 years or more for a tree to reach great size, letting several trees per hectare continue to grow older than the surrounding forest is necessary to provide future woodpeckers and other hole nesters a place to rear their young.

WHAT ABOUT THE INSECTS?

One reason foresters have long opposed the preservation of old forest stands is the fact that insect populations were thought to boom there. However, it is now clear that leaving snags for woodpeckers usually provides a forest with better insect protection, rather than less, as the hole nesters clean up on destructive pests. Today, many foresters agree that fire, safety, and timber-management goals can be met while still maintaining habitats for cavity nesters. In Missouri's Mark Twain National Forest, scattered portions of forests away from roads or recreation areas have been left to grow for 200 years. Instead of applying the "cut 'em all" rule to snags, California now "leaves 'em all" except those that are fire and safety hazards.

PROTECTING SNAGS

USFS wildlife biologists in Arizona and New Mexico recommend that seven good quality snags per hectare be protected from cutting if they stand within about 150 meters of forest openings and water, five per hectare over the remaining forest. Just as important, they make provisions for future snags: spike-topped trees with cavities and obvious "cull trees" are left for future cavity-nesting bird habitat. And many foresters are now tagging suitable snags to protect them from campers scrounging for firewood in intensively-used areas.

A Carolina chickadee has chosen a fine hole for raising a family.

Karl H. Maslowski

Larry West

A raccoon kit watches the cameraperson from the safety of its tree house.

Ruth Byers

Don't prune or cut down all your dead trees if you want to conserve wildlife.

One bird that many other creatures depend on for shelter should benefit greatly from these new efforts: the pileated woodpecker. Each year, as part of its mating ritual, this bird selects a dead tree in which to excavate a nest. After woodpeckers are finished with these nests, they provide homes for wildlife ranging from bufflehead ducks to salamanders. Later, when pileated woodpecker holes are enlarged by insects or weathering, they are often occupied by great-horned owls, and raccoons, and sometimes even martens and fishers.

WE CAN ALL HELP

Safeguarding the future of these cavity nesting birds will require massive habitat preservation programs. Homeowners can help by leaving snags standing on their own property. If you have a dead or dying tree in your yard, don't cut it down unless it is endangering your property.

A hollow log—once a tree that provided shelter for wildlife—may become a den for a gray fox.

Steve Maslowski

Similarly, if you own a woodlot, resist the temptation to cut every dead tree. Dead trees don't take up soil nutrients or water, and don't affect the growth of trees nearby. A big dead tree full of holes is worth a lot to the wildlife on your land, especially in winter, and the chips on the snow indicate how much foraging has gone on to find insects in the dead wood.

If you have a woodlot with mostly small healthy trees, you can create cavities by stub pruning. To do this, cut off a seven- or eight-centimeter diameter limb about 15 centimeters from the trunk. This will expose the stub to fungal attack, and over the years a natural cavity will form.

A better way to produce cavities is to girdle a few trees per hectare by removing the bark and cambium in a several-centimeter-wide band around the trunk. Select trees at least 30 centimeters in diameter. If you manage forest land for timber, choose crooked trees that probably won't be much good for lumber anyway.

It surprises some people to learn that many birds need dead trees to survive. But the living forest needs these birds as much as they need snags. So don't just plant trees for wildlife. Leave plenty of dead ones standing, too □

THE DUTCH ELM DISEASE

by Howard Bloomfield

ADMIRED by homeowners and city fathers as the finest landscape trees, American elms have flourished in 41 of our mainland states. It avoids only the driest and hottest states. As magnificent specimens on village greens and in arching avenues of shade, elms numbered 77 million in incorporated areas alone in 1930.

THE DAMAGE

But in Cleveland that same year a few elms showed yellowing leaves in their upper branches and then mysteriously wilted away to death. After this first appearance, Dutch elm disease spread slowly for some years before it was recognized as a calamity. By last count in 1976, the elm population was down to 34 million, a loss of 54 per cent. In the northeast states, where the beloved elms were planted in great number, 75 per cent had died.

Dutch elm disease has broken out in every county in 23 northeast and midwest states, and it still spreads. Embattled communities, with civic beauty and pride at stake, are spending $30 million annually to protect their remaining elms. Protection by spraying and injection costs far less than does the removal of dead elms.

The forces against the disease gathered strength and cohesion in November 1977, in the first national symposium of Dutch elm disease experts at the National Arboretum in Washington. The arborists expect no cure, ever, for the disease. They see themselves in a holding action to preserve, they hope, millions of the present elms. They report improvements in techniques and management that limit losses in some areas to a mere one per cent. They also report successes in the development and propagation of resistant elms. The nonprofit Elm Research Institute in Harrisville, New Hampshire has made $500,000 grants to 10 universities for research on Dutch elm disease.

Grant Heilman

This elm, beside the round church of Richmond, Vermont, became diseased and had to be cut down. A young maple grows in its place.

Dr. Frank S. Santamour, Jr., a National Arboretum geneticist says of the disease: "This is not the baffling situation of the chestnut blight. That was airborne, with no means of control. Dutch elm disease has a weak link in the chain. It travels on a vulnerable insect, the elm-bark beetle."

THE BEETLES

As with so many of the world's astonishingly different 850,000 known insect species, Nature wove a special pattern for the elm-bark beetle. It breeds only in dying or dead elms and cut logs. Dead and dying elms send out an aroma not emitted by a healthy elm. The scent summons ready-to-mate beetles within a radius of about one and a half kilometers.

The arrivals add strength to the message by giving off sex scents called pheromones. The females send out an attractant for males, and the males issue their own invitation for females. The sum total of attractants draws traffic jams of excited beetles.

The beetles penetrate the bark and

Elm Research Institute   Elm Research Institute

Before and after. All the elms of Gillet Avenue in Waukegan, Illinois, became victims of the Dutch elm disease. This has happened in numerous towns.

directly under it cut a network of little channels called galleries. Here the beetles mate, and the female lays about 50 eggs. The eggs hatch in a week. For four or five weeks the larvae bore feeding tunnels, which end in a pupal chamber. In each miniature chamber a maturing larva encases itself in a pupal wrapping, from which it will emerge as a mature beetle.

The beetle flies off to feed in the crown of a healthy elm, on two-to-four-year-old twigs. It goes directly to the crotches, because these hold the richest store of food. Yet even on this first day, if the special scent is in the air, the beetle may bypass the feeding stage and go at once to a dead elm to begin breeding.

The elm-bark beetle carries a fungus, which infects and destroys American elms.

Elm Research Institute

American elm-bark beetles have always been common in the United States and Canada, but their meals of sap have never deterred the growth of our elms. In 1909, however, a specimen of European bark beetle was collected in Cambridge, Massachusetts. Only about 2 millimeters long—smaller than its American cousin—the beetle probably had arrived on a shipment of European elm logs.

THE DISEASE: A FUNGUS

Presumably, if the beetle were the only thing that arrived on those logs, American elms could have accommodated themselves to the new guests with no substantial damage. But the invaders carried on their outer coverings the sticky spores of a fungus (*Ceratocystis ulmi*) that originated in Asia and had devastated elms in Europe. The results of its arrival in America were to be catastrophic.

The fungus, which is the Dutch elm disease, is inseparable from the beetle. It transmits itself to the gallery walls where the beetles mate. It attaches to their larvae. It is in their pupal cell. It is with the mature beetle as it flies to feed on a healthy elm. And there it transmits itself to the elm's sap stream.

The little European beetles are much more numerous and aggressive than the American. They have two generations a season while the Americans have one. Meanwhile the native beetles also have become spore carriers.

Holland has no special responsibility for the calamity. It is called Dutch elm disease because Dutch scientists were the first to isolate the fungus and determine its life cycle.

Unfortunately, the elm, in defensive reaction to the infection, becomes its own enemy. It produces a gummy substance to seal off the fungus. The gummy compound clogs and blocks the flow of the tree's liquids. Foliage wilts and yellows as the deprived branches die.

The disease often spreads fast enough to kill the tree in the same season, though it sometimes takes up to three years. In the dead and dying wood the blocked ducts show up as areas of brown discoloration.

TEN PER CENT AND GONE

The arborist's first attack on the Dutch elm disease is to prune out wilting branches as far as streaks of discoloration run under the bark. And for safety prune away another 3 to 5 meters of clear wood. But most experts agree that if the wilt covers 10 per cent of the elm's crown, the tree is past saving. It should be destroyed before it can become a beetle-breeding tree.

A ban by the U.S. Environmental Protection Agency on outside burning but not on burning wood in stoves or fireplaces irks some arborists, who must locate landfills to bury diseased elm. If logs are kept, they must be debarked.

Ideally, all-out sanitizing to end the disease in an area calls for trained personnel, with full access to private property, to scout every elm every two weeks from mid-May to September.

Although wilt is the signal for action

Elm Research Institute

The bark beetle bores into the inner bark of weakened elms in order to lay their eggs.

and some mistakes have to be accepted, the only really positive test for the disease is a laboratory culture. Geneticist Santamour tells of a fine elm wilting on public ground near his home. He halted the removal crew, to get a culture. The cause of the wilting was not the Dutch elm disease. Next season found the tree in full leaf, and it has flourished ever since.

Fungus that enters through roots is even more deadly than fungus that starts from beetles feeding in the crown. The roots meet and graft themselves together, and the infection passes from a diseased tree to its healthy neighbor. The fungus, rising with the sap stream, gets a quick and thorough distribution.

In Britain, where elms were planted in long hedgerows for generations, root-grafting rapidly spread the fungus. The clasping roots unite a hedgerow into a solid chain of infection and death. All 20 million of Britain's elms are considered doomed. In America, too, the root-grafts have destroyed fine avenues of shading elms.

On the inner surface of the bark and on the sapwood the beetle bores an egg gallery.

Elm Research Institute

At the end of a feeding tunnel, the larvae mature into adult beetles, which fly off to feed.

Elm Research Institute

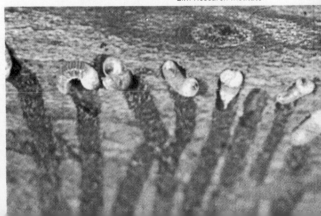

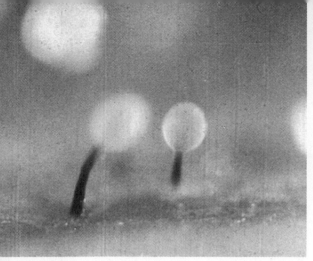

The fungus, which kills the elm, produces spores that multiply by yeastlike budding.

INJECTION OF FUNGICIDES

But a new and fast-expanding technique is aiding the contest against the Dutch elm disease. It is the injection of elms with fungicides that move through the sap along the same course the fungus would take. The technique is too new to know just how successful it will be, but experiments are bringing increasingly good results. Inoculation safeguards trees that have been pruned for crown wilt, and is being used as a preventive in thousands of healthy trees.

The inoculant Lignasan BLP was approved in 1976 by the U.S. Environmental Protection Agency. It is sold under the trade names of Correx, Agway Elmosan, Pratt Elm Tree Noculate, Arboral Fungicide, and Ulmasan. Under observation by Arthur D. Costonis of Massachusetts is the antibiotic Nystatin. It was injected by gravity into elms near Beacon Hill in Boston in 1978.

Still under trial are different pressures of injection: gravity, low pressure, and high pressure. Trees are usually injected close to the ground, at the flare of the trunk. One injection pattern is to bore holes 15 centimeters apart, one centimeter in diameter, and five centimeters deep. A belt of hose from a tank of chemical encircles the tree and is tapped into each hole.

More effective than trunk injections are root injections, as practiced by Edward S. Kondo of the Canadian Forest Service. The inoculant is sent through a hose clamped around the severed root. The technique takes more work and time, but when the inoculant rises with the sap, it gets better distribution. Trunk injection protects for a year; root injection works for two years.

Kondo declared at the National Arboretum symposium, "For the first time we can choose the elms that we want to preserve or maintain." He blamed some past failures to protect elms on opposing theories held by "I only want to inject" arborists and "All diseased elms must be destroyed" arborists. The best protection, he said, calls for good judgment in combining the techniques of both groups.

DDT was formerly used as a dormant spray in early spring to kill beetles before their deadly freight of spores could brush off. Since it was banned, methoxychlor has taken its place. A thorough coating poisons beetles arriving to feed in the twigs.

PHEROMONE TRAPPING

And beetles can be killed by the millions with the lure of sex pheromones, according to experiments by Gerald B. Lanier of the College of Forestry, State University of New York. Lanier and his associates developed three insect-attracting compounds to bait posters which are tacked to utility poles. Over a period of 100 days, each poster releases pheromone attractment equal to that of 2,000 virgin female beetles. Lanier credits

Pruning infected branches is the first and expensive step in checking Dutch elm disease.

Left: holes are drilled into the trunk to innoculate the elm with Lignasan. Right: spraying in early May with Methoxychlor is proving effective.

the traps with a significant reduction of the disease in a dozen experimental areas.

The subtle, lasting persistence of pheromone caused a researcher's embarrassment at a ball game while seatmates stared at the insects arriving and landing on him.

The U.S. Forest Service has used pheromone trapping to cut down beetle populations in heavily infested Detroit, in Evanston, Illinois, and in Fort Collins, Colorado. But as a total destroyer of beetles, trapping contends with the possible emergence of a million beetles from one large dead elm.

SOME ELMS ARE RESISTANT

The experts expect that many more elms will die because it is impossible to keep them all under capable management. But as elms die, resistant trees will stand out for easier identification.

Of all species of elms, the American variety is unfortunately the most susceptible to the Dutch elm disease. Yet even among American elms resistant ones, just beginning to wilt, have by themselves kept the disease from destroying them. These trees are being propagated.

Good resistance is showing up in European and Asiatic species, and in hybrids of the two. Some of these trees are chunkier than ours. Other species promise the graceful height of the American elm. Resistant elms are under development at the National Park Service Ecological Laboratory, the U.S. National Arboretum, and other research centers, and are being propagated by bud grafts for further testing.

The 2,700 elms in Washington, D.C. stand tall and handsome in random arrays from the Capitol west to the Lincoln Memorial, and from Lafayette Park and the White House south to the Jefferson Memorial. They are under the watchful eyes of Park Service principal plant pathologist Horace V. Wester of the Ecological Laboratory, and pathologist James L. Sherald, who says, "Any elm removal here is a drastic loss."

Like Santamour, Wester sees no repetition of the avenues of the elms. "Monocultures are asking for trouble." But elms in more random patterns, "planted no closer than 25 meters" and interspersed with other desirable shade trees, show promise.

Forty years of contending with the disease in old elms and the study of new ones leave Wester emphatically optimistic: "'We'll always have elms—including elms taller and more vigorous than the fine ones we've been learning how to save" □

SELECTED READINGS

"Dutch elm disease: good news, bad news" by J. Murphy. *Country Journal,* July 1978.

"Dutch elm disease" by M. W. Staples. *Flower and Garden,* April 1978.

"Elm-leaf beetle: what to do?" *Sunset,* August 1978.

"The elm forest is doomed, but twin cities are ready" by F. Graham, Jr. *Audubon,* July 1977.

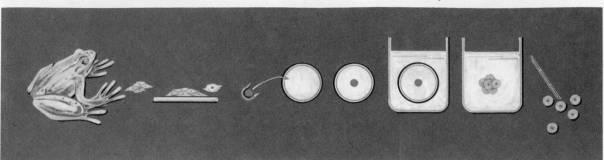

2. Cells from the tissue are cultured.

4. The egg develops into an embryo.

1. A bit of skin tissue is taken from a frog.

3. The nucleus from one of the cells is transplanted into a recipient egg (the nucleus of which has been removed).

5. Embryo cells are separated.

CLONING
by Damon R. Olszowy

CLONING is suddenly in the news, thanks to revolutionary techniques developed by genetic engineers and other new breeds of biologists. The newspapers are full of stories describing how scientists can produce a clone, or an identical carbon copy, of an organism from just a single cell. Biologists now have the ability to clone various plants and animals. Can people be far behind?

All of this seems frightening to many, not quite right to some, just plain startling to others. Perhaps the basic question is: how can cloning experiments contribute to the future welfare of people?

WHAT IS A CLONE?

A clone is an organism or a group of organisms created from a single parent. The process of cloning is really a form of asexual reproduction. You know that sexual reproduction involves the union of sex cells: the sperm from the male parent and the egg from the female parent. The nucleus of each sex cell—called a pronucleus—contains only one set of chromosomes with their genes and not the two sets that are found in the nuclei of all other cells, called body cells, and which give each species its characteristic chromosome number. The union of sperm and egg in fertilization produces two full sets of chromosomes. It is the first step in the creation of a new and unique individual with traits and characteristics inherited from both parents.

Cloning is asexual. There is only one parent. And the offspring has the hereditary traits of that single parent.

The word "clone" comes from the ancient Greek root, *klon,* meaning a twig or slip. Taking a twig or cutting from a plant and growing it into another plant is actually cloning the plant.

Today, however, the word "cloning" is used in a slightly different way. It has come to mean the production of an organism from just a single cell taken from the body of a plant or animal. This single cell, being a body cell and not a sex cell, contains two sets of chromosomes—one set from its mother and one set from its father. It thus has all the genetic information necessary to produce a complete individual if it is stimulated to grow.

CLONING PLANTS

Cloning is easier to do in plants than in animals because plant cells are simple in structure. Most young plant cells also have the ability to divide again and again. Individual plant cells are cultured in a special growing medium that contains the proper nutrients. The cells can divide, grow, and develop into new plants with leaves, roots, and flowers. Indeed, scientists have been able to do this in the laboratory with plants such as carrots, pine trees, and African violets.

This technique of cloning plants enables scientists to select a desirable plant and produce as many identical copies of it as they wish from each cell that is cultured.

A CLONAL FROG

The technique used to clone an animal is more difficult. First the nucleus of an egg

Illustrations by W. Hortens

Cloning a frog is relatively easy because frog eggs develop by themselves in water.

6. The nucleus from an embryo cell is transplanted into another recipient egg.

7. The egg develops into a clone of the original frog.

cell is removed. Then a nucleus from a body cell of a donor of the same species (either male or female) is placed into the egg cell. The egg cell now has a nucleus that has a complete chromosome complement and not half as its own nucleus had. This technique is called "nuclear transfer."

In 1952 U.S. scientists Robert Briggs and Thomas J. King tried the technique with frogs. They destroyed the nucleus of an unfertilized frog egg cell with radiation. Then they transplanted the nucleus from an ordinary body cell of a young tadpole (the juvenile stage in a frog's life) into the egg cell. The egg with transplanted nuclei survived and developed into a normal frog. The result of this experiment is a tadpole that is a genetic twin of the tadpole that donated the nucleus.

Ten years later British biologist John B. Gurdon tried using a nucleus from a skin cell of an adult frog. The results were unsuccessful: many abnormal and deformed frogs resulted. This happened because the egg cell divided more rapidly than the body cell from which the nucleus was taken. In other words, there was a discrepancy between the division rate of the egg cell and the division rate of the donor nucleus.

The key to success in cloning experiments is to transplant the right kind of nucleus into an egg cell. In this case "right" means that both divide at the same rate. Gurdon refined his experiment by first transplanting a nucleus from a skin cell into an enucleated egg cell and then growing the embryo until it was a very young tadpole. Then he separated the body cells of the young tadpole and transplanted the nuclei from these tadpole body cells into other enucleated frog egg cells. The new clones grew

from these eggs. This time many more normal frogs developed into adults.

This procedure was successful because the nuclei from the younger cells—in this case, from the tadpoles—divided at the same rate as the egg cells. This procedure is called "serial transfer" because it happens in series of steps involving two or more nuclear transplants.

CLONING MAMMALS

The cloning of mammals is even more difficult. The eggs of mammals are smaller and more fragile than the eggs of frogs. It requires microsurgery to transplant a nucleus without damaging the egg. In 1975 J. Dereck Bromhall of Oxford University, in England, tried to clone rabbits, but the results were unsatisfactory: the embryos grew abnormally. Since then, however, new techniques and instruments have been developed so that now a nucleus from a donor cell can be transplanted successfully into an egg cell of a mouse, a rabbit, or even a human.

Another major difference that makes cloning mammals more difficult than cloning frogs is that their embryos grow differently and have different needs. A frog is an amphibian, and its eggs can develop by themselves in water. In contrast, the embryo of a mammal must be protected inside the uterus of its mother if it is to complete its growth and development.

Today scientists can remove eggs from a female mammal, and replace the egg's nucleus with a nucleus from a body cell of a donor. They then implant the egg back into the uterus of the same female or into another female, which then acts as a substitute mother. In the uterus the embryo can complete its growth and development. Substitute

mothers have, in fact, given birth to mice, cows, and even to a baboon. The young produced in this way are not even related to their substitute mothers, since they do not contain any of the substitute mother's genetic material.

MICE MADE TO ORDER

U.S. biologists Clement L. Markert and Peter Hoppe of Jackson Laboratory in Bar Harbor, Maine, have worked on the cloning of mice. First they removed an egg from a female mouse just after it had been penetrated by a sperm cell. Then, using the techniques of microsurgery, they removed either the egg pronucleus or the sperm pronucleus before the two pronuclei united in the essential and final part of the fertilization process.

The egg cell then had one pronucleus. A pronucleus, you remember, has only one set of chromosomes—or half the normal chromosome number. They then stimulated the chromosomes in the pronucleus still in the egg cell to duplicate themselves. They then had an egg cell with a full chromosome complement, but all of it from one parent.

The egg continued to divide and develop into an embryo. At an early stage of its development, the embryo was implanted into a female mouse, which acted as a substitute mother. Of course, more than one egg can be implanted and, in fact, several were implanted. Seven offspring were born.

All the baby mice were female. Five of them had all their genes from a female pronucleus, and two had all their genes from a male pronucleus. Males cannot be produced in this experiment because each pronucleus carries only one type of sex chromosome. The production of males in mammals re-

quires the presence of two different types of sex chromosomes—an X and a Y sex chromosome. (A female pronucleus contains only the X sex chromosome; the male pronucleus contains either the X or the Y sex chromosome, but not both. When either pronucleus is stimulated to duplicate its chromosomes, only one sex chromosome in double dosage, so to speak, can result, and thus only females can be produced.)

You may notice that this procedure is different from the method used to clone a frog. It is true that all the genes in the mouse embryo come from a single adult mouse. However, the genes in its embryo consist of two copies of only *half* of the donor's genetic material rather than a complete set of genes representing a single copy of every gene present in the donor. The offspring could be considered semi-clones since they have only one half of all the possible genes that the donor has. Because of this condition, semi-clonal mice are not identical to the donor.

By repeating the experiment and starting with a semi-clone, a completely clonal mouse could be produced. An egg is taken from a semi-clonal mouse, and the chromosomes in its pronucleus are stimulated to duplicate themselves. This produces a complete nucleus with two chromosome sets. Then the embryo is implanted into a substitute mother. The resulting offspring will have exactly the same genes as its semi-clonal mother. It will be a true clone, a clone of a semi-clone.

CLONING A HUMAN

Scientists believe that much of the technological knowledge already exists to clone a human. The creation of a human by cloning

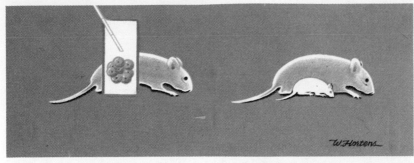

In this method of mouse cloning normal mating occurs, and then the sperm nucleus is removed. The female chromosomes double, and the developing embryo is implanted into another female.

6. The embryo is implanted in a substitute mother.

7. The substitute mother gives birth to a mouse whose genes are derived solely from the original mother.

would, however, be a very complex and risky laboratory procedure.

First, a healthy egg would be removed from a woman. Instead of fertilizing the egg with a sperm cell, scientists would destroy the nucleus in the egg and replace it with a nucleus from a donor cell. This step is the biggest challenge.

The nucleus of the egg cell and the nucleus of the donor cell must first be separated from their surrounding cytoplasm. Then the donor's nucleus must be transplanted into the empty cytoplasm of the egg cell. Although this has been done successfully in frogs and mice, the chances for success with human eggs are less because human eggs are much smaller and more delicate. However, cells can now be united by using a method called cell fusion.

In this case, the nucleus is removed from the donor cell with radiation. Then certain chemicals or viruses are used to help make the nucleus fuse with the empty egg cell. But even with cell fusion, some of the cytoplasm from the egg cell can get mixed up. Some scientists believe that the disruption of the cytoplasm can alter the production of a clone. (The disruption of egg cytoplasm is easier to avoid in the cloning of other species because non-human eggs are larger, less delicate, and easier to handle.)

For the purposes of this discussion, however, let's assume that the nucleus from the donor was transplanted into the human egg cell without disrupting the egg cytoplasm or damaging the egg. The egg would then be cultured in the laboratory until the embryo reached the blastocyst stage of development in which it is a hollow ball of cells. It would then be implanted into the uterus of a

woman—a substitute mother—so that it could complete its development.

The baby born would not be genetically related to its "mother" since it would not have any of her hereditary characteristics. The baby would have only one parent—the donor that provided the nucleus. The baby would be, in fact, a genetic copy of the donor—its identical twin, a generation or more removed.

BUT . . .

Although the cloning of a human seems possible, there are still technological problems involved. More important, there are serious ethical questions involved.

One danger is the possibility of a mutation in the nucleus of the donor. The chance of a mutation occurring depends to a large extent on the kind of cell that is used as the nucleus-donating cell. A skin cell or any other body cell could theoretically be used. It has a complete nucleus and can provide the necessary chromosome number. But the risk of a mutation is greater in body cells because these cells have already divided many times and the more cell divisions the greater the chance for a mutation.

If it were a male to be cloned, the donated nucleus could be taken from a sperm cell. But, as you remember, a sperm-cell nucleus—or more correctly, a pronucleus—has only half the chromosome complement for humans. A child cloned from such a cell would have only one half of the genes of the donor and would not be a true clone, but rather a semi-clone. There is also a greater chance of a recessive lethal gene showing up in a sperm cell than in other types of cells.

What kind of cell then should be used to

This tricolored mouse was formed by joining three eight-cell mouse embryos from mice of three different colors. By 25 hours the 24 cells had joined together, forming a single embryo, which was transferred to the uterus of a foster mother.

Clement Markert

clone a human male? Some scientists believe that the best choice is a spermatogonium, or sperm-producing cell. These cells are found in the testes. They possess all the donor's genes to clone a complete individual.

The appropriate cell to use to clone a female has not yet been identified.

NOT A CARBON COPY

How similar would a human clone be to its donor? It surely would not resemble the adult donor from the start. The human infant would have to go through the normal stages of growth and development. It might resemble the donor during certain comparable stages of life—for example, the clone at five years old might resemble the donor when he or she was five years old.

In terms of genetics, the clone would be as similar to the donor as an identical twin would be. Mutations could, however, cause differences between the donor and clone even though they originally have the exact same genetic makeup.

There could also be other differences in the clone. No one, for example, really knows the effects of the egg's cytoplasm on the developing embryo. There are also the largely unknown effects of the substitute mother's hormones and general health and nutrition during pregnancy.

Even more probably, differences between the clone and its human donor would result from the two having different histories, environments, life-styles, and diseases throughout life. Certainly the notion that a human clone would be an exact duplicate of the donor is very questionable.

THE FUTURE

We are back to our original question—namely, how will cloning contribute to the welfare of people? The techniques of cloning can improve our methods of producing desirable plants and animals. The day may come when we will be able to select prize animals and plants with superior genetic traits and produce exact copies of them in large quantities in less time than it would take under natural conditions. This could have an important effect on the world's production of food.

Cloning techniques could also be used in basic biological and medical research. Clonal mice and rats, for example, could be used to study genetic diseases, cancer, and other disorders.

But what about human cloning? At the present time, most researchers are not concerned with human cloning. There are serious ethical questions to be considered as well as practical doubts about the consequences of human cloning. To cite just one of the complex problems involved: who is to decide which hereditary traits are desirable and to be continued via cloning and which traits are not? Is musical talent more valuable than scientific talent? Is blond hair preferable to red hair? These are the unanswered and perhaps unanswerable questions □

SELECTED READINGS

"Cloning era is almost here" by Gene Bylinsky. *Fortune,* June 19, 1978.

"Test-tube potatoes." *Scientific American,* June 1978.

The ladybug was imported from Australia to control a citrus insect pest.

BIOLOGICAL CONTROL OF INSECTS

by William H. Jordan, Jr.

MOST farmers in America have not yet realized that insects naturally interact with, intervene with, and control one another. And farmers usually don't think in terms of populations. In nature, as long as one fertilized female survives, the population can regenerate, the species can survive. It doesn't matter in the overall view if, say, 90 per cent of the individuals succumb, because a few females can start a whole new population.

Insects are amazingly skilled reproducers. A single aphid capable of bearing 50 young in its lifetime could theoretically be responsible for 318,750,000 aphids within just one month. In one year it could be responsible for a mass of aphids 90 million miles in diameter.

So not only do insect populations survive with remarkable vigor, they can also adapt genetically with electrifying speed. The people who develop insecticides have learned this at great expense and labor, as product after product has been rendered obsolete by insect resistance.

PLANT EATERS AND PREDATORS

Obviously, that female aphid didn't end up reaching her reproductive potential—the world is not overrun with aphids. The reason is biological control. Biological control occurs continuously in nature as parasites, predatory insects and insect diseases—frequently introduced by humans—constantly regulate populations of plant-eating insects. Regulation, however, depends on predator multiplication. In a relationship called density-dependence, the numbers of predators vary in direct proportion to the host's density. As the plant eaters multiply, the predators multiply. As the plant eaters decline, their predators decline.

A second property of predator multiplication is the lag effect: The predators multiply after the prey have started to increase, decline after the prey have started to decline. Actually, the relationship could work no other way, because plant eaters must be present as food and sustenance when predators and parasites arrive. This means, however, that the predator and parasite populations always lag a half step behind the plant-eating population. The ultimate effect is that biological control expresses itself as an endless rise and fall of populations—a predictable, dependable, and inexorable process. Yet it is a fragile process, too, and we can easily disrupt it.

I think natural control is somewhat of a miracle, as well as a mechanism. Mysterious instincts, macabre jaws, stingers that lay eggs, supersensitive antennae—all evolved for searching out and attacking prey. These boggle the mind, especially when one realizes that they all contribute to the natural systems of control. Every garden is full of insects struggling away in combat with one another, each using its deadly little tools and weapons. All of us have probably chanced on their Lilliputian conflicts without any awareness of what was going on among them.

THE APHID AND THE SYRPHID

Last summer, for instance, my landlady asked me to examine one of her rose bushes. She was very concerned that aphids were about to drain all the sap from it. Sure enough, aphids were clustering on the fresh buds and honeydew was glistening on the older foliage beneath. It looked like an absolute disaster.

To the untrained eye it was a disaster. But as I looked closer, I suddenly noticed another circumstance: Two aphids that were just reaching reproductive age sat side-by-side on the underside of a leaf. Arranged in a triangular pattern around them lay three sausage-shaped eggs glued onto the surface. These were eggs of a syrphid fly. Larval syrphids are voracious aphid-eaters. But the real beauty of the situation was the timed arrival of those eggs, because in a day or so, after the two aphids had produced a few infants, the young syrphids would hatch next to aphids small enough for them to kill and eat.

The adult syrphids, driven by an instinct synchronized to their prey's development, had searched out aphids just reaching maturity and laid eggs nearby—all the more miraculous when you consider that syrphid larvae are blind and must feel around with their heads until they touch their prey. Groping, an infant larva must encounter its first victims before it uses up all the energy stored in its little body.

MORE PREDATORS

This was not the only conflict on the rose bush. A greyish-green creature standing at the edge of an aphid group was lifting an aphid with jaws like ice tongs. This was a lacewing larva in the act of sucking the juices from its victim. And in the middle of the colony were several mature aphids that were not green, but tan. Somehow, in some ineffable

The syrphid larva emerges from its egg and blindly eats surrounding aphids.

Harry Rogers/Photo Researchers

Some gardeners say that every garden should have several mantises and a skunk to keep in check the insect population.

J. H. Robinson/Photo Researchers

way—a static look, a stiffer posture—they seemed different from their green companions. On looking closely I saw the telltale hole on the top of each abdomen and realized that these individuals were shells of the once-living insects. Aphid parasites were also in the neighborhood and were attacking the aphids. Insect parasites stalk their prey, puncture them with an ovipositor (the familiar "stinger" of larger bees or wasps) and inject an egg, which hatches into a legless grub that devours the prey from inside, finally killing it. The larvae of this particular parasite, after finishing their growth, line the inside of the aphids with silk and convert them into tan cocoons or "mummies."

ORGANS FOR HUNTING AND DEVOURING

The most amazing thing about predatory and parasitic insects is the methods they have evolved to track down, attack, and devour their victims. If you watch a hunting parasite, you'll see it scurry over and under twigs, buds, and axils, excitedly examining every nook and niche that could hide a host. It turns out that special nerve cells line their antennae, so they can detect faint odors from the prey themselves or from the prey's saliva smeared on the chewed leaves.

Furthermore, an insect parasite usually specializes in attacking just one or a few closely related species of plant-eating insects and won't take others. For biological-control programs this ensures that the "good bugs" will control only the pests they're supposed to control and not attack some innocent, otherwise beneficial species.

The point of all this is that it takes a thief to catch a thief. Learning to use insects against other insects is a better tactic than trying to depend entirely on pesticides. Natural enemies do a more thorough, more dependable job without polluting.

SUCCESSFUL BIOLOGICAL CONTROLS

Actually, biological control has been used in American agriculture for many years. It started with the spectacular control in 1888 of the cottony cushion scale, which was destroying California's citrus industry. The vedalia beetle, a ladybug, imported from Australia along with a parasitic fly, completely dominated the pest. Imported parasites and predators have also controlled the olive scale, the citrophilus mealybug, and the walnut aphid, saving millions of dollars in California alone.

These are called "classic successes" because they follow the ecological theories about how things happen in nature. Theory assumes that plant eaters are normally regulated by predators and parasites in their native environments. It also assumes that if an eater of plants should happen to invade a new region by hiding in the myriad cracks and crevices that cargoes always have, the insect finds a boundless source of food and no natural enemies. It multiplies unchecked, and then we call it a pest.

According to the theories, to reestablish natural control, we simply discover the pest's home territory and import its natural enemies. These then thrive and spread, and biological control develops. Once stabilized, a classic situation takes care of itself, not requiring any additional human intervention.

Indoors, where the environment is too simple for natural control to continue indefinitely, programs of artificial biological control have been worked out for certain crops. In England and Holland entomologists have developed programs for maintaining a greenhouse environment. Such programs favor predators and parasites and stimulate them to control their prey. One program for chrysanthemum pests actually controls spider mites, whiteflies, aphids, and leaf miners. In the world under glass, with its regulated environment, biological control is becoming a kind of biological engineering.

COMBINING TWO CONTROLS

By itself, however, biological control can't always hold plant-eating insects and mites below levels that cause economic damage. Then pesticides or cultural methods have to be used. In the past this was the point where biological control vanished. Then the delicate natural relationship among predator and prey was torn apart by routine applications of chemicals. But in the last 20 years an approach called *integrated control* has been scientifically devised to use pesticides, as well as other weapons, according to our knowledge of insect ecology.

Integrated control is based on biological control that is operating at the time. Therefore, pesticides must be used in judicious doses at just the right times not to ruin this natural foundation. For integrated pest management you've got to know the important mites and insects in an ecosystem. You've got to know how they react to weather, to the seasons, and to other insects and mites.

COTTON PLANT VERSUS BUGS

Scientists at the University of California have developed an excellent program of integrated control for cotton. For organisms like lygus bugs, bollworms, mites, and even for the cotton plants themselves, they've gathered all kinds of data. Such data include reproductive capacities, food requirements, growth rates at various temperatures and humidities, and the rising and falling populations of insects and mites.

Researchers have found, among other things, that cotton plants will often tolerate large populations of pests like bollworms, lygus bugs, and mites before losing yield. This tolerance also varies during the season.

In order to control the cotton boll weevil, scientists have learned about their life cycle and exactly how they fit into their physical and living environments.

Using too much pesticide destroys the natural biological controls.

Bollworms, for example, do not always affect the crop if they infest the plants early in the season, because up to 80 per cent of the flowers and young bolls drop off in the course of the season, regardless of insect activities.

As another example, if lygus bugs have not reached a particular population density by the middle of July, they too will not bother the crop, so the researchers recommend not spraying. At times like these, pesticides would only kill insects that do no real damage, as well as kill the predators and parasites that keep other species of plant eaters in check. Heedless spraying creates pests from species that are normally harmless.

WEAK SPOT IN LIFE CYCLE

On the other hand, spraying is beneficial and worthwhile if the "weak spots" in a pest's life cycle are discovered. For instance, although lygus bugs are cotton pests, they begin the season by breeding in safflower, the only crop available early in the year. Then, when the safflower begins to dry out, they migrate in multiplied hordes to cotton. This safflower period, though, is their most vulnerable time. They cannot fly while maturing. They don't burrow into the plant like bollworms, so they can't escape or find protection from chemical sprays. Until they molt into adults they're stuck in the field.

What science has taught us to do, then, is simply wait until the growing population is 80 to 90 per cent composed of immature bugs. Then we spray once, trapping in the field millions of lygus that would have infested cotton. Integrated with biological control, the pesticide in this case does not disrupt the predators and parasites in cotton. Thus the integrated program gives better regulation, eliminates pollution, and does not create other new pests. Sometimes it reduces pesticide use by as much as 80 percent.

INSECTS AND THE FARMER

Insect populations have an amazing ability to adapt to their environment. Some individuals in a population are not poisoned by a certain insecticide. Then within a relatively short time a whole population is resistant to the pesticide. And resistance is steadily growing, make no mistake about it. A recent report from Cornell University reveals that insects did about twice as much damage to food and fiber crops in 1972 as they did every year from 1942 to 1951. Yet we now need more than 10 times as much pesticide per year—100 million pounds in 1947 compared to 1.4 billion pounds in 1972—to get only half the control □

SELECTED READINGS

"Applied ecology: showing the way to better insect control" by Jean L. Marx. Science, March 4, 1978.

"Microbial pesticides: coming but slowly" by J. Arehart-Treichel. Science News, January 7, 1978.

"USDA's profound change: to help farmers naturally" by J. Cox. Organic Gardening and Farming, September 1977.

THE 1978 NOBEL PRIZE IN PHYSIOLOGY OR MEDICINE

by Margot Slade

THE 1978 Nobel Prize in Physiology or Medicine was awarded to two U.S. scientists: Hamilton O. Smith and Daniel Nathans, both of Johns Hopkins University Medical School, and to Werner Arber of the University of Basel Microbiological Center in Switzerland for their work with restriction enzymes and its application to genetic research. In naming the winners, the Nobel Committee of Sweden's Karolinska Institute of Medicine formally recognized that the achievements of the three microbiologists were built one-upon-the-other.

Arber, while a visiting researcher at the University of Southern California and the University of California at Los Angeles, discovered restriction enzymes, enzymes that chemically sever, or cut, the cell's genetic material. At Johns Hopkins, Smith built on Arber's discovery by demonstrating how the restriction enzyme in bacteria "precision cuts" the DNA, or genetic material, in the middle of a specific symmetrical sequence of its component chemicals. Nathans then applied these findings to pioneer the application of restriction enzymes to genetic research.

Restriction enzymes are substances that become catalysts for chemical reactions in cells. They act as chemical scissors, cutting strips of the genetic material DNA, or deoxyribonucleic acid, into fragments of precise length. Using restriction enzymes, scientists can analyze the chemical structure of genes and map their sequences. They can separate out specific genes and investigate how they function to determine specific hereditary traits. Researchers can also use restriction enzymes to study hereditary diseases, and they hope, one day, to use them to unravel the mysteries of cancer.

CHEMICAL SCISSORS

Both Smith and Nathans agree that the basis of their achievements lies primarily in Arber's research, which began in the late 1950's. Arber first postulated the existence of restriction enzymes in the 1960's while he was studying viruses that invade bacteria. He labeled such a virus with a radioactive isotope, and this enabled him to trace the activity of the virus in the bacterial cell. Arber found that when the virus entered the bacteria cells, most of the viral DNA was destroyed. He hypothesized that the bacteria were manufacturing a substance that "cut" the viral DNA into small pieces. The bacteria's own DNA, Arber reasoned, was protected from similar dismantling by other enzymes. He also suggested that the cutting enzymes—called restriction enzymes—pinpoint specific cutting sites along the viral DNA strand.

Werner Arber

Werner Arber

PINPOINT ACCURACY

Smith advanced this enzyme research one step further in 1969. He was studying the ability of bacterial cells—in his work, influenza bacteria—to take up naked DNA—that is, DNA not enclosed in a cell or protective covering—from the surrounding culture medium. Smith noticed that the bacteria produced a substance that cut the DNA at specific points. He actually saw a restriction enzyme in action.

In two classic papers, published in 1970, Smith described the discovery and how the substance seemed to operate. Most important, he actually demonstrated the enzyme's specificity: each time it singled out a particular sequence of chemicals making up the DNA strand and severed the strand at that precise point.

PIECE BY PIECE

Nathans was conducting research in Israel in 1969 when Smith wrote to him and told of his discovery. Referring to the exchange of letters, Nathans has said it "sparked my interest that restriction enzymes could be used" to cut up DNA in the same way that enzymes in the human digestive system break up protein in the foods we eat.

Nathans applied Smith's discovery to his work with SV40, a monkey virus known to cause cancer in animals but not in humans. In 1971 Nathans found that by using restriction enzymes he could break SV40 DNA into 11 discrete fragments and determine the specific genetic function of each fragment. In so doing, he gave scientists a method for mapping DNA structure, a method that could be used with the DNA of other, more complex organisms. At the same time, Nathans suggested several ways in which restriction enzymes could be used in genetic research, particularly in the controversial field of recombinant DNA research.

100 NOW KNOWN

Scientists now recognize approximately 100 restriction enzymes that act on specific sites along the DNA molecule. Many of them have been identified through the screening of a large number of bacterial strains by Richard J. Roberts of the Cold Spring Harbor Laboratory in New York. The application of these enzymes to the study and engineering of DNA molecules has revolutionized the fields of molecular biology and molecular genetics.

Restriction-enzyme use is also beginning to have important medical applications. Researchers have, for example, recently found ways of using restriction enzymes to test for the presence of particular genetic diseases before birth. It is, however, the use of restriction enzymes in recombinant DNA research that has attracted the most attention.

USE IN RECOMBINANT DNA WORK

Recombinant DNA research involves the rearranging of genetic material to create new or altered life forms. Many scientists are very concerned about recombinant DNA research. They fear, among other things, that some mutant virus or bacteria against which mankind has no defenses or weapons could escape a research laboratory and perhaps cause an epidemic. Some scientists have even contested the right of any individual or

Hamilton O. Smith

Johns Hopkins Univ.

Daniel Nathans

group to experiment with basic genetic material and urged strict government regulation and supervision of research as well as stringent safety standards for all laboratories involved in DNA research.

Ironically, Nathans, who began dismantling cancer-cell DNA in 1970, ended in 1974 by joining a group of influential scientists in urging caution and a slowing-down of recombinant DNA work. Arber took a different stance, saying that research cannot be slowed.

Many of the fears about recombinant DNA research have, to date, proved groundless, and the U.S. National Institutes of Health has even recently modified the stiff requirements for DNA research facilities. And much very promising recombinant DNA work is being done. One group of scientists has, for example, succeeded in using recombinant DNA techniques to manufacture human insulin in bacterial cells.

POTENTIAL RECOGNIZED

In awarding the Nobel Prize to the three researchers, the Karolinska Institute said that their work has "increased knowledge in [an] area [which] should help in the preven-

tion and treatment of malformations, hereditary diseases, and cancer." Echoing this statement, Nathans has noted that to have any hope of understanding the complex genetic structure of cancer and of birth defects or of comprehending human development, "we have to break it up one piece at a time."

Today Nathans continues to examine the pieces, looking at DNA in cancer cells and trying to understand the mechanisms that transform a normal cell into a cancerous one. Smith is again working with influenza DNA, and Arber is continuing his research at the Basel Microbiological Center.

Werner Arber was born in Gränichen, Aargav, Switzerland in 1929. He studied at the Federal Institute of Technology in Zurich and then at the University of Geneva. After working for several years with leading geneticists in the United States, he returned to the University of Geneva where he did most of his award-winning work. Since 1970 he has been associated with the University of Basel Microbiological Center in Switzerland.

Hamilton O. Smith was born in New York City in 1931. He received his undergraduate degree from the University of California at Berkeley and his M.D. from Johns Hopkins in 1956. After internship and residency, he turned his attention to research in microbial genetics, working at the University of Michigan from 1962 to 1967. Since 1967 he has been associated with the department of microbiology at Johns Hopkins University, where he is now a professor of microbiology.

Daniel Nathans was born in Wilmington, Delaware, in 1928. He was awarded a bachelor of science degree from the University of Delaware and received his M.D. from Washington University in 1954. He worked at the Rockefeller Institute for Medical Research (now Rockefeller University) and the Columbia-Presbyterian Medical Center, both in New York City, and at the U.S. National Cancer Institute in Bethesda, Maryland. He then became associated with Johns Hopkins, where, like Smith, he rose through the academic ranks. Today he is a professor of microbiology and director of the department of microbiology □

Tadder/Baltimore

At the Baltimore, Maryland, Learning Center underachievers of all ages are learning to read, to reason, and to do basic mathematics through the medium of computerized programs.

COMPUTERS & MATHEMATICS

COMPUTERS AND MATHEMATICS
REVIEW OF THE YEAR

IBM Corporation

Drs. Humberto Gerola and Philip Seiden used a computer to simulate the evolution of galactic forms. In this photo their computed pattern overlays an actual photo of a galaxy known as M101. The scientists believe that a chain reaction of exploding stars may be responsible for the spiral shapes of galaxies.

Physicians of the University of Wisconsin Medical Center have programmed this computer with information they received from interviews of hundreds of depressed patients. The computer predicted 90 per cent of those who attempted suicide.

Tom Rust, University of Wisconsin

Computer Trends. In 1978 there was a growing trend toward large, general purpose computers with faster, more powerful logic circuits and greater, more advanced memory systems. There was also a continuing trend toward more powerful, less expensive computers. Microprocessors, those tiny silicon chips containing computing units, are becoming "smarter" and less expensive and show promise of being built into many more electronic devices in the near future. ■ Computer firms also experimented with fiber optics during the year. Glass fibers, which transmit data by light waves, can carry more information, are cheaper, and much harder to "bug" than are copper wires that transmit signals electrically. ■ Two newcomers to the memory technology market began to fill the gap between high speed, but costly memory systems and cheap, but slow systems during the year. These newcomers: magnetic bubbles and CCD's, or charge-coupled devices, are discussed in the article "New Computer Memories," which begins on page 99.

Expanding Use in Science. CCD's have not only mundane uses in computers and electronic cash registers, but they also have "other-worldly" uses. Since CCD's can detect subtle differences in light intensity and are quite sensitive in the red and infrared regions of the spectrum, they are being used by astronomers and astrophysicists for planetary observations and for studying distant galaxies. So far CCD's have detected clouds in the atmosphere of Uranus and faint holes around certain galaxies. Princeton University scientists, led by David T. Wilkinson, hope to use CCD's to study primordial galaxies—galaxies at the "edge" of the universe and so distant that by the time their light comes to us, we are seeing them as they looked billions of years ago when they first formed. ■ CCD's will also be used by the U.S. National Aeronautics and Space Administration (NASA) for the Space Telescope planned to be carried aloft in the Space Shuttle in the early 1980's and for the Galileo Project, an upcoming space probe to the planet Jupiter. Special flight control and data-collecting microcomputers that can withstand Jupiter's intense radiation field are also being designed for the Jupiter orbiter. ■ Computers are also being used to study the evolution of spiral and elliptical galaxies and the formation of stars from interstellar gas clouds.

In chemistry, computers have been designed to use with infrared spectrometers to aid organic chemists in such things as rapid quality control analysis, and special computer programs have been developed to determine the shapes of complex molecules and to describe certain processes that occur in complicated chemical reactions. ■ Biologists are using computer simulation studies to try to understand growth processes that occur in embryonic cells, and earth scientists are using computers to study seismic phenomena. California Institute of Technology scientist Carl Johnson has developed a special system to monitor seismic events and pinpoint their locations so that scientists can analyze earthquake activity as it occurs.

Computers and People. Can a computer determine whether or not a person is suicidal? A computer programmed by doctors at the University of Wisconsin Medical School interviewed hundreds of depressed patients and correctly predicted 90 per cent of those who attempted suicide within nine months after the interview, while therapists who had given personal interviews correctly identified only 30 per cent.

In a program that began in February 1978 computers at the Baltimore Learning Center in Maryland are helping "functionally illiterate" adults to improve their reading and mathematics skills so that they will be able to get better jobs. After about 23 hours with the program, students were able to advance almost one grade in reading, and after 30 hours with the program were able to advance a little more than one grade in mathematics.

Now there's a computer that "speaks" Chinese. Robert Sloss and Peter Nancarrow of the Faculty of Oriental Studies of Cambridge University developed a model that uses a grid to assign a numbered code to each Chinese ideograph (character), which can then be entered into the computer. The computer "understands" Chinese, can draw ideographs and display them on a video screen, and, it is hoped, will be able to be used for typesetting Chinese newspapers and for translating.

In other news from Great Britain, systems called Teletext and Viewdata have turned the television set into a computerized video-display system. At the touch of a button, Teletext displays weather maps, theatre listings, stock-market results, or news headlines on the television screen. Viewdata, by using the telephone in addition to the television, ensures direct contact with the Viewdata computer, thereby giving even faster service and allowing subscribers to send messages to one another. Both systems should be available in the United States in 1979.

Mathematics. Elementary-school students in Mt. Vernon, New York, are becoming lightning-fast calculators simply by using their fingers. The special finger-counting method, developed by Mr. Hang Young-Pai, is known as Chisanbop, and is a modified version of a hand-calculation system used in the Far East. Basically the fingers of the right hand represent single units, while the thumb stands for 5; the fingers of the left hand stand for tens, while the thumb represents 50. Using both hands, all adding, subtracting, multiplying, and dividing up to 99 can be done.

In another special-mathematics program, students at Theodore Roosevelt Elementary School on Long Island, New York, are learning mathematics at an accelerated pace. Third graders learn long division; sixth graders learn algebra. The children learn to visualize how a problem should be done before they do it. Most of the students, many of whom come from low-income families, are now doing superior work in mathematics, and other schools are starting to use the apparently successful program.

In August 1978 four young mathematicians—Daniel Quillen of the Massachusetts Institute of Technology, Charles Fefferman of Princeton University, Pierre Deligne of the Institut des Hautes Etudes Scientifiques in France, and G. A. Margulis of the Soviet Union—were awarded Fields Medals at the Eighteenth International Congress of Mathematics in Helsinki, Finland. The Field Medal, the "Nobel Prize of Mathematics," is awarded to mathematicians under 40 "in recognition of work already done and as encouragement for further achievement."

Jane Samz

NASA

Astrophysicists are now aided by computer scientists in testing out their astronomical theories and calculations. Here Richard H. Miller of the University of Chicago (seated) and Bruce F. Smith of the NASA Ames Center watch a computer-graphics display in their study of galactic dynamics and evolution.

A sixth-grader at Theodore Roosevelt Elementary School solves an algebra problem at the blackboard.

Newsday

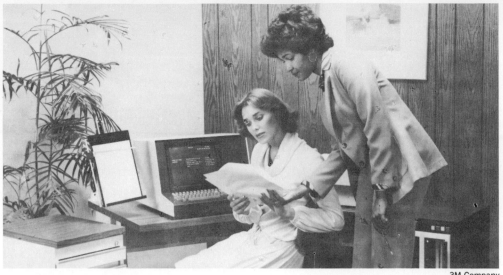

WORD PROCESSING

by Jane Samz

IT took a lot of time and the efforts of a number of people to produce the article you are now reading. After researching the topic of word processors, the author sketched an outline and wrote a rough draft of the article. The rough draft was then revised and typed. The first typed version was then revised (articles tend to read differently once they are transposed from longhand to type) and retyped. The article was then checked for typographical errors, clarity, and readability, after which the finished manuscript was sent to the editor.

The editor made revisions for clarity, readability, flow, length, and style. The edited copy was retyped and sent to the author for comment and then returned to the editor. The author's comments duly noted, the final edited and approved copy was retyped and sent to the typesetter.

At the typesetters, the manuscript, which may have again been retyped, was set in type. The typeset copy was then proofread. Final revisions were made by the editor, provisions for text and illustrations to fit were made, and the article was at last sent to the printer.

Unfortunately in order to produce a book or magazine, or even an important business letter, a great deal of time and effort is spent retyping manuscripts each time there are major revisions in the text. The problem is compounded by the necessity of proofreading each retyped version for typographical errors. How much better it would be if only the revised sections, rather than the whole text, had to be retyped. This is one of the major functions of word processors.

ELECTRONIC AID

Word processors electronically speed the writing, editing, and transmitting of documents by eliminating the necessity for completely retyping revised or previously typed material. Errors are less likely to occur if only the edited material needs to be retyped. This is an aid to authors and editors as well as to secretarial personnel, since then only the revised and retyped parts need be proofread.

The word-processor revolution essentially began with the introduction of the International Business Machines (IBM) magnetic-tape *Selectric* typewriter in 1964. The *Selectric,* with a magnetic-tape memory, allowed the user to record and play back documents as many times as necessary. With this machine and others like it, revisions and retyping could be made on only the part of the copy that needed it. Then, about 1969, the IBM magnetic-card *Selectric* typewriter came on the scene. With this machine, documents are typed onto magnetic cards that are capable of storing a full page of copy. Changes are made simply by typing over errors, and the changes are recorded on the magnetic card. Once all revisions have been made, error-free copies are produced automatically simply by placing a blank piece of paper in the typewriter and pressing a button. The *Selectric* then types out a copy at the rate of 150 words a minute.

Today other electronic typing systems featuring magnetic cards, magnetic tapes, or single and dual-cassette tape systems as well as systems that can handle information from both cards and tapes make up an important segment of the word processing market. Some more sophisticated systems can automatically index documents and act as "electronic filing cabinets." Others, equipped with time-saving carriages that can print in both directions, function as high-speed duplicating and printing systems. Still others are capable of inserting variable information into a standard format such as a letter.

Additional features make word processors a valuable helping hand. Text searches allow the operator to zoom in on and change a given word or phrase anywhere in a document rapidly. Margins, tabs, line spacing, column alignment, underlining, and attractive right hand margins can all be handled automatically.

WITH A TV SCREEN

More advanced word processors come equipped with single-line display windows that are suitable for minor text revisions. There are also video-display units, usually cathode-ray television-type screens that can accommodate a full page display or zoom in on a given section of text. Global search systems allow a specified word or phrase to be automatically changed every time it appears in a document. For example, the processor can be made to change Mr. Smith's address from 730 East 35th Street to 730 East 37th Street every time it appears. And even whole paragraphs can be moved around on such a system.

At least one cathode-ray tube word processor highlights the copy being edited by displaying it in "reverse video." The edited sections are displayed by reversing the standard text character and background colors. If, for example, text is displayed as green characters on a black background, the edited portion will appear as black characters on a green background. Redactron Corporation's *Redactor II* system uses this method.

Video-display systems also allow the user to type or edit one document while previously completed manuscripts are being printed. The printing is usually done with the aid of a "daisy wheel," a print element with one type character on each spoke. This print wheel is bidirectional and very fast, generally capable of printing about 360 words a minute. It saves time by not having to return to the left margin every time a new line is printed.

Still other video-display systems can be programmed to automatically process frequently used forms or letters. And some word processors feature a security system in which a designated code or password is programmed into the machine in order to restrict access to classified information.

AND THEY TALK

Some companies are now designing communications systems that can be used in

The interior of a word-processing computer is extremely complicated.

conjunction with word processors. There are video-display units and special communication typewriters that can communicate over telephone, Telex, or TWX lines with other video-display units, communicating typewriters, computers, document printers, and TWX and Telex terminals.

AND READ

As word processors become both more common and more sophisticated, the distinction between them and data processors may become harder and harder to define. Data-entry and electronic mail have been incorporated into some word processing systems, while others are capable of sorting information in the same manner as a computer.

Along with this trend toward more sophistication is the introduction of optical-character recognition (O.C.R.) machines into word processing systems. O.C.R. "reading" machines were originally designed to help speed the entry of data into computers. Now, smaller versions of these machines have been created to read typed material—up to four pages a minute—into word processors. There is, however, one drawback. A number of these O.C.R.'s can read only a special printing type, or font, so that only information typed on typewriters capable of using several different type elements can be used. O.C.R.'s do enable materials typed on *Selectric* typewriters to be read into word processors and into Telex and TWX systems as well.

AND TRANSLATE

Then there's the computer just recently introduced that will help human translators speed the translation of documents from one language to another. According to the manufacturer, a human translator with the aid of its computer, should be able to handle more than 2,400 words an hour. The computer provides literal translations, and the human translator acts as editor and interpreter. The machine is actually a word processor—an electronic typewriter plus video display—tied into a minicomputer.

The foreign-language manuscript to be translated is typed out and a word-for-word translation appears on the video display. Changes in translation—to be made by the translator—are typed out and the corrected version processed. Where there is more than one meaning for a word, the computer lists all definitions and the translator chooses the appropriate one. The system, called the Multi-Lingual Word Processing System, is manufactured by Weidner Communications Systems, Inc. of La Jolla, California. It was introduced in a Spanish to English version, but provisions are being made to accommodate Japanese, Russian, Arabic, Hebrew, and about five other languages. In addition, a computer designed to assist four translators at one time will also be available.

AND HEAR? NOT YET

With all the different types of word processors on the market, the buyer is faced with the task of finding suitable equipment for the present without getting locked into a system that may become obsolete in a few years. Manufacturers are therefore providing add-ons that are compatible with older equipment and up-to-date modular systems that allow the buyer the same sort of flexibility now available in modular data-processing systems.

Ultimately, it is hoped, voice-recognition word processors will be developed. Such systems would allow documents to be composed and revised verbally, with copy to be edited displayed on a video screen. A computer system would then check the document for grammar and vocabulary, and finally, after filing a copy electronically, would transmit the finished document by electronic mail.

So, word processing, which began with a power typewriter that enabled the user to type in revisions without retyping the whole document, may one day lead to a voice-to-machine system that allows for revision, filing, and distribution of documents swiftly and electronically, without the use of pen, typewriter, or even paper □

SELECTED READINGS

"Amazing daisies; industry competition for daisy wheel printing system." *Forbes,* August 1977.

"Linotypes' risky dive into word processors." *Business Week,* May 8, 1978.

"Word processing equipment." *American City and Country,* December 1977.

NEW COMPUTER MEMORIES

by Bro Uttal

PIONEERING a new kind of computer memory is likely to be a money-losing game. The memory market is tempting, all right—currently around $5,000,000,000 and growing at about 25 per cent a year. But the ticket for research, development, and pilot production can easily exceed $10,000,000, and the chances of ending up with a winner are slim.

Existing memory technologies are embedded in the designs of computer systems, and prices fall so steeply and inexorably that newcomers seldom catch on unless they have some compelling performance advantage. The history of the memory business is littered with devices of great technical merit that lost out because they could not catch up with the declining production costs of their established competitors.

THE CCD

Lately, though, some of the biggest bettors in the computer and electronics industries have been putting sizable amounts of money on two new technologies that seem to be sure winners—at least on paper. Both were developed at Bell Labs. One of them is the charge-coupled device, or CCD. It is a relative of the conventional semiconductor-memory chip, that tiny sandwich of silicon that can store thousands of bits of data on a surface 1/36 the size of a postage stamp.

The CCD is slower and simpler than the standard memory chip—the metal-oxide semiconductor RAM, or random-access memory.

However, the CCD seems capable of storing data for one-third the price of RAM storage, or even less. The market is small now, but at least one computer scientist estimates that the new chip could ring up sales of about $70,000,000 by 1980, even if it sold for half as much per bit as RAM storage.

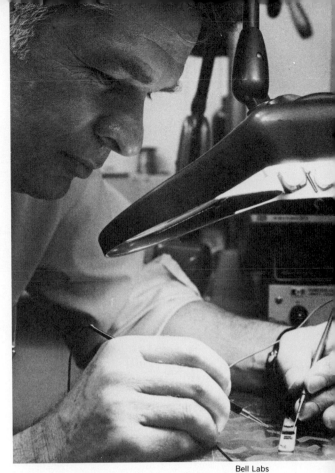

Bell Labs

Bell Labs scientist Andrew H. Bobeck makes a final adjustment on a magnetic bubble chip.

MAGNETIC BUBBLE

The other contender in the memory market is the magnetic-bubble memory. The magnetic-bubble memory reads bits—the 1's and 0's of the computer's binary code—by detecting the presence or absence of minute magnetic "domains"—that is, bubbles. It has attracted even more big names and big money than the CCD. According to one knowledgeable bubble scientist, more than 500 engineers are working on the technology in the United States, and cumulative research-and-development-investment by all U.S. companies probably tops $150,000,000.

GAP FILLERS

What excites the companies backing these new technologies is that they look like "gap fillers." Because of their technical properties and likely manufacturing costs, they should fit into an unoccupied niche of the memory market—between very fast but ex-

Bell Labs

The CCD memory chip was invented by W. S. Boyle and G. E. Smith, who demonstrate a TV camera that uses CCD memory chips.

pensive semiconductors and very cheap but slow magnetic disks and tapes. If the eventual cost and performance of CCD's and bubbles actually do qualify them as gap fillers, they should run away with hefty shares of the memory market because of the big boost they will be able to give to the performance of computer systems.

Gap fillers should alleviate a perennial difficulty of computer-system design—namely, the limited range of options for trading off memory cost and speed, or in other words, the problem of cost versus speed. Semiconductor memories can record or disgorge a bit of data in several millionths of a second, but each bit of capacity costs about 1 cent, or roughly 1,000 times the cost per bit in a large, much slower, disk file. So, while designers could maximize performance of the computer's lightning-fast logic by using only the fastest memories, it makes more sense to store a lot of infrequently needed data on disks and tapes.

But even the fastest disks need about eight-thousandths of a second to find a bit and are therefore much slower than the computer's logic circuits, which operate in terms of billionths of a second. Thus, when the computer system fails to find needed information in the fast semiconductor memory and switches over to the slower disk, its central processor stands idly by, waiting. Such idle time can typically exceed 75 per cent of the processor's capacity. Even with the best software, or programming systems, one maker of computers estimates that the performance of some large systems might be

improved two or three times if there were a memory technology faster than disk and cheaper than semiconductor. And that's exactly where CCD's and bubbles come in: they are faster than disk but not so expensive as the very fast semiconductors.

COMPACT—YET MANY USES

The basic physical characteristics of CCD's and magnetic-bubble memories give them added advantages. Unlike disks, they have no moving parts, so they are much less likely to fail in the catastrophic ways for which disks have become notorious. Both CCD's and bubbles are compact, and need no elaborate supporting apparatus. They can be wired directly onto computer printed-circuit boards. So they seem ideal for many systems where disk drives are too unreliable, too bulky, or too expensive. And that range includes applications as diverse as memories for mammoth computers, on-line storage for text-editing typewriters, and backup memory for the microprocessor, or "computer on a chip," that has found its way into automobiles, cameras, and microwave ovens.

EARLY USERS

Customers for the new technologies are using them both for replacing other technologies and for new applications. Instead of costly disk files, Burroughs is now using CCD's to speed up the performance of its largest machine, an array of sixteen processors called the Burroughs Scientific Processor. Some companies that make disk drives already have seen the writing on the wall and will soon be introducing CCD-based memory devices. For example, Data Terminal Systems, a small Massachusetts company, is using CCD's to replace conventional chips in its top-of-the-line electronic cash registers.

Bubbles have been designed into a variety of products. Data Systems Design has announced a bubble-based replacement for "floppy disks," or very small drives that use flexible disks. The company hopes to slash access time, or the time needed to deliver

Lower costs will come when some companies get enough production volume and experience to start improving their "yields,"—that is, improving the number of usable devices produced in every batch. In the industry, it's called "riding the learning curve." This is a very important goal for success. Unless healthy demand materializes within a few years, though, no producer can afford to keep on bearing the costs of getting a start on the curve.

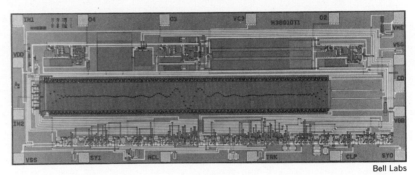

Enlarged view of a CCD chip. It stores and transfers binary-code information in the form of packets of electrical charges.

Bell Labs

data from the computer memory to its processing unit, from a range of 200 to 700 milliseconds to around seven milliseconds. Analog Precision sees a bubble-memory system as an ideal substitute for a floppy-disk drive in a process-control system for a candy factory. Because of all the powdered sugar in the air, a disk could become contaminated. The solid-state bubble should lick that special problem. Another company is talking about a bubble-based data file to complement its CCD memory.

TO BROADER MARKETS

These early applications, however, are limited. To make any money, the component manufacturers will have to bring bubbles and CCD's to much broader markets. And that requires getting the price down. Says the engineering vice president of one computer company: "We judge a new technology on ten criteria. The first eight are cost. Then come performance and reliability." But achieving costs low enough to give CCD's and bubbles wide appeal is a chicken-or-egg problem: low price requires high production; high sales volume needs low price.

OLDIES GAINING

Meanwhile, the price reductions and performance improvements of existing technologies may close off the opportunity for getting any volume for the new memories. The price of semiconductor memory, for example, has been falling at 35 to 40 per cent annually, and the number of bits that can be squeezed onto a single chip has quadrupled roughly every two years. (It now stands at more than 16,000.) Storing a bit on disks costs about 20 to 25 per cent less every year than it did the year before. In effect, the companies that have bet on the new technologies have to create markets that current production costs cannot justify. "It is," says Toombs of Texas Instruments, "one big balancing act."

What's more, CCD's and bubbles are competing with each other for some parts of the market. Though the technologies are very different in terms of performance, whichever becomes widely available first will be designed into many computer products for lack of anything better. Timing is then crucial.

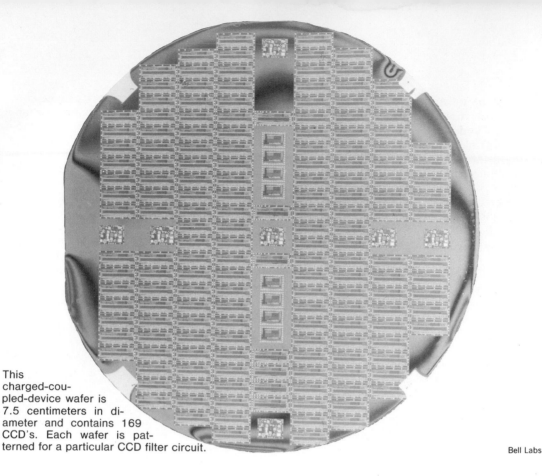

This charged-cou-pled-device wafer is 7.5 centimeters in di-ameter and contains 169 CCD's. Each wafer is pat-terned for a particular CCD filter circuit.

A MATTER OF TIMING

The commercialization of the CCD illustrates how much difference timing can make. In principle, the technology looks very promising. Like conventional semiconductor random-access memories, the CCD is an assembly of microscopic circuits etched and deposited on silicon. But instead of using transistors and capacitors to store information in the way RAM's do, the CCD continuously moves small packets of electrical charge along a series of wells arranged as a closed loop. The presence or absence of a packet indicates a 1 or a 0 of the computer's binary code.

Though significantly slower than its semiconductor relatives, the CCD is inherently simpler to manufacture. The size of the cells it uses to store bits is smaller than that of the cells in a RAM, and the chip requires fewer circuits to support and control its cells. Because of those differences, the CCD can carry up to four times as many bits of information on a chip of roughly the same size—and of about the same cost.

In addition, the composition of CCD's is so similar to that of RAM's that they can be made on conventional production lines. Thus the strategy for introducing the CCD has been straightforward: make them in much the same way as ordinary chips, at the same price per chip, but with up to four times the number of bits.

Fairchild introduced the first commercial CCD in 1975. It was a device capable of storing 9,000 bits, or 9 kilobits. According to the semiconductor industry's rule of thumb, it takes between eighteen months and two years after a component is introduced for it to achieve high volume as a result of being designed into new products. But the CCD is still produced in only limited quantities. Problems in design, production, and especially timing, have retarded its progress. The original 9-kilobit chip cost more than the memories with which it competed and never did well. By the time Fairchild had come up with a 16-kilobit CCD, a 16-kilobit RAM was already on the horizon. Since both were likely to sell for about the same price per bit, the new technology had no advantage, and customers failed to materialize.

Intel, which had launched a 16-kilobit CCD before Fairchild and designed it to work well with the company's own highly successful microprocessors, has done much better and is the acknowledged leader in shipments. Intel, however, is also beginning to suffer from timing problems.

To keep up with the 16-kilobit RAM, Intel planned to introduce a 64-kilobit CCD. But it is not yet available—and may never be. Because customers have been slow to incorporate CCD's in their products, Intel has diverted engineers and equipment to RAM's, which have been in short supply. Says Gordon Moore, president of Intel: ". . . I'm even less sure now that the CCD has a place in the sun than I was five years ago."

RELIABLE BUBBLES

Unlike the CCD, the slower magnetic-bubble memory is almost immune to competition from semiconductors, because it is potentially so much cheaper. Its competitors are disk memories.

The bubble memory consists of a thin wafer of nonmagnetic garnet crystal with an even thinner film of magnetic garnet deposited on top of it. The film contains crystalline cells in alternating, serpentine strips that are polarized in opposite directions. When a magnetic field is applied perpendicular to the film, some of those strips contract into micron-size bubbles. (A micron is equal to about 0.001 millimeter.) The bubbles are moved about by means of a metal track charged with its own magnetic field; it pulls the bubbles through the garnet at speeds up to 1,000 centimeters a second. As they pass a detector circuit, they register as 1's or 0's.

Because the bubble is based on new materials, mastering the production process is difficult. But since the bubble memory requires only three major laminations—the film, the track, and a third layer for control circuits—it is significantly simpler in design than semiconductors, which require up to seven critical alignments. Along with the prospect of creating bubbles smaller than a micron in diameter, that relative simplicity of design has led some analysts to project bubble memories for the 1980's that will contain between 1 and 4 megabits (million bits) on a chip.

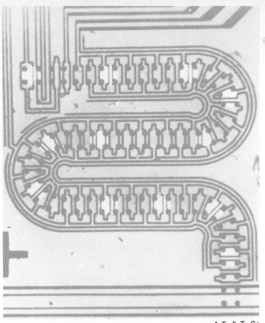

A.T. & T. Co.

The "large" white dots are the magnetic bubbles of the bubble memory. These memories will be used in electronic telephone-switching systems.

One special virtue of bubbles is that they are nonvolatile. Unlike all forms of semiconductors, including CCD's, they do not lose their data if power is cut off. Instead, according to bubble engineers, the information is likely to remain in a perfect state for at least 100 years. That promise of reliability has made bubbles a prime choice for telephone companies, which place a very high premium on low maintenance costs. Western Electric has set up a full-scale production plant, which has been turning out 68-kilobit chips used to store voice messages in the Bell System's recorded-announcement machines.

Some commercial users are bound to turn to bubble memories for the same reasons the telephone companies have, but they will not provide the kind of volume the manufacturers need to drive down the costs of bubbles to the point where they will compete heavily with disks. To help get volume, Texas Instruments has designed a 92,000-bit bubble into its own model 765 portable terminal. The potential demand for bubbles seems so strong that manufacturers expect to see a seller's market for several years.

Texas Instruments, though, is wrestling with the still unpredictable behavior of bubbles, and has yet to announce the next generation—a 256-kilobit bubble memory. The lead may now pass to Rockwell, which has

CUBIC FEET

for 1 million characters of storage

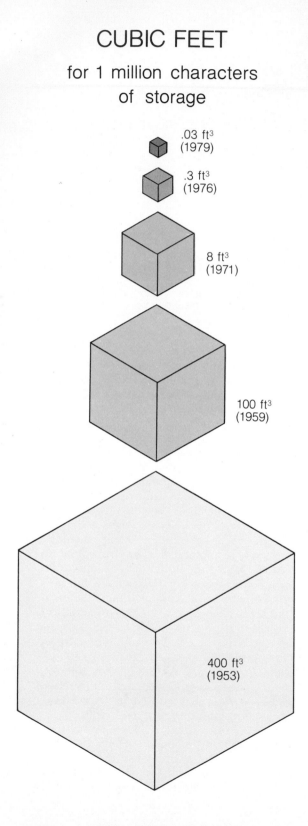

.03 ft³
(1979)

.3 ft³
(1976)

8 ft³
(1971)

100 ft³
(1959)

400 ft³
(1953)

demonstrated a laboratory version of a bubble memory that stores one megabit and has already made available a 256-kilobit device. But interest in the field is so intense that a clear winner won't emerge for years.

Many bubble makers think they will have to start producing a one-megabit memory in order to have a good shot at pushing the price below 1 millicent per bit, the price at which it would be giving stiff competition to a lot of disk drives. Nobody expects to see a commercial megabit component before the early 1980's.

By then the "access gap" may have narrowed considerably and "gap fillers" may no longer be needed. RAM's are likely to keep on doubling in density every two years, and the price per bit of RAM storage will keep on dropping.

SPECIAL USES

But even if RAM's close off the access gap, CCD's and bubbles may well achieve sizable markets in specialized applications. CCD's for example, seem sure to gobble up most of the $150,000,000 market for fast, relatively expensive disks used for temporary storage. If CCD's can maintain any kind of cost advantage over RAM's, they should keep showing up in products such as point-of-sale terminals, where low power consumption is more important than speed.

Bubbles may have their brightest future as auxiliary memories for the microprocessors that are finding more and more everyday uses. Some bubble makers think that this application of bubbles will be worth more than $200,000,000 a year in the early 1980's. It could be even bigger if teams of specialized microprocessors succeed in taking over the various processing chores of large computers, as some computer scientists predict. Such a proliferation of microprocessors could draw behind it a huge swarm of bubbles that would make this newcomer of the 1970's a dominant technology of the 1990's □

A chronological comparison of computer size and the memory bits they can handle.

COMPUTER LOGIC

by James Toth

FOR most of us, electronic calculators and electronic computers are playing a steadily increasing role in life. Gas, telephone, electric, and other bills now have the holey look of the computer punch card—mainly because that is exactly what they are. Also, for most of us, the inner goings-on of these devices is about as understandable as magic. Just what makes these things tick, anyway?

BASE-TWO MATH

As you may have heard, "base two" is the heart and core of electronic calculating. Why? Let's first ask, why is base ten the heart and core of human calculating? The answer is, because it's convenient. People happen to have ten fingers, and that's how early calculating was done. Had we been created with 8 or 12 fingers, you can bet that you would now be doing your computing in base 8 or 12.

Likewise, base two happens to suit the way electronic circuits are. A circuit can be on or off. Current flows or it does not. In short, only two states are possible for an electronic circuit. Similarly, only two digits are used in base two: 0 and 1. 1 can stand for an "on" condition, and 0 can stand for an "off" condition.

You say your calculator uses ten digits? Actually, it displays the answer using ten digits, and it accepts information from you using ten digits, but it does the calculating in base two.

As we will be using base-two arithmetic from here on, it may be a good idea to try some base-two computing. For instance:

$$0 + 0 = 0$$

Also,

$$0 + 1 = 1$$

And,

$$1 + 1 = two$$

but we aren't allowed to write the digit 2 in base two. Only 0 and 1 are permitted. So,

$$1 + 1 = 10$$

In other words, base two has place value just the same as base ten. In base ten, the number—say, 3,047—stands for three thousands, zero hundreds, four tens, and seven ones. It's as if we had columns headed ones, tens, hundreds, thousands, and so on. Then we just fill in digits under the appropriate column headings, like this:

. . . 10,000's	1,000's	100's	10's	1's
	3	0	4	7

The same thing happens in base two, except that the column headings are different:

... 16's	8's	4's	2's	1's
			1	0

Notice that in base ten you get the column headings by starting with one and continually multiplying by ten, while in base two you multiply by two.

Two, then, is represented in base two by one two and no ones, or a 1 in the two's column and a 0 in the one's column, or 10.

Continuing with our base two addition,

$$10 + 1 = ?$$
$$(two) \quad (one) \quad (three)$$

The digit 3 can't be written in base two either, so three is broken up into one two and one one, or 11.

Similarly,

$$11 + 1 = 100$$
(one four, no twos, no ones)
$$100 + 1 = 101$$
$$101 + 1 = 110$$
$$110 + 1 = 111$$
$$111 + 1 = 1000$$
and so on.

LOGIC: TRUE OR FALSE

A logician's main job is deciding whether conclusions are true or false. True or false—two conditions. Notice how nicely that fits in with the duality that has been running through this discussion.

In logic it is customary to let letters like P and Q stand for statements. For example, let P represent "It is raining" and let Q represent "The birds are singing." Then "P and Q" would stand for "It is raining and the birds are singing," and "P or Q" would stand for "It is raining or the birds are singing."

This gives rise to questions like this: If P is true and Q is true, is "P and Q" true? Well, if it is true that it is raining, and if it is true that the birds are singing, then the compound statement "It is raining and the birds are singing" would have to be true, too.

Okay, then suppose that P is true but Q is false. What about "P and Q" now? The statement "It is raining and the birds are

singing" has to be false, because even though it *is* raining, the birds are not singing also, as the compound statement says.

TRUTH TABLES AND CIRCUITS

In other words, "P **and** Q" is true only if P and Q are true simultaneously. This can be shown in what are called "truth tables" like this:

P	Q	P and Q
T	T	T
T	F	F
F	T	F
F	F	F

Now consider the circuit below. Let's let

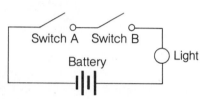

a closed switch or a lighted light be represented by a 1, and an open switch or an off light be represented by a 0. Clearly, the light will be on only when both switches are closed, and the following table, much like a truth table, can be made:

A	B	L
1	1	1
1	0	0
0	1	0
0	0	0

Notice that this table of electronic conditions has the same pattern as the logical—**and**—truth table. Because of this, switches in series (or any combination of transistors, diodes, and the like behave in this fashion) are referred to as "AND logic gates" and are symbolized like this:

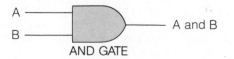

P-OR-Q LOGIC

A similar sort of thing occurs with the logician's "P **or** Q" combination. If both P and Q are true, of course "P or Q" is true too. But if just P is false, or if just Q is false, then "P or Q" is still true. That is, "It is raining or the birds are singing" is a true statement as long as at least one *or* the other of those two things are indeed happening.

The "P **or** Q" truth table looks like this:

P	Q	P or Q
T	T	T
T	F	T
F	T	T
F	F	F

Now look at the circuit below. The light

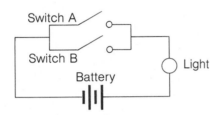

will go on if either (or both) of the switches is closed. Using the same 0 and 1 notation as before, this fact can be put into table form too:

A	B	L
1	1	1
1	0·	1
0	1	1
0	0	0

This time the table of electronic conditions shows the same pattern as the logical—**or**—truth table. Therefore, switches in parallel (or any of the combination of electronic components that behave in this fashion) are referred to as "OR logic gates" and are symbolized by:

To keep the AND and OR gate tables straight in your head, think of them this way: Think of AND gates as being very difficult things to push electricity through—a voltage has to be applied at both input terminals before a voltage appears at the output terminal. On the other hand, think of OR gates as being very easy to push electricity through—a voltage at either input terminal is enough to cause a voltage to appear at the output.

Many other logic circuits exist, and one more that we will need is the NOT circuit. As its name implies, it negates things. Put in a 1, and a 0 comes out. Put in a 0, and a 1 comes out. In table form it is:

A	Not A
1	0
0	1

It is symbolized as:

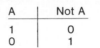

HALF-ADDER CIRCUIT

The arrangement below of two AND gates, an OR gate, and a NOT circuit will add—sort of. It has its limitations so it is called a "half adder."

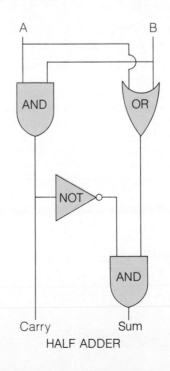

HALF ADDER

Let's try using it to do $0 + 0$, meaning apply 0 at points A and B and see what appears at "sum" and "carry." By the wiring arrangement, 0 will go into both input terminals of both the first AND gate and the OR gate. Of course, 0 will come out of both gates. 0 now appears at the "carry" point and 0 goes into the NOT circuit. 1 emerges from the NOT circuit and goes to one input of the second AND gate. Since 0 is at the other input (from the OR gate), 0 appears at "sum," and that's the answer. $0 + 0 = 0$. So far, so good.

Now let's try $1 + 0$, meaning apply 1 at A and 0 at B. By the wiring, 1 and 0 go into the first AND gate, and 0 comes out. So 0 appears at "carry" and 0 enters the NOT circuit, meaning 1 comes out of it and appears at one of the second AND gate's inputs. Also by the wiring, 1 and 0 go into the OR gate, meaning 1 comes out and arrives at the other input of the second AND gate. 1, then, is at both input terminals of the second AND gate, so 1 comes out at "sum," and $1 + 0 = 1$.

Try tracing $1 + 1$ through the half adder in the same way, and you'll find that 1 appears at the "carry" position and 0 appears at the "sum" position, making the answer 10, which is correct.

But this is as far as a half adder can go. You can add no more than two one-digit base-two numbers, and that's a pretty heavy limit. Something more complex is needed.

FULL-ADDER CIRCUIT

Enter the "full adder" circuit. The full adder, shown at upper right, is composed of two half adders and an OR gate.

A full adder works pretty much like a half adder does, but it has the added bonus of three input terminals. This means that it can handle something that turns up in addition all the time, but which the half adder can't do.

For example, consider the problem

$$\begin{array}{r} 27 \\ +16 \\ \hline \end{array}$$

When doing this, you first add the two digits 7 and 6 to get 13. You then write down the 3 (which is like a digit appearing in the sum position in our adders) and then carry the 1 and write it above the 2.

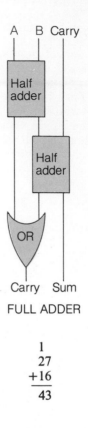

A B Carry

Half adder

Half adder

OR

Carry Sum

FULL ADDER

$$\begin{array}{r} 1 \\ 27 \\ +16 \\ \hline 43 \end{array}$$

Now you add the three digits, 1, 2, and 1, to get 4, which you then write down beside the 3. The answer, then, is 43.

The important thing to notice is that in doing addition, it is sometimes necessary to add three digits at a time, not just two, and full adders can handle this.

Full adders still have their shortcomings, though. They can't handle base-two numbers like $101 + 11$ ($5 + 3$) because each input terminal can take only one-digit numbers, and here we have a three- and a two-digit number to be added. Now what?

SEVERAL FULL-ADDER CIRCUITS

The solution is to arrange a number of full adders shown on the next page. This arrangement can do $101 + 11$. The addition process goes like this. For the 101, the following entries appear at the following input terminals: 1 at A_4, 0 at A_2, and 1 at A_1. For 11 it goes: 0 at B_4, 1 at B_2, and 1 at B_1.

Tracing the electrical impulses through the system, this is what happens: A_1 and B_1 (1 and 1) into the first full adder yields 10, or 0

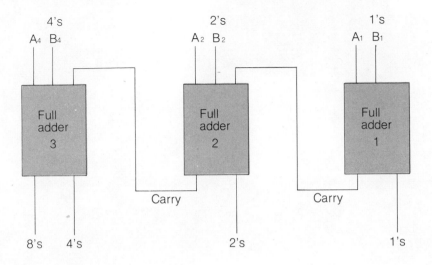

4's · A₄ B₄ · 2's · A₂ B₂ · 1's · A₁ B₁ · Full adder 3 · Full adder 2 · Full adder 1 · Carry · Carry · 8's · 4's · 2's · 1's

in the first output position and 1 in the first carry position. This carried 1, together with A_2 and B_2 (0 and 1) in the second full adder yield 10, or 0 in the second output position and 1 in the second carry position. This carried 1 and A_4 and B_4 (1 and 0) are now added by the third full adder to get 10, or 0 in the third output position and 1 in the fourth output position.

The answer according to this circuit, then, is:

$$101 + 11 = 1000$$
(five) (three) (eight)

which is correct.

Larger sums, such as $11010 + 1110$, can be handled by simply adding more full adders to the circuit. True, base—two numbers can be rather long, but then, size is no object—modern technology can produce extremely complicated circuits on extremely small integrated circuit chips.

MULTIPLICATION, SUBTRACTION, AND DIVISION

Now that we can add any two numbers, there is the matter of other mathematical operations. How are they done? If simple adding gets this involved, they must be super-complicated, right?

Actually, no. *Adding is the key to everything, and we have that mastered.*

Take multiplication, for example: Can 4×9 be done by adding? Yes, like this:
$4 + 4 + 4 + 4 + 4 + 4 + 4 + 4 + 4$ or this:
$9 + 9 + 9 + 9$

And this is true for problems like 347×9698, too. If you can add any two numbers in less than a split second (and computers and calculators can), then adding nine thousand six hundred and ninety eight 347's is no trick at all. So much for multiplication.

Subtraction and division? Why, they are just the inverse operations of addition and multiplication respectively.

And the really hard stuff, like trigonometric functions maybe? They can be done with no more than addition, subtraction, multiplication, and division, too—provided you remember little things like:

$$\sin X = X - \frac{X^3}{3!} + \frac{X^5}{5!} - \frac{X^7}{7!} + \ldots \square$$

SELECTED READINGS

"Computer Arithmetic" by H. Chamberlin. *Popular Electronics,* July and September 1978.
Basics of Digital Computers, Vol. I by John S. Murphy. Hayden, 1970.

© Lynn McLaren/Rapho-Photo Researchers

MATH ANXIETY

by Sheila Tobias

IN 1972 Lucy Sells, a Berkeley, California, sociologist, surveyed a sample of incoming freshmen at the University of California at Berkeley. Her area of concern was the number of years of high-school mathematics they had studied prior to entering college. She found that of the entering male freshmen, 57 per cent had taken four years of high school math. For women, it was eight per cent.

After a minimal inquiry into the structure of course prerequisites at Berkeley. Sells concluded that without four years of high school mathematics 92 per cent of all the women at Berkeley would be ineligible for introductory courses in economics, calculus, chemistry, physics, engineering sciences, statistics, and computer science. Without these courses these math-poor women would not be able to major in 22 of the 44 fields offered.

MATH—A VOCATIONAL FILTER

The significance of math avoidance among so many girls and women is evi-denced not only in the number of girls who drop out from math courses in high school, but also in women's occupational choices. Mathematics is a vocational filter, Sells points out. People who are steered away from mathematics early in their careers will have their options severely limited later on.

In 1977 Sells, now at the University of Maryland, repeated her study with a sample of more than 300 entering freshmen. Her findings are shown in the accompanying chart.

Mathematics is not only a vocational filter for college graduates. Sells and others estimate that knowledge of algebra and geometry alone may make a difference of up to 25 per cent in scores on entry-level tests for civil service and industrial jobs. In monetary terms, taking algebra and geometry in high school can mean the difference between an $8,000 and an $11,000 starting salary for a high school graduate.

In addition, adults who have avoided

Number of Entering Freshmen with Four or More Years of High School Math

	Number with 4 years	Total in sample	Percent
White men	49	86	57
Black men	18	78	23
White women	17	83	20
Black women	8	77	10

mathematics may find themselves in mid-career unable to move ahead into management because they are uncomfortable with "data," confounded by balance statements, and frightened of "planning" and "modeling." One woman I interviewed confided that because she was not able to get the facts from her figures she was severely hampered in her work as a vice-president of a major food chain.

Part of the reason women (and possibly even black males) avoid mathematics is the pervasive ideology that math and science are men's (or white men's) turf. The adolescent female, confronted by increasing difficulty in mathematics in junior- and senior-high school, may be permitted by parents and teachers to drop math because it is considered of no great use in the kinds of careers usually open to females and minorities. But considerable discouragement also comes from a generally held view that some inferiority in math is innate and irreversible.

THE MYTHS OF MATH ABILITY

So much myth pervades the discussion of "mathematical ability" that it is useful to remember three things: 1. That most bright adults of both sexes cease learning mathematics at some time in their lives. 2. That many hundreds of students dislike math intensely. 3. That adults who do not directly use mathematics in their work may be quite incapable of recalling even "simple" arithmetic.

What is particularly pernicious about the math mythology is the notion that from the outset people either have or do not have a "mathematical mind." The idea that one is either verbal or mathematical is precisely what causes many young women to avoid mathematics. They fear they will lose some-

Although there are many fine female mathematicians, mathematics does act as a vocational filter, often screening out females from math-oriented vocations such as engineering.

Hugh Rogers/Monkmeyer

Going up to the black-board in front of a class can be threatening for many people.

thing they value (being feminine), if they succeed at doing math.

If it were not for these psychological elements, the problem of mathematics avoidance might be cured by an intelligent campaign to get women and minority students to take more math in high school. But the solution is not that simple. After three years of work in a math clinic at Wesleyan University, we have come to the conclusion that math avoidance is both a cause and a result of "mathematics anxiety," we learned that the cures for this problem are more complex and far-reaching than the mere rewriting of guidance materials.

WHAT IS A MATH CLINIC?

A math clinic is a place to which undergraduates and adults can bring their personal-learning problems with mathematics. (The technique has been tried only minimally with high-school students.) Out of a "mathematics autobiography," carefully elicited by a trained learning counselor, comes a whole collection of memories associated with learning math.

These math autobiographies show that students and even adults who have been away from math for a very long time remember failing at math as an experience like that of sudden death. Despite reasonable success up to the point of failure, people remember being certain that they had come to the end of their capability in math (or science). They recall that they could never master the new material, and, even worse, that they had been "faking math" for years.

This perception of helplessness, together with the guilt and shame with which it is associated, accounts in part for the development of a true anxiety about doing math. The student—for reasons that will be developed shortly—feels essentially out of control in the math classroom and, in the case of women and girls in particular, out of place as well.

REASONS FOR MATH ANXIETY

Why is there so little confidence, so little reserve of good feelings about math to carry the learner over an obstacle that is not at all beyond her capability? There are many clues to the sources of this disability. For one thing, the typical math classroom is fraught with ego-threatening consequences. For example, going to the blackboard to reveal one's "stupidity" in front of everyone else. Timed tests, which put a child under inordinate tension. Emphasis on the right answer. No room for discussion and debate. A feeling that the mind is blank.

Another general reason is that many people find the mode of explanation in mathematics to be generally unclear and unhelpful. For example, an application or a proof may not provide enough of an explanation. Indeed, among the mathematics autobiographies that have been collected so far, the most frequently remembered frustrations had to do with actual (or perceived) ambiguity in the language being used in class. This resulted in difficulty in "translating" mathematical ideas into words or pictures.

For these reasons, math remediation may prove to be ineffective unless it is accompanied by personal counseling and sup-

Dr. Stanley Kogelman of the Mind Over Math clinic holds a math-anxiety-clinic demonstration at Barat College, Lake Forest, Illinois.

port. Feelings about mathematics appear to get in the way of learning unless the feelings are identified and treated.

TREATING THE MATH ANXIOUS

How does a treatment take place? In the case of adults, a group of eight to 12 are brought together under the direction of a math teacher and a counselor, for the purpose of sharing math autobiographies and explaining why and how their math block gets in the way. During the initial period, the members get to know one another and experience the heady discovery that they are not alone in their disability. In fact their helplessness in regard to math may have been learned.

As the members of the math clinic build up confidence and group cohesiveness, the teacher will introduce some mathematics in small bits and never for very long. The purpose of teaching math at this stage in the process of desensitizing is to give the group members something to work on, while they observe themselves. Their "self-talk" and defeatism as they do math becomes obvious right away.

Since this kind of session is never taken for credit, and there is no syllabus to follow, the group can determine its own agenda ("What is it you have always wanted to understand in math? Let's do that one right now.")

During the periods between class sessions, participants are asked to think about their behavior as they do math and, when possible, to try tackling more and more complicated mathematics in their everyday life. These experiences are noted and "processed," too, in the same way that the discussion of the math autobiography was processed at the outset. People assist one another in countering their own defeatism. They notice constructive action when it is taken and, above all, they nurture and protect one another.

Some will argue that this process of relearning mathematics must be slow. But if one accepts the notion that much of the mathematics one needs in everyday work life has already been "entered" into the mind, then the goal is not to accumulate additional increments of knowledge, but rather to facilitate retrieval. The person who cannot recognize a problem in fractions, when the problem is encased in words, may not have forgotten fractions in the ordinary sense of the term "forgotten." For example, some people may be incapable of applying what they know about fractions because they have become so tense and feel so very much out of control when they have to deal with a word problem involving fractions.

At Mind Over Math, in New York City, a gentleman who had never been able to learn long division did not have to be "taught" it in the conventional sense of that word during desensitization sessions. He reported one Monday night that his brother-in-law had taught him long division the previous weekend. The question is not what technique was his brother-in-law suddenly able to use, but rather why this man was now "ready" to learn long division and what had blocked him from mastering it in the past.

COMPUTERS AND MATHEMATICS   113

CONSTRUCTIVE ACTION

The concept that difficulty with math may be an anxiety problem, and that one need not go back to fourth grade when the problem started in order to correct it, can be immensely useful in getting people to give themselves another chance. Having conceded long ago that they did not have a "mathematical mind," such people have not been able to take constructive action until now. And constructive action is what math-anxiety treatment is all about.

What does this tell us about how children learn and how we might improve the mathematics staying-power of the generation currently in school?

There is little experience to date in directly treating math anxiety in younger people. Part of the problem is that, like psychotherapy, the process presumes that the victim is highly verbal, intuitive, and able to introspect. Children who are in the process of learning everything for the first time may not understand what is being asked for in a "mathematics autobiography."

Still, there is some data that is encouraging. The Dalton School, a private school in New York City, experimented a year ago by having two math therapists come into one of their math classes one day a week. The teacher found that the students lost nothing by missing one of their regular math classes each week. Instead, they became active participants and accomplished more in the remaining two classes than they had done in the three classes per week.

Sidney Spindel, a mathematics instructor in the developmental-math program of Prince George's Community College in Maryland, asked his psychiatrist-wife to sit in on his math classes in order to train him in listening for psychological information. Since that time, he has offered "Math-Anxiety" sections. He now claims that his effectiveness with slow learners has improved.

Lenore Blum, Nancy Kreinberg, and others at the Lawrence Hall of Science Program at the University of California at Berkeley bring in junior- and senior-high school girls for special programs in math and science. By providing role models, hands-on experience (on the computer, for example) and open discussion about "mathematics and sex," the designers of this program hope to influence women's attitudes toward mathematics and career choice.

Perhaps the most important implication for teaching and learning in the lower grades will be an acknowledgment and acceptance of the mathematics anxiety that exists among many elementary school teachers, social workers, and librarians. They may have chosen their field in part because it is without a math requirement. Then they discover in mid-career that if they are to do their job properly, they are going to have to learn math.

Some school districts are considering math-anxiety desensitization for in-service teachers. Persis Herold of the "Math Center" in Washington, D.C., hopes to work with teenagers and their parents in reducing math anxiety, by holding evening sessions for both.

Wherever it is being tried, this system is meant to engage individuals—whether they are professionals or children—in the process of dealing with their own math anxiety.

Even competent mathematics professors experience math anxiety. Indeed, fear that one may not be able to solve a problem one has never seen before seems to be common to people doing math at all levels. One of the truths about math anxiety that the disabled in math never seem to learn is that math anxiety can never be eliminated. The point is to manage it, as those who work in the field of mathematics learn to do □

SELECTED READINGS

"Math hangups: learning how to lose them" by S. Koslow, *Mademoiselle,* March 1978.

Overcoming Math Anxiety by Sheila Tobias. Norton, 1978.

"Who's afraid of math, and why" by Sheila Tobias. *Atlantic Monthly,* September 1978.

USGS photo

Increasing research is going into earthquake prediction. Here geologists check motion along a fault by means of portable instruments that are sensitive to displacement of 1 millimeter in 16 kilometers. Overhead, a plane measures magnetic variations.

EARTH SCIENCE

EARTH SCIENCE
REVIEW OF THE YEAR

Alain Keler/Sygma

Aftermath of earthquake in Iran. In eastern Iran centered around a crack in the earth's crust, called the Nayband fault, a violent earthquake killed about 26,000 people.

John Horner, a Princeton University paleontologist, is shown with his assemblage of a baby hadrosaur, which is about 60 centimeters long. Horner located a nest of 15 hadrosaur young in Montana.

Princeton University Press

Earthquakes and Seismology. During the first ten months of 1978 there were eight major earthquakes, each registering 7 or higher on the Richter scale, a widely used measurement of ground motion during a quake and one indication of a quake's severity. The largest—7.7 on the Richter scale—occurred in eastern Iran in the Tabas region near a crack in the earth's crust known as the Nayband fault system. Some 26,000 people were reported killed and tremors were felt as far away as Tehran, 600 kilometers away.

Seismological research was concerned mainly with earthquake prediction. In the United States special funds for research were made available by the Earthquake Hazards Reduction Act. Plans were also made to improve the Worldwide and National Seismological Networks. ■ Japan continued its extensive efforts in earthquake research. The Japanese Meteorological Agency installed the first ocean-bottom seismological network. Located off the southern coast of Honshu, about 200 kilometers south of Tokyo, it consists of a line of four seismometers, each 50 kilometers apart. Data gathered by these devices are telemetered to a recording station on land and used in various earthquake-research projects.

Volcanoes and Volcanology. Volcanic activity during 1978 produced fewer and less spectacular eruptions than in 1977. Probably the largest explosive eruption occurred in the Aleutian Islands when Westdahl Volcano erupted in early February. ■ In September activity at Guatemala's Santiaguito Volcano triggered a mudflow that caused the year's only known volcano-related fatality. ■ Despite the decrease in the number of dangerous eruptions, worldwide efforts to learn more about volcanoes and their hazards continued in anticipation of expected vigorous activity in many of the world's major volcanoes. Hawaii's Mauna Loa, for example, appears to be continuing its slow but ominously persistent buildup toward its next major eruption, and usually active Kilauea Volcano on Mauna Loa's east flank has not had a major eruption since September 1977.

Volcanic activity also continued to play a role in other geologic processes. During the summer of 1978 a submarine eruption at Kavachi in the Solomon Islands built an island—but only for a while: marine erosion quickly destroyed it. ■ In July increased activity of Iceland's Krafla Caldera produced a gradual uplift of the land and large fissures, or cracks, in the land, the study of which is providing information on the processes responsible for sea-floor spreading.

Paleontology. The known age of vertebrates on earth was pushed back some 40,000,000 years with the year's major paleontological find. The remains of a jawless fish, named *Anatolepis*, was found in northeastern Wyoming rocks dating from Late Cambrian time, more than 500,000,000 years ago.

Dinosaur biology and the evolutionary relationship of dinosaurs and birds continued to generate much interest. A nest containing the remains of 15 baby dinosaurs born about 75,000,000 years ago was found in Montana during the year. The specimens, about 60 centimeters long and about 25 centimeters high, were identified as hadrosaurs, a type of duck-billed, plant-eating dinosaur. A mature hadrosaur was about 3 meters tall and about 11 or 12 meters long.

Paleontology also continued to provide clues to an understanding of the earth in earlier times. The finding of certain vertebrate remains in widely separated areas provided further evidence that there was once a broad land connection across the North Atlantic. And fossil amphibians and reptiles found in Antarctica appear to confirm that Antarctica, Australia, Africa, South America, and the subcontinent of India were once joined to form a huge landmass known as Gondwanaland. ■ Fossil plant communities added to our knowledge too. The U.S. Geological Survey used them to show that dramatic changes have occurred in the earth's magnetic axis in the past 70,000,000 years. ■ And in yet another contribution of paleontology, the study of fossils of microorganisms is revealing much about ocean sediments and the oceanic and land environment long ago.

Environmental and Engineering Geology. Pressing problems and needs in the fields of energy and environmental studies increasingly involved geology during 1978. Accelerated interest in offshore oil development created new interest in marine-engineering geology. Studies of the ocean floor involved obtaining profiles of bottom-surface features, determining the stability of bottom sediments, and detecting submarine faults and slides. Information such as this is used in determining conditions that might affect oil-drilling towers, some of which are being placed in 300 meters of water and cost more than $1,000,000 each. ■ Geologists also concerned themselves with the location and development of geothermal energy sources and with the location of dams and nuclear power plants. The location of such facilities in areas free from known geologic hazards such as faults or cracks that might make the area earthquake prone is extremely important. As a result of one such study, the location of General Electric's nuclear research reactor in Vallecitors, California, was reconsidered. ■ In some of these studies and in others monitoring strip-mining activities and potential landslide areas, geologists used remote sensing equipment with imagery and other data relayed to earth from orbiting earth satellites.

Geologists also attacked several environmental problems. The disposal of solid wastes, especially toxic chemicals and nuclear wastes, received particular attention as repeated studies found health problems resulting from the presence of even trace amounts of arsenic, copper, zinc, cadmium, lead, and other chemicals in the soil and water. Geologists continue to find salt deposits as the most likely rocks in which to store hazardous wastes, but they are investigating the use of shale, basalt, and granite, among others.

Hydrologists directed their attention to problems associated with surface waters and ground water. Various government agencies investigated the relationship of water resources to other basic social and economic factors, and special "environmental action teams" studied the effects of flood control, flood-plain land use, and urban development and its effects on water quality. ■ Specific urban geologic problems, such as California's Bluebird Canyon landslide, which dislodged 24 houses and seriously damaged 16 others, also received special attention.

William H. Matthews III

U.S. Geological Survey/UPI

A huge dome of lava boils upward 17 meters high in an eruption of Kilauea volcano on Hawaii Island. An eruption can disgorge tens of cubic kilometers of lava, which spread out, increasing the area of the island.

In the volcanic-prone areas of the earth's crust are certain spots that leak heat from the mantle. In some of these places the heat can be put to use, as is being done at the Geysers Geothermal Plant in Sonoma County, California.

U.S. Geological Survey

HURRICANES

by Robert C. Cowen

IF hurricanes didn't happen, meteorologists wouldn't feel compelled to invent them. And therein lies the paradox of the most violent storms on earth, according to hurricane analyst William M. Gray.

In their peak season, hurricanes, typhoons, and other tropical cyclones, as the weaker forms of these storms are called, supply 10 to 15 per cent of the world's rainfall. That includes 20 to 30 per cent of the Northern Hemisphere's share. They also feed Northern Hemisphere winds with 10 to 15 per cent of their energy—a contribution that may even reach 20 to 30 per cent when the storms are particularly active.

NATURE DOING IT THE HARD WAY

Yet, Gray, a Colorado State University meteorologist, notes, for all of this vast pro-duction in late summer and autumn, the total contribution of tropical cyclones to the world's annual rain and energy budgets is only about 2 per cent. This could easily be made up by a modest increase in the number of mild disturbances that occur all the time in the tropics. Furthermore, he adds, there is little in present knowledge of atmospheric physics to suggest that nature has to do it the hard way by generating something like 80 cyclones somewhere in the tropics every year, half to two thirds of which grow to hurricane strength.

Why then, he asks, do we have hurricanes?

Meteorologists have learned a lot about how these violent storms grow from the low pressure circulations called tropical cyclones. They can model the process on computers and predict hurricane development. But why the cyclones themselves form remains a mystery. Until scientists solve that mystery, their knowledge of hurricanes will remain unsatisfactorily incomplete, Dr. Gray said in outlining the challenge at a recent conference on tropical meteorology at Britain's Royal Society.

As a start, Dr. Gray has summarized the statistics of the cyclones and constructed a composite model of them. These have given him some insight into the place these enigmatic storms hold in world and tropical weather.

CREATURES OF THE SEA

To begin with, tropical cyclones, and the hurricanes and typhoons they become, are creatures of the sea. They feed on its warmth and moisture and evolve out of the air circulation, which flows largely over the tropical ocean.

Dr. Gray has identified half a dozen climatological factors that he believes influence cyclone formation. They include such things as the spin of the earth, the warmth of the sea, moisture in the air, and the nature of the general wind field in which a disturbance is embedded.

Earth's spin is important because it supplies the force that makes air flow around regions of low atmospheric pressure rather than rushing in to smooth out the pressure difference. In the Northern Hemisphere it makes winds blow counterclockwise around a "low." (In the Southern Hemisphere it makes winds blow clockwise.)

A hurricane couldn't get going without the influence of earth's spin to whirl its winds. Since this factor weakens toward the equator, tropical cyclones don't form less than 4 or 5 degrees north of the equator.

Ocean warmth and moisture aloft affect the energy flow and convection, or movement, of the storms. If middle-level air has less than 50 to 60 per cent relative humidity, this inhibits convection over tropical oceans, in contrast to convection over land. Also, tropical storms need warm water to develop. They die out when they move over land and tend to cool down ocean areas over which they pass. A vigorous hurricane can influence the water to 60 meters depth. Tropical

Image Bank

Palm trees bend with the wind during a hurricane in Miami, Florida.

cyclones need water at temperatures above 26° Celsius down to depths of some tens of meters to draw upon.

WIND FEEDING

While such factors are important, Dr. Gray believes it is the character of the general wind field that is decisive in determining whether or not a tropical disturbance will spawn a cyclone. This goes against usual approach, which has looked for clues in the nature of individual disturbances themselves.

However, Dr. Gray points out, disturbances such as clusters of convective clouds appear in the tropics all the time. Even when most conditions seem to favor cyclones, there's no way to tell from watching a given disturbance whether or not it will develop. What does make the difference, Dr. Gray says, is certain characteristics of the surrounding wind field.

One of the most important of these is an abstruse quantity called vorticity. It's a measure of the rotational motion of the air. If the surrounding air flow supplies vorticity to a disturbance, this helps spin up cyclonic winds. If the environment can't feed it with vorticity, a tropical disturbance is unlikely to become a cyclone, let alone a hurricane.

The way wind flows through a disturbance is also important. If there is too much ventilation, Dr. Gray explains, moisture and energy can't accumulate in the disturbance and it won't grow.

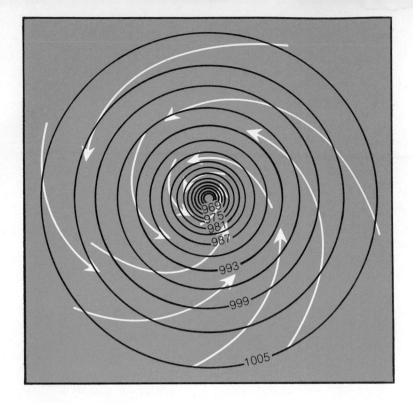

The circles indicate isobars, and the arrows indicate wind direction in a hurricane. The air pressure in the "eye" of this pattern is about 957 millibars. Note how close the isobars are toward the "eye."

ENERGY FOR WINTER

Dr. Gray has put his six climatic factors into an index which he finds accurately specifies the general statistics of tropical cyclones. It outlines where they do and do not form and predicts their general seasonal occurrence.

To judge from this research, Dr. Gray says it looks very much as though the cyclones are a direct manifestation of tropical climate. But paradoxically, he adds, they seem to have very little effect on that climate themselves.

Tropical cyclones form in the western Atlantic, the eastern and western Pacific, and the Indian Ocean. About two thirds of them occur in the Northern Hemisphere. Again, about two thirds form in the Eastern as opposed to the Western Hemisphere, and the western North Pacific has about one third of the globe's tropical cyclones.

Relatively few of them occur in the spring when global rainfall over land is abundant. They come in the autumn when such rainfall is more sparse so that hurricane rains help make up the difference. They also feed large amounts of energy into Northern Hemisphere winds at a time when that circulation is building up for winter. It's as though the storms were part of a mechanism by which the atmosphere taps the energy store of the tropics when an extra supply is needed.

NEED FOR MORE STUDY

Putting all this together, Dr. Gray believes it is important to solve the mystery of tropical cyclones. Meteorologists must understand them to learn more of how the atmosphere operates. And, because they so often grow into typhoons and hurricanes, the genesis of the cyclones needs to be understood to aid forecasting.

In this connection, Dr. Gray says he is encouraged that it is the air flow in which disturbances are embedded that seems decisive. This is much easier to monitor than are the individual cloud clusters or other disturbances from which cyclones form. To make progress, he says, it is time to stop attacking the problem piecemeal and put tropical cyclone research on a coordinated, global basis □

SELECTED READINGS

"Don't call the wind Maria" by T. Young. *New Times,* June 26, 1978.

"Foul weather forecast" by S. Mennear-Dubas. *Family Health,* September 1977.

"Swept away; danger to coastal communities from hurricanes" by B. Funk. *New York Times Magazine,* September 18, 1977.

Musee Guimet-Paris

TSUNAMI!

by Richard A. Kerr

TSUNAMI (soo nah′ me), wrongly called tidal wave, prediction is not a glamorous field of research today, as earthquake prediction is, but the stakes are still high. Large earthquakes are the most common cause of tsunamis. One large quake in one part of the Pacific can create waves capable of suddenly inundating villages and cities on the coasts of both North and South America, Asia, and the islands in between. The destruction can be staggering.

A tsunami in 1896 killed 27,000 people in Japan. One, in 1960, destroyed or severely damaged every Chilean town along 800 kilometers of coast. But tsunami prediction, a reality since 1948, has helped minimize the loss of life during the four major tsunamis that have crossed the Pacific since 1948.

The reliability of tsunami warnings has improved during the 30-year history of the Tsunami Warning System, now a cooperative international organization operated by the U.S. Weather Service. However, prob-

lems still remain. Improvement has been due largely to increased experience and the expansion of the system's network of observation stations throughout the Pacific. Now, a new way of monitoring possible tsunami-generating earthquakes may soon help to reduce the number of false alarms and increase public cooperation in areas, such as Alaska and Hawaii, where the most rapid warnings are required.

WATCHES AND WARNINGS

The present observation network of the Tsunami Warning System allows experts to locate and measure the magnitude of large earthquakes that may cause tsunamis, as well as to detect a tsunami itself and follow its progress across the Pacific. The system includes seismographs, machines that provide one measure of an earthquake's magnitude, and tide gauges that are installed throughout the Pacific and linked to the Tsunami Warning Center in Hawaii.

If an undersea earthquake appears from seismological data to be large enough to cause a tsunami, a watch is issued, alerting threatened populations to the possibility that a tsunami has been created. If a tsunami is actually observed by the tide gauges in the system, a warning is then issued. Because most watches and many warnings are not followed by destructive tsunamis, the effectiveness of the system has at times been impaired.

UNPREDICTABLE NATURE

One reason that some unnecessary alerts must be called is that a great deal remains to be learned about how tsunamis behave once they are formed. A tsunami, which is actually a series of waves, like ripples from a pebble thrown into a pond, moves quite predictably across the deep waters of the Pacific. Its great speed in the open ocean, about 800 kilometers per hour, contrasts with its small height of less than a meter. The variation of a tsunami's speed with water depth is well understood, so that arrival times thousands of kilometers from the earthquake can be accurately predicted.

Unfortunately, the size that a tsunami will be when it reaches land remains rather unpredictable. Eventually, it may rear up to as high as 30 meters within a few hundred meters off shore as it slows to about 50 kilometers per hour. Or it may disperse its energy before arriving at a particular beach and not cause any damage. Attempts to understand the basis of these differences have met with limited success.

PROBLEM WITH TIDE GAUGES

The tide gauges of the warning system can record the passage of a tsunami and provide the first proof that a tsunami has been indeed created. But they cannot be used for predicting how large it will be at another location. In addition, initial tide gauge reports may not arrive at the warning center until two hours or more after the quake because of the travel time involved and the sometimes indirect communication links with remote stations. Plans to link the network by a satellite have not yet progressed beyond a single experimental link.

An alternative to waiting for tide gauge reports would be to issue a warning solely on the basis of reports from several readily accessible seismograph stations. This is more rapid but considerably less reliable. It may take only a few minutes if the quake is within a dense network of instruments such as the one that comprises the Alaska Regional Tsunami Warning System. To predict whether or not a tsunami has been formed, the location and magnitude of the earthquake must be known. It is relatively easy to determine whether a quake is in the ocean, where it can cause a tsunami. Determining its magnitude is more difficult.

As a general rule, destructive tsunamis are generated by earthquakes of magnitude 8 or larger on the Richter scale. But not all tsunamis follow the general rule. For example, the 1946 Unimak Island quake in the Aleutians had a Richter magnitude of only 7.2 (about eight times smaller seismic wave amplitudes than magnitude 8.0), but it gen-

International Tsunami Information Center

A seismologist at a tsunami warning station inspects a seismograph, which records earth tremors.

erated tsunami waves of 9 to 17 meters in Hawaii, killing 159 people.

BETTER SAFE THAN SORRY

Currently, the only way to avoid overlooking a dangerous earthquake is to put a conservative lower limit on the magnitudes that will trigger a tsunami watch. Any earthquake within the Pacific basin greater than magnitude 7.5 automatically initiates a watch. A warning is issued for the Pacific only if tide gauges detect a tsunami. No warnings have been issued by the Hawaii Warning Center since 1967, but there are about two watches each year.

When the threatened coastline is close to the location of an undersea earthquake, the only practical basis for a timely warning is seismological data. For example, the Alaska Regional Tsunami Warning System will issue a warning, not a watch, for an area within several hundred kilometers of any Alaskan coastal quake of magnitude 7.0 or greater, rather than the usual 7.5. In the period 1968–1978, the Alaska Warning Center issued three warnings, but no significant tsunamis were generated.

FALSE ALARMS

These necessarily numerous watches and warnings can reduce public confidence in the warning system. A striking example from the earlier years of the warning system is the 1960 Chilean tsunami. In spite of being warned six hours before the first wave arrived, 61 residents of Hilo, Hawaii, were killed. As a public tsunami-information pamphlet puts it: the victims apparently believed that the warning had been "just another false alarm."

LONG-PERIOD SEISMIC WAVES

Many researchers believe that the reliability of tsunami predictions would be improved by the use of specially designed seismographs. A wide range of seismic waves with different periods, or times between successive high points, can be produced by earthquakes. Very-short-period waves often result from the sharp snap of rocks under high stress, while very-long-period waves are usually due to the slower movements of large sections of the ocean floor. Because it is gen-

International Tsunami Information Center

A geostationary satellite is used to transmit seismic and tidal data.

erally thought that the up-or-down movement of these large blocks causes most tsunamis, some researchers suggest that the strength of seismic waves of very long periods would be the best guide to an earthquake's ability to generate a tsunami.

Most seismographs in use today are not sensitive to very-long-period waves. Thus, they cannot "see" that aspect of an earthquake thought to be most responsible for tsunamis. The familiar Richter magnitude scale, which is useful as a measure of ground shaking and possible damage to buildings, was first calculated from the amplitude of seismic waves with periods of only about one second. This scale is now derived from 20-second waves so that large earthquakes, which produce a larger proportion of long-period waves than smaller quakes, can also be accurately measured. In the present Tsunami Warning System, shorter-period waves are used to locate the earthquake, but 20-second waves are used to calculate the magnitude.

A tsunami of about 35 meters high devastated Seward, Alaska on March 28, 1964.

UNDETECTED ENERGY

A number of seismologists and tsunami researchers, including James Brune of the University of California at San Diego and Hiroo Kanamori of the California Institute of Technology, believe that even 20-second waves do not accurately reflect the true magnitude of some earthquakes and that 100-second waves should be used instead. It has already been shown by the work of Brune, Kanamori, and others that a large part of the energy released by some large earthquakes goes undetected unless the movement that produces very-long-period waves is included in the calculation of its magnitude. For example, the Chilean earthquake of 1960 had a magnitude of 8.3 when calculated on the basis of 20-second waves. But its magnitude was 9.5, more than 10 times larger in wave amplitude and more than 60 times larger in energy released, when calculated by Kanamori's method. His method attempts to include the energy release represented by very-long-period seismic waves.

It is this possible underestimation of magnitude that has prompted tsunami specialists to include a safety factor of up to one magnitude unit, or a factor of 10, in the seismological criteria for issuing watches and warnings. Scientists now believe that there would be fewer alerts if very-long-period seismological data was available.

SPECIAL DETECTORS

Such data have begun to be collected, but it has not yet been integrated into the Tsunami Warning System. Very-long-period seismographs have been in use for more than ten years, but only recently have any instruments been devoted to tsunami studies. Two very-long-period seismographs incorporating recent technical advances have been set up under a Soviet-U.S. exchange program. One is in Hawaii and the other on the Soviet island of Yuzhno-Sakhalinsk northeast of Vladivostok. Project IDA (International Deployment of Accelerometers) uses identical seismographs in the study of the excitation or "ringing" of the whole earth by large earthquakes. A third station is being created by the modification of a conventional instrument at the Alaska Warning Center in Palmer on the south Alaskan coast.

Now, tsunami specialists must wait for enough large earthquakes and any tsunamis that result to see whether very-long-period seismology can actually make a contribution to tsunami prediction □

SELECTED READINGS

"International Tsunami Warning System" by George Pararas-Carayannis. *Sea Frontiers,* January 1977.

Tsunamis in the Pacific Ocean, edited by William M. Adams. University Press of Hawaii, 1970.

CAN ANIMALS ANTICIPATE EARTHQUAKES?

by Evelyn Shaw

CHICKENS and pigeons balked at entering their coops; cattle bellowed mournfully and refused to graze; dogs howled in chorus all over town; rats scurried from their hideouts and marched fearlessly through houses; catfish leaped out of their ponds; horses neighed, trembled, and ran wildly around their corrals; and snakes slithered from their hibernation holes only to freeze to death on winter ice.

Opening scenes from a monster movie? No.

Opening scenes of an earthquake? Perhaps.

Unusual behavior by animals as divergent as ants, parakeets, sardines, and yaks has been noted in many countries prior to the onset of earthquakes. Some of the behavior, as reported from China, Japan, the United States, Guatemala, and Italy, took place weeks before the quake, some only hours or minutes.

Soviet scientists in recent years have become interested in using animal behavior to predict all kinds of natural disasters. They report that before tremors and storms, shrimps crawled on dry land, ants picked up their eggs and moved in mass migrations, and pheasants chorused an alarm.

MANY EXAMPLES

In 1964, the year of the great Alaska earthquake, kodiak bears emerged from hibernation two weeks before their normal winter sleep would have ended and headed for the hills.

In 1975, in California, a strong earthquake struck the Oroville region, a rural area about 130 kilometers northwest of Sacramento. Two days later, a visiting reporter was overwhelmed by accounts of anomalous behavior of farm animals, seen minutes, as well as weeks before the event.

San Diego Zoo

Pigmy chimpanzees appear to be restless a day before an earthquake.

A scientist attached to the Max Planck Institute of Berlin visited northeastern Italy after the disastrous Friuli earthquake of 1976. While there he was told innumerable tales of strange animal behavior, such as fowl refusing to roost, cattle panicking in their barns, mice and rats leaving their hiding places, and cats moving out of the area.

Finally, a man in San Francisco reported the odd behavior of pet bullfrogs that had metamorphosed just two weeks earlier. One Sunday, the man noticed that the frogs had increased their jumping activity and were hopping about more than usual. But he was particularly baffled the next day when he heard the young frogs croaking loudly at noon and then saw them swimming in clockwise circles. That evening at 7:45 a moderately severe earthquake struck the Bay area. Normally, frogs vocalize as adults. Males croak during the reproductive season and occasionally before an oncoming storm. Consequently, the vocalizations of the young frogs were out of the ordinary and may have been a reaction to some otherwise undetected physical stimulus.

These reports, no matter how widely separated their places and times of origin, share certain attributes in common: increased animal irritability and vocalization, restlessness, and greater activity often leading to migrations.

CHINESE SUCCESSES

Although many of the tales of unusual animal behavior are anecdotal in nature, the tales have enough substance to cause the People's Republic of China to take them seriously. The Chinese have distributed publications to farmers and other rural residents instructing them in what to watch for in their animals so that every household can join in helping to predict earthquakes. The government of the People's Republic claims that the location and time of origin of about fifteen earthquakes have been successfully foretold in recent years. The predictions have relied heavily on bizarre behavior among domestic animals, which can be easily observed without technical equipment or special training.

The Chinese are particularly proud of their prediction of the major earthquake in Haicheng on February 4, 1975. The town was totally destroyed but very few persons were killed, even though about 1,000,000 lived near the quake's epicenter, because the population had been evacuated. Foremost among the precursory events of that earthquake was the discovery in mid-December that normally hibernating snakes had left their holes and frozen to death on the ice. In

Retna
Bullfrogs seem to anticipate earthquakes as indicated by increased jumping and croaking.

the month preceding the major tremors, the earthquake alert became more intensive as "hundreds to thousands" of people reported odd animal behavior, centered on an area that later proved to be the quake's epicenter.

FISH STUDIES

In the 1930's, earthquake swarms occurred with such regularity in Japan that several scientists were able to test the sensitivity of catfish to earthquake precursors. Working at the Asamushi Marine Biological Station, two researchers discovered a correlation between the response of catfish to a mechanical stimulus and the subsequent occurrence of an earthquake. The catfish were kept in aquariums filled with water drawn directly from a local creek. The aquariums were installed on wooden tables on which the researchers tapped three times a day. Their studies showed that if the catfish did not react to the tapping, no earthquake tremor would occur; but if they did respond—by jumping—a slight tremor would take place, usually six to eight hours later. The researchers claimed a correspondence of 80 per cent between the catfish reaction and the occurrence of earthquakes, indicating sensitivity to even slight seismic disturbances. Subsequent Japanese experiments with catfish also showed that some relationship existed between catfish sensitivity to minute electrical changes and changes in the earth's electric field associated with the occurrence of earthquakes.

Kodiak bears in Alaska ended hibernation two weeks early before the 1964 earthquake.

Bruce Coleman

In Japan studies have been made on the ability of catfish to detect earth tremors.

Bruce Coleman

CHIMPS BECOME RESTLESS

With earthquake prediction in mind, a new look was taken at data collected at the Stanford Outdoor Primate Facility in California for the purpose of studying long-term changes in chimpanzee behavior associated with maturation and hormonal variations. Several intriguing deviations in behavioral frequencies were found to have taken place one day before a mild earthquake occurred in the vicinity of the facility, which is located close to the earthquake-prone San Andreas fault. Observers reported a "significant elevation of restlessness," as well as significant increases and decreases in the time the chimpanzees spent in certain areas of the facility. Similarly, a day before another earthquake, increased restlessness was also observed, but in that case space-utilization changes occurred only on the day of the quake. Although of slight magnitude, these earthquakes were apparently sensed by the chimpanzees about eight hours before they took place.

NO SPECIFIC DETECTORS

The probability that any animal would be subject to intense seismic stimuli during its lifetime seems fairly remote. Very strong earthquakes do not, fortunately, occur frequently, and the chance of an animal with a normal life span considerably shorter than that of a human being in the particular region struck by a quake is very low indeed.

Thus it is difficult to believe that animals would have developed specific systems for the recognition of earthquake cues. There is simply very little chance that such a warning system would be useful to them. It seems therefore that animals sense earthquake warning events through sensory detectors developed and used primarily for another purpose—namely, to gather information about small daily changes in their own particular environment.

Let's assume then, that no specific earthquake detectors exist in animals and that detection takes place through available sensory equipment. But what particular stimuli do the animals react to? One major problem in determining this is that the cluster of physical components involved in earthquakes is not necessarily identical from one earthquake to the next. Earthquakes have individual characteristics: modifications occur in acoustic waves, air-pressure levels, the tilt of the land, electrical conductivity, electromagnetic fields, electrostatic discharges, gas emissions, groundwater level, and temperature, for example, but these events do not always appear in identical patterns. The time of onset, frequency, duration, and magnitude of each may vary, as well as which particular physical events are present. To confound the experimenters further, physical changes that take place are often of such small magnitude that they fall within the range of normal fluctuations regularly experienced by the animal.

Before earthquakes, people have observed horses to neigh, tremble, and run wildly in their corrals.

Retna

If animals do indeed sense oncoming earthquakes, they must be able to distinguish an earthquake signal from an array of background "noise," perhaps through a filtering system. Moreover, animal responses tend to differ according to the season, time of day, age, and previous experience. Thus, given that we do not have complete information about animal detection capabilities, and that our knowledge of the physical events preceding earthquakes is also incomplete, we can only guess as to what the animals are actually sensing.

MAGNETIC SENSORS?

Animal sensors that discern light, sound, odor, touch, and temperature are well known. Less well known are sensors that detect changes in the earth's magnetic field. That they exist is currently being revealed by scientists studying orientation, navigation, migration, and homing among birds, bees, and other species. For those who believe in animals as earthquake predictors, the discovery that some animals distinguish small shifts in magnetic fields is very exciting since it has long been thought that variation in geomagnetic fields is intimately involved with earthquakes.

The earth's geomagnetic field is measured in units known as gammas. One gamma, which is a very weak field, is 1/50,000 of the total average earth field. At the earth's surface, the geomagnetic field is variable. When analyzing the sensitivity of animals to earthquakes it is therefore important to remember that within their normal daily foraging adventures, animals may be subject to magnetic fields that vary by as much as several hundred gammas. More important perhaps is the day-to-day variation of thirty to fifty gammas that results from the interaction between the earth's magnetic field and charged particles coming to the earth from the sun.

The changes recorded in local magnetic fields before earthquakes are only of one to ten gammas—well within the range of normal daily fluctuations. How, then, do animals detect a difference? Although the amplitude of these normal fluctuations may be small, we do not know their frequencies. Could normal fluctuations and earthquake-produced fluctuations differ in frequency? We do not know. But let us examine research that reveals the capacity of some animals to detect magnetic field changes. Certain invertebrates show a capacity of detection.

Earthquake devastation. What is it that some animals may feel before a quake?

BEES DON'T ERR

In the early 1970's the sensitivity of honeybees to magnetic fields was demonstrated by the work of German scientists who had studied with Nobel laureate Karl von Frisch. As long ago as the 1920's, von Frisch established that honeybees communicate the distance and direction of food supplies to members of their colonies by means of dances. The direction of the dance within the hive relative to the angle of the sun informs fellow hive members of the direction of nectar-laden flowers; the duration of the waggle in the dance indicates the distance.

Using that information as a model, two German investigators discovered what seemed to be an "error." The direction of the dance was always a little off, yet the bees found the food with unerring accuracy. Obviously, some factor in addition to the position of the sun was involved. The researchers tracked the diurnal variations in the strength of the earth's magnetic field and found that the so-called errors in the bees' dances corresponded to those magnetic changes. If the earth's magnetic field was artificially reduced to zero within the hive, the researchers showed that the direction of the dance fol-

lowed the route they predicted from the model. Moreover, the bees evidently sensed magnetic fluctuations as small as ten gammas, again well within the range of normal fluctuations in terrestrial magnetism. The bees' magnetic detectors, however, remain unknown.

BIRDS GOOD TOO

Homing pigeons similarly sense changes in the magnetic field and may use the information for orientation on overcast days. A research team at Cornell University in New York found that although the sun's position is the pigeon's main directional cue, pigeons can still navigate successfully on cloudy days. Small bar magnets attached to the pigeons' backs had no effect on their navigation on sunny days but caused confusion and interfered with typical directional choice when the birds were released some distance from home on cloudy days. Researchers at the State University of New York at Stony Brook actually forced a new orientation, rather than merely disrupting the expected one, by attaching electrical coils to pigeons. When the current flowed counterclockwise in the coils of some birds and clockwise in the

Russ Hamilton, Cornell University

A homing pigeon outfitted with magnets to change the surrounding magnetic field. Changes in the pigeon's heart rate could indicate that the bird has perceived the magnetic change.

coils of others, the birds headed in opposite directions from each other. It thus appears that pigeons use cues from the magnetic field as directional guides when they cannot use the sun.

Other studies in the United States and in Europe also have shown birds affected by magnetic-field changes. And recent field studies seem, at least indirectly, to reaffirm the laboratory results. One field project visually tracked nocturnally migrating perching birds and correlated their loss of accuracy in orientation with disturbances in the magnetic field. But the investigators cautioned that magnetic field disturbances may not directly affect the birds but may act through such intermediaries as weather patterns, which are also modified by the earth's magnetic activity.

Another field study found that man-made electromagnetic-field fluctuations caused turning or changes in altitude among nocturnally migrating birds. Evidence thus accumulates that birds are capable of sensing small fluctuations in magnetic fields. Animal behaviorist William T. Keeton of Cornell University, who conducted the experiments on homing pigeons, believes that experimental refinements may eventually demonstrate that birds and bees are capable of detecting changes in magnitude as small as one gamma, well below the amplitude of the earth's field. In addition, Keeton points out that homing pigeons sense small shifts in barometric pressure and can also detect extreme low-frequency sounds—physical events that are associated with earthquakes.

Although the studies of birds and bees were not directed at detecting sensitivity to earthquakes, they suggest fruitful directions for further inquiry along that line. Recent research on the sensory perception of fish has also not been directed toward earthquake prediction. Nevertheless, fish, like birds and bees, have sensory capacities that may permit them to react to earthquake precursors, such as small electrical voltage changes.

BUT IS IT USEFUL?

Granted that many animals seem to be acutely sensitive to various premonitory events associated with earthquakes, the basic question remains of how this behavior can be put to use in earthquake prediction. Can we learn just what stimuli particular species are reacting to? Can we then design instruments of comparable discrimination and sensitivity? And even with such instruments, do the premonitory events take place sufficiently in advance of major tremors to make long-term predictions, and the concomitant evacuation of large populations, a realistic possibility? Only further experimentation will provide the answers ☐

📖 SELECTED READINGS

"Earthquakes: prediction proves elusive" by R. A. Kerr. *Science,* April 28, 1978.

"Earthquake research and political tremors in China; study by Carl Kisslinger" by D. Meredith. *Technology Review,* October 1978.

"Prediction of tremors can create new hazards" by S. Aaronson. *Science Digest,* April 1978.

YOU AND THE WEATHER

by H. E. Landsberg

ARE Mrs. Jones' aching, arthritic joints really beating the U.S. National Weather Service's computer forecasts? And what does Mr. Smith mean when he says he is "under the weather"? Is Bill O'Bryan making the right move, when he retires, to change his abode from Maine to Florida because "the climate is better"?

None of these questions has easy answers. All raise age-old scientific questions about how weather and climate affect human beings. The answers are being sought by the science of biometeorology. Workers in this field are trying to establish the interaction between two of the most complex systems on earth: the vagarious atmosphere and the mysterious functioning of living organisms.

AGE-OLD INTEREST

The notion that human health and disease are closely linked with daily and seasonal weather probably predates written history. But it was nailed down in writing by the Greek physician Hippocrates (about 400 B.C.), who recorded different reactions of human beings to hot and cold winds and related epidemics to seasonal weather changes. Very little was added to Hippocrates' discerning observations for over two thousand years.

Careful scientific investigations have been made only over the past few decades. These have begun to unravel some intricate interactions. One of the great difficulties in these studies is the fact that no two human beings are exactly alike. We do not come uniformly and well calibrated from a factory. We have different genes, different statures, different states of nutrition. And above all we change with age.

Quite in contrast, our information on the atmospheric environment is precise.

The aged find it hard to ignore weather conditions as their internal heating and cooling mechanisms begin to break down, and bones and skin become very sensitive.

FPG

Temperature, humidity, pressure, wind are all measured with precision and so are their changes from day to day or season to season. You can readily see that it first confuses and then exasperates the research worker in the field if, say, a sudden drop in temperature causes aches and pains in ten per cent of a sample population, seems not to affect eighty per cent at all, and exhilarates the other ten per cent. However, the same people react almost invariably the same way to various weather stimuli.

WEATHER, BIRTH, AND DEATH

Rapid weather changes seem to initiate responses in the body. These phenomena have been analyzed by classifying them according to weather phases. These follow the common sequences of weather in that part of the world under the effect of the westerlies. All told, six phases represent fairly well the complex totality of weather. We start with cool, high pressure, with a few clouds, and moderate winds or phase 1. This is followed by perfectly clear, dry, high-pressure and little wind in phase 2. Then we get into considerable warming, steady or slightly falling pressure, and some high clouds in phase 3.

After that warm, moist air gets into the lower layers, pressure falls, clouds thicken, precipitation is common, and winds pick up in phase 4. Then, in phase 5 an abrupt change takes place: showery precipitation is accompanied by cold, gusty winds and rapidly rising pressure and falling humidity. Finally with further rising pressure and diminishing clouds, temperatures reach low levels and humidities drop in phase 6.

Of course, these phases are not equally long either in one sequence or in the course of the year. In winter all of these phases may follow one another in less than three days. Some phases may be so short that it looks as if they had been omitted but they are usually there, even if in vestigial form. In summer it may take two weeks for a weather sequence to pass.

These weather phases have been very successfully correlated with the joys and tragedies of human life. In order to do that one has to rely essentially on hospital records.

You need little imagination to speculate that the quiescent weather phases 1 and 2, the "beautiful weather," stimulate the body very little. They generally make few demands on us and most of these can be met by proper clothing and adequate housing.

Quite in contrast, weather phases 4 and 5 are often turbulent and violent. Somehow or other, they stir us up. Let's look at some of the statistics. You probably wouldn't believe that the precise date and hour of your birth was determined by the weather. The end of human pregnancy is uncertain by about plus or minus 10 days of the anticipated birth date. If we distribute the large numbers of cases of births among the weather phases it shows that in far more cases than statistical accident would permit, labor starts in days with weather phase 3, often followed by birth in phase 4.

These same phases seem to follow us toward the termination of life. Coronary thrombosis, the so-called heart attack, also shows a peak in weather phases 3 and 4. It shows a minimum in phases 1 and 6. Bleeding ulcers occur more often in phase 4. So do migraine attacks. Spasmodic diseases seem to be more prevalent in phases 4 to 6 than during the other weather conditions.

Weather not only affects our physical health and disease, birth and death, it also rules our moods and behavior. This is generally far more difficult to establish than precise events, such as birth and death. But, unfortunately, some moods sometimes lead to the latter event: suicide. Here again, there is a clear increase in weather phase 3.

Weather phase 3 also leads in cases of behavior problems among school children, according to a few available statistics. Comfort and discomfort play a role here. When it is hot and sticky, children do not learn well. This has been conclusively shown by comparison between air conditioned and non-air conditioned classrooms. Uncomfortable atmospheric conditions also are more conducive to riots than comfortable weather.

NARROW SURVIVAL LIMITS

None of us is immune to the atmospheric environment. Human beings are really creatures of the intertropical regions, physically adapted to a narrow range of temperature. Our metabolic mechanism is in best harmony with air temperatures around 25° Celsius. There is a limited range above and below this temperature where survival is possible. At lower temperatures greater muscular activity will raise metabolic heat. This can include involuntary shivering. At higher temperatures another mechanism—sweating—can restore normal temperature. Evaporation of the sweat will use extra heat energy taken from the body. But this process will only work well when humidities are low.

At high humidities the evaporative cooling will not work. Overheating occurs and heat stroke can result. Thus combinations of temperatures of 45° Celsius and 10 percent relative humidity; 35° Celsius and 40 per cent relative humidity; 30° Celsius and 60 per cent relative humidity; and 27° Celsius and 100 per cent relative humidity define a danger limit. If these limits are exceeded, heat prostration, heat stroke, and heat death may occur. Infants, whose heat regulatory mechanism is not yet fully developed, and old people, who often have impaired circulatory systems, are most likely to suffer.

On the cold end of the scale, wind becomes an important influence. It blows away a thin protective air layer near the skin. We try to keep this insulation intact by wearing progressively thicker clothing as exposure to cold increases. Various combinations of air temperature and wind speed have been combined into a wind-chill index, expressed in form of an equivalent temperature reflecting the cold sensation with calm air. Thus a temperature of 10° Celsius and wind of 4.5 meters per second gives a wind chill equivalent of 4.5° Celsius in calm air. To give some

The body's natural cooling system is hindered at high temperatures by humidity, and heat prostration may occur.

other examples: 0° Celsius and 8.9 meters per second wind are equivalent to −14° Celsius; and −18° Celsius and 2.2 meters per second wind to −25.2° Celsius.

THE COMMON COLD

The classical case of a disease allegedly related to weather is the common cold. Is it really a meteorotropic, or weather-caused, ill? There is no easy answer.

A cold is a virus-caused disease, with the virus spreading from person to person. Obviously enough, the virus does not survive in extreme cold. There are no colds in the isolation of the polar night. Colds are only imported there by visitors. But in the moderate latitudes colds occur more frequently in winter. That is the time people are confined indoors; schools are in session and the virus spreads epidemically. It is very difficult to discern whether it is the close indoor person-to-person contact more common in winter or the weather itself that affects the incidence of the common cold.

There have been experiments, albeit on very limited numbers of persons, where people were exposed to both cold temperatures and to virus, while control subjects were exposed only to virus. The number of those coming down with the miserable sniffles in both groups showed no significant difference.

Statistical studies present a problem. There are no reliable statistics on daily numbers of individuals showing first cold symptoms.

Thus, all statistics are case information from clinics or individual physicians and often in the analysis of such data with weather conditions, use has been made of only the readily available meteorological observations, such as maximum and minimum temperature. These are decidedly inadequate. Modern multiple-correlation screening techniques, which have studied the relationship of the common cold to various weather phenomena, have not been used on adequately large samples to give conclusive results. However, a review of bulk information on the incidence of colds seems to point definitely toward the wind-chill factor as a contributing weather element. Perhaps further work will yet verify another Granny tale.

What about the cold and other virus diseases? We know very little about virus transport by atmospheric currents and virus survival times in relation to weather.

ALLERGIES

We are much better informed about airborne allergens, or substances that can produce an allergic reaction in sensitive people. The best known of these are various plant pollen. Turbulent winds carry these. On sunny days during the warm season the atmosphere does not have a stable temperature, and strong vertical air currents are common. These currents are often strong enough to prevent pollen from falling to the ground. The pollen may stay afloat and be carried long distances. People sensitive to

Close indoor contact and warm, moist air may lead to colds.

EPA-Documerica

them will then develop allergic reactions, such as hay-fever miseries, or even asthmatic attacks.

More insidious even than pollen are spores of fungi. These are generally smaller and lighter than the pollen and can, therefore, be carried greater distances, sometimes 2,000 kilometers. Heavy wind storms may stir some of these fungi out of the ground and carry them along. One such fungus, which resides in both tame and wild-bird excrement, causes histoplasmosis, a lung disease that often mimicks pulmonary tuberculosis.

The same atmosphere which stirs up these natural irritants also eliminates them. Washout by rain cleanses these as well as man-made pollutants out of the atmosphere. The more frequently it rains, the cleaner the air. In many parts of the United States, airborne dust generally stays airborne less than five days in the lower air layers.

WEIGHT AND SKIN

Between the dangerous limits of heat and wind chill, there are sensations of comfort and discomfort. These, again, are widely differentiated, often governed by the state of nutrition. Obese persons suffer more from heat; malnourished individuals are very sensitive to cold.

Many weather-related ailments are transmitted via the skin. The skin separates the body from the external world. It senses and transmits to the body and the brain many of the changes taking place in the atmosphere. As long as the skin is unimpaired the system works well. But when the skin becomes scarred or deformed, atmospheric temperature, moisture, and possibly electrical changes may induce a tension between the healthy skin and the scar tissue resulting in a flash of pain.

PHANTOM PAIN

Let's go back a hundred years. In the United States, it was the time after the Civil War. Many soldiers had suffered serious wounds and amputations. They felt the weather changes. Many with amputated limbs reported feeling pain in the missing limb. The first systematic study of these pains—often called phantom pains—was undertaken by S. Weir Mitchell, M.D. In the

Stephen Jennings

People who have lost limbs often report "phantom" pain in the amputated limb when atmospheric conditions change abruptly.

April 1877 issue of the prestigious American Journal of Medical Sciences he related the case of Union Captain Catlin, who after his leg was amputated below the knee, made a rapid recovery—except for neuralgic pains. Catlin kept a detailed diary of the onset and duration of his pains. Dr. Mitchell interpreted these pains in terms of the coincident weather conditions and concluded that an approaching storm with the combination of conditions—falling barometric pressure, rising temperature and humidity, followed by rain—was most frequently giving his patient pains. It was an astute deduction.

Enter now Claus Thurkow, a German soldier who lost his right arm in 1945 at the end of World War II, and Otto Hoflich, a Ph.D. candidate in meteorology at the University of Hamburg. The scenario is the same in this case: Thurkow kept records of his pains for five years and Hoflich looked at the meteorology. Unlike Mitchell a century earlier, Hoflich had access to a computer and used sophisticated statistical methods to correlate the pain intervals with the meteorological conditions. The end result, now established beyond reasonable doubt by tests of significance, is almost identical to Mitchell's discerning analysis: falling pressure, reaching a minimum in 24 hours, and high probability of rain—the typical symptoms of a warm front—caused pain. But there were also pain reactions with cold fronts and shower rains as well as possible relations to atmospheric electric phenomena.

Stephen Jennings

Arthritics often suffer great pain when humidity and air pressure systems change.

ARTHRITIS FLAREUPS

Very similar meteorological conditions, which have been termed *biotropic,* affect the arthritics, an experience which has found folklore expression in the old English ditty:

"Hark how the chairs and tables crack,
Old Betty's bones are on the rack."

This is a clear allusion to humidity changes. But according to all observations rising humidities alone are not enough to cause discomfort: the barometric pressure has to fall too. In fact, this has been verified objectively by Dr. J. L. Hollander of the University of Pennsylvania. He placed some arthritic volunteers in an isolated hospital room in which most atmospheric conditions could be controlled and changed at will. Changes simulating the passage of high and low-pressure systems were induced in the room, where the patients were on a regular hospital routine. Lo, and behold, when pressure falls and humidity increases were programmed for the chamber, the patients noted pains. Even more convincing were the objective findings of swollen joints occurring at the same time. However, we still don't know how atmospheric changes penetrate the body. Could it be that the membranes in a joint act like an aneroid barometer and exercise a pressure on fluids in the bursa, or fluid-filled sac surrounding a joint, and that this causes the pain?

MUCH RESEARCH NEEDED

It is clearly impossible to give more than a few examples of how the weather affects our bodies. We must also admit that only in a few instances have we unravelled the complete chain of events. Statistical correlations tell us nothing about causal linkages. They only alert us to the possible existence of a relationship that suggests cause and effect. Much painstaking research needs yet to be done to make the information useful for maintenance of health and for management of disease.

In this latter area lies a complex of questions which needs urgent exploration: the relation of weather to the effects of drugs. We live in an age of pill-popping and some evidence suggests that the same dosage will have greater or lesser effects on the ailment the drug is to control on one day than the next. Most of these drugs are taken for chronic diseases, with patients administering the drugs themselves. They only see their physicians infrequently so that no consistent information on drug action is available. In some drugs, weather-steered responses have been reported but we know very little which diseases and which remedies are affected. That's a real gap in knowledge.

More sensitivity to health-related information by those who issue weather forecasts is also something to be desired. These forecasts, rightly so, include warnings against severe storms and floods. In some localities air-pollution alerts are issued when necessary. But it is also desirable to give predictions of chill factors in winter and humithermal conditions in summer.

Weather-sensitive persons can also contribute to the unraveling of the many puzzles about weather and health. They may learn how better to cope with the atmospheric steering of their own symptoms. And all of us will have to reckon with the fact that the atmospheric environment plays a major role in our "pursuit of happiness" □

SELECTED READINGS

"Biometeorology seeks clues to health" by R. Wolkomir. *Science Digest,* August 1977.

"Weather link with health" by J. Arehart-Treichel. *Harpers,* April 1976.

"What the weather does to you" by M. Brenton. *Family Health,* August 1976.

History repeats itself. During World War II (1941–1945) the gasoline shortage was caused by the war. Thirty-five years later the shortage is caused by increased use of cars, a falling-off of domestic oil finds, and international politics.

ENERGY

ENERGY
REVIEW OF THE YEAR

Westinghouse

A bed-coal gasification unit by Westinghouse. Tests at this pilot unit have demonstrated that the gasification process can be used to produce fuel gas from coal for generating electricity.

Interior of coal mine in West Virginia. Bituminous coal miners board steel-top cars, which will take them to the "working face," where the coal is smashed and shoveled by enormous dozerlike machines.

National Coal Association

Creating a national energy policy is "with the exception of preventing war, the greatest challenge our country will face during our lifetimes." So began the nationally televised address in which U.S. President Jimmy Carter introduced his National Energy Plan on April 18, 1977. Some 18 months of Congressional debate resulted in the National Energy Act, which, although it did not contain much of the original content and bite of Carter's plan, was, however, an ambitious first step toward establishing a coordinated energy policy. It attempted for the first time to account for the synergistic impact that the use of coal, natural gas, and oil—the nation's three major fuels—has on both the economy and the availability of future energy supplies.

To encourage fuel conservation Carter would have used increased taxes to raise fuel prices without giving producers windfall profits, but Congress chose instead to issue a complicated battery of regulations and tax subsidies to encourage conservation. The only Carter tax to survive was one to be applied toward future automobile models with poor fuel efficiency.

The most controversial part of the energy package was price control, particularly natural-gas price decontrol. Congress voted to let gas prices climb gradually toward complete decontrol sometime in the mid-to-late 1980's. For oil, Congress chose not to maintain artificially low oil prices but at the same time chose not to increase them. They left that to Mr. Carter, who earlier had pledged to raise oil prices to world levels within two years. ■ The energy act also required changing fuel-price structures to encourage conservation and offering tax credits for expenditures on insulation and other energy-conserving investments.

Coal. Only a few years ago the belching smokestacks of coal-fired boilers appeared to be an endangered species in a United States committed to cleaning its environment. The 1973 Arab oil embargo changed that into a national policy that crystallized in 1978. Carter energy strategists decided that the only way to shift the United States' dependence away from oil— one-half of which came from foreign sources in 1978—without bankrupting the economy was to shift back to reliance on coal, which is plentiful in the U.S. In fact, the first regulation to come out of the new energy legislation was the Fuel Use Act, which mandated just that: a switch from oil and gas to coal.

Although the primary reason for shifting away from oil was to halt the flow of "petrodollars" out of the country, the proposed shift has another attraction. Compared to most other energy options, coal is still a relatively inexpensive source of power. But even in that, winds of change blew in like a hurricane in early 1979 when a 110-day coal strike shut down 3,295 of the nation's 4,889 normally operating coal mines. Attendant shortages of coal and natural gas, coupled with record low temperatures and snowfall in parts of the northeastern and midwestern United States resulted in massive school closings, industrial disruptions, and temporary layoffs. The strike's economic impact, together with the wage increase given the coal miners, brought home the intimate tie between energy and economics.

138

Oil. While the U.S. oil industry spent most of 1978 concerned with Congressional action on oil-price decontrol, much of the rest of the world wrestled with finding new oil and gas supplies. And there was some cause for optimism. Estimates of the oil recoverable in the Peoples' Republic of China appeared close to 70,000,000,000 barrels, roughly equal to the potential of Alaska's North Slope. More unexpectedly, estimates of Mexico's store of recoverable "black gold" soared, so that by the end of 1978 some experts speculated that Mexico's oil might turn out to rival Mideast oil reserves.

The global picture appeared bleak, however. In 1976, for the first time, the year's oil-production rate surpassed the oil-discovery rate. "This means the answer to the question, 'Will there be a shortfall of oil supply in the late 1980's?' must be 'Yes,' " according to Friedrich Bender, a German oil expert, "particularly so if the demand surpasses the expected four to five billion tons production of oil in 1985." And the 1977 output was already 3,000,-000,000 tons, he told representatives of more than 30 nations attending the 1978 biennial Circum-Pacific Energy and Mineral Resources Conference in Hawaii.

Nuclear Power. Prospects for the expansive development of nuclear power predicted in the 1960's plummeted further than ever in 1978. Organized protests by antinuclear groups strengthened, spawning large rallies. Court injunctions citing environmental issues temporarily halted the construction of the Seabrook nuclear plant in New Hampshire at great cost to the local utility. Political troubles for nuclear power were not limited to grassroots protesters, however. As part of his nuclear nonproliferation policy, President Carter fought the commercial reprocessing of nuclear fuel. Not reprocessing nuclear fuel would cut deeply into any economic edge that nuclear power might have over competing technologies. Carter also fought completion of a breeder-reactor demonstration plant in Oak Ridge, Tennessee. He had earlier, in 1977, vetoed breeder funds, and in 1978 kept the fate of funds for breeder reactors in a state of limbo. For more on nuclear power, see the article, "The Accident at Three Mile Island," on page 301.

Antinuclear protests also occurred in other countries. Massive protests halted plans for nuclear power plants in West Germany. A referendum calling for nuclear development in Austria was strongly defeated by the electorate, and dissatisfaction over nuclear issues toppled the Swedish Parliament's ruling party for the second time in succession.

Solar Energy. May 2, 1978 marked Sun Day in the United States. It was a nationwide celebration of solar energy patterned off Earth Day and developed by the same people. Businesses, public-interest groups, labor unions, schools, government offices, and churches all joined in festivities to learn more about developing solar technologies and to view demonstrations of what commercial solar systems can deliver today. In Sun Day ceremonies at the Solar Energy Research Institute in Colorado, President Carter unexpectedly announced that an additional $100,000,000 would be added to the U.S. Energy Department's solar-research budget, bringing the total to more than $500,000,000.

Janet Raloff

UPI

In October 1978 anti-nuclear demonstrators of the Boston Clamshell Alliance climbed over a fence at the Seabrook, New Hampshire, nuclear station site.

Former Governor of Massachusetts Michael Dukakis takes part in a Sun Day ceremony at Boston Common on May 3, 1978. The Governor tends a coffee pot, being heated by a solar stove. Note the reflector at the base.

UPI

UPI

At Americology recycling plant, in Milwaukee, paper, ferrous metals, aluminum, and glass are separated for reuse.

BIOMASS

by Roberta Navickis

PERHAPS the most commonplace and practical plan for using solar energy is to tap energy supplies stored in biomass. What is biomass?

Biomass is almost everything under the sun—everything from sewage to sweet sorghum. The word is a catchall, covering the many living, or derived from the living, materials or substances that potentially could be used as energy sources. Lumped together in this category are wood and wood wastes, agriculture products and wastes, algae, animal wastes, municipal sewage, and so on.

APPEALING IDEA

Biomass energy is appealing for many reasons. Like other types of solar energy, it is infinitely renewable, and unlike direct collection of solar energy, there is no storage problem. The energy is stored in trees or algae or municipal wastes.

The technologies proposed for using biomass are not far-fetched in most cases. Agriculture and forestry operations are already a workable part of the economy and a desirable use of land. An additional advantage of biomass is that it addresses not only the problem of energy production, but also that of waste disposal, a major environmental source of pollution. Biomass, in itself, being low in sulfur, is less polluting than many fossil fuels.

BIG PRICE TAG

But the use of biomass as an energy source is not without problems. The chief ones are the same reasons why wood was abandoned in favor of coal in the 1800's. Biomass raw material is often quite low in energy content. Coal, oil, and natural gas have a much higher energy content.

Biomass usually contains a lot of water and is mostly composed of carbohydrate. Carbohydrates don't contain as much energy per molecule as the hydrocarbons found in the fossil fuels. Biomass can be converted into fuels that are of high energy content, but that takes energy and money.

There is also a problem of scale with biomass. Not enough biomass material is available in one location for collection and generation of power to be efficient and economical.

These two problems add up to a high price tag for biomass energy. But with rising costs of petroleum, the depletion of natural gas, and the development of better ways to process and convert biomass to more energy-rich fuels, the price tag may not look so bad in a few years.

ALREADY USED

In fact, biomass is being used for energy now. In 1977, one and one-half per cent of the United States' energy came from biomass. That's approximately one half of the energy derived from nuclear power. Wood wastes burned for fuel by the pulp, paper, and forest industries account for most of the biomass use.

But at least 20 U.S. cities have built or are considering plans for "resource recovery" plants that can generate fuel from organic garbage. An Oklahoma firm provides Chicagoans with methane (natural gas) made from feedlot wastes of cattle. More exotic forms of biomass energy—plantations of petroleum-producing plants and huge kelp farms in the ocean—are projected for the future.

Biomass can be used on either a small or a large scale. Small-scale energy-from-wastes projects are coming into increasing use throughout the world. Methane-producing "digestors" are popular, especially in Third World nations. The digestors, usually installed near homes, consume animal wastes and produce methane that is then used for cooking, providing, almost, the proverbial free lunch.

FORESTS TO THE ANSWER

Much planning is afoot for large-scale farms of trees, which would be used for fuel. A 400-hectare pilot-scale plantation on the Savannah River in Aiken, South Carolina, is being funded by the U.S. Department of Energy (DOE). DOE is also funding a broader program at The Solar Energy Research Institute in Golden, Colorado, on ways to produce biomass and convert it to fuel

efficiently. Thomas B. Reed, the project's director, estimates that as much as 40 per cent of the current U.S. energy needs could be produced from biomass around the year 2000. Others are more conservative about the potential contribution of biomass. Almost everyone agrees that energy from biomass will never meet all U.S. energy needs. Nevertheless, DOE is taking biomass seriously, with a 30 per cent increase in its total long-range allocations for biomass in 1979.

Charles D. Scott, associate director of the chemical technology division of Oak Ridge National Laboratories in Oak Ridge, Tennessee, predicts that in the next 20 years forest products will be the major source of biomass energy. According to one estimate, total biomass growth in the approximately 200,000,000 hectares of U.S. commercial forests—forests producing about one-and-one half cubic meters of stemwood per hectare per year—about 12 per cent of current energy needs each year. The U.S. National Research Council estimates that the yields could be doubled if the forests were better managed. Most forests are not now actively managed for production, except for the 13 per cent that are industrially owned.

In still another estimate, two Princeton University scientists calculate that in Con-

DOE photo by Schneider

John Goss, Professor of Engineering, University of California at Davis, has developed a gas-producing prototype unit that uses farm and forest residues to produce methane gas. The gas is used to fire a boiler that heats and air conditions a building on the Davis campus. Here he is operating an electric generator, which is powered by the methane gas.

DOE photo by Schneider

Courtesy of the University of Georgia

This four-year-old stand of sycamores will be harvested, and their stumps will sprout new trees.

necticut as little as 22,000 hectares could support a 150 megawatt power plant, providing 4.3 per cent of that state's energy needs.

WOOD PELLETS

Forest management taken to the extreme is short rotation forestry. Projects such as the one in Savannah River apply intensive agriculture techniques to growing trees. Trees are planted close together and propagated from cuttings. More productive types of trees are selected for. In Canada, The Ontario Ministry of Natural Resources has selected fast-growing hybrid poplars whose trunks in 5 years measure 20 centimeters in diameter, compared with normal diameters of 5 centimeters.

Such intensive forest management requires big doses of water, phosphorus, and nitrogen. And the threat of attack by pests, especially insects and rodents, always looms.

But, all in all, growing trees is relatively cheap. The processing is what is expensive. Collecting and hauling trees is labor-and time-consuming. A mobile chipper that chomps trees to wood chips is now available and will make things easier. But wood chips still have a low energy content relative to the fossil fuels. It takes many more wood chips than coal chunks to fire a furnace.

But even this problem may soon be solved. According to Peter Schauffler, the co-ordinator of the Bio-Energy Council in Washington, D.C., there is now a machine that can make wood economically competitive with coal in some areas. The machine compresses wood so much that wood's heat content per kilogram becomes comparable to coal's. The wood pellets can be burned in the place of coal or burned with it.

But most homes, schools, and businesses are not at present equipped to burn wood, other types of biomass, or coal directly. So efforts are being made to find ways to convert biomass into more conventional fuels. The techniques developed to gasify coal can be modified to gasify wood. Gasification of biomass is easier than coal gasification because biomass contains more volatiles.

SUGAR CANE

Agriculture crops are also sources of fuels. A classic example is sugar cane. The cut cane is crushed with water. The washing water goes to an evaporator for extraction of sugar and the cellulose residue (bagasse) goes to the boilers where it is burned, providing steam to run the machinery of the mills. Excess steam can be used to generate electricity. The sugar cane can be fermented to alcohol and used as a fuel.

In January 1978, Brazil the largest sugar cane grower in the world, was meeting about 10 per cent of the fuel requirements of the state of Rio de Janeiro with alcohol from sugar cane, and hopes by 1982 to have 20 per cent of liquid fuels be alcohol. Brazil's success is partially attributable to cheap labor and land, and a semi-tropical to tropical climate. Sugar cane can't be grown in most of the United States, and land is by no one's estimate cheap or available.

In fact, one of the most frequent objections raised against the biomass-for-fuel programs is that they use land that would otherwise be used for raising food and could cause a food shortage. Advocates counter that some biomass could be grown in marginal land that is today nonproductive. But water and nutrients are often limiting factors on marginal land.

Other problems with agricultural wastes are that they are even less energy dense than trees, and are only available at harvest time, not year round, like an oil well. In this, trees have an advantage in that they can be stored "on the stump" and harvested at any time.

FUEL-AND-FOOD GROWING

Edward S. Lipinsky of Battelle Laboratories in Columbus, Ohio, says that the answer to some of these problems lies in adaptive systems, ones that integrate the fuels-for-biomass with the production of food and materials. The economics of growing fuel are much improved if one combines fuel crops with some other useful crops. Sugar cane yields bagasse and sugar; corn yields stalks and corn kernels. The two-purpose crop concept is particularly attractive in areas less favorable to fuel farms than those with abundant sunshine. By-products such as fertilizer can also be derived from biomass.

Lipinsky says that sweet sorghum, a grain that can be fermented to alcohols with yields comparable to those of Louisiana sugar cane, can be grown on the same land as corn and soybeans. When it is unprofitable to raise the standard crops, sweet sorghum can be grown. He writes "Knowing when and where to switch from emphasis on food and materials is just as important as knowing how to produce fuels."

SYNFUELS

Biological methods to convert crops to synfuels such as methane, methanol, and ethanol, are advancing rapidly. George Tsao of Purdue University has produced a breakthrough in converting cellulose into glucose and other fermentable sugars which, in turn, can be converted into alcohol and other chemicals. He has found an organic acid that facilitates the attack of fungal cellulases on lignocellulose, formerly a very undigestible component of plants. This finding makes wastes such as corn cobs, stalks, and other parts, much more valuable.

Methanol can now be produced for about 12 to 14 cents a liter from biomass, according to Schauffler, making it competitive with 1978 gasoline prices. Methanol can be the sole fuel for car engines, provided the engines are modified slightly. Today's engines can run on "gasohol," a mixture of ethanol and gasoline. Ethanol costs about 33 cents a liter to produce from biomass and so isn't economical at this time, he said, but could be if petroleum prices keep rising.

GASOLINE FARMS

Some plants store energy in hydrocarbons rather than carbohydrates and could be used to produce gasoline directly. Melvin Calvin of the Laboratory of Chemical Dynamics at the University of California at Berkeley proposes petroleum plantations of such plants. These plantations could be on semi-arid, currently unproductive, land. He has raised a small crop of gopher plants (*Euphorbia lathyris*) in southern California and estimates that such hydrocarbons can be grown today for $20 a barrel. Others think his estimate may be overly optimistic, because water scarcity may reduce yields on such large-scale "gasoline farms."

Near Guymon, Oklahoma, is a plant that can process 500 tons of cattle waste daily. The plant will produce enough methane to meet the energy needs of 3,500 homes.

Courtesy of Thermonetics

This proposed quarter-acre test farm will demonstrate commercial feasibility of farming giant kelp and converting it into methane and fertilizer.

AQUATIC SCHEMES

Water is no problem for algae and other water-based biomass. In fact, processing of algae has not been attractive because it has not been possible to concentrate algae to more than 4 per cent by weight. Now, however, a group at the New Mexico Solar Energy Institute has developed a technique (a slurry of algae put on a moving endless belt of very fine mesh nylon screen) to concentrate algae to 20 to 28 per cent.

Water hyacinths, fast-growing floating aquatic plants that feed on raw sewage, and at the same time clean the water around them, are also being investigated as sources of biomass.

The most grandiose aquatic scheme for the harvesting of energy is to establish large sea kelp farms. Kelps, which grow 60 to 90 centimeters a day under good conditions, could be converted to methane and other products. The kelp plants will be attached by their holdfasts to a grid of nylon lines suspended 18 meters below the surface so that the fronds of the mature plants will float just below the surface where they will receive sun-light and be able to make their own food. The American Gas Association and General Electric Company's Environmental Systems Division at Philadelphia are involved in a $3,000,000 project on a 1,000-square meter area of seabed eight kilometers offshore from Laguna Beach.

MOVE TO FRONT BURNER

Solid-waste conversion of organic garbage is receiving the most attention now. Methane is being obtained by sinking wells into already existing land fills, or by sorting out garbage fresh from collecting trucks. But this source of methane will always be relatively minor. Biomass's potential lies in such deliberate energy farms—be they of kelp, trees, or petroleum plants.

The bioenergy field is rapidly developing after years on a back burner. The scope is vast. Artificial biomass systems, such as synthetic leaves, may also be in the future. But that's another story □

📖 SELECTED READINGS

"And if all else fails: cattails" by K. A. Matichek. *Science Digest*, October 1977.

"Photosynthetic solar energy: rediscovering biomass fuels" by A. L. Hammond. *Science*, August 27, 1977.

"Plant crops as source of fuel and hydrocarbon-material" by P. E. Nielsen and others. *Science*, December 2, 1977.

An oil burn-off in the newly-found oil fields of Mexico.

Wolf von dem Bussche, LIFE Magazine, © 1979, Time Inc.

THE ENERGY PICTURE: 1985-2000

by Earl T. Hayes

THE problem of supplying energy for a growing U.S. economy is a real and a permanent one. Our natural resources have finite limits, and we have been consuming them at an ever increasing rate for many years. Like all spendthrifts living beyond their income, we have resorted to the charge account. And so we have increased our import bill for foreign oil from $3 billion to $45 billion in 6 years.

Sooner or later the United States has to reduce its imports to more manageable levels. Doing so will require a difficult transition from the rapid energy growth of the last 25 years to a slower one. In the wake of the 1973 oil embargo came the first general realization that there might be supply difficulties ahead.

Americans continue to believe that we can have all the oil and gas we will ever need at 1970 prices without digging coal or building nuclear plants. This attitude slows down or stops planning for the inevitable—a less energy-intensive U.S. society.

Aside from the predictions of energy-supply problems by a few individuals and a handful of government agencies, the country did not have adequate background information on energy in 1973. Since then, we have been inundated with energy-demand and supply studies, ranging from responses to presidential requests to minutiae. Among the overall studies since 1972 have been those conducted under the auspices of the Department of the Interior, Project Independence, the Ford Foundation, the Energy Research and Development Administration (ERDA), the Committee on Nuclear and Alternative Energy Sources (CONAES), Project Interdependence and the Department of Commerce.

THE AVAILABILITY FACTOR

There are two approaches in energy-and-supply studies. The economist's, who reasons that there will always be a supply of a commodity if the price is right. The engineer's, who sees declining grade, institutional constraints, and physical geography placing finite limits on availability.

In this article I am mindful of the economist's approach, but I give much more weight to the availability factor. I discuss natural resources of energy, analyze the probable domestic and import supply of each major energy sector. And I arrive at the dismaying conclusion that energy growth will all but stop in another decade. In this analysis I do not address the economic, social, and political problems that will ensue and will dwarf the technical ones.

Table I summarizes the energy supply expected to be available to the United States in 1985 and 2000, as well as the past supply record. The following sections provide documentation for each estimate. The values in Table 1 represent the energy that can probably be made available for consumption under normal development and at prices up to twice those of today.

U.S. PETROLEUM LIQUIDS

It must be recognized that the United States never had and never will have the petroleum resources to sustain indefinitely the production levels of the last 25 years. In effect, we have been living off our capital all this time and cannot postpone the day of reckoning indefinitely. Talk of rising petroleum (and gas) production for long periods is both immoral and nonsensical. Whatever slight gain might be achieved for a very few years will be at the expense of the youth of today.

Burmah Oil & Gas Co.

Oil production in the United States has been falling off since 1970.

Predictions of sustained increased production deny the records of 50 years of experience with the exploration, development, and extraction cycle of liquid hydrocarbons. There is a finite amount of easily recovered petroleum in the United States. No act of

Table 1. Annual energy supplies for the United States, 1940 to 2000. Values are quadrillion (10^{15}) Btu's (quads)* per year.

Year	Petroleum liquids		Gas		Coal	Hydro	Nuclear	Other†	Gross total†	Gross (quads per year)
	Domestic	Imported	Domestic	Imported						
1940	7.5		2.7		12.5	0.9		1.4	25.0	1.02
1950	13.5		6.2		12.9	1.4		1.2	35.2	1.04
1960	16.8	3.3	12.5	0.2	10.1	1.7		1.0	45.6	2.25
1970	22.8	6.7	21.2	0.8	12.7	2.7	0.2	1.0	68.1	1.60
1977	20.0	17.4	19.1	1.0	13.0	2.7	2.7	1.8	77.7	1.13
1985	17	22	15	2	19	3.0	6.0	2.7	86.7	0.55
2000	15	17	9	1	32	3.5	11	6.5	95.0	

* Equivalents of 1 quadrillion Btu's: 1 trillion cubic feet of natural gas, 170 million barrels of oil, 40 million tons of bituminous coal, or 100 billion kilowatt-hours of electricity.   † Includes biomass figures not carried in all energy summaries.

Congress or false optimism of government, industrial, or academic planners can add to our natural resource base.

The difference between estimates of how much oil we can really expect to find in the United States seems to have been resolved on the pessimistic side. Undiscovered petroleum liquid resources are now placed at 100 billion barrels, give or take 25 billion.

Notable among forecasters is M. K. Hubbert. He accurately predicted more than 20 years ago—when we were being assured of oil and gas forever—that there would be a peak in production near 1970 and an unavoidable decline in production forever after. Each passing year shows the accuracy of his projections. Now we realize that U.S. resources of conventional oil will be seriously depleted by the year 2000.

Proved U.S. reserves of petroleum liquids peaked at 47 billion barrels in 1970 and then declined to the present level of 37 billion barrels. This occurred in spite of the one-shot addition of 10 billion barrels from Prudhoe Bay, Alaska, in 1970. Production and reserve figures for oil and natural gas liquids are given in Table 2. In the 1950's we found 1¼ barrels of oil for every barrel we extracted, but by the late 1970's this had dropped to about ½ barrel. Estimates of production in 1985 and 2000 from some of the current reports are given in Table 3.

H. Franssen, the leader of Project Inter-

Paolo Koch-Rapho Guillumette

Our overuse of motor vehicles has gotten the United States into petroleum debt.

dependence, has pointed out that to achieve a production rate of 11 million barrels per day in 1990, it would be necessary to add 4 billion barrels a year to our reserves. However, there is no resource base to support claims of increased oil production. Aside from the one-of-a-kind Prudhoe Bay discovery, we have not found that much petroleum in any one of the last 30 years. In fact, as Table 2 shows, lately our reserves have been

Table 2. Annual estimates of proved U.S. reserves of crude oil and natural gas liquids.

Year (end of)	Crude oil (billion barrels)		Natural gas liquids (billion barrels)		Natural gas (trillion cubic feet)	
	Proved reserves	Production	Proved reserves	Production	Proved reserves	Production
1946	20.9	1.73	3.16	0.129	159.7	4.0
1950	25.3	1.94	4.27	0.23	184.6	6.3
1955	30.0	2.42	5.44	0.32	222.5	9.4
1960	31.6	2.47	6.82	0.43	262.3	12.8
1965	31.4	2.67	8.02	0.56	286.5	16.0
1970	39.0	3.32	7.70	0.75	290.4	21.9
1971	38.1	3.26	7.30	0.75	278.8	22.5
1972	36.3	3.28	6.79	0.76	266.1	22.5
1973	35.3	3.19	6.45	0.74	250.0	22.5
1974	34.2	3.04	6.35	0.72	237.1	21.4
1975	32.7	2.89	6.27	0.70	228.2	19.7
1976	30.9	2.83	6.40	0.70	216.0	19.5
1977	29.5	2.86	5.99	0.70	208.9	19.4

People stand beside their cars while waiting in line for gasoline during the shortage of 1974.

going down by 1¼ billion barrels a year. Just to maintain current production would require a discovery rate 50 per cent higher than that of the last 10 years.

OTHER FOSSIL FUELS

There is an estimated 2 trillion barrels of oil dispersed in shale in Colorado, Utah, and Wyoming. But only 80 million barrels of this might be classed as a favored resource. Each ton of this shale contains 10 to 40 gallons of

Table 3. Estimated U.S. production of petroleum liquids. Values are millions of barrels per day.

Source	1977	1985	1990	2000
CONAES (5)	10.0	9.0	8.0	6.0
Project Inter-dependence		10.9	11.4	
Department of Commerce		8.6		6.2
Hubbert*		8.0	7.0	4.0
Exxon		8.0	10.3	

* Estimated from graph.

kerogens, which can be released by heating at the fairly low temperature of 480°.

The logistics of producing 1 million barrels of oil a day are nearly overwhelming. For surface retorting it would be necessary to mine about 2 million tons of shale a day, transport it to retorts, process it, and then dispose of the spent shale in an environmentally acceptable manner in a desertlike atmosphere. Rising oil prices, however, will lead to the conversion of some of these resources to reserves, and production could reach ½ to 1 million barrels a day by 2000.

Two-thirds of all the oil ever found is still in the ground waiting for an economical recovery process. Secondary or tertiary recovery methods involving water pressure, reinjection of natural gas, carbon dioxide and steam, surfactants, and so on provide limited yields. By using such methods, it should be possible to add ½ to 1 million barrels of oil a day to our production by the year 2000.

I estimate a production of 7½ million barrels of petroleum liquids per day in 2000. This is basically a projection of the data in Table 2 and the Hubbert bell-shaped curve, augmented by shale oil and enhanced recovery.

PETROLEUM IMPORTS

Foreign oil resources are much larger than those of the United States, but they too have finite limits. The Project Interdependence report has this to say: "Half of all the oil that has ever been produced has been taken from the earth in the last 10 years. This gives a perspective on the escalating growth in world energy demand. Even in the OPEC countries (Organization of Petroleum Exporting Countries) as in most producing basins of the world, most of the oil has already been found. So great is the accelerating demand for energy that the years of abundant supply of conventional liquid hydrocarbons will be relatively few." The same report states that the world is approximately halfway in its ultimate petroleum exploration.

At the end of 1976, the recoverable world reserves of crude oil amounted to 567 billion barrels, of which 380 billion were in the OPEC countries. Saudi Arabia and Kuwait had a total of 180 billion barrels—six times the reserves of the United States.

World production of petroleum liquids has gone from 24.5 million barrels in 1960 to 45.7 million in 1970 and 55.4 million in 1975. Sixty per cent of the last figure comes from four countries: the United States, Saudi Arabia, Russia, and Iran. It is estimated that world productive capacity will peak in the next 15 years in a range from 65 million to 90 million barrels per day, depending on whether deliberate curtailment is imposed.

There should be sufficient oil in the world to permit imports of 11 million barrels a day in 1985. This could cause a further worsening of our trade balance and further threaten our national security.

My estimate of 8½ million barrels of imported oil a day in 2000 takes account of the expected worldwide peak followed by a decline in production in the 1990's. The United States will experience at least a 25-per-cent decline in availability from 1985 levels as it competes with the rest of the world for available oil.

U.S. NATURAL GAS

Among the fossil fuels, natural gas has the starkest outlook. An insistence that it be sold at a fraction of its replacement cost is resulting in a squandering of the most valuable nonrenewable resource we possess. For the past 10 years we have been using 20 trillion cubic feet (TCF) a year and finding only 10 TCF.

The whole story is told in Fig. 1. The desirable reserve/production ratio of 12 to 1 governs the average rate at which natural gas reservoirs can be drawn down to achieve maximum resource recovery. The United

Figure 1. U.S. natural gas picture: proved reserves; addition and production.

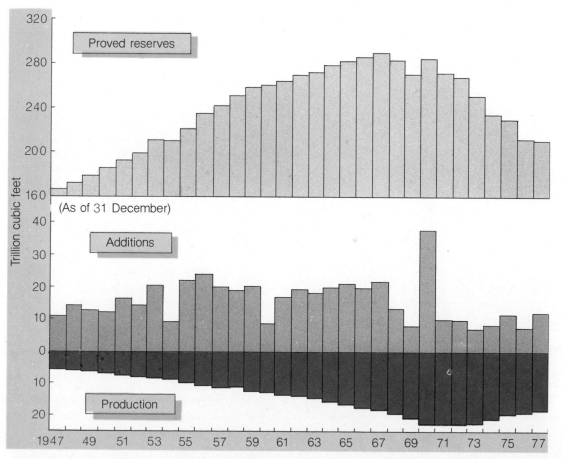

States reached a production peak of about 22 TCF in 1971 to 1973. This declined to about 19 TCF in 1977. Lowered production follows from the fact that proved reserves went through an earlier peak of 290 TCF in the late 1960's and dropped to 209 TCF in 1977 (Table 2). Projecting the proved reserve figures and holding the R/P at 12 gives production figures of 13 TCF in 1985 and less than 5 TCF in 2000.

UNCONVENTIONAL SOURCES FOR NEW GAS

There are three possible sources of additional natural gas: tight sandstones, Devonian shales, and geopressured zones. The tight sandstones of the western basins, ranging from the northern tier states to the Mexican border, have marginal gas supplies at 1978 prices near $2 per thousand cubic feet. These three sources will make a modest contribution to overall supply.

Devonian shales, along with coal beds roughly covering the Appalachian area, contain large quantities of gas. But the dilute nature and low pressure of the gas hinder its large-scale production. The Office of Technology Assessment believes they may furnish 1 TCF per year by 2000.

The Gulf Coast region supposedly has large geopressured areas at great depths containing water with dissolved gas. So far, this is mostly an interesting hypothesis and very small amounts of gas have been produced. The pumping problems for large-scale gas recovery would be formidable.

I estimate 15 TCF in 1985, assuming that decontrolling natural gas prices will add to our reserves by making it profitable to extract additional gas above the projection of

Fig. 1. My estimate of 9 TCF in 2000 includes 5 TCF from conventional sources, 3 TCF from unconventional sources (currently supplying about 1 TCF), and 1 TCF from Prudhoe Bay. With complete deregulation and price levels twice that of today, it is quite possible that unconventional production could be doubled. The estimate of 9 TCF is admittedly conservative. It is based on projections of Table 2 coupled with the fact that in 10 years our finding rate for natural gas has dropped from 560,000 to 220,000 cubic feet of gas per foot of hole drilled.

NATURAL GAS IMPORTS

Natural gas imports will be more limited and expensive than oil imports. The United States has imported 1 TCF a year from Canada for several years. This will probably continue until around 1985, and the amount imported will decline to zero by the early 1990's. Liquid natural gas imports from non-Canadian sources such as North Africa and the Middle East will reach 1 TCF by 1985 and rise for a few more years before declining in the 1990's. Other sources such as Indonesia and especially Mexico will add to these figures.

An estimate of 1 TCF of imported natural gas in 2000 appears generous in light of the predicted decline in reserves and production of world oil and gas starting in the middle 1980's. Use of gas near the source for energy-intensive industries such as the petrochemical and aluminum industries could imperil such imports.

COAL

The United States possesses about 31 per cent of the world's known coal resources.

Donald Sims/FPG

The oil tanker has become a symbol of our reliance on other nations for oil and gas.

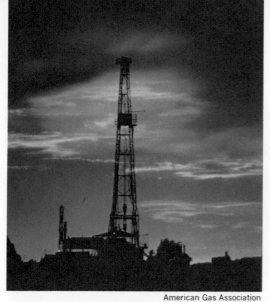

American Gas Association

Our natural gas reserves are disappearing. Tight sandstones and shale will produce some gas.

The Bureau of Mines estimates there are 437 billion tons of coal in deposits that can be mined under present economic conditions with current technology. About two-thirds of this is underground. Recovery of coal in place varies from 40 per cent for some underground methods to more than 90 per cent for strip-mining operations. This results in a fairly certain estimate of more than 250 billion recoverable tons of coal.

No matter what figures are used—the reassuring conclusion is that coal is available in increasing quantity to tide us over the transition to a society demanding less energy. Regardless of the present environmental and sociological constraints on its use, coal is the only abundant domestic energy resource capable of substantial expansion to keep our energy supply growing, albeit slowly.

Recent estimates of future U.S. coal production are shown in Table 4. The United States exported 54 million tons of coal in 1977, and it is assumed that the amount exported will grow to 80 million tons in 1985 and 110 million tons by 2000. This would make available to the United States 19 quads of net coal energy in 1985 and 32 quads in 2000. (A "quad" is a quadrillion, or 10^{15}, Btu's per year.)

These projections would require coal production to increase 50 per cent in the decade 1975 to 1985 and 300 per cent in the period 1975 to 2000. In itself this will require a tremendous effort in capital formation, training of a quarter-million miners, and production of mining and transportation equipment. There will be even larger expenditures in downstream facilities such as transportation and electricity-generating systems to make this coal useful.

NUCLEAR ENERGY

The story of nuclear energy is one of decreasing expectations. In 1973 the Atomic Energy Commission predicted 240 gigawatts (GW) of installed electricity-generating capacity by 1985; by 1977 their forecast had dropped to 163; in 1978 this dropped drastically to 110 GW. Part of the high figure was based on pure optimism. The decrease resulted from continued public opposition to nuclear reactors, rising capital costs, and a decreasing electrical energy growth rate.

In the United States coal is the only abundant and cheaply usable energy resource to maintain our lifestyle and economy until science and technology make other sources available.

DOE

Table 4. United States coal production estimates, 1985 to 2000. Values are millions of tons.

Source	1985	1990	2000
Project Interdependence	940	1225	
National Energy Plan	1050	1250	
Department of Commerce	890		1860
CONAES	995	1250	1700
Project Interdependence Blueprint	1100	1300	

The story of nuclear energy is one of decreasing expectations.

In the second quarter of 1978 nuclear energy was furnishing 48 GW of power, and there was a reasonable expectation that plants under construction would add another 52 GW by 1985, for a total of 100 GW. This results in a forecast of 6 quads in 1985, as shown in Table 1.

In addition to the constraints on the development of commercial nuclear energy, there is a more far-reaching one of limited natural resources. This one may be the most telling constraint of all. The uranium resources of the United States may not support a light-water reactor program more than twice as large as the program for 1985.

Domestic uranium resources in June 1977, estimated by ERDA, are shown in Table 5. Even the Department of Energy questioned the validity of including possible and speculative resources in hard planning data. In normal ore-estimating procedures, the most optimistic analysis would include only the reserves and probable resources. Inclusion of the number of reactors in such data is highly misleading.

The CONAES Supply Panel found markedly lower values. Their consensus was that the reserve figure of 680,000 tons of U_3O_8 might diminish to 450,000 tons of recovered U_3O_8 when mining losses were taken into account. The CONAES best estimate for a total was 1,070,000 tons of reserves and probable resources of U_3O_8—far below the ERDA estimate of 3,370,000 tons of U_3O_8 at $30 a pound.

FEEDING A ONE-GIGAWATT REACTOR

A 1-GW reactor requires 5,500 to 6,000 tons of U_3O_8 over its life-span of 30 years. Therefore, the 100-GW of installed capacity by 1985 will require 550,000 tons of U_3O_8, which is just about the CONAES estimate of today's known reserves. A total of 200 GW by 2000 would require 1,100,000 tons of U_3O_8 or all the known and yet to be discovered economical resources, as seen by CONAES.

Table 5. Domestic uranium resources on 1 June 1977. Values are thousands of tons of U_3O_8. The numbers in parentheses represent the number of 1000-megawatts reactors that can be supported for 30-year operating lifetimes by the amount of uranium in the associated resource category. It is assumed that each reactor consumes approximately 5500 tons of uranium during its lifetime.

Uranium resources	Forward cost category*	
	$30 or less	**$50 or less**
Reserves†	680(125)	840(150)
Potential resources	2690(490)	3330(605)
Probable	1088(190)	1370(250)
Possible	1188(215)	1420(260)
Speculative	484(85)	540(95)
Total	3370(615)	4170(755)

* Forward costs are those yet to be expended, and do not include sunk costs, taxes, profits, or amortization of existing capital equipment, and therefore do not represent prices at which U_3O_8 will be marketed.   † Does not include the 140,000 tons of U_3O_8 estimated to be available as a by-product of phosphate and copper production during the period 1977 to 2000.

The reserves plus the probable categories of the Department of Energy estimates would suffice for about 400 1-GW-reactors. This gives a total estimate for the ultimate U.S. capacity of 200 to 400 GW. The high figure is very optimistic when it is realized that a reactor on the drawing board today depends on uranium yet to be discovered for its fueling.

We have seen that the problems of nuclear energy are low public acceptance, capital costs, past track record, lack of fixed plans for spent fuel processing and waste disposal, cancellations, and primarily ore availability. In light of these problems it would appear that nuclear energy will not exceed 185 GW (11 quads) in the year 2000. Current orders are slightly over 200 GW. World competition for uranium will constrain U.S. imports. Investment enthusiasm would be diminished if a $1-billion plant were dependent on foreign ore sources.

The present political uncertainty and the development costs preclude the breeder reactor from being a factor in energy supply in this century. The cost of a reactor just to test materials going into a breeder reactor rose from an initial $87 million to almost $1 billion in a few years. Materials, engineering, and financing problems continue to plague the development of a demonstration reactor. Yet, from a resource viewpoint, we have no choice but to work on a system that, in effect, would increase our uranium reserves 70 times.

SOLAR ENERGY

The lure of free power from the sun has blinded many people to the economic facts of life. No other part of the energy spectrum generates as much optimism, emotion, and misinformation as this one. However, we are in danger of being carried away with too much spending too rapidly in a narrow area that has unlimited long-range but restricted short-range returns. A fallacy in this area is that because the sun's radiation is free, technology will convert it to a cheap source of inexhaustible energy.

The bright hopes for widespread use of solar energy will not be realized by 2000. Sunlight is a dilute form of energy and is available only part of the time. Therefore, the processes by which it can be put to use are inefficient by our present standards or economics. The most promising immediate use is in passive collectors, which heat water for use directly or for heating buildings.

The use of passive collectors is near the edge of present economics and can be expected to have an impact on the design and construction of every new structure in the coming years. About 22 per cent of U.S. energy consumption is for heating houses, businesses, and water. A rough estimate is that up to 10 per cent of this, or 2 quads, might be supplied by solar in 2000.

OTHER FORMS OF ENERGY

This amount of energy will be passed by biomass energy production. In 1976 and

The hope for widespread uses of solar energy will most likely not be realized by 2000. Sunlight is a dilute form of energy and available only part of the time. It can be changed to electricity but not yet in the amounts we require.

DOE

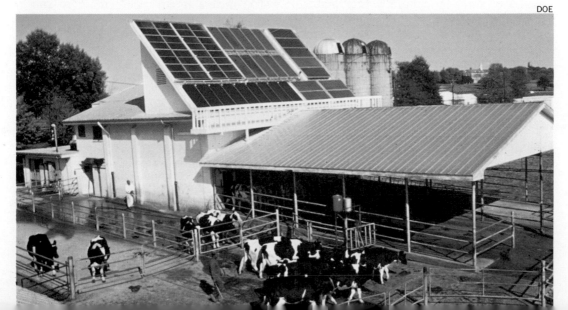

DOE

Energy from the wind will help slightly by 2000, but its future is unpredictable.

1977 the contribution from this area was about 1.6 quads from wood and wood wastes and 0.2 quad from other wastes. (This is unaccountable energy in most forecasts.) The wood-waste contribution is strictly one of derived demand and depends on activity in the pulp and paper industry.

D. A. Tillman has estimated that by the year 2000 the energy available in biomass will be 5.67 quads, consisting of 4 from wood, 0.67 from agricultural wastes, and 1.0 from municipal solid waste. This assigns very minor roles to such items as methanol and energy plantations. All of these estimates appear to be optimistic, in view of probable lower industrial growth rates. Attainment of 3 to 4 quads for the year 2000, about twice the current level, appears to be possible.

Wind, tide, ocean thermal, solar electric, geothermal, and other proposed energy sources do not show promise of delivering more than 1 quad of energy by 2000. They do not fit the economics of our times since the true cost of delivered energy from these sources would be several times today's prices.

This adds up to 6 to 7 quads in 2000, which is higher than most estimates. Project Interdependence estimated about 2 quads in 1990, and the Department of Commerce estimate was 5 quads in 2000. The period 2000 to 2010 should see a marked gain.

HYDROPOWER

It has taken more than 50 years of effort to reach a level of 57 GW of installed generating capacity, which produces 2.7 quads of energy from hydropower. The better sites have been used, and even an accelerated effort (the current Administration has a deceleration policy) will produce only a modest addition. About 14 GW can be installed in existing structures and 8 GW in structures being built. A conservative estimate is that hydropower will produce 3 quads in 1985 and 3.5 quads in 2000.

DISCUSSION

There are seers who indulge in wishful thinking. Their reports are laced with phrases such as "assuming all-out government funding," "pending successful demonstration," "development of necessary technology," and "a determined conservation program." The public and the scientific community must recognize that there is a long gap between speculation and delivery of energy to the consumer. In a speech at Massachusetts Institute of Technology, Frank Press stated:

"We still hear echoes of solutions to the energy problem based on back-of-the-envelope calculations that tell us: that the earth's geothermal energy at an average depth of 6000 meters is equivalent to more energy than we will ever need; that the deuterium in the world's sea water could release through fusion the energy equivalent of 500 Pacific Oceans of petroleum; that the amount of uranium in the world's granitic rock could provide the world's energy at X times the current rate of consumption for thousands of years, or that the sunlight falling on X per cent of the earth's land area could give us the same amount of energy for as long as the sun shines. . . . There are even those who believe that there are still huge supplies of oil and gas available to be tapped, if only the price were right.

Serraillier-Rapho

Dams for hydroelectric power have already taken the best sites; little more can be expected.

Figure 2. Energy growth for 1940 to 2000. Net growth lags far behind the gross growth.

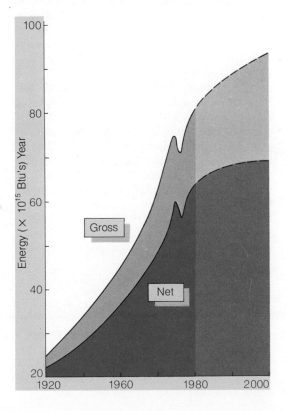

"Such wisdom would seem to indicate there is no energy crisis, merely a few technological problems and restrictions on the free market, between us and an energy millennium. But we know differently, and not only in terms of energy but of material resources, food, water and all our other human needs. There are no ultimate or singular technological fixes, nor is everything available or possible, simply by providing enough incentive."

We will still be locked in to fossil fuels in 2000. By that year an as-yet-undetermined amount of coal will have been converted to supplementary industrial gas, coal liquids, or other refined forms.

Figure 2 portrays energy growth from 1940 to 2000 based on the projections in this article. It portends disaster because energy and the gross national product have gone hand in hand at a growth rate of 3 to 3½ per cent for almost 40 years, and there is little hope of maintaining even 1 per cent energy growth in the 1990's. Although there is no proof that such an energy growth rate must be maintained, it is more than just coincidence that the nations with higher living standards are the largest energy consumers.

So far, I have discussed only gross energy. There is another figure known as net energy, which is the amount delivered to the consumer after conversion losses. For instance, in converting fossil fuels to electricity there is a two-thirds loss of energy. In petroleum refining 11 per cent of the barrel is required for refinery energy. At present, the average net energy is slightly more than 80 per cent of the gross, which means that the consumer received about 63 of 78 gross quads available in 1977.

The trend toward greater use of electricity and coal conversion points to a lowering of the net energy factor to about 75 per cent in 2000. In that case, 95 quads gross in 2000 would be more nearly comparable to 90 quads at 1978 conversion factors. This would have the practical effect of bringing energy growth almost to a halt in the 1990's, as shown in the net energy curve of Fig. 2. We will have an additional 40 million people in the United States by 2000, and just transporting and housing them will use the expected gain in energy.

The American economy in much of the

Larry Fried/Image Bank

period in Fig. 2 was built on oil at $3 a barrel, coal at $4 a ton, and natural gas at $0.16 a thousand cubic feet. In 1978 dollars this translates to a fossil energy price of roughly $0.55 per million Btu's compared to a current weighted figure of $1.70.

The seller's market of the 1990's, when world petroleum and gas production will have passed its peak, will lead to wholesale costs more than double those of today. Some signs are already here: obtaining oil from shale will cost $20 a barrel ($3.45 per million Btu's); coal liquids, $30 to $34 a barrel ($5.17 to $5.86 per million Btu's); and Syngas from coal, $3.50 to $6.50 per million Btu's. Alaskan natural gas will cost $4 to $6 per million Btu's at the border, depending on the final cost of the pipeline, which is now targeted as $10 billion.

The 95-quad estimate could be low by a few quads, or the peak in world oil production could come a few years later. (For example, there could be significantly more Mexican oil than the present reserve figures indicate.) But this would not change the overall picture in the long run. The time for planning and husbanding our natural resources is now, and not after the inexpensive sources have been dissipated.

The necessary expansion of coal utilization and the development of solar sources and the breeder reactor will not happen quickly. Furthermore, there is no guarantee that the latter two will ever produce energy at even what we consider high costs today. And only national planning at a high level can prevent the collapse of our economy built on cheap energy sources.

CONCLUSIONS

The facts point to the inescapable conclusion that exponential growth of energy supply is coming to an end in the United States. Energy and gross national product have risen 3 to 3½ per cent a year since 1940. And a decrease in the energy growth rate to less than 1 per cent a year by 2000 will occasion some fundamental national problems for which we have no precedent. The involuntary conservation brought on by higher prices and decreased supplies will be exceedingly painful for an unprepared American public.

We have sufficient energy resources to supply our basic needs for many decades, but the costs will rise continually. The country still does not understand the problem. Most people want to believe in inexhaustible, cheap gasoline. And in this they have been supported by many unsubstantiated claims.

The time has come to realize that no miracle is imminent, and we must make do with what we have. We will never again have as much oil or gas as we have today, nor will it be as cheap. Nuclear fission energy has been a major disappointment. And nuclear fusion energy is still a long way off. Solar energy will be slow in developing and, contrary to popular opinion, quite expensive. Coal is the only salvation for the next few decades.

In the last analysis, we have entered into a massive experiment to determine what effect energy growth has on economic growth. Or put another way: How much can we slow down the machine and still maintain a democratic, capitalistic form of government? ☐

📖 SELECTED READINGS

"America's energy resources: an overview." *Current History,* May 1978.

"U.S. energy demand and supply" by R. Rycroft. *Current History,* March 1978.

"World oil production" by A. Flower. *Scientific American,* March 1978.

Illustration by Diana Coleman

HOMEMADE HEAT

by Dorothy Behlen

A CHILL night, soft music, good company, and a crackling fire in the fireplace—few scenes are as romantic as this one. But there's nothing romantic about a fire that won't start or one that smokes all night long, or a fire that heats inefficiently or causes a dangerous buildup of brown or black condensate, called creosote, in the pipe or chimney.

BACK TO WOOD

Until a century ago wood was the primary source of energy in the United States. Today one third of the world's population still depends on wood for heating or cooking. The modern U.S. concept of fireplaces and wood-burning stoves is that they are quaint and nice to have but serve no practical purpose. But as the supplies of oil, gas, and coal diminish, people are turning back to wood, not just as a supplemental energy source but in some cases as the primary heating source.

In 1970 Oregon had fewer than 32,000 homes using wood as a primary energy source. In 1978 that figure rose to 75,000 homes, 10 per cent of all households in that state. The New England office of the U.S. Department of Energy reports that by 1985 wood could replace 50 per cent of the No. 2 grade oil used in Maine as fuel. Burlington, Vermont already produces 10 per cent of its electrical power by the use of wood chips and burnable wood wastes. These wood forms are fueling electric generators, and the cost of power in northern Vermont has been reduced from three cents per kilowatt-hour to 2.3 cents per kilowatt-hour.

ENERGY WOOD

To fuel this new trend, the United States is turning to her forests. Luckily, wood is a renewable source of energy, and the sun is the ultimate source of that energy. But no mass cutting need be undertaken and no woodlands wiped out. According to studies done in New England, large amounts of unmerchantable wood (rough and rotting trees) could be used to fuel energy projects. In fact, the removal of this material could increase the productivity of the forest.

Firewood in the form of driftwood is plentiful in certain areas on the coasts of Oregon, Washington, and British Columbia.

EPA-Documerica

According to a report given at the Wood Energy Institute's Wood Heating Seminar held in April 1977, "As a rule of thumb, an acre of unmanaged forest land will produce half a cord of wood per year. But with proper management this could be doubled. A hardwood forest on a good site should be able to produce a cord per acre per year."

A cord is the standard measurement for firewood. It contains 128 cubic feet of wood and when stacked stands eight feet long, four feet high, and four feet wide. Two thirds of the stack is wood, and roughly one-third is air space.

The American Forestry Association has coined the term "energy wood" to describe generally unmerchantable wood good for fuel. It encompasses such wood fibers as low-grade or cull trees, logging wastes, precommercial thinnings, insect or disease-damaged trees not suitable for pulp or lumber, wood from land-clearing operations or from special fuelwood plantations and mill wastes.

"CLEAN" POLLUTION

As the United States turns to increased burning of wood, there may be some initial difficulties with air-pollution standards and the smoke and ash that the burning of wood produces. But the pollution from burning wood is different from that produced by the burning of coal or oil. Wood contains little sulfur—only .01 to .05 per cent, compared to the three per cent from coal or oil. Also, the carbon dioxide released into the atmosphere from the burning of wood is no greater than that released had the wood been allowed to decay on the forest floor.

Use of wood-burning generators may become widespread in the future, but what most homeowners are dealing with are their own fireplaces, wood-burning stoves, and fuel-supply problems.

GOOD AND BAD

Among the advantages of wood are that it is a renewable supply of fuel; it contributes little to air pollution; and it can be burned independent of other energy sources. Among its disadvantages for the home user are that it is heavy and bulky, and requires a great deal of storage space. Also, it requires attention while burning, and poor burning can result in creosote buildup and fire danger.

BUYING WOOD

The most expensive but also the most convenient way to get firewood is to buy it from a dealer already cut, split, and seasoned. Cost for a cord of this firewood can vary from $25 to $175 per cord.

Remember: a full cord is four feet by four feet by eight feet. Other amounts, usually differing in width, are available. An amount, called a run is 16 inches wide, and amounts known as ricks and face cords can have widths varying from 12 to 24 inches. Specify just what kind of cord you want.

Shop around, try different dealers, and get prices on a full cord. Before you go, know what you want to buy—the species of wood, wet or dry, the size, and amount. The more you buy, the cheaper it should be. Buying wood in the off-season (spring, summer, early winter) brings the price down, as does splitting your own logs. Be sure to ask if the price includes stacking.

Make sure you are getting dry wood if that is what you ordered. Green wood is heavier, about two times the weight of dry wood, and if you knock a wet log with another, you'll get a dull thud rather than the sharper, ringing sound of a dry log. Freshly cut logs show a clear growth ring. Dry logs have dark-colored ends and cracks radiating from the center. Don't pay for water.

And don't buy by weight either. A cord can vary in weight according to species; shellbark hickory weighs in at 4,439 pounds per cord, white oak at 3,821 pounds per cord, and white pine at 1,868 pounds per cord.

FELLING A TREE

There are sources of firewood other than dealers, but they all mean more work. You can visit dumps, landfills, and construction sites in search of firewood, or a state or national forest that has a cutting program where you can get a permit and cut your own trees. If you go to a woodlot where you will be felling your own tree, that means even more work as you fell the tree, cut it, split it, and stack it so it can season, or dry out, for six months to a year.

When cutting, consider how much wood you will need for a season. A tree with a 12- to 14-inch base should yield about half a cord of wood, the trunk and branches each supplying a quarter of a cord. This size tree is easy to handle and a good width for splitting. Make sure when cutting that you have a permit, that you're cutting on the right property, and that you clean up your debris.

Felling your own tree can be a formidable chore and should not be undertaken by a novice. The best way to learn to properly fell a tree is to practice with an expert. The best time is in the winter. Cutting then allows plenty of time for the wood to dry before the next season.

In order to fell a tree you need several basic tools: a manual or power saw, an axe, a splitting maul, several wedges, and eye protection. Ear protection is a good idea too when using a power saw. Chainsaws are available in a variety of engine sizes and with a variety of options and safety features. Choose one to fit your own needs. If you are doing the cutting manually, the standard poleax is a good compromise between all the various types of axes. Select one with a handle about as long as your arm from armpit to fingertips. Avoid axes with varnished or painted handles; they can be dangerously slippery.

LIMBING AND LOGGING

Once the tree is down, the limbs and branches must be removed. To limb a tree, stand on the side of the trunk opposite where you want to cut, and swing with the growth grain, working from the base of the tree up. Avoid making overhead swings, and keep your work area free of obstructions.

The next job is to cut and split the logs. For splitting you need a chopping block, a splitting axe, a sledgehammer, a splitting maul, and several wedges.

Georgia Forestry Commission

You can buy your wood in a wood market, or you might have a cord or two delivered to you.

Enclosed metal or ceramic stoves are much more efficient than fireplaces.

STACKING

When all of the wood has been chopped, stack it so it can season. The most effective stack is the log-cabin style, with corners every three feet. Start the pile with two rows of logs end to end and parallel to each other; put layers on top at right angles. The pile may be braced to hold it more securely.

If the wood is not kept in a shed, consider covering it with plastic sheeting to keep it dry. Wood should be aged for at least six months after cutting to reduce the moisture content to roughly 20 per cent. Moisture content is the weight of moisture lost during oven drying, divided by the ovendry weight, not by its original weight. So wood with a moisture content of 100 per cent is not all water, but rather is 50 per cent water and 50 per cent wood. Some species take a full year to dry; oak may take two. But don't store too long. Wood stored too long may rot, and rotting decreases the wood's energy output.

Another important aspect of fuelwood is its density. Ovendry wood of almost every species has the same energy within a few per cent. The major difference is in the weight or density. No common wood type is truly unsuitable as fuelwood.

LAYING A FIRE

Of the two most common wood-burning chambers used in the home, the stove is by far the most efficient. Wood-burning stoves have an efficiency of from 50 to 60 per cent. Fireplaces have an efficiency of only about 10 per cent (low because of the open front).

Some oil burners may have a 65 to 70 per cent efficiency.

The more efficient the burner, the less wood it will use. These wood burners vary in efficiency with heat-output capacity, steadiness and duration of output, tendency to form creosote deposits, safety, durability, and ease of loading and unloading.

Laying a proper fire is important. You need a mixture of hardwoods and softwoods, and if possible some fruit or nut wood thrown in for aroma. But you need to know what you are mixing. Pine, for all its aroma, has only 65 per cent the heat value of a mixed-hardwood fire. Good hardwoods to use are ash, birch, beech, hickory, hard maple, and oak. Conifers have a high resin content and may cause creosote problems, but softwoods do make good kindling and are excellent for starting a fire.

Mixing green and dry wood makes a slow-burning fire. Softwoods burn faster and hotter than hardwood; hardwood burns longer and generates more coals. The denser the wood, the more time it takes to be consumed. The radiant heat of a flame is weaker than that of coals. Since heavier wood is more dense, it will lay down more coals. So the rule is: the heavier or denser the wood, the hotter the fire.

A fireplace can keep one or two rooms comfortably warm even if the thermostat is set very low. In heating an entire house a woodstove is more effective and efficient. The thermostat should be in the same room as the heating source—either the fireplace or the wood-burning stove.

Stack your split wood so that air can flow through the pile easily, thus aiding it to dry as quickly as possible. A cover will keep it from getting wet.

RESIDUE PROBLEMS

Wood ashes are a solid residue from almost complete combustion. They form a perfect base for a fire and catch and store live coals. You can bank a fire, covering it with ashes, and keep coals alive up to 12 hours. Leftover ashes are good for the garden; a cord of firewood can supply 20 pounds of lime, 30 pounds of potash, and half a pound of phosphoric acid.

One of the problems with burning wood is that a dark brown or black condensate with an unpleasant odor is left on the walls of the pipe or chimney. This substance is creosote. "The name creosote is given to a variety of conditions found in a flue pipe and/or chimney when burning other than seasoned hard or softwood under certain conditions," according to John Dunn in his book *Wood Burners Secrets*. The tarlike buildup greatly increases the chance of a chimney fire.

If you must burn green wood, burn it in a small hot fire rather than a big slow fire; slow burning enhances deposition. Creosote buildup depends on the density of smoke, fumes, and the temperature of the surface onto which it is condensing. To minimize condensation, reduce the amount of wood used in each fire and add extra air.

PREVENT FIRES

If you should have a chimney fire, suppress it by limiting the air supply and adding salt and water to the fire. Call the fire department immediately so that the chimney fire does not become a house fire.

Have your chimney and stove or fireplace checked periodically. Keep them clean and look for creosote deposits. In a stovepipe the creosote is likely to be runny and in a more liquid form than the tarlike buildup found in chimneys. This is because the deposition occurred on a cooler surface. Whether in liquid or solid form, the creosote deposits should be removed. Chemical chimney cleaners are available, and a stiff wire brush is good for removing the hardened creosote. A risky but effective tactic is to start a small, controlled chimney fire to burn off the creosote. But the most effective, thorough, and safe cleaning job is done by a professional chimney sweep. With the increase in popularity of woodstoves and fireplaces, this profession is making a comeback.

Fire extinguishers should be handy. Also consider installing smoke detectors. Have escape plans from each room. Every member of the family should know what to do and where to go in case of fire □

SELECTED READINGS

The Woodburner's Encyclopedia, Wood as Energy by Jay Shelton and Andrew W. Shapiro. Vermont Crossroads Press, 1978.

"Wood as fuel," by F. S. Langa. *Popular Science,* February 1978.

Wood Burners Secrets by John E. Dunn. Dunn Publishing, 1978.

"Wood stoves glow warmly again in millions of homes," by J. S. Trefil. *Smithsonian,* October 1978.

"Working Up Firewood." *Country Journal* October 1977.

DEGREE DAYS

FACED with high fuel costs, possible fuel shortages, and unusually severe winters in some areas of the United States and Canada, prudent homeowners are stocking their energy-saving arsenals with every weapon they can muster. These include insulation, storm windows, lowered thermostats, and windbreak plantings. But one tool is generally overlooked—and it is potentially of great value. It is the "heating degree day."

As early as 1915 the fuel industry was searching for improved methods of predicting fuel consumption and thereby of adjusting production and distribution schedules. In 1927 the American Gas Association found that fuel consumption varies directly with the difference in the average daily temperature when it falls below a base temperature of 65° Fahrenheit.

A spokesman for the American Gas Association explains: "The 65-degree reference point is the temperature above which no daytime heating is required to maintain temperatures within the range of human comfort. As the average daily temperature falls below that base temperature, heating requirements and, thus, fuel consumption increase proportionally."

HUMAN COMFORT

But what is the range of human comfort? Dr. Murray Mitchell, a climatologist with the U.S. National Oceanic and Atmospheric Administration's Environmental Data Service, describes it this way:

"Americans feel uncomfortable when daytime house temperatures fall below 70° Fahrenheit. This is a subjective evaluation of comfort, however. If Americans were acclimated to the same standards of comfort as the British, for instance, then the heating degree-day reference point would probably be lowered to 60°, or even 55° Fahrenheit."

In other words, any temperature will serve as the basic heating degree-day reference point, as long as the temperature selected reflects the social habits of the community, geographical area, or nation concerned.

"Because Americans demand higher house temperatures as a standard of comfort, Dr. Mitchell continues, "the basic figure of 65° was arrived at, representing the average of mean daytime temperature of 70° Fahrenheit and a mean nighttime temperature of 60° Fahrenheit. It is the agreed-upon dividing line between where some amount of furnace heat is ordinarily required to provide the average American with a comfortable indoor temperature, and where it is not."

BUT WHAT IS A DEGREE DAY?

A degree day is a measure of the amount of fuel needed to maintain indoor comfort according to typical American standards of comfort. When the average temperature for a given day falls one degree below 65°, that counts as one-degree day. If it falls two degrees below 65°, that counts as two-degree days, ten degrees below 65°, then ten-degree days.

The degree-day concept assumes that the same amount of heating fuel is needed for any combination of cold and duration that add up to the same number of heating degree days. For example, ten days at 64°, five days at 63°, and two days at 60° all equal ten-degree days.

FUEL INDUSTRY USE

Fuel manufacturers use degree-day data to plan production and distribution of supplies. They are aware that fuel requirements vary with population changes, business growth, and community development. Taking degree-day data and all other factors into consideration, they estimate probable fuel consumption in a given geographic area and shunt supplies to that area.

Heating engineers use degree-day data in designing heating and ventilating systems for buildings and in diagnosing architectural reasons for heat loss. The data is also often used in checking consumption and thus the operating efficiency of actual heating installations.

Retail fuel companies are concerned primarily with predicting the needs of their customers. Good service depends on it. By combining the individual's record of fuel consumption with degree-day averages compiled over long periods of time and adjusting that number according to temperatures or degree-day predictions, the retailer can predict a homeowner's needs as much as one month ahead of time. Ever notice how the fuel truck shows up just as the tank is about to run dry?

CONSUMER USE

Consumers can apply the same methods used by manufacturers, engineers, and retailers to estimate their own fuel bills. Consumers do not have to do such complicated figuring, however. Most consumers are concerned with only one household, whereas producers and retailers attempt to predict the needs of diverse architectural types, floorspace, building use, and ventilating systems. Consumers, therefore, have a much simpler system at their fingertips, and by planning well in advance, can stem the consumption that threatens their pocketbooks.

Insulation, storm windows, sealing doors, and humidifiers all produce dramatic reductions in fuel consumption and a real saving in fuel bills. But with the dramatic rise in energy costs, the degree day, as a tool, can also be used to cut these costs still further.

In his book *Climatology: Fundamentals and Applications,* Dr. John R. Mather likens a house to an individual, ". . . producing heat internally through the burning of fuel, and losing it to the cold, outside environment as a result of conduction, convection, and radiation." Obviously then, temperatures below 65° Fahrenheit are not the only factor influencing heating requirements. Variations in fuel consumption occur with overcast or clear skies, windy conditions or calm periods, or combinations of both. But happily, Dr. Mather, after studying the correlations between degree days and fuel consumption and between degree days in combination with various meteorological conditions and fuel consumption, found that correlations with degree days alone were quite significant.

Degree-day data alone can then help the consumer. By computing past fuel consumption in terms of degree days a consumer can form a basis for estimating near-future fuel requirements. And in cases where those requirements are projected to rise dramatically, the consumer can take measures to cut down costs.

The Corning glass house is a model that easily shows where insulation should be installed.

Owens-Corning Fiberglas

GETTING THE DATA

The degree day has proven to be such a reliable fuel-management tool for both business and home that climatologist Mitchell suggests that newspapers, radio, and television should include the number of degree days normal for a given month, a running account of the number of degree days as they accumulate during a month, and the National Weather Service's degree-day forecast in their presentations. Energy-conscious groups have also suggested that fuel retailers include the number of degree days that accumulated during a billing period, thus providing consumers with baseline data on a continuing basis.

BILLS NOT TOO USEFUL

A record of last year's fuel consumption in your home is the key to using the degree day to save fuel—and money. Records are essential.

Most consumers equate their fuel consumption to the size of their fuel bills, attributing high fuel bills to the greed of suppliers, the venality of oil-exporting countries, or honeymoon relationships between power companies and the commissions appointed to monitor rate hikes. Fuel bills in and of themselves are, however, poor indicators of fuel consumption. Most large energy bills reflect combinations of high-fuel costs, inefficient heating systems, and large accumulations of heating degree days. When expressed in dollars and cents, this combination pro-

vides a shaky foundation on which to base consumption figures. Therefore, fuel consumption should be expressed in kilowatt-hours, gallons of oil, or cubic feet of gas. Not in dollars.

COMPUTING YOUR FUEL CONSUMPTION

The first step in computing the fuel consumption baseline for your home is to dig out last year's energy bills and separate them so they are grouped into calendar months. Some of the bills will, of course, include a few days of the preceding or subsequent month, but this slight overlap will not seriously affect your monthly baseline figures as expressed in degree days.

The table on page 166 shows a tabulation of the actual degree days accumulated each month in some major cities in the United States during the winter of 1976–77. Find the number of degree days accumulated during a given month in your area. Then divide the amount of fuel you consumed that month by the number of degree days accumulated that month. Repeat the process for each month. A fuel-consumption baseline expressed in terms of degree days will emerge.

Let's take an example. Say you live in the Washington, D.C. area. According to the table, there were 652 degree days during the month of November 1976 in your area. And your fuel bill for that month tells you that you used 68 gallons of oil that month: 68 divided by 652 equals 0.104. You used 0.10 gallons of oil for each of the 652-degree days.

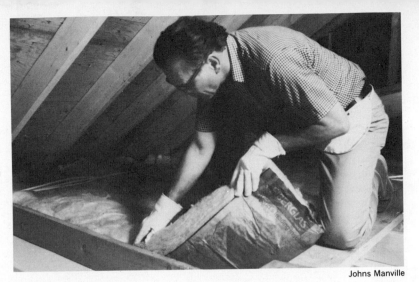

Installing battens, or strips, of insulation is not a difficult job. In an attic they are simply layed between the floor joists before the flooring is put down. For insulating walls, a heavy-duty stapler is required to staple the battens to the uprights.

In January 1977 you used 120 gallons, or approximately 0.09 gallons per each of the 1,221-degree days that month.

In computing the fuel consumption per degree day for all of the other months, you soon find that no matter how cold the weather was, about 0.10 gallons of oil per degree day were used. And because this figure will remain the same—unless you make a drastic change in heating system, such as adding insulation or modifying the furnace—the consumption rate will remain reasonably constant.

In our example, we used oil, but the same relationship can be determined for kilowatt hours of electricity or cubic feet of gas. And because the fuel consumption per heating-day degree is reasonably constant, this figure provides an excellent tool in managing your fuel consumption.

LISTEN TO FORECASTS

The U.S. National Weather Service's National Meteorological Center routinely publishes a chart that estimates whether temperatures are expected to be normal, above normal, or below normal for each geographic area during the subsequent 30 days. The chart is based on an analysis of meteorological observations from a major part of the Northern Hemisphere. Accompanying the chart is a table containing the normal number of heating-degree days each month for each of the major cities and predictions about whether each city will have fewer degree days than normal, more degree days than normal, or just about a normal amount. Armed with all this information, you can act.

USING THE INFORMATION

When the monthly outlook predicts a large increase in heating-degree days—that is, below normal temperatures—you can take steps to limit your fuel use. You can, for example, close off unneeded rooms, especially on the shady side of the house. You can seal off the space between the floor and the bottom of doors to the outside or to closed-off rooms with scatter rugs. You can keep window draperies open on the sunny side of the house during the day and closed at night. You can break out sweaters, extra blankets, quilts. Or, if the fuel bills haven't already depleted your bank account, you can consider taking a vacation in a warm-weather area.

EAT BOILED DINNERS

Another good measure to conserve fuel is to increase the humidity in your house. Dry air increases the evaporation rate of moisture from the skin. When combined with reduced thermostat settings, the low humidity makes rooms feel chilly—cooler than they really are.

Higher humidities can be maintained—and therefore greater comfort with lower thermostat settings—by placing pans of water on radiators or near heating vents and by boiling meats and vegetables without lids on the pots. In fact, this last device is excellent because it adds moisture to the room's atmosphere. Baking, broiling, and other forms of cooking that do not involve boiling tend to dry the air, lower the humidity, and make rooms feel uncomfortable even though actual room temperature is higher. So—when it's cold outside, eat boiled dinners □

MONTHLY HEATING DEGREE DAYS 1976–1977

	OCT.	NOV.	DEC.	JAN.	FEB.	MAR.
ALBANY, N.Y.	564	895	1345	1526	1127	764
ALBUQUERQUE, N. MEX.	367	726	985	1084	674	669
AMARILLO, TEX.	464	790	846	1075	592	464
ANCHORAGE, ALASKA	972	1028	1294	1017	900	1241
ASHEVILLE, N.C.	411	706	884	1239	768	437
ATLANTA, GA.	277	618	775	1099	640	300
AUGUSTA, GA.	191	490	635	906	565	206
BILLINGS, MONT.	582	885	1032	1452	759	896
BIRMINGHAM, ALA.	241	581	732	1026	566	252
BISMARCK, N. DAK.	726	1152	1550	2062	1147	956
BOISE, IDAHO	434	720	1097	1418	868	772
BOSTON, MASS.	393	688	1109	1290	956	623
BUFFALO, N.Y.	573	921	1328	1579	1123	755
BURLINGTON, VT.	654	954	1505	1667	1240	831
CHARLESTON, S.C.	159	418	501	811	516	186
CHARLESTON, W. VA.	475	814	1047	1482	888	482
CHARLOTTE, N.C.	299	621	799	1075	636	306
CHICAGO, ILL.	520	960	1388	1695	1058	622
CINCINNATI, OHIO	498	894	1157	1640	980	571
CLEVELAND, OHIO	519	932	1287	1672	1113	689
COLUMBIA, MO.	487	898	1169	1587	891	548
COLUMBUS, OHIO	538	925	1241	1659	1071	601
DENVER, COLO.	509	759	907	1105	749	771
DES MOINES, IOWA	527	964	1333	1700	981	624
DETROIT, MICH.	540	938	1341	1609	1100	721
DULUTH, MINN.	860	1280	1875	2017	1334	1033
EL PASO, TEX.	215	601	709	623	492	469
EUREKA, CALIF.	324	375	535	537	400	577
FAIRBANKS, ALASKA	1267	1466	—	1709	1574	—
FARGO, N. DAK.	788	1247	1797	2119	1327	1015
FORT WAYNE, IND.	540	938	1322	1723	1107	662
FRESNO, CALIF.	63	375	566	636	313	386
GRAND RAPIDS, MICH.	591	999	1415	1616	1177	765
GREEN BAY, WIS.	667	1152	1730	1918	1254	861
HARTFORD, CONN.	467	794	1242	1429	1035	684
RICHMOND, VA.	332	660	869	1227	680	366
ROANOKE, VA.	452	735	945	1275	786	385
SALT LAKE CITY, UTAH	432	689	1096	1175	813	839
SAN ANTONIO, TEX.	160	382	461	643	337	144
SAN DIEGO, CALIF.	0	39	129	143	94	224
SAN FRANCISCO, CALIF.	127	231	494	549	326	432
SAULT STE MARIE, MICH.	728	1121	1706	1818	1420	1119
SEATTLE, WASH.	307	510	625	786	451	591
SHREVEPORT, LA.	199	471	574	815	399	188
SPOKANE, WASH.	556	871	1089	1324	832	824
SPRINGFIELD, ILL.	497	905	1260	1693	989	543
SPRINGFIELD, MO.	415	797	975	1421	752	476
ST. LOUIS, MO.	456	832	1125	1541	839	471
SYRACUSE, N.Y.	556	869	1303	1520	1086	767
TALLAHASSEE, FLA.	100	359	456	649	434	166
TAMPA, FLA.	11	122	208	422	214	28
TOLEDO, OHIO	596	976	1393	1708	1135	718
TUCSON, ARIZ.	45	112	390	435	221	287
WASHINGTON, D.C.	306	652	907	1221	729	389
WICHITA, KANS.	404	793	966	1253	646	456

Illustration by Vala Kondo

The Environmental Protection Agency has proposed the ''bubble concept'' of air pollution. The EPA would regulate only the total pollution coming from the ''bubble,'' instead of from individual factories.

THE ENVIRONMENT

THE ENVIRONMENT
REVIEW OF THE YEAR

The year 1978 was a "mixed bag" for the environmental movement: some accomplishments and some setbacks, with many issues still unresolved. In the United States, the 95th Congress adjourned with a spotty record. The lawmakers did approve some legislation safeguarding wildlife and wilderness and forestry areas and did enact the National Climate Program Act, which set up a special office to foster the collection, evaluation, and dissemination of climatological data. The House of Representatives also sustained President Carter's veto of a water-projects bill that would have had unsound environmental impacts. On the other hand, Congress weakened the Endangered Species Act, passed a rangelands bill with a public-grazing feature that many fear will hasten soil impoverishment, and failed to enact legislation that would have set aside certain parts of Alaska for wilderness and wildlife preservation.

A dark cloud—jobs and money *vs.* the environment—seemed to hang over many environmental issues during the year. Accusations were made and reechoed that regulations and laws enacted to protect human health and the environment generally are inflationary, cost jobs, and inhibit industrial growth. Although some segments of some industries have made these claims before, the issue heated up during the year. Environmentalists counter the inflation argument by pointing out the benefits and cost savings of improved health and a clean environment. They also point out that although some jobs are lost due to the closing of industrial plants for environmental or health reasons, more often than not these plants were obsolete and due to be closed for inefficient operation and that, in fact, pollution control has actually produced more jobs than it has lost. Environmentalists also point out that pollution control inhibits only unwise and unsafe industrial growth while stimulating responsible industrial innovation. Nonetheless, the spectre of inflation and increased taxes is leading some politicians to consider a roll back on environmental, health, and conservation programs. Interestingly, public opinion does not support the contention that environmental spending is too high. In fact, a national survey, conducted in the summer of 1978 at a time when interest in tax relief was running high, showed that "given a choice between paying higher prices to protect the environment or paying lower prices and having more air and water pollution, protecting the environment is chosen by a six to two margin."

Toxic Substances. 1978 was the year of the Love Canal disaster. Residents of a region near a canal used 30 years ago as a dump for waste chemicals were found to have an abnormally high rate of miscarriages, birth defects, epilepsy, liver abnormalities, skin rashes, and a host of other medical problems. This disaster—probably the environmental story of the year—focused attention on the toxic-waste disposal problem, a problem many scientists fear may become worse before solutions are found. ■ The discovery of very high levels of mercury in the Meadowlands in New Jersey in late 1978 and early 1979 kept the issue in public focus. For a discussion of the Love Canal disaster and related problems, see the article "Love Canal, U.S.A." on page 185.

Judy Greenberg/NYC-EPA

Many new automobiles are not meeting pollution-control standards, and more and more states are now requiring yearly inspection of auto emissions.

High levels of mercury contamination have been discovered in the Hackensack Meadowlands, which has become the home of a giant sports complex.

UPI

Testing chemicals for their effects on humans and on the environment in general continued to be a difficult and expensive problem during the year. The U.S. Environmental Protection Agency (EPA) missed its November 1, 1978 deadline for publishing guidelines and regulations for the testing of chemicals before they are allowed on the market. The reasons for the failure were the complexity of the task, bureaucratic inertia, and the vociferous opposition of some companies that must perform the tests.

Air Pollution. Although health standards were violated for ozone, carbon monoxide, sulfur dioxide, oxides of nitrogen, and total suspended particles in the air in each of 43 U.S. cities monitored by the President's Council on Environmental Quality (CEQ), both the severity and frequency of violations showed a downward trend. Major industrial polluters include steel mills, with less than one half of the major producers in compliance with air-quality standards or on schedule to reach compliance; major copper, lead, and zinc smelters with fewer than one half in compliance; and large coal and oil-fired power plants with about one fourth not in compliance. ■ The EPA estimates that one fourth of the automobiles that came off the assembly line in 1978 did not meet government pollution-control standards and that as many as 80 per cent of the cars on the road do not meet the standards. Yet cars today produce 60 to 80 percent less pollution than did 1960's models.

Water Pollution. Oxygen depletion, excessive suspended materials, oil and grease, heavy metals, and toxic chemicals continue to degrade our water quality. As monitoring and measuring devices become more sophisticated, we continue to discover the presence in the water of minute but harmful quantities of chemicals. The CEQ states that industrial discharges still affect 72 per cent of U.S. water basins, but the pollution from non-point sources such as runoff from agricultural and forestry lands, from construction sites, and from streets and highways is still probably the most serious and widespread problem.

Drinking water supplies have also been found to contain known and suspected carcinogenic (cancer-causing) compounds as well as other substances that can produce a wide range of toxic effects. However, the EPA and individual states and local governments were not able during 1978 to agree on the need, cost, and benefits of installing activated-charcoal-filtration systems to remove these harmful substances.

Pesticides. Faced with the increasing awareness of possible hazards of pesticide use, rising pesticide costs, and growing resistance of pests to pesticides, farmers in increasing numbers are using a new pest-control program. Called integrated-pest management, or IPM, the program relies on a balanced control strategy using planting and cultivating practices, natural predators to pests, genetic manipulation to make plants more resistant to and less attractive to pests, crop rotation, repellants, attractants, traps and other means for making the agroecosystem inhospitable to pests. Chemical pesticides are used only when needed to prevent significant economic damage and then only under carefully controlled dosage and timing conditions. For a more complete discussion, see the article "Biological Control of Insects" on page 85.

Solid Wastes. During 1978 Connecticut, Delaware, and Iowa joined four other states in having legislation requiring a deposit on beverage containers. These "bottle bills" are aimed at reducing roadside litter.

Louis S. Clapper

Judy Greenberg/NYC-EPA

A record of a suspended-particle sampling device is being monitored by a technician of the New York City Department of Air Resources.

The Integrated Pest Program, whose goal is to reduce the use of pesticides, is studying the effectiveness of wasps in controlling the alfalfa weevil.

USDA

This 300-meter-high smoke stack spews acid-forming smoke to the winds and neighboring lands.

ACID RAIN UPDATE

by James Gannon

THE birds are back in Hyde Park. That's the good news from London. And its implications go far beyond a mere ornithological happening. The birds are a sign of London's triumph over its deadly smog, smog that killed 4,000 people in a terrifying four-day inversion in 1952. During a thermal inversion, a layer of warm air traps a layer of cold air near the ground. There are no strong air movements and the cold air becomes laden with pollutants. The birds are a good sign because air that can support birds can also support people—and can help to sweep away the dark memories of the world's worst air-pollution disaster.

From Scandinavia the news is bad. Acid rain and snow, a form of pollution unknown before the 1950's, have caused massive fish kills in the past two decades. Ironically, England is a major contributor to the Scandinavian pollution. The birds live in Hyde Park while the fish die across the North Sea in southern Norway and Sweden.

At first glance the trade-off may seem favorable to some observers—even when you count the fish kills in Canada and the United States from North American sources of pollution. No massive toll of human beings of the magnitude that London experienced in 1952 can be remotely linked to acid rain. Not even one human death.

SERIOUS THREAT

But to a leading U.S. authority on acid rain, Gene E. Likens of Cornell University in New York, the fish kills are a "disaster." Likens, an ecologist, is alarmed by what he perceives to be a threat to the natural-life systems.

"One has to be very seriously concerned about this kind of environmental insult on the natural systems," he warned. "There is a limit to the stress they can withstand. The forests and the lands are life-support systems. Without those life-support systems to cleanse the air and the water, to provide food for us to eat, our health is just as much in jeopardy as if something is affecting us directly."

These are some of the signs of stress that concern Likens:

• Acid rain has wiped out commercial salmon fishing in much of southern Norway and Sweden and has destroyed sport fishing in parts of Scandinavia, eastern Canada, and the northeastern United States.

• Acidic lakes and streams do not simply kill fish. They also eliminate other forms of aquatic life, including microscopic forms, and affect larger animals that feed on fish.

• In waters where the fish are not all gone the acidity contributes to higher levels of mercury contamination in the most desirable game fish, and the contamination can be passed on to humans.

• Acid rain may leach nutrients from soils and impede the growth of vegetation, including plants for food and timber; it has done so, at least, in laboratory experiments.

TIPPING THE BALANCE

Acids do occur naturally in the atmosphere and have always fallen to earth in precipitation. But nature's marvelous system of checks and balances has neutralized them—until recently. Now the excessive loading of man-made acids on vulnerable land surfaces tips the balance against nature. These acids usually originate in the burning of fossil fuel for electricity and other uses and in the smelting of ores for industry.

But they don't start out as acids. Sulfur and nitrogen oxides are emitted from the stacks and are oxidized into the dehydrate of sulfuric and nitric acids. Water in the atmosphere does the rest, turning the substances into sulfuric acid and nitric acid. Measurements by Likens at the Hubbard Brook Experimental Forest in the White Mountains of New Hampshire confirm the acid components of rainfall to be as much as 65 per cent sulfuric and 25 to 30 per cent nitric. Other monitoring stations have detected these acids in slightly lesser amounts. Both are highly corrosive acids. They can destroy plant and animal cells—destroy life—on contact.

The rainfall is still almost all water. The acids occur only in minute amounts, never in

Gene Likens

Collecting rain in Norway in a study of acid pollution from upwind countries.

strengths greater than the acids in the human stomach for example, but often—and here's the danger—in strengths greater than the acids in nature.

TRAVEL FAR AND WIDE

Acid rain can fall anywhere downwind of urban or industrial pollution. In cities it is simply one more element undermining air quality. It contributes to the corrosion of buildings and monuments and has subtle, long-term effects on human health.

But acid rain is more remarkable for transferring what has been an urban problem to the countryside. You do not expect to find the effects of air pollution in the Canadian wilderness or among the stately mountains of New England and northern New York—but you find them there now.

The pollutants come from near and far, and they travel in all directions without respect for international boundaries. A report prepared for the Canadian-American International Joint Commission shows that Lake Superior receives significant acid fallout from points as distant and scattered as St. Louis, Missouri; Cincinnati, Ohio; Pittsburgh, Pennsylvania; and Sudbury, Ontario.

The U.S. cities are all more than 800 kilometers away from Lake Superior. If conditions are favorable, the pollutants can go

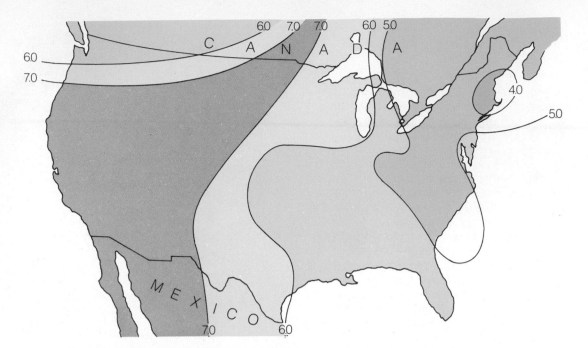

"Acid rain" has been operationally defined as rain (or snow) at pH values of less than 5.6. The first data for pH precipitation for the entire mainland United States was collected between 1964 and 1966. Acidification is intensifying in New England, and it is also generally spreading towards the Southwest.

that far in a day. They've been known to stay airborne for weeks, although Swedish scientists estimate that the average time aloft is two to four days. There's time, in any case, for pollution originating in North America to travel across thousands of kilometers of ocean to Sweden and Norway. It is not uncommon for acid rain that falls in Scandinavia to be "made in the U.S.A."

That's a bit startling, but it is consistent with what is known about the global transport of atomic and volcanic clouds. Tall industrial smokestacks built in the past quarter century to help clean up cities like London may account, in large measure, for long-range pollution.

GROWING PROBLEM

The danger is growing. Acid rain is so widespread today that the average rainfall in the eastern half of the United States and southeastern Canada—regions of heavy industrialization—is about twenty-five times more acidic than it would be if the rain contained acids from natural sources only. As recently as the late 1960's, that sort of acid intensity could be found only in the northeastern states and around the nickel mining

center of Sudbury, Ontario. But today there are more than 200 tall stacks in the United States alone, rising some 125 to 375 meters above power plants and smelters and spewing the sulfur and nitrogen compounds into the atmosphere. The acid-rain problem could become even more acute with construction of many more coal-generating facilities.

AND NOW COAL

The Carter Administration's energy plan for the United States, given to the U.S. Congress in the fall of 1977, calls for an 80 per cent increase in the use of coal for electrical generation. Under a 1977 clean-air law, the best available air-cleaning technology will be required for new coal-fueled generating plants. Right now that means "scrubbers," devices that can trap 90 per cent or more of the sulfur dioxide from a plant's flue gas. But a huge environmental battle has been brewing about the pollution controls needed to check the emissions from all these new plants. Meanwhile, there are no significant standards for nitrogen oxides—a huge part of the acid-rain problem—and little research on technology to control that pollutant.

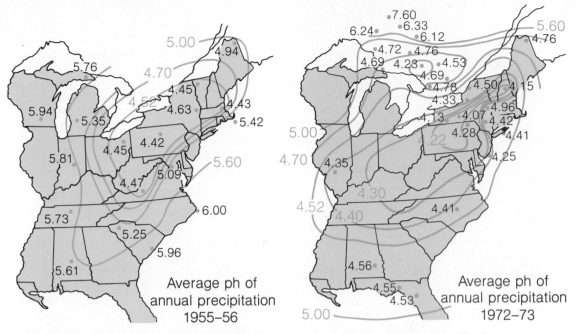

The symbol pH expresses degree of acidity and alkalinity on a scale from 0 (totally acid) to 14 (totally alkaline). The midpoint, pH7, is neutral—neither acid nor alkaline. Each shift of one unit downward means a tenfold increase in acidity. The normal pH for rain is 5.7.

MOST VULNERABLE AREAS

The danger from acid rain is greatest in lakes situated in hard-rock areas where the rocks and soils are low in neutralizing chemicals, such as the calcium carbonate in limestone. All soils have these buffering chemicals to a greater or lesser degree, but many underlying rock formations do not. Rocks made of granite or lava, for example, simply do not react with acid. So acid rain can gradually, almost imperceptibly, disrupt the surface ecosystem.

The entire Canadian Shield, made of Precambrian rock formed 600,000,000 to 4,000,000,000 years ago, is vulnerable. It stretches from the Arctic Circle across most of Greenland and the eastern half of Canada into the United Staes below the Great Lakes. Combined with other pockets of hard-rock formations, it adds up to some 260,000,000 hectares of acid-sensitive land surface in North America.

Lakes in hard-rock areas, said Likens, are the "clearest and most dramatic example" of acid-rain's effects. An acid lake is a death trap for fish. For the newly spawned, should they survive the spawning, it is almost instant death. For older fish, more resistant to the toxic effects of acid, it is a slow and tortured death. However it comes, death is inevitable, for fish and for other forms of life, as the acid level slowly rises.

THE POOR FISH

Richard J. Beamish, a scientist for Environment Canada, has probably spent as much time as anyone in North America studying what acid does to fish. For many years Beamish used the acidic lakes around Sudbury, site of the world's richest nickel deposit and the world's largest single point source of sulfur pollution, as his "laboratory."

Beamish and his colleagues found that adult fish became emaciated, stunted, and deformed under acid stress. Far more destructive for the fish populations, however, was the failure of female reproduction. "Eggs were developed," Beamish discovered, "but they were never passed from the ovary and fertilized." It made the premature deaths of adult fish a moot point, he theorized, because without the recruitment of new fish into the population, the species is inexorably reduced to zero.

That happened to one species after another in lakes that Beamish studied. Some prime game fish, smallmouth bass and walleye, were the first to be eliminated. Northern pike and lake trout were next. Even the most acid-tolerant fish, such as lake herring, perch, and rock bass, eventually succumbed to the lethal acid.

Beamish estimated—"conservatively"— that two hundred to four hundred lakes within an 80-kilometer radius of the Sudbury smelters have few or no fish remaining. Since the construction of the world's tallest smokestack at Sudbury, acid pollution has reached out to Ontario's popular resort areas of Muskoka and Haliburton where the lakes are on the edge of disaster. Pollution made in the United States will undoubtedly share blame for the disaster.

In Scandinavia the problem is even more severe. Lars N. Overrein, director of a comprehensive Norwegian study of acid rain, reported that the "majority of inland waters . . . have completely lost their fish populations." That runs to "thousands of localities."

In New York's Adirondack Mountains the fish are gone from about a hundred lakes and streams at higher elevations, and ecologists fear the loss of "buffering capacity," and ultimately the loss of fish, in the lower valleys.

The spring snow melt, when acid levels can rise precipitously from winter-snow accumulations, is the most dangerous time for fish. A late winter thaw in 1975 killed trout by the thousands along the Tovdal River in southern Norway.

SOIL SUFFERS TOO

It's difficult to tell what happens to forests and agriculture from acid rain. So many hazards—fungus, insects, bacteria, drought, and other manmade pollutants—can afflict a plant in the natural environment that sulfur dioxide and acid rain are merely additions to a long list. But scientists have clearly shown in laboratory experiments that simulated acid rain, with other negative influences factored out, is destructive to vegetation.

Acid rain has a capacity to "leach out" nutrients that can affect the environment in different ways. Falling directly on plants, it causes leaf lesions, reducing the area for photosynthesis and limiting growth. In the soil it impedes root development.

Swedish scientists predict that acid rain

This smoke-scrubbing system in Chalmette, Louisiana, includes 125 "bag houses" (at bottom center and right). They replace the smokestack. This company is no longer polluting the air, and downwind areas will have less acid rain.

UPI

C. A. Peterson/Rapho Guillumette

Alesund, Norway's largest fishing harbor on its west coast, receives acid rain.

will leach calcium from their nutrient-poor woodland soil, leading to a reduction of forest growth of 10 to 15 per cent by the year 2000. If true, that will be a serious economic loss.

METAL LEACHING

The leaching property of acid rain also draws out heavy metals from the earth and atmosphere. Metals such as aluminum, mercury, lead, cadmium, tin, beryllium, and nickel are drawn into the freshwater systems and held in solution by the acid.

One result of this is even more fish death. Carl L. Schofield, a Cornell University biologist, discovered this from observations in the Adirondacks. In this case, aluminum combined with nitric acid is the deadly weapon. "We found," said Schofield, "that the aluminum in this situation is very toxic to fish. You get a much higher toxicity for a given level of [acid] than you would otherwise."

Mercury is one of the better known threats to human health. The human race has had quite enough experience with it to hold it in respectful fear. It kills or maims in any form. As methyl mercury, one of its organic forms, it accumulates in fish—a major source of protein for humans.

The worst outbreak of mercury poisoning from fish occurred in the 1950's in Mina-mata, Japan. More than one hundred people died, and several hundred others suffered symptoms ranging from mild tingling of the skin to reduced motor coordination, mental retardation, and impaired sight and hearing—effects that are permanent because mercury causes irreversible damage to the cells of the central-nervous system.

That tragedy came from the industrial discharge of mercury waste into Minamata Bay, where it contaminated fish and shellfish eaten by local people. Industrial dumping of mercury into Ontario's English/Wabigoon River system and other freshwaters of North America has brought fear and consternation closer to home. This is true especially among native populations who make a steady diet of fish.

ACID CONNECTION

The "acid connection" to mercury contamination of fish is more subtle. It occurs in the same waters vulnerable to human-generated acid pollution: softwater lakes situated on hard-rock strata. Mercury enters the water in a metallic inorganic state, then falls to the bottom sediment where it is converted by microorganisms to an organic form, methyl mercury. Methyl mercury passes easily into the food chain and, because it does not pass easily out, accumulates in fish regularly eaten by humans.

THE ENVIRONMENT 175

George Hunter

Around Sudbury, Ontario, the clear lakes are dead—killed by acid.

A Swedish scientist, Arne Jernelov, has established a clear correlation between the acid levels of lakes and mercury levels of fish. He has found that the more acid added to a lake's water, the more mercury in its fish, up to the point where the acid kills the fish outright.

Many, many people go fishing in Ontario each year. Increasingly, they are fishing in troubled waters. According to Ontario's Ministry of the Environment, 336 lakes and rivers, excluding the Great Lakes, have at least some contaminated fish at levels officially considered unsafe for prolonged human consumption. The highest levels were found in the predator game fish, walleye, and northern pike.

But sport fishermen have no cause for alarm, according to John M. Wood, director of the University of Minnesota's Freshwater Biological Institute. "They don't get sufficient exposure to mercury-contaminated fish to really seriously be threatened. You have to have a diet of fish for a significant period of time to be affected."

Like the diet of the Canadian Indians, for example. They eat fish almost daily in the

summer, and they have cause for alarm. In a recent survey by Health and Welfare Canada, 42 per cent of 764 Indians tested in Quebec, Ontario, and the Canadian Northwest Territories had abnormally elevated mercury levels, which is poisonous, in their blood or in their hair.

DEAD LAKES

Fish are not the only casualties. Around Sudbury, Ontario, the acid lakes look pure because they are so clear. But that's an illusion. They are clear because, for all practical purposes, they are dead. The organic life has been virtually erased: fish, amphibians, invertebrates—all gone. Plankton, gone. Algae, bacteria, severely reduced or chemically altered. The entire aquatic ecosystem snuffed out—perhaps irrevocably. Beamish said at least one hundred lakes near Sudbury fit this description, and he doubts that they can be restored. When the chain of life is broken like this, the higher animals are also affected. Fish-eating birds and vertebrates have left the lakes.

Parts of the barren landscape around Sudbury will resemble what the earth will be like when life is gone entirely. The vegetation has been destroyed by the direct fallout of sulfur dioxide. But 40 kilometers away the land looks normal—at least to the untrained eye.

NATURE OR INDUSTRY

It's the Indians trying to live close to nature who are most immediately threatened by acid rain. The threat is magnified at the tiny Ojibway Village on Lac La Croix by the prospect of an 800-megawatt power plant close to home.

The Indians there shun welfare and are trying to live off the wilderness, fishing, hunting, and trapping. Their only outside source of income comes from guiding U.S. fishermen in the summer, and they pick up a few extra dollars from the declining number of beaver pelts they gather in winter. The thought of acid rain has them virtually paralyzed with fear.

Lac La Croix, a softwater lake on the hard-rock Canadian Shield, rests directly on the Canadian-American border. The Indians live on the Canadian side. Ontario Hydro, a government corporation, plans to build a large coal-fired power plant near Atikokan, only 80 kilometers from the village. That's why the Indians are afraid.

"The economic base of our reservation is the surrounding environment. If that's destroyed, our whole economic base is destroyed," says Chief Jourdain.

ENTER POLITICS

Chief Jourdain could as easily fear for the present. Things are bad enough without the power plant, just from the effects of a small nearby smelter combined with long-range pollution. It is hard to see how the new power plant can do other than make things worse. The utility has said it will use low-sulfur coal and claims it will not need expensive scrubbers for sulfur removal.

In contrast to the United States, scrubbers are not in use in Canada, but pressure for them may increase with an acceleration in Canadian development. Environmentalists, fearing for the entire surrounding wilderness, have turned the issue into an international controversy that has reached diplomatic levels.

EPA-Documerica

Sulfur and nitrogen oxides from smoke become sulfuric and nitric acid in the moist air.

WHY NOT BEFORE?

Because the use of fossil fuels is the source of the acid-rain problem, the obvious solution is to stop using fossil fuels. As utopian as that may sound, that solution is not only plausible, it is inevitable. Fossil fuel reserves will be exhausted, according to some current estimates, in about 200 years.

While we bend to the task of finding alternative sources of energy, it matters how we use the remaining fossil fuels. The speed and magnitude of our fossil-fuel consumption, for example, and whether we extract the sulfur or trap the nitrogen from power-plant emissions can all have an effect. And it matters how fast we find safe alternatives. Because we have no choice about finding alternatives, why not act sooner rather than later, to save what's left of the wilderness and to safeguard our health? □

SELECTED READINGS

"Aluminum pollution caused by acid rain kills fish in Adirondacks lakes." *Bioscience,* July 1978.

"Forecast: poisonous rain; acid rain" by A. Rosenfeld. *Saturday Review,* September 2, 1978.

"The sulfur we breathe" by J. W. Sawyer. *Environment,* March 1978.

The manatee inhabits warm-coastal water, feeding on seaweed and fresh-water plants.

WHAT HAPPENED TO THE ENDANGERED SPECIES?

by Philip Shabecoff

THE Endangered Species Act itself may be endangered. Recent developments in which the protection of endangered species is in conflict with the construction of public works have culminated in the fight over the eight-centimeter snail darter and the completion of the multimillion-dollar Tellico Dam in Tennessee, which will destroy the fish's only habitat. Some members of the U.S. Congress have proposed changes in the endangered-species law, which would enable specific projects to proceed even if certain species become extinct in the process.

LOUSEWORTS AND DARTERS

The Furbish lousewort, despite its unprepossessing name, is not without a certain modest charm when it first emerges in the springtime along the steeply sloping banks of the St. John River in Maine. Its leaves are delicate and fernlike, its stem is slender and, in due season, it diffidently puts forth two or three pale yellow blossoms. By the time the boreal forest of northern Maine has donned its brilliant autumn foliage, however, the lousewort has turned into a brown, blowzy, utterly inelegant growth. Its leaves are curled and brittle, its stalk is withered, and its seed pod, gaping and empty, droops like a tired slattern. Standing among clumps of vivid red fireweed, the aging lousewort is all but invisible.

Yet this little weed created a furor in the spring of 1977 when it was reported that the plant might block construction of two massive dams planned for a $700,000,000 hydro-electric project bigger than the Aswan Dam in Egypt. Widely believed to be extinct, the little-known lousewort was spotted growing in the path of the proposed Dickey-Lincoln power project in the summer of 1976. Because it is in danger, the lousewort has been placed on the Endangered Species List maintained by the Fish and Wildlife Service of the U.S. Department of the Interior. Long before the discovery, however, construction of the dams had been under attack by environmentalists for other reasons.

A similar situation occurred with the snail darter. After local conservationists in February 1976 brought a lawsuit to halt further work on the Tellico Dam on the Little Tennessee River, the river was found to be the "critical habitat" of the snail darter. Conservationists found that the eight-centimeter fish, an endangered species, lived in the last 60 kilometers of clear, free-flowing water on the Little Tennessee River. It cannot live in the still water that would be created by the dam impoundment.

Because of the growing concern that some obscure species of life may block multimillion-dollar projects, Congress has been studying proposed revisions for the Endangered Species Act of 1973 that sponsors say would make the act "more flexible." The act, which restricts only projects involving the U.S. Federal Government, was set up to prevent the elimination of species, subspecies, and population segments of plants and animals. Some of the proposed changes would enable some projects to proceed even if certain species are made extinct in the process.

POLITICAL SCAPEGOAT

Environmentalists have regarded the 1973 act as a first line of defense for the growing number of animals and plants facing extinction. In the course of safeguarding the life of these species, however, conservationists have come up against unexpected dilemmas. The Furbish lousewort is a case in point. It was seen for the first time in 30 years in 1976, when Dr. Charles D. Richards, a botanist from the University of Maine who was working on an environmental-impact statement for the U.S. Corps of Engineers,

came across a clump of the weed along a stretch of the St. John river bank. The Corps of Engineers has long had plans to construct a pair of dams on the St. John. The Dickey-Lincoln hydroelectric project would flood much of the river valley and, in so doing, destroy one-half of the 800 louseworts on the river banks.

To those fighting the Dickey-Lincoln project, the plight of the Furbish lousewort poses a particularly sticky problem. While they are against any deliberate attempt to extinguish a species, they recognize that the weed is being turned into something of a political scapegoat by proponents of the dam. "The lousewort is actually damaging to our efforts to save the river because people think it is ridiculous that a weed should hold up a project costing millions of dollars," said Wayne Cobb, former assistant director of the nonprofit Natural Resources Council of Maine, which is leading the battle to save the St. John from drowning.

"There are a lot of good reasons for not building those dams," said Mr. Cobb. He explained that the dams would destroy one of the last wild rivers in the eastern United States and eliminate many kilometers of some of the best white-water canoeing anywhere. It would submerge some 35,000 hec-

The controversy over the snail darter (above) has held up construction of the Tellico Dam.

BIRDS AND FISH VS. HIGHWAYS AND DAMS

The primary cause of extinction of plants and animals is the alteration or destruction of their habitats. Protection of the endangered species shown here has led or may lead to blockage of major Federal projects.

HIGGIN'S EYE PEARLY MUSSEL

PEREGRINE FALCON

BROWN PELICAN

GRAY BAT

EL SEGUNDO BLUE BUTTERFLY

RED-COCKADED WOODPECKER

| Dam | Space Shuttle | Highway | River Channeli-zation | Bomb Testing | Airport | Power Plant | Timber Manage-ment |

tares of valuable timberland while supplying virtually no power to impoverished northern Maine because most of the electricity that would be generated by the proposed power plant is destined for the Boston area.

"If you look at the energy crisis and the economics of the dam," says E. Lee Rogers, attorney for the council, "you realize Dickey-Lincoln is not the right answer— there really are better alternatives. For in-stance, estimates are that the dam would eventually cost $1,000,000,000. A study by the Audubon Society shows that if you were to take the money and insulate the buildings in New England, you'd have a much greater energy savings."

It appears now that if the dam is blocked, it will not be by the Furbish louse-wort. Keith M. Schreiner, manager of the endangered-species program for the Fish and

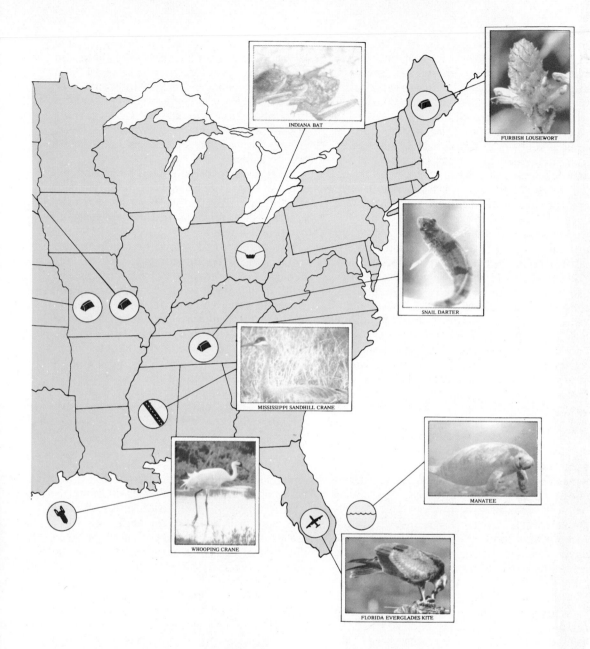

INDIANA BAT

FURBISH LOUSEWORT

SNAIL DARTER

MISSISSIPPI SANDHILL CRANE

MANATEE

WHOOPING CRANE

FLORIDA EVERGLADES KITE

Wildlife Service, feels that a number of ways might be found to resolve the issue, after consultation with the Army Corps of Engineers. He says: "It's possible you could establish a population upstream from the impounded area. Or you could arrange for the full protection of the Furbish lousewort populations that already exist below the dam as well as in Canada." These solutions seem easy and practical.

IMPASSE

It is the case of the Tellico Dam and the snail darter that has officials stymied. Attempts at transplanting several hundred fish into another river have been made and, according to the Tennessee Valley Authority, have thus far been successful. But transplanting an animal population is simply not as easy as transplanting a plant population. "One of the hardest things in wildlife management is to establish a viable breeding population of animals in a new habitat," says Mr. Schreiner. "For every 100 attempts, there are 95 failures." He adds that it takes years before a population can be considered successfully established.

Without a compromise, matters quickly came to a head. The protest by Congressmen from Tennessee and other supporters of the dam led to Senate subcommittee hearings on the Endangered Species Act amendments, and the case of the Tellico Dam vs. the snail darter is also before the Supreme Court.

Partisans of the dam argue that it would provide flood control, recreational and industrial development, and more power. They also assert that it would be ridiculous not to use a dam that is already almost entirely completed at a cost of $117,000,000. Defenders of the snail darter, on the other hand, are making a strong case that the dam is a "pork-barrel" scheme that would benefit relatively few people. They also argue that the Little Tennessee River should be saved as the last free-flowing portion of the abundantly dammed Tennessee River system.

MANY COMPROMISES

At the Senate subcommittee hearing, witnesses for the Carter Administration, which backs a strong endangered species law, pointed out that hundreds of conflicts between construction projects and endangered species have been resolved through compromise solutions and only three cases have gone to court. One concerned the Meramec Park Dam in Missouri and the Indiana bat. The Fish and Wildlife Service indicated that the dam would jeopardize the bat's existence, but a U.S. District Court ruled in favor of the completion of the dam, saying that the entire species was not jeopardized.

Nevertheless, many Congressmen continue to feel that the Endangered Species Act is in need of revision, and several amendments have been proposed. The one considered to have the best chance of enactment is sponsored by Senator John Culver, Democrat of Iowa and chairman of the subcommittee that held the hearings, and Senator Howard H. Baker of Tennessee, the Republican Senate leader. The amendment would create an interagency review board of high-level-Government officials who could permit a Federal project to destroy a species of life if the project benefits "clearly outweigh" the value of the species. Senator Culver explains that this action will stave off other, more drastic amendments that would seriously cripple the Endangered Species Act. Not everyone agrees.

"It is just not necessary to amend the act," says Mr. Schreiner of the Fish and Wildlife Service. "Tellico Dam has been the only absolute impasse. In other cases, some compromise has been worked out." He and others who testified before the subcommittee worry that, if the amendment is passed, the Federal Government will be placed in the position of having to consciously extinguish a harmless species. Michael Bean of the Environmental Defense Fund, who called the 1973 act "a determined attempt to keep the concept of the biblical ark afloat," commented: "Along the way, it is true that a lot of species have fallen off the ark. Some have been unwittingly crowded off by man himself, but never before has any species been intentionally thrown overboard."

ABOARD THE ARK

In 1973 there were 418 species listed as endangered. Today, there are 662 life forms being protected and another 2,000 being reviewed for possible inclusion on the list. As each species is added to the endangered list, the prospects increase for conflict between the right of plant or animal to exist and the demands made by humans on the land and its resources.

A Federal dredging operation was halted to protect the critical habitat of the Higgin's eye pearly mussel.

The El Segundo blue butterfly, which lives in only a few square meters that happen to be at the end of the runway of the Los Angeles airport, is blocking expansion of the airport.

A biological opinion given in early 1977 indicated that the Columbia Dam in Tennessee would jeopardize the existence of various endangered mussels and snails. Local representatives and senators have introduced legislation to exempt the dam from the Endangered Species Act.

U.S. Fish & Wildlife Service

Whooping cranes breed in the Wood Buffalo Park in Canada and hibernate in the Aranas Wildlife Refuge on the coast of Texas.

Federal officials denied a permit to the Florida Power and Light Company to build a nuclear power plant in an undeveloped 4,000-hectare coastal site in southern Dade County, near Miami. The power plant was to occupy a hundred or so hectares, with the rest of the land kept wild, but that tract was in the critical habitat of the manatee, an endangered species of aquatic mammal. The irony in this case is that the power company will probably have to sell the land, and the most likely buyer would be a real-estate developer who, unaffected by the endangered-species law, could drain the area for private housing. In the view of many conservationists, the Endangered Species Act is not strong enough in that it restricts only projects in which the Federal Government is involved.

SPEEDED UP EXTINCTION

Extinction has been a common fate for almost all species that have appeared on earth. Sooner or later, even the most powerful, dominant forms, such as dinosaurs, pass from the scene. But in modern times, human activity has speeded up the pace at which species vanish at an alarming rate. In prehistoric times, it is believed, one species became extinct every 10,000 years. Around the year 1600, the rate was about one every thousand years. Now, estimates of the extinction rate range from one a year to 20 a year, although the latter figure is regarded as high. One environmentalist figures there are now 1,000,000 species, subspecies, and general populations in trouble. "A lot of them will be extinct before we know they exist," he says.

The culprits in this acceleration of "unnatural extinction" are people. Hunting, particularly commercial hunting, is one way in which humans have wiped out species. Far more frightening is the rapidly increasing toxification of the earth by industrial society. The Eastern peregrine falcon was wiped out by the pesticide DDT, which made the bird's eggs too fragile to hatch. As more and more poison seeps into the air, the land, the lakes, streams, rivers, and oceans, the number of endangered species will swell rapidly.

PEOPLE AND BULLDOZERS

But by far the most devastating impact on wild animals and plants comes from the destruction of their natural habitats by human activity. As forests are leveled, wetlands drained, water tables lowered, and natural ecosystems paved over for roads, dams, shopping centers, and suburbs, the elbow room and nutrients required by a broad range of species are rapidly diminishing.

"The primary cause of extinction is not bad hunters shooting defenseless animals," says Fish and Wildlife's Keith Schreiner. "It is the change and destruction of habitat. People's ability to change the earth has increased 20-fold over the past 50 years with the use of bulldozers and cranes and other earth-moving equipment. If enough people care, we can slow the process. But common sense tells me the future is bleak."

So bleak is the picture, in fact, that the bulldozer and not the atomic bomb may turn out to be the most destructive invention of the twentieth century. The protection of critical habitats is the most publicized aspect of the work of the Fish and Wildlife Service, in large part because of the brawl between the snail darter and the Tellico Dam. Sometimes the federal government acquires land to give a species room to exist. Several years ago, for example, it bought land in the Florida keys to provide living space for the vanishing key deer. More recently, the U.S. Federal Highway Administration agreed to buy some 800 hectares around the site of a proposed highway interchange, and turn them over to the Fish and Wildlife Service, thus preserving the critical habitat of the Mississippi sandhill crane.

Perhaps the most famous effort to save

Jeff Foott

The endangered brown pelican dives into the water for its prey, whereas white pelicans do not.

an endangered species involves the whooping crane, a stately wading bird with a haunting cry. Hunted for its beautiful feathers, the bird had all but vanished by the early 1940's, with only about 15 left in the wild. Careful nurturing by the wildlife's research center on the Patuxent River in Maryland, and in other such centers, kept the species going. In 1978 there were about 100 whoopers alive and the species has moved a few steps back from the edge of extinction. Nine areas in seven states have been set aside as critical habitats. And 12 whooper eggs placed in sandhill-crane nests at Grays Lake National Wildlife Refuge in Idaho hatched.

VALUABLE "WORTHLESS" CREATURES

Arguments for the effort and cost of protecting species are often couched in esthetic or ethical terms such as the beauty of diversity or the arrogance of people in assuming that the earth was created solely for their benefit. "There is probably nothing more criminal than destroying a life form," says Mr. Schreiner. "You are not talking about a single life but an entire species!"

One problem that is viewed with growing seriousness is the reduction of the earth's aggregate gene pool with the passing of each species. By allowing plants and animals to pass out of existence, it is argued, we may be losing things of incalculable and irreplaceable value to people, if we only knew it. Who knew the value of bread mold 50 years ago? But the discovery of penicillin has saved countless lives.

Other discoveries—such as the use of the blood of horseshoe crabs as a detector of toxins in intravenous fluids, or the chemical in a plant that was used to develop birth-control pills—suggest that "worthless" creatures and weeds may be very valuable indeed. "We don't actually know that the Furbish lousewort is not useful," says botanist Charles Richards when asked why the little weed should be saved. "Perhaps it could be used as a part of a gene pool for breeding. Perhaps it might have some medicinal value we haven't discovered yet."

EARLY WARNING SYSTEM

Increasingly, scientists and environmentalists are coming to the conclusion that the destruction of species is directly related to the viability of the human race itself. The disappearing life forms are likened to the canaries that coal miners used to carry down into the shafts before the advent of the safety lamp. If the canary died, it was an indication that poison coal gas was in the vicinity and that the miners were in grave danger.

Today, the endangered species are an early-warning system indicating that the human habitat is becoming dangerous. Dr. George Woodwell, director of the Ecosystems Center at the Marine Biology Laboratory in Woods Hole, Massachusetts, finds the loss of species "very frightening" and says that "it has a direct bearing on and cannot be separated from a larger problem—the biotic impoverishment of the earth, which is reducing the capacity of the environment to produce services. It is one of the great issues of our time, right up there with nuclear proliferation, the stability of government, and health care. The ultimate resource is the biota—there is no other. And we are destroying it."

Environmentalists say they are accused of being alarmists. "But when you think of the tropical forests being destroyed," said Mr. Schreiner, "when you see the rampant stream pollution, the soils full of pesticides, animals poisoned to the point where they can't reproduce, well, you've got to believe we are putting ourselves out of business. And that may not be far away."

So ask not for whom the Furbish lousewort lives. It lives for you □

📖 SELECTED READINGS

"Endangered species law reviewed" by C. Holden. *Science,* June 16, 1978.

"Wild species vs man: the last struggle for survival" by E. Eckholm. *Living Wilderness,* July 1978.

An infrared photo of the filled-in Love Canal (center), once a dump for drums of chemicals.

LOVE CANAL, U.S.A.

by Michael H. Brown

IN the years since Rachel Carson's *Silent Spring,* a great national concern has arisen over air and water pollution. It now appears that pollution seeping into the earth itself has gone largely unnoticed. And it may in some cases be far more dangerous as a direct cause of cancer and other severe human illnesses. "Toxic chemical waste," says John E. Moss, former chairman of the U.S. House of Representatives Subcommittee on Oversight and Investigations, "may be the sleeping giant of the decade." Not until the nightmare of the Love Canal unfolded in Niagara County, New York, in the summer of 1978 did people become aware of the vast dangers of ground pollution. But the problem since then seems only to be worsening.

Each year, several hundred new chemical compounds are added to the 70,000 that already exist in the United States, and the wastes from their production—over 40,000,-000,000 kilograms a year—are often placed in makeshift underground storage sites. U.S. federal officials now suspect that more than 800 such sites have the potential of becoming as dangerous as those at the Love Canal and some are probably already severely hazard-ous to unsuspecting neighbors. The problem is how to find them and how to pay the enormous costs of cleaning them up before more tragedy results. So far, Federal, state, and local governments have been, for the most part, reluctant to face the issue.

WHAT HAPPENED AT LOVE CANAL

Sometime in the 1940's the Hooker Chemical Company, which is now a subsidiary of Occidental Petroleum, found an abandoned canal near Niagara Falls, and began dumping countless hundreds of large waste-filled drums there. In 1953, the canal was filled in and sold to the city for an elementary school and playground (the purchase price was a token $1), and modest single-family dwellings were built nearby. There were signs of trouble now and then—occasional collapses of earth where drums had rotted through, and skin rashes in children or dogs that romped on the field—but they were given little thought until the spring of 1978. By then, many of the homes were deteriorating rapidly and were found to be infiltrated by highly toxic chemicals that had percolated into the basements.

Fifteen miles from Charleston, West Virginia, Union Carbide maintains a well-regulated landfill for hazardous wastes from its petrochemical plant. The closed cabin and air tank protect the dozer driver from pollutants.

The New York State Health Department investigated the area and discovered startling health problems: a disproportionately high rate of birth defects, miscarriages, epilepsy, liver abnormalities, sores, rectal bleeding, headaches—not to mention undiscovered but possible latent illnesses. In August 1978, President Carter declared a federal emergency. With that, the state began evacuating residents from the neighborhood along the Love Canal. Two hundred homes were boarded up, the school was closed, and the nation got a glimpse of what New York Senator Daniel Patrick Moynihan called "a peculiarly primitive poisoning of the atmosphere by a firm."

NOT UNIQUE

But it was clearly not so peculiar. Since then, new dumping grounds have been reported in several precarious places. Under a ball field near another elementary school in Niagara Falls health officials have found a landfill containing many of the same compounds as those found in the Love Canal area. It was discovered because the ball field swelled and contracted like a bowl of gelatin when heavy equipment moved across it.

Officials have discovered, too, that Hooker disposed of nearly four times the amount of chemicals present in the Love Canal not too far west of the city's municipal water-treatment facility, and residues have been tracked inside water-intake pipelines. Across town, near Niagara University, another large Hooker landfill contains such killers as Mirex, C-56, and lindane—essentially chemicals that were used in the manufacture of pest killers and plastics. This area has been found to be fouling a neighboring stream, Bloody Run Creek, which flows past drinking-water wells. About 80,000 tons of toxic waste are said to have been dumped there over the years.

Still worse, as the company recently acknowledged, it buried up to 3,700 tons of trichlorophenol waste, which contains one of the world's most deadly chemicals, dioxin, at various sites in Niagara County between 1947 and 1972. Investigators immediately sought to determine whether dioxin had seeped out and, indeed, the substance was identified in small quantities in samples taken from the periphery of the Love Canal, an indication that it may have begun to migrate. There are now believed to be an estimated 64 kilograms of dioxin in the canal site—and as much as 900 kilograms buried elsewhere in the county.

The Love Canal is above the city's public water-supply intake on the Niagara River but nearly one-half of a kilometer away; the other sites are closer, but downstream of the intake. However, the Niagara River flows into Lake Ontario, which Syracuse, Rochester, Toronto, and several other communities make use of for water supply. Although health officials regard the dioxin discovery as alarming, they do not yet consider it a direct health threat because it is not known to have come into contact with humans or to have leached into water supplies. Academic chemists point out, however, that as little as 85 grams of dioxin are enough to kill more than 1,000,000 people. It was dioxin, 1 to 5 kilograms of it, which was dispersed in Seveso, Italy, after an explosion at a trichlorophenol plant: dead animals littered the streets, hundreds of people were treated for severe skin lesions, and some 400 hectares had to be evacuated.

Lowell, Massachusetts, has a problem with the remains of a defunct chemical company.

In January 1979, New York State health officials began to examine and conduct studies of residents and workers in the area because of the dioxin concentrations. One local physician there expressed concern over an apparently high rate of respiratory ailments, and union officials say that workers in industries alongside the landfill are suffering from emphysema, cancer, and skin rashes. Cats have lost fur and teeth after playing near Bloody Run.

IN FACT—HUNDREDS

So far, there are at least 15 dumps in Niagara County alone that have been discovered to contain toxic chemicals. But no one in the county, or anywhere else in the country, is sure exactly where underground dumpsites are. Of the thousands of covered pits suspected of containing toxic wastes in the United States, the U.S. Environmental Protection Agency (E.P.A.) says it is a fair estimate that as many as 838 are, or could become, serious health hazards. But the machinery to carry out the kind of monitoring and inspecting now being done in Niagara County does not generally exist elsewhere. And the E.P.A., internal memorandums reveal, has not been eager to set it up because of the extraordinary expense and political problems that would present themselves.

In at least one known case there are symptoms disturbingly similar. Just 120 meters from a residential area in Elkton, Maryland, is a disposal area that, according to E.P.A. files, was used both by the Galaxy Chemical Company and by a suspected, unidentified midnight hauler who dumped wastes. Residents have complained of sore throats, respiratory problems, and headaches, all reminiscent of the early days of trouble at the Love Canal. So far, however, there is no evidence of direct human contact with leachate, as occurred at Niagara Falls; nor have residents demanded evacuation.

In Rehoboth, Massachusetts, some 750 cubic meters of resins left over from a solvent redistilling process were recently ordered removed from a dumpsite that the owner had placed within 3 meters of his own house. In Lowell, Massachusetts, some 15,000 drums and 43 tanks of assorted toxic wastes are at present being removed from a site within 200 meters of homes, while chemicals leaking from the drums are appearing in sewers and a nearby river.

The U.S. Comptroller General, at the request of Congress, has mapped out stretches through much of the eastern United States, Texas, Louisiana, and parts of Oregon, Washington, and California as regions with the greatest potential for trouble.

LONG IGNORED PROBLEM

The tendency not to connect health problems with ground pollution has certainly been widespread. Before the summer of 1978, ground pollution was never a major concern in Niagara Falls, either. Because that city is relatively small and has a cheap source of hydroelectricity for chemical firms, most of its people have lived their whole lives on top of or near the hidden strains and goo of industrial pollution. Children near the chemical dumpsites often played with phosphorescent rocks. Dirt on the old canal turned white, yellow, red, blue, and black. Cesspools of caustic sludge gushed from several locations. But these manifestations were viewed more as a matter of esthetics than as a health problem.

But indiscriminate dumping, dumping whatever wherever, has been a national way of life. Though U.S. manufacturers of plastics, pesticides, herbicides, and other products that produce huge amounts of toxic wastes are now beginning to deposit them in centralized landfill sites—which may insure a closer inspection—the common practice has been to dispose of residues and forget

In Seveso, Italy, a chemical plant exploded, sending a toxic defoliant gas into the air, which caused skin rashes, internal disorders, and birth defects.

Francois Lochon, Gamma-Liaison

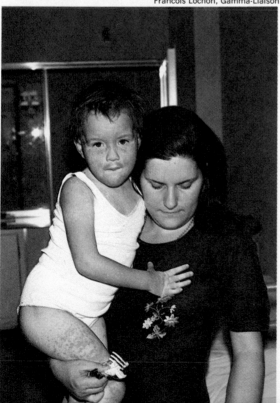

about them. This has been true of private individuals as well, from independent haulers to local farmers.

CONTAMINATED CATTLE

Farmlands, because they make for nicely isolated dumping grounds, have posed special problems. In 1974, a 258,000-hectare pastureland around Darrow and Geismar, Louisiana, was found to be contaminated with hexachlorobenzene (HCB). HCB, produced by wastes dumped into pits, is a by-product of the manufacture of carbon tetrachloride and perchloroethylene. It is known to cause liver deterioration, convulsions, and death.

During a routine sampling of beef fat by the U.S. Department of Agriculture 1.5 parts per million of HCB was tracked in the meat of a steer from the Darrow region. Further samplings showed that cattle were carrying the same toxin. Soil and vegetation were likewise tainted.

The dumps were covered with plastic and dirt, and 30,000 cattle were ordered destroyed. The cattle were fed special diets instead of being slaughtered, however, and moved away from the area. Their toxin levels receded to an "acceptable" point, and only 27 were deemed unmarketable and killed. No one can be sure how many cattle, grazing near dumpsites elsewhere, have made it to the dinner table undetected.

Several years ago in Perham, Minnesota, 11 persons suffered arsenic poisoning from grasshopper bait that had leached into the soil. Those struck with contamination worked for a building contractor who drilled a well six meters from where bait had been buried by a farmer 30 years before. Severe neuropathy cost one of the employees the use of his legs for six months.

MUCH ILLEGAL ACTIVITY

Much of past dumping has been plainly illegal. New Jersey, one of the most industrialized states in the United States and one whose cancer rate has been found to be substantially higher than the national average, has been a favorite spot for midnight haulers, or "scavengers." Companies pay midnight haulers to cart off wastes and unload them in swamps, sewers, pits, or abandoned wells to

For decades parts of the Hackensack Meadowlands, New Jersey, were used as dumps for anything. It now bleeds poisonous liquids into its many drainage channels.

avoid paying for disposal at approved sites. In Coventry, Rhode Island, officials found an illegal and highly toxic dump on a pig farm. It contained one suspected cancer-causing agent, carbon tetrachloride, and another compound that will ignite at 22° Celsius.

More blatant violators have been known simply to loosen tank-truck valves and get rid of contaminants along roadways in the dark of night. The owner of a New York company that reprocesses electrical transformers is currently on trial on charges of deliberately spilling out polychlorinated biphenyls (PCB's) from his truck onto 430 kilometers of a highway in North Carolina.

THREAT TO DRINKING WATER

Ground pollution's greatest threat is to the national drinking supply. More than 100,000,000 people in the United States depend upon ground water as the major source of life's most vital fluid. Springs and wells, as opposed to rivers and lakes fed by running streams, are the main drinking reservoirs in 32 states. Florida's population, for example, is 91 per cent dependent on ground water. Pouring tons of chemicals into the earth can be comparable, in an indirect way, to disposing of poisonous wastes upstream from a municipal river intake.

Chemical landfills never lie dormant. When water penetrates buried wastes, it removes soluble components from the wastes, producing a grossly polluted liquid leachate that extends out from the dump. Therein resides the danger. Leaching can continue, at any given site, for more than 100 years, pick-ing up dangerous, stable materials and spreading them around a surprisingly large area. E.P.A.'s Office of Solid Waste has guessed that the average landfill site, about seven hectares in size, produces over 17,000,000 liters of leachate a year if there are 25 centimeters of rainfall.

In the spring of 1978 the Comptroller General reported that nearly 4,000,000,000 liters of ground water had been polluted near an Islip, Long Island, New York, landfill. A contaminated aquifer spoiled some drinking-water wells, which had to be sealed off and the homes connected to another source. In humid regions, where rainfall exceeds evaporation, the problem is most acute: the more water in the ground, the more leaching occurs.

In the early 1970's the Union Carbide Corporation contracted with an independent hauler to remove an unknown number of drums from its Bound Brook, New Jersey, facility. Inside the drums were wash solvents and residues from organic chemical and plastics manufacture. Instead of going to the Dover Township landfill, much of the waste was dumped on a former chicken farm in the Pleasant Plains section of Dover. The owners had leased the farm to some one else who took the drums. When the unknowing owners began to smell pungent odors emanating from the property, they investigated the land and found thousands of containers, both buried and strewn about the surface. Additional drums were discovered in a wooded area near the Winding River, some six kilometers away.

Above, a landfill area for hazardous wastes, in Cranston, Rhode Island. No one knows when, if ever, poisonous chemicals will seep into the water table.

The drums were hauled away under court order, but the damage had been done. Sufficient quantities of chemicals had already entered the environment, and early in 1974 residents of the area began tasting and smelling strange things in their water. Dover's Board of Health, in emergency action, passed an ordinance forbidding the use of 148 wells and ordering that they be permanently sealed. Although there were no documented cases of illness as a result, it is difficult to determine how many residents had consumed potentially harmful substances before the odors were noted. Equally difficult is determining where and how far the leachate traveled.

The U.S. federal governmment itself has been the cause of serious ground-water contamination. Careless storage at the Rocky Mountain Arsenal, formerly an Army production center for chemical-warfare agents, led to the contamination of nearly 8,000 hectars of shallow aquifer near Denver and, in turn, to the abandonment of 64 wells used for drinking water and irrigation. Waterfowl in the area died, and poisoned soil turned sugar beets and pasture grasses a sickly yellow. An estimated $78,000,000 will be needed to complete the proposed cleanup, but there is no way of recovering the chemicals that have already escaped. One irrigation well that shows traces of contamination is less than two kilometers south of the city of Brighton's public well field.

LAW TO PROTECT US

In 1976, President Ford signed into law the Resource Conservation and Recovery Act. It may become an important piece of legislation, if the E.P.A. decides to implement it. This new law provides for a hazardous-waste regulatory program, control of open dumping, an inventory of disposal sites, and grants and programs for communities to set up solid-waste management systems. The passage of that law was provoked by the fact that toxic-waste disposal not only has gone unwatched, but is indeed increasing at an alarming rate. The chief reason for the increase is, paradoxically, the imposition of air and water pollution regulations that have stepped up the practice of burying materials in the ground. Issuance of new disposal regulations was supposed to have been made within 18 months of the President's signature, but the E.P.A. predicts that they will not be ready before 1980.

BUT . . .

Spurred by the Love Canal crisis, Representative Moss's House subcommittee met in the fall of 1978 to determine what was happening to the law. It was a discouraging hearing. Hugh B. Kaufman, an E.P.A. official assigned to look for landfill problems, told the Congressmen that the agency's policy has been to avoid finding such situations. "There were no guidelines in this memorandum [on landfills] for the regional office to alert the public to the potential dangers," Kaufman testified. "In fact, the memo further instructed the regions not to find new problem sites because they might be required to provide this information to Congress and the public." On July 16, 1978, according to Mr. Kaufman, Steffen Plehn, head of E.P.A.'s Office of Solid Waste, told him to stop looking for imminent hazards. Mr. Plehn admitted that Mr. Plehn admitted that Mr. Kaufman's statement was essentially true, but the reason, he said, was that jurisdiction for such matters was being defined under the agency's enforcement division while his unit was culling a "data base." The problem, according to Mr. Plehn, was bureaucratic.

As long ago as April 20, 1978, and more than three months before officials recognized the Love Canal as an emergency, Mr. Kaufman wrote John P. Lehman, E.P.A.'s Hazardous Waste Management Division director, and said it was "imperative" that dumpsites across the country be cleaned up immediately. "We are receiving reports that, for the most part, the state of hazardous-waste management in the U.S. is as bad or worse than it was when Congress passed [the Resource Conservation and Recovery Act]," Mr. Kaufman wrote, "I recommend that we shift our policy emphasis and not close our eyes to the fact that hazaradous-waste facilities located in many states are presenting hazards to the public." Neither E.P.A. officials nor regional offices paid much attention to that advice. When Mr. Lehman warned E.P.A.'s regional office for Ohio that a chemical facility in Akron might be an "imminent hazard" (it appeared to be leaking chemicals into drinking wells), the office sent back a pointed note reprimanding him for "loosely"

UPI

With landfill areas saturated with poisonous chemicals, neighboring home owners express their concern.

using the term "imminent hazard" and stating that the region's Air and Hazardous Material Division did "not intend to send any person from this office out to inspect the facility at this time." At about the same time, Mr. Plehn wrote Mr. Lehman a memorandum suggesting that he "put a hold on all imminent-hazard efforts."

But the agency cannot be held as the sole culprit. Its large volume of responsibilities—from car emissions to microwaves—is an awesome task. And it often gets little help from state, county, and city agencies. The Niagara County health department and the city government did not consider the Love Canal situation an emergency, for example, and, in fact, played down the problem, and the New York State Department of Environmental Conservation did little in the way of investigation. Not until the state Department of Health stepped in was the matter regarded as urgent.

Drilling in Love Canal to learn about soil and water conditions, where long-buried chemicals are seeping to the surface.

NO TOTALLY SAFE SYSTEM

Much of the randomness with which chemical companies have chosen their dumping grounds over the years will no doubt continue until the Resource Conservation and Recovery Act is implemented. Even then the problem will not go away. There is simply no such thing as a totally secure, self-contained landfill, a fact even those in the business admit. "There is no proof a landfill, 100 years from now, won't leach," says Paul Chenard, president of SCA Chemical Waste Services Inc. He says disposal methods have been improved. Pits can be lined with a special plastic. Waste-disposal firms can excavate on clay-based soil, compact the ground, install standpipes to pump out leachate, and slope the final cover to minimize rain infiltration. But the state of the art is new and no one issues guarantees.

AND THE INNOCENT SUFFER

An E.P.A. memorandum has listed more than 32,254 storage, treatment and disposal sites, both on and off industrial premises, as existing in the United States. In an earlier breakdown, California ranked first, with 2,985; Pennsylvania, New York, Ohio, and Texas were not far behind. Those statistics, officials emphasize, refer only to known sites. And even at the known sites the quality of the treatment is questionable. One estimate is that less than 7 per cent of the more than 40,000,000,000 kilograms of chemical waste generated each year receives proper disposal.

After working in Niagara Falls for several months, Dr. David Axelrod, New York State Health Commissioner, says the overall problems of improper disposal and treatment "are incredibly immense." The Hooker Company, which says that it did not know the possible dangers and was simply disposing of wastes as everyone else did, is already faced with claims against it in excess of $2,-000,000,000, and citizens' demands upon the state are only just beginning. New discoveries of dioxin are prompting new demonstrations, new arrests of demonstrators, and new requests for evacuation and relocation. Patricia Pino, whose home in Niagara Falls is now unmarketable, was one of those arrested. "We request a reprieve from death row," she telegraphed Gov. Hugh Carey. "We are innocent of any crime." Her two children have liver abnormalities, and she has learned that she herself has cancer □

SELECTED READINGS

"EPA and toxic substances law," by J. Walsh. *Science*, November 10, 1978.

"Laboratory chemicals may come under costly OSHA restrictions," by A. J. Smith. *Science*, Nov. 3, 1978.

"Regulation of the chemical industry," by P. H. Abelson. *Science*, Nov. 3, 1978.

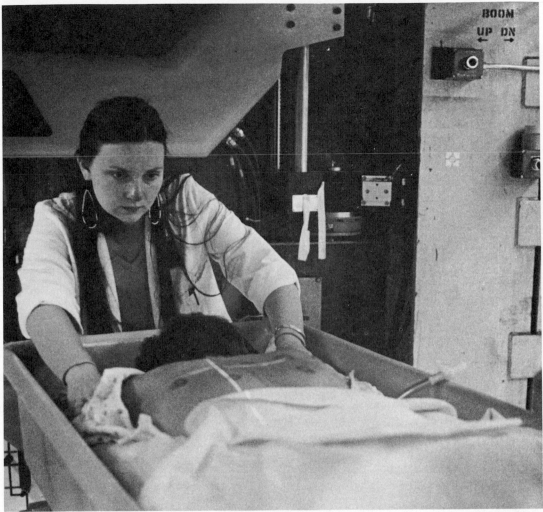

Los Alamos

Atomic particles called pions are now being used in tumor therapy at the biomedical facility of the particle accelerator at Los Alamos, New Mexico. Pions are easier to manage than X rays.

HEALTH & DISEASE

HEALTH AND DISEASE
REVIEW OF THE YEAR

UPI

Based on U.S. Surgeon General's Report on Smoking, HEW Secretary Joseph Califano has been spearheading a drive to convince smokers in the United States to end their deadly habit.

The Surgeon General's Report on Smoking points out that "women who are pregnant and smoke stand a greater chance of retarding fetal growth" and that "the children of women who smoke are more likely to have measurable deficiencies in physical growth and development."

American Cancer Society

Smoking and Health. Cigarette smoking is the "largest preventable cause of death in the United States," according to the 1,200-page U.S. Surgeon General's Report on Smoking and Health released in early 1979. The conclusion was based on a digest of the more than 30,000 articles in the world scientific literature dealing with the social, psychological, medical, and biological aspects of smoking. Coming 15 years after the first such report, the new report presented additional evidence of cigarette smoking's adverse effects on human health and clearly stated that smoking is "far more dangerous than was supposed in 1964."

The new report devoted much more attention to the hazards that smoking poses for women and for the fetuses of pregnant women. The report points out the sharp rise in cigarette smoking among young women over the last decade, to 15.3 per cent from 8.4 per cent, in the age group from 15–24. Dr. Julius B. Richmond, the U.S. Surgeon General, said that "women who are pregnant and smoke stand a greater chance of retarding fetal growth" and that "the children of women who smoke are more likely to have measurable deficiencies in physical growth and development." The report continued "Babies born to women who smoke during pregnancy are on the average 200 grams lighter than babies born to comparable women who do not smoke. Twice as many of these babies weigh less than 2,500 grams compared with babies of non-smokers."

The lighted cigarette generates about 4,000 compounds, and the report identified carbon monoxide, nicotine, and tar as the most likely among many other contributors to the health hazards of smoking. It pointed out that smoking affects the liver's enzymes, thereby modifying the breakdown and effects of drugs taken to treat illnesses.

Overall, the report said, current cigarette smokers have about a 70 per cent greater chance of dying from disease than non-smokers. Heart disease is the chief contributor to the higher death rates among smokers, with lung cancer and chronic obstructive lung disease following. ■ 'The report also said that several studies have shown more stomach and duodenal (peptic) ulcers among men and women who smoke cigarettes. The risk of dying from peptic-ulcer disease is about twice as high for smokers as for non-smokers. ■ The chance of premature death for smokers is directly related to the amount and duration of smoking, and is higher both for those who began smoking at younger ages and for those who inhale. Yet, stopping smoking reduces the hazard of an earlier death. After 15 years, death rates for former smokers approximate those for individuals who had never smoked.

A clear interrelationship between cigarette smoking and occupational exposure to chromate, nickel, coal gas, asbestos, and uranium and death from lung cancer was reported. But because only a small part of the smoking population is exposed to these industrial carcinogens, or chemicals that are cancer-producing, the report said these agents could not account for the rising lung cancer risks in the general population.

The Autopsy. The autopsy, one of the most time honored and instructive procedures in medicine, attracted unusual attention during 1978 because of a bizarre disaster and because of concern about a continuing drop in the autopsy rate in U.S. hospitals.

The disaster was the deaths of 911 (according to best available count) members of the People's Temple in Guyana, described as the largest non-natural, non-military disaster in recent history. It was a situation that called for autopsies by pathologists who specialize in forensic medicine and work as medical examiners. Yet, the disaster may go into history with many medical questions unanswered. Few autopsies were done by Guyanese officials before the bodies were flown to the United States, and because there is no U.S. federal law permitting autopsies, government officials reluctantly agreed to request autopsies on just seven of the victims. The bodies were badly decomposed when the autopsies were done four weeks after death. Pathologists said that preliminary results showed that the leader of the Temple, the Rev. Jim Jones, and one of his followers were shot and that the cause of death of the other five may never be determined.

The autopsy is a systematic external and internal examination of a body. Pathologists make surgical incisions in the body to look at vital organs with the naked eye and to obtain specimens. The specimens are chemically tested and microscopically examined in a search for foreign substances and anatomical abnormalities. From information learned at autopsies and from medical records, pathologists attempt to determine the precise cause of death.

Autopsies usually are carried out in hospitals with permission from relatives of the dead person. But when a death is believed to be murder or suicide or to have resulted from an accident with implications for public safety, medical examiners and coroners have the power to conduct autopsies without such permission. Autopsies often produce surprising findings about the cause of death. Sometimes they detect evidence of previously unsuspected disease that may shed light on the individual's behavior or the events preceding death. Sometimes the evidence is at variance with theories of the death based on information from people with only limited knowledge of the individual or his or her death.

In recent years, interest has been growing in forensic medicine, the speciality devoted to medico-legal autopsies. The reasons for this range from public attention to errors in the medical investigation of President Kennedy's assassination to the increasing litigation over insurance questions and other issues related to the causes of a person's death. Specialists in forensic pathology are trained to look for hidden bullet wounds, needle punctures, bruises, cuts, fractures, and other evidence of physical trauma that might point to the cause or circumstances of death. Even in catastrophes such as an airplane accident autopsies are done to determine if the cause of death of the pilot was a heart attack and to determine the pattern of injuries. Knowing the pattern of injuries in crashes has helped engineers design safer planes.

Just as the Guyana situation led medical examiners to criticize the government for failing to appreciate the need for autopsies, so too have medical leaders criticized the declining autopsy rate in U.S. hospitals. The rate has dropped to 22 per cent from about 50 per cent in the late 1940's. Medicine has advanced beyond the stage where autopsies are the sole key to progress. Autopsies have, however, contributed significantly to many recent advances in medicine, such as the finding that surgically removable tumors can cause high-blood pressure and ulcers and that a form of cancer known

UPI

Mass death in Jonestown, Guyana. Few autopsies were done by Guyanese doctors before the bodies were flown to the United States, where only 7 of the 911 victims were autopsied—partly because of the advanced state of decomposition.

Note the sickle-shaped red-blood cells in the photograph. This condition produces a disabling and frequently fatal anemia. There is now a prenatal test for this disease. The test uses a few drops of amniotic fluid from around the fetus.

NIH

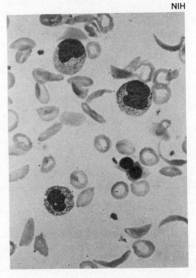

195

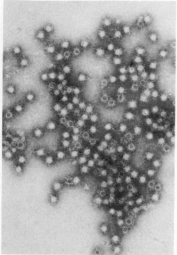

U.S. Center for Disease Control, E. H. Cook

A new hepatitis virus has been identified and is presently referred to as "non-A, non-B virus" because it is neither the two hepatitis viruses called A and B. The virus appears to be spherical, and tests show that the new virus is chemically different from A and B.

Elisabeth McSherry, M.D., measures out baking soda for a patient to prevent an hereditary growth impairment caused by a rare kidney disease. Dr. McSherry and other researchers found that large doses of common baking soda substantially increased the height of a small group of very short children with this disorder.

University of California, San Francisco

as mesothelioma can result from exposure to asbestos dust in the workplace. Autopsies are among a doctor's best teachers. The procedure is valuable in checking the effectiveness of surgical and drug therapies and is the profession's chief means of verifying diagnoses. Often the autopsy results change the presumptive diagnosis made when the person was alive. The findings can be important both to the family and to the doctor involved in a malpractice litigation. Because fewer pathologists are doing fewer autopsies, research in this field has slowed. But specialists argue that more research is needed because the knowledge gained about the major killers might well lead to better therapies and ways of prevention.

Sickle-Cell Anemia. In an application of a Nobel Prize-winning molecular biology technique, researchers at the University of California at San Francisco have developed a safe and rapid test to detect sickle-cell anemia in unborn infants. Similar tests can be developed to detect many other genetic diseases and birth defects, the researchers say.

Sickle-cell anemia is a hereditary disease limited almost exclusively to blacks. The disease is caused by a minor defect in hemoglobin, the oxygen-carrying protein in red blood cells. The defect—a change in one amino-acid component of the protein—changes the red-blood cell from oval to sickle shape and produces a severe and disabling anemia. The severe form of the disease results when the child inherits defective genes from both parents. Inheritance or just one defective gene produces the sickle-cell trait, but does not result in serious clinical symptoms.

Previously the only way to detect sickle-cell anemia before birth was to test a sample of blood from the fetus. This method, developed by Dr. Yuet Wai Kan, required great obstetrical skill and had a death rate for the fetus of up to ten per cent. Now, Dr. Kan and Dr. Andree M. Dozy have developed a test that avoids the risks of fetal-blood testing.

The new test uses a few drops of amniotic fluid, the fluid that surrounds the fetus in the mother's uterus and which can be withdrawn during pregnancy through the technique of amniocentesis. They add to the amniotic fluid sample a specific restrictive enzyme. Restrictive enzymes are a particular type of bacterial enzymes that slice a cell's hereditary material at specific sites and in characteristic ways. By studying the fragments produced by the enzymes, or, in other words, by studying where and how the enzyme slices the fetal hereditary material in the amniotic fluid, the researchers can detect the presence of the defective gene for sickle-cell anemia.

The test takes one week to complete and can be done as early as the 16th week of pregnancy. The researchers predict that the test will be useful in about 60 per cent of the pregnancies at risk for sickle-cell anemia, and they hope to be able to apply the same technique to detecting the presence of other hereditary diseases in the unborn.

Baking-Soda Therapy. There was help for another hereditary disease during the year—and again the work was done at the University of California at San Francisco. The work involved children who suffer from a rare hereditary kidney disease known as classic renal tubular acidosis, or RTA. Children with this disease do not grow normally and remain physically stunted. Researchers found that large doses of common baking soda substantially increased the height of a small group of very short children with this disorder. The baking-soda therapy, which works only for children with the uncommon disease and which can be dangerous for those who do not have this particular disorder, led to rapid growth spurts in the children. They continued to grow two or three inches a year until they reached normal size. Some who might have become dwarfs played varsity sports and others showed dramatic improvement in their school work.

The key to developing the new therapy was in the observation that growing children with the disease excrete in their urine large amounts of bicarbonate, which is baking soda. The researchers discovered that the doses of baking soda had to be constantly increased to offset the amount that the bodies of the children wasted. When the larger doses were given, the rate of growth in the children in the test group increased by up to three times.

New Hepatitis Virus. Scientists at the U.S. Center for Disease Control Laboratory in Phoenix, Arizona, reported that they have discovered a virus that they believe causes most cases of hepatitis resulting from blood transfusions. Several viruses, including those that cause yellow fever and infectious mononucleosis, can cause hepatitis, which means inflammation of the liver. But the word "hepatitis" is generally used to describe illnesses produced by the two common hepatitis viruses, called A and B, or sometimes 1 and 2. The new virus has been called "non A; non B virus."

The new virus was isolated from samples of two commercial lots of blood factor used to treat people with hemophilia and was identified using photographs taken with an electron microscope. The virus particles appear to be spherical, about the size and shape of hepatitis A virus, and somewhat smaller than the hepatitis B virus. Tests have shown that the new virus is chemically different and distinct from the hepatitis A and B viruses. Scientists think that there may still be other undiscovered viruses that cause hepatitis.

Smallpox. For a year the world was without smallpox. From October 1977, when a 23-year-old man in Somalia recovered from a moderately severe case, until the fall of 1978 not a single case of smallpox was reported in the world and scientists believed that they had succeeded in eradicating the disease. Then, two cases, one fatal, occurred in England. The cases resulted from the accidental escape of the deadly virus particles from a laboratory in Birmingham, England. The patients were a woman who worked in the hospital where the laboratory was located and her mother. The outbreak led to pleas for tighter controls on laboratories that still have stocks of the smallpox virus and to discussions about whether indeed a stockpile of the virus particles should be maintained for research purposes.

Meanwhile, the United States Public Health Service ended smallpox vaccination requirements for travelers arriving in the United States. (They had previously ended smallpox vaccination requirements for people living in the United States.) Now no vaccinations of any kind are required to enter the United States from any country. Cholera vaccination requirements were stopped in 1970 and yellow fever vaccination requirements were stopped in 1972.

Lawrence K. Altman, M.D.

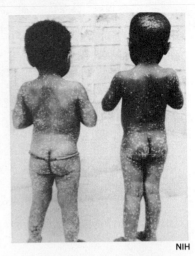

NIH

Probably throughout the life of mankind smallpox has killed hundreds of millions of people, and blinded and scarred millions more. In 1967 the World Health Organization organized an immense team of physicians and health workers to stamp out the disease, and they have succeeded.

A wood engraving from an 1883 issue of *Harper's Weekly* showing a western-bound train carrying immigrants while a doctor vaccinates them against smallpox.

National Library of Medicine

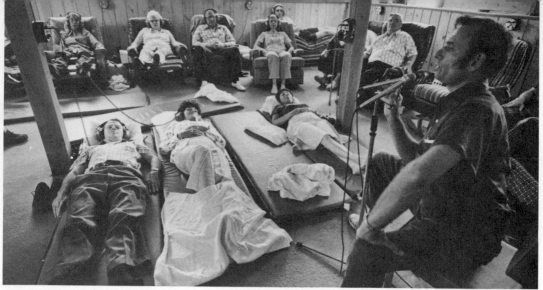

Getsug/Anderson; *Medical World News*

Dr. C. Norman Shealy conducts a pain clinic in La Cross, Wisconsin.

PAIN

by Jonathan B. Tucker

A terrible car accident left Barbara Loew with excruciating pain in her neck and back. At first her doctor thought it was severe whiplash. Months passed, but the pain never lessened. She tried sleeping tablets, Valium, and dozens of painkillers. None could relieve the agony that had become a daily part of her existence. Like 20 million other American victims of chronic pain, Barbara undertook a frustrating search for relief.

Several years after the accident, her doctor told her of a revolutionary new drug. "I haven't prescribed it to any of my other patients yet," he said hesitantly, "but the drug appears to be totally safe—it's nonaddictive, there's no buildup of tolerance, and it doesn't put you to sleep."

To Barbara's astonishment there were only two pills in the glass container given her by the pharmacist—a prescription that was supposed to last a month. The directions read, "Take one tablet every 24 hours." By the end of the second day, she was discouraged—nothing had happened. But on the morning of the third day, the aching pain that had plagued her for so long was gone. Even more startling, the relief lasted for a whole month.

"How does it work?" Barbara asked her doctor.

"It's really your body that does the work," he explained. "The body has its own defense against pain—an opiatelike substance naturally produced in the brain that controls the amount of pain you feel. The drug I gave you gradually increased the levels of this brain chemical to provide long-lasting relief."

Although Barbara Loew's story is fictitious, preliminary tests conducted on a group of chronic-pain patients in 1978 indicate that the wonder drug in this story may already exist. The potent analgesic properties of this drug were not discovered accidentally. Rather, the finding was precipitated by rapid developments in our understanding of pain only during the last decade—advances that promise to provide powerful new tools for treating chronic pain by exploiting the body's own pain-inhibitory system. But before we can discuss these exciting developments, we first need to know more about pain itself.

ARE THERE PAIN SENSORS?

Pain physiologists have long debated whether specific pain sensors exist or whether pain results from the excessive stimulation of sensory cells that respond to touch, temperature, and pressure. The existence of specific pain sensors was recently demonstrated by physiology professor Edward R. Perl of the University of North Carolina School of Medicine identified nerve endings that are activated only if the stimulus is of sufficient intensity to be painful. These nerve endings have fine interwoven branches and are located in the deep layers of the skin, the internal organs, the membrane covering the bones, the cornea of the eyes, and the pulp of the teeth.

When a region of the skin is injured, the death of the cells in that area is believed to cause the liberation of chemicals associated with inflammation, such as histamine and bradykinin. These substances in turn trigger volleys of nerve impulses in the pain sensors. One of the actions of aspirin is to inhibit the manufacture of bradykinin, so that the generation of pain is blocked at the wound site.

The impulses generated in the pain fibers enter the spinal cord and travel through it to the cerebral cortex, of the brain, where the location of the painful stimulus is pinpointed on the body surface. The limbic system—a doughnut-shaped region surrounding the core of the brain—appears to mediate the emotional component of pain.

The prefrontal cortex located just behind the forehead may also participate in this aspect of the pain experience. Frontal lobotomy, a type of psychosurgery formerly used to treat chronic pain, involved severing the connections between the prefrontal cortex and the rest of the brain. After the operation, patients reported that the pain was still there but that it didn't bother them. They simply no longer cared about it and often forgot that it was there. But the personality changes resulting from lobotomy—loss of spontaneity, reduced intelligence, and lowered responsiveness—often made the cure more terrible than the disease.

ATTACHMENT SITES FOR OPIATE MOLECULES

A major breakthrough in the understanding of the physiology of pain came in 1973 with the discovery in the central nervous system of specific receptors, or attachment sites, for the molecules of morphine

and other drugs of the opiate family. The "opiate receptors" were highly concentrated in regions of the brain and spinal cord traditionally associated with the perception of pain. These regions are the central gray matter of the brain stem and the limbic system.

As it typically happens in science, the answer to one puzzling question—how an age-old drug exerts its influence—soon presented a more baffling mystery. Why did the brains of human beings and other mammals evolve with receptors for a chemical in the sap of the opium poppy? A rapid series of discoveries soon revealed that the brain manufactures its own opiates.

The unparalleled painkilling properties of morphine (the active ingredient of opium) are made possible because the drug mimics the natural opiates produced in the brain. As Stanford University pharmacologist Avram Goldstein points out, it is "one of nature's

This diagram illustrates a theory about addictive and non-addictive drugs. An exact-fit non-addictive opiate molecule pushes out an inexact-fit addictive opiate molecule.

Illustration by Frank Senyk

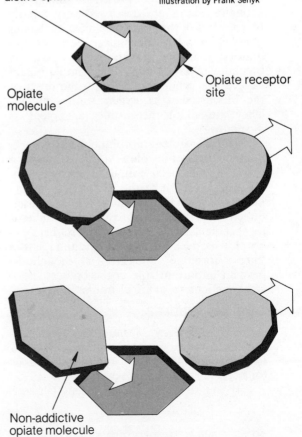

Opiate molecule

Opiate receptor site

Non-addictive opiate molecule

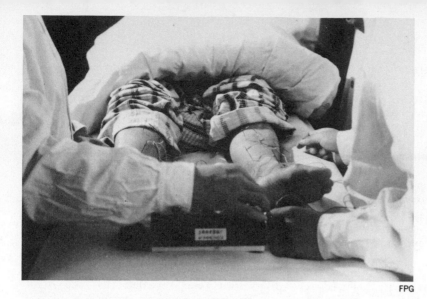

The stimulation by acupuncture needles may release enkephalins in the brain and central nervous system, which somehow block pain transmission from rising to the brain.

FPG

most bizarre coincidences" that the molecular configuration of a natural chemical in the brain should match that of a molecule found in the opium poppy.

"IN-THE-HEAD" MOLECULES

The first of the brain's opiates to be discovered was termed "enkephalin" (from the Greek, meaning "in the head"). This molecule consists of a chain of five amino acids—the building blocks of protein. Although enkephalin chains are destroyed very rapidly by enzymes in the brain, chemical analogues of enkephalin have been prepared in the laboratory that are resistant to enzymatic breakdown. These analogues stimulate pain suppression when injected into the brain or the bloodstream of experimental animals. They are about three times as potent as morphine.

Another potent morphinelike substance, named beta-endorphin ("the morphine within"), has been found in the pituitary gland at the base of the brain. Beta-endorphin appears to be a hormone that is released directly into the bloodstream, which carries it to specific target organs. Because beta-endorphin is released at the same time as the "stress hormone" ACTH, it is thought to play an important role in the body's defensive reactions to physical trauma and stress.

TWIRLING NEEDLES

The discovery of natural opiate substances in the brain has provided new clues to how both acupuncture and the witch doctor's craft may actually work.

If the wisdom of the ancient Chinese was ever in doubt, certainly their methods of exploiting the brain's natural opiates in the treatment of pain and suffering were highly advanced. Acupuncture has long aroused the suspicions of Western skeptics. Now, 2,300 years after the ancient art was first developed, a link has been found between its anesthetic action and the opiates the brain produces.

David Mayer of the Medical College of Virginia subjected normal people to experimental pain and found that acupuncture effectively reduced the pain. He then gave the subjects naloxone (a drug that blocks the action of enkephalin) and found that it significantly reduced the analgesic effects of acupuncture. This finding suggests that the stimulation of nerve endings by acupuncture needles triggers the release of enkephalin in the brain or spinal cord, thereby decreasing the amount of pain information that reaches conscious awareness.

PLACEBOS AND OPIATES

Nonetheless, faith in acupuncture may be an additional factor in its success. It has long been known that a patient's expectations may affect his response to treatment. The success of the witch doctor, often the most highly esteemed member of primitive tribes, may be largely attributable to the patient's belief in the cure. Modern researchers call this phenomenon the "placebo effect." Nearly one third of all patients recuperating from severe postsurgical pain report marked relief after being given a placebo—an inert compound such as a sugar pill or saline solution that the patient genuinely believes is a potent analgesic. ("Placebo" comes from the Latin "I shall please.")

Evidence now suggests that the placebo effect is not just in the mind but also in the physical brain. Again, the natural opiates produced by the brain seem to be involved. Researchers at the University of California at San Francisco gave placebos to patients who suffered pain after wisdom-tooth extractions. As expected, the placebo brought about a significant reduction of pain in one third of the patients. When these patients were subsequently given a drug that inhibits the actions of beta-endorphin, their pain increased back to almost the same level reported by patients who had not responded to the placebo in the first place.

STRESS IN PAIN REDUCTION

Why placebos trigger the brain to release internal opiates in some patients but not in others remains a mystery. Researchers following this line of investigation speculate that stress may be the crucial factor. Indeed, two related observations—that patients under extreme stress often respond best to placebos, and that beta-endorphin is released from the pituitary simultaneously with the stress hormone ACTH—certainly lend plausibility to this theory.

The role of beta-endorphin in stress may also explain peculiar aspects of pain tolerance, such as how athletes in the midst of competition and soldiers in battle can sustain severe injuries without becoming aware until later that they have been hurt. "One feels a single cut from a surgeon's scalpel," wrote Montaigne in the seventeenth century, "more than ten strokes of the sword in the heat of battle."

CONSCIOUS-CONTROL OF BRAIN OPIATES?

Could individuals learn to consciously control the release of opiates within their own bodies? Followers of Eastern religions who practice self-discipline and meditation in order to achieve inner awareness have long known how to control involuntary responses such as heart rate, respiration, and body temperature.

It would not be surprising to discover

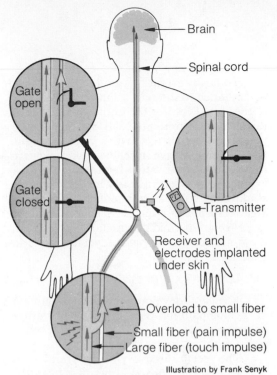

Illustration by Frank Senyk

Dr. Ronald Melzak of McGill University has suggested that at times the nerves in the spinal cord refuse to transmit the signal that the brain recognizes as pain. This theory of pain blockage is known as the gate theory. Pain impulses travel along two kinds of pain fibers on either side of the spinal cord. Gentle electrical stimulation may activate the large nerves to close the "gate" in the spinal cord by means of enkephalins, thus blocking the pain message to the brain. Acupuncture and hypnosis might have the same effect as electrical stimulation.

that the trancelike state Oriental mystics enter before walking over beds of burning hot coals or passing needles through their flesh somehow enables them to regulate the release of internal opiates. For less mystically oriented Westerners, biofeedback training may someday provide the key to gaining control over this seemingly involuntary response.

ELECTRICAL IMPULSES AND BRAIN OPIATES

In the last decade, however, approaches to pain therapy have changed radically owing to our new knowledge of the body's own pain-suppressing system. There has been a move away from the surgical treatment of pain to the electrical stimulation of peripheral nerves and parts of the brain involved in the pain-inhibitory system.

Today, current is applied with electrodes taped to the skin or implanted directly in the spinal cord or the brain so that the patient can intermittently activate them when the pain becomes too severe. This technique has proved effective in relieving chronic pain that is unresponsive to other therapies. However, it is not yet known whether excessive stimulation will lead to a reduction in the analgesic response over time or whether the presence of permanent metal electrodes in the brain tissue will have adverse long-term effects.

LAB-MADE ENKEPHALINS

A second development in the treatment of chronic pain has been to devise new drugs possessing the beneficial qualities of morphine without the bad ones.

The recent discovery of the brain's own opiates naturally raised hopes that modified forms of these chemicals might provide the long-sought nonaddicting analgesics. Enkephalin was chosen for the preparation of analogues because its molecule consists of only five amino acids. But to create a medically useful enkephalin, it first had to be stabilized so that it would not be immediately destroyed, and chemically modified so that it would pass through the "blood-brain barrier" into the brain.

Chemists at a major drug company in Basel, Switzerland, overcame these formidable obstacles. They managed to stablilize the molecule and enhance its activity so that one enkephalin analogue, designated FK-33824, is 30,000 times more potent than enkephalin.

Excitement about enkephalin analogues was quickly dampened, however, when it was found that they, too, are addictive. When rats are regularly treated with enkephalin or beta-endorphin, they develop many of the symptoms of morphine addiction. Nonetheless, the recent discovery of the analgesic properties of neurotensin has aroused interest in its possible drug applications.

Snyder personally believes that a different approach may untimately prove more fruitful. "Making enkephalin analogues is just like making morphine," he says. "My own prejudice is that if we can find the enzyme in the brain that specifically destroys enkephalin and isolate it, then we could develop a drug that would inhibit this enzyme and thereby indirectly raise enkephalin levels. This would be a different way of juicing up the system, perhaps in a more gentle fashion than by having something that just mimics enkephalin."

ENHANCING THE EFFECTS OF THE BRAIN OPIATES

Snyder's "prejudice" must have been well founded. Recently, Seymour Ehrenpreis of the University of Chicago Medical School reported that an old drug called D-phenylalanine (DPA) inhibits the action of carboxypeptidase, the enzyme that destroys enkephalins. This discovery has raised hopes that the pain-reducing action of the enkephalins could be sustained. DPA has now been tried on 11 chronic-pain patients. Nine of these patients became either pain-free or experienced less pain.

Furthermore, DPA usually required only two days of treatment in order to obtain relief from pain for as long as a month. Ehrenpreis believes that this prolonged analgesia is the result of a long-term buildup of enkephalin levels in the brain. Laboratory tests with 200 mice have also found DPA to be nonaddictive, giving support to Snyder's contention that this method would prove to be a gentler way of "juicing up the system."

The enormous growth in the understanding of the body's natural mechanism for coping with pain has not only revealed a scientific explanation behind esoteric methods for treating pain. It has also suggested a cure that comes from within the body and the brain itself, especially through drugs that enhance the pain-suppression system without disrupting it to the point of addiction. Never before have the prospects of conquering man's oldest and most relentless enemy looked so promising □

SELECTED READINGS

"The great pain plan" by Joan Arehart-Treichel. *Science News,* October 14, 1978.

"Solving the mysteries of pain" by Laurence Cherry. *The New York Times Magazine,* January 30, 1977.

"The brain makes its own narcotics" by Richard Restak. *Saturday Review,* March 5, 1977.

FOODS THAT BLOCK CANCER

by Jane Brody

CANCER researchers have discovered that a number of common substances, including certain food additives, pesticides, vitamins and constituents of vegetables, can block the action of carcinogenic, or cancer-causing, chemicals.

Among the effective agents, studies in animals and people indicate, are the preservatives BHA and BHT, which are commonly added to cereals and baked goods, and a group of chemicals naturally present in such vegetables as cabbage, Brussels sprouts, and broccoli. Vitamins C and E and certain

chemical relatives of vitamin A have also shown effectiveness against cancer-causing chemicals, as have several sulfur-containing pesticides.

The findings offer a wide range of possible new approaches to cancer prevention. Some, in fact, are already being tested in people who are highly susceptible to developing certain types of cancers. Others require further study to be certain that they prevent cancer rather than promoting it or causing some other damage. Research is showing that what we eat is critical to our health.

Robert Miller/The New York Times

The Millers have shown that chemicals have to be activated before they can cause cancer.

NEW TECHNIQUES

The new techniques stem from chemical carcinogenesis, the process through which chemicals cause cancer. The investigation of this process—still not completely understood—began with the discovery more than 30 years ago by Drs. Elizabeth and James Miller that chemical carcinogens had to be activated in the body before they could change normal cells to cancer cells.

Dr. Elizabeth Miller, a University of Wisconsin biochemist, explains the current understanding of carcinogenesis as follows:

Most of the substances now thought of as carcinogens are actually precarcinogens. These may be either detoxified in the body to form harmless compounds or they may be activated into "proximate" and finally "ultimate" carcinogens.

The ultimate carcinogen can attach itself to critically important target-cell molecules, including DNA, RNA, and proteins that are involved in transmitting genetic information from one cell generation to the next. Once attached to its target, the carcinogen can initiate the development of cancer by altering the genetic message of the cells. Next, researchers believe, promotion of the initiated cells occurs. A second substance, such as a hormone, acts as a promoter, causing the initiated cells to grow into a clump of similar cells and finally into a full-blown cancer.

"In terms of cancer prevention," Dr. Miller says, "if you interrupt these processes anywhere along the way, you stop tumor production."

KEEP CARCINOGENS OUT

In light of this understanding, Dr. Lee Wattenberg of the University of Minnesota outlines four possibilities for cancer prevention. "By far the best thing you can do, of course, is avoid exposure to the carcinogen," he said, adding that this is and probably always will be the most potent weapon for cancer prevention.

A second approach is to block the chemical formation of carcinogens within the body. One example of this approach would be to block the hookup of nitrites with amines from foods to form nitrosamines, which are potent carcinogens. Studies described by Dr. Steve Tannenbaum of the Massachusetts Institute of Technology showed that ascorbic acid (vitamin C) and alpha-tocopherol (a free form of vitamin E) can inhibit the formation of nitrosamines in the stomach and large intestine of experimental animals. However, Dr. Wattenberg said his own research revealed no anticancer effect of vitamins C or E.

Studies are under way in Canada and South America as well as in the United States to test the ability of ascorbic acid and alpha-tocopherol to prevent cancers of the stomach and large intestine in people known to be highly susceptible to these cancers.

INTERCEPT THEM

A third tactic—the one Dr. Wattenberg, among others, is focusing on—is to intercept the carcinogen before it hooks up to its target. This can be done either by preventing the chemical from reaching its target or by blocking its link-up with the target. In studies of this approach, an inhibiting agent is given before or simultaneously with the carcinogen.

Dr. Wattenberg reports that BHA, an antioxidant used as a food additive, can block a rather large group of carcinogens, including nitrosamines, polycyclic hydrocarbons—which are believed to be important in smoking-caused cancers—and urethan, an industrial carcinogen. It works by altering enzymes, thus preventing activation of the precarcinogen and increasing the amount of the chemical that is detoxified. BHT, another antioxidant food additive, has a similar effect but is too toxic to consider.

Disulfiram—the alcoholism drug known as Antabuse—and related chemicals used as pesticides also block the activation of precarcinogens, but these are also too hazardous to be used against cancer, he added.

However, certain naturally occurring chemicals called indoles that are found in plants of the cabbage family are potent and apparently safe inhibitors of certain carcinogens. In addition to cabbage, these indoles are found in broccoli, Brussels sprouts, turnips, cauliflower, and related vegetables.

In animal studies, two such indoles markedly reduced the ability of a carcinogen to cause breast cancers according to Dr. Wattenberg. And a detailed diet study by Dr. Saxon Graham of the State University of New York at Buffalo revealed that people who eat a lot of cabbage, Brussels sprouts, and broccoli are less likely to develop cancer of the colon.

Other plant constituents called coumarins, found in a variety of fruits and vegetables, are also able to block carcinogen-caused mammary cancers in experimental animals.

DON'T PROMOTE THEM

Dr. Paul McCay of the Oklahoma Medical Research Foundation has described yet another dietary approach to inhibiting carcinogens—a low-fat diet. In worldwide studies, diets high in fat have been linked to an increased risk of developing cancers of the colon and breast. Dr. McCay reports that when animals are placed on a low-fat diet, the detoxifying action of enzymes appears to be encouraged. Fewer cancers develop in response to a carcinogen and those that do develop grow more slowly.

However, the reverse occurs when the animals are fed a diet high in fats, particularly polyunsaturated fats. In Dr. McCay's opinion, "eating as little fat as possible is the best idea."

Another way to inhibit carcinogens, Dr. Wattenberg has reported, is to flood cells with decoy targets that tie up the carcinogen, thereby preventing its link-up with heredity-determining molecules. One such effective trapping agent is a compound called glutathione.

Dr. Wattenberg also cautions that car-

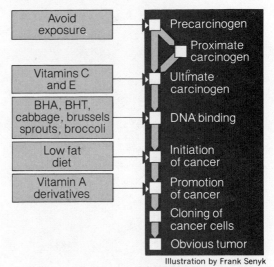

Illustration by Frank Senyk

The right column of this diagram shows the steps in tumor formation, starting with the presence of a precarcinogenic chemical. The left column shows five factors that stop cancers from forming. Four of these factors are found in food.

cinogen inhibitors can be unpredictable. Some may actually promote the action of certain carcinogens while blocking others. Timing is also critical: the drug phenobarbitol, for example, suppresses cancer when given before exposure to the carcinogen, but it fosters the development of cancer if it is administered after the carcinogen.

In the fourth approach, carcinogenic action may be blocked after the chemical has linked up with critical cell molecules and initiated the cancer process, probably during the promotion phase. Dr. Michael Sporn of the U.S. National Cancer Institute has reported that a derivative of vitamin A called 13-cis retinoic acid is being tested as a cancer preventive in patients who face a very high risk of developing bladder cancers. The compound may also be able to inhibit cancers of the breast, lung, pancreas, colon, and esophagus □

SELECTED READINGS

"Animal studies link nitrites to cancer," *FDA Consumer,* September 1978.

"Cancer and your diet," by J. Powell. *Science Digest,* September 1977.

"Link between cancer and nutrition," by Jane Brody. *American Home,* August 1977.

Sybil Shelton/Monkmeyer

OBESITY

by Jane E. Brody

RECENT studies suggests that many of the factors thought to cause obesity are actually its results.

The new research challenges the long-standing notions that most people who are fat get that way because of their genes, because they are lazy, greedy, or weakwilled or because they are psychologically disturbed or cursed with a low metabolism. Rather, the studies show, many of these characteristics are the consequences of eating too much and weighing too much in a society oriented toward slimness.

While offering no panacea to the millions of overweight Americans who have been unable to shed excess weight permanently, the new findings help explain why obesity is such a persistent problem for so many people and why most popular solutions fail in the long run.

The findings also suggest alternative approaches, starting in infancy, to the prevention and treatment of serious weight problems. And they emphasize the need for some people to come to terms with the fact that they were never meant to match society's widely advertised standard of fashion-model slenderness.

ROLE OF EMOTIONAL FACTORS

Researchers have found that the obsession with slimness has precipitated serious disturbances in some people. Anxiety over being slightly overweight, they say, and perpetually gaining and losing weight cause more physical and emotional harm than the excess weight ever would.

Of even greater concern is the appearance of a serious new eating disorder that is brought on by the social pressure to be thin. Increasing numbers of slender young women who want to be thinner are being caught in a physically and psychologically damaging cycle of starvation, binge eating, and punishing purges.

College health officials report that this syndrome, which two Cornell University psychologists have named "bulimarexia," is fast becoming widespread. One off-the-cuff estimate is that as many as one-quarter of freshman women may be afflicted.

CAUSE AND EFFECT

Yet for an estimated 40 million Americans, overweight is a real and perplexing problem, causing damage to mind and body that is hard to ignore. Recent research on the causes and consequences of obesity has raised the following key points:

- Environment is a far more important cause of obesity than heredity.
- Low metabolism is more likely to be a result than a cause of obesity.
- Likewise, psychological disorders are commonly consequences of obesity but rarely cause it.
- Many fat people, conditioned early in childhood to overeat, eat in response to emotional disturbances and environmental cues instead of real hunger.
- Obese people are inactive because of their excess weight, rather than the other way around.

Obesity afflicts only seven per cent of the children of parents who themselves are normal in weight. Research shows, however, that 40 per cent of the children with one fat parent and 80 per cent of those with two fat parents also become fat. But this can result from an environment that fosters overeating as well as from inherited tendencies.

Studies of adopted children and identical twins reared together and apart have shown somewhat conflicting results. But the preponderance of evidence indicates that environment plays a stronger role than heredity. A genetic predisposition to be fat will be expressed only if the environment in which the person is raised permits it. A study in England showed that the pets of fat people are twice as likely to be fat as those of thin people.

INSULIN, APPETITE, AND OBESITY

Dr. Judith Rodin, a psychologist at Yale University, pointed out that fat people produce higher levels of insulin, a hormone that promotes the storage of calories as fat. High levels of insulin also cause hunger and result in increased food consumption. The faster a person eats, and the more calories and carbohydrates the meal contains, the more insulin is released, creating a cycle of more eating and more insulin. In a Vermont study, prisoners of normal weight were fed two to three times more calories than they normally ate. This overfeeding resulted in a 26 per cent weight gain along with hormonal and metabolic changes as those seen in the obese.

CALORIC REQUIREMENTS

"The obese person with extremely low metabolism is a rarity," Dr. Rodin said. "Ninety-eight per cent of the housewives who say they can't lose because they have a low metabolism are wrong."

However, Dr. Jules Hirsch of Rockefeller University in New York said studies of extremely overweight people have shown that they need a third to a half fewer calories to maintain their weight than people of normal weight (and same height). This is largely because fatty tissue requires less energy (which is what calories measure) than lean body mass.

But even after the obese reduce to normal weight, their caloric requirements are slightly lower than those of people who have never been fat, Dr. Hirsch said. Whether this is a lasting result of obesity, the consequences of inactivity, or a sign of a genetic predisposition to obesity is unknown.

PROBLEM OF BEING FAT IN OUR SOCIETY

The studies also suggest that psychological disorders are more likely to be the result than the cause of obesity. Being fat in our society can lead to self-disdain and rejection by others, which can, in turn, produce emotional disturbances. Dr. Albert Stunkard, a psychiatrist at the University of Pennsylva-

Carbohydrates stimulate the production of insulin, which in turn increases appetite. Fasting limits insulin production, thereby limiting appetite.

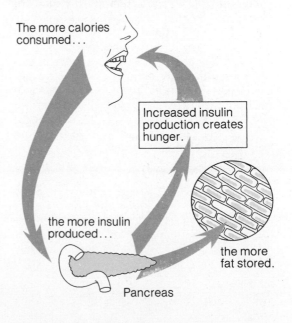

The more calories consumed...

Increased insulin production creates hunger.

the more insulin produced...

the more fat stored.

Pancreas

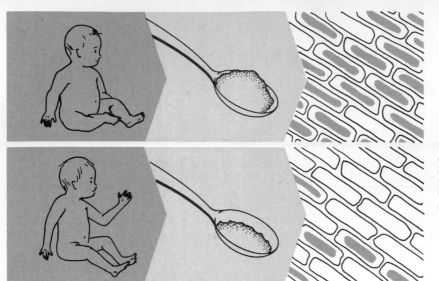

Young children who overeat produce more and more fat cells under the skin tissue. These will require filling for the rest of their lives.

nia, showed that although obesity was six times more common among women in the lower social classes than among upper-class women, the latter were far more likely to be emotionally disturbed as a result of a weight problem.

Although the files of psychotherapists contain many cases of severe emotional disturbance among overweight people, a study of New Yorkers conducted by Dr. Stunkard showed only a "trivial" difference between normal-weight and obese people in the amount and degree of mental illness.

However, when obese people lose a lot of weight, a large percentage of them become depressed and anxious. Dr. Hirsch said that many such people feel "deprived, left out, lonesome and empty in a global sense." Similar feelings are experienced by normal-weight people who are starving. For many of the formerly fat, the feelings are severe enough to cause them to overeat and regain the lost weight.

Dr. Rodin believes that the constant vigilance required by dieters spells their eventual doom. Continual restraint leads them to feel compelled by food until their restraint weakens. She advises that the overweight "get off diets as such and learn to live more normally with food."

EARLY EATING HABITS

Regardless of genetic tendencies, early eating patterns can make an enormous difference in a person's later struggle with excess weight. Research by Dr. Jerome Knittle, of Mount Sinai Medical Center in New York, and others has shown that fat babies and fat children are more likely to grow up to be overweight adults because they develop a permanent excess of fat cells. This leaves them with a lifelong storehouse of fat cells in want of filling. Controlling weight-gain in early childhood may therefore thwart a tendency to later obesity.

Among those who become overweight as adults, the existing fat cells enlarge but do not increase in number. When such people lose weight, the cells shrink to normal size.

The latest research suggests that most fat people probably start out metabolically normal and gradually develop derangements in their internal chemistry when they gain weight. As many fat people have complained, these derangements can cause "everything" they eat to turn to fat and result in weight gain even though they do not seem to overeat.

THE PARENTAL INFLUENCE

Dr. Hilde Bruch, a psychiatrist at Baylor University School of Medicine in Houston and an expert in the psychology of eating disorders, believes that many parents unwittingly "program" their children to overeat by feeding them for the wrong reasons or at the wrong times.

"It doesn't take much to distort the programming of the brain," Dr. Bruch said in an interview. "All the mother has to do is give children food whenever they cry, no matter what the reason for the distress. Or mothers may not feed them when they are hungry because it's not yet time to eat again." The re-

Courtesy of Albert J. Stunkard

Dr. Stunkard, a psychiatrist and author of *The Pain of Obesity*, found no correlation between obesity and degree of mental illness.

sult of such treatment, she believes, is that the child's brain never learns to recognize hunger as distinct from other sensations, such as boredom, anger, anxiety, disappointment, and depression.

"These are the jolly fat people who never get angry but always eat," Dr. Bruch observed. "They are also the people who say they have no will power. When they start eating, they can't stop."

Dr. Rodin suggests that to help develop normal responses to internal signals of hunger, infants should be fed whenever they are hungry rather than on a schedule. She adds that children should not be made to eat when they are not hungry.

Parents also teach children to use food as a reward, Dr. Rodin said, adding: "But both overweight and normal-weight people reward themselves with food, so it's not by itself a cause of obesity." However, she noted in an article in the magazine *Human Nature* that fat people tend to overestimate the passage of time. And, as a possible corollary, they are more likely to eat when they are bored than are normal-weight people, but less likely to eat when they are involved in absorbing work.

CLUE TO WEIGHT-WATCHERS

This finding, she said, should be a clue to weight-watchers to keep busy with something interesting at all times. It may also explain in part why many fat people have no trouble refraining from overeating all day, but go overboard in the evening, when life quiets down.

In studies with Donald Elman and Stanley Schachter at Columbia University, Dr. Rodin found that overweight people also tend to eat more when they are emotionally aroused. This seemed to be true regardless of whether the feelings are positive or negative. And, they found, emotions of all sorts are more easily aroused in obese people than in those of normal weight.

Earlier studies by Dr. Schachter showed that so-called external cues—such things as the sight, smell, and taste of food and the knowledge that it is mealtime—have an unusually strong influence on fat people, even if they are not hungry. In one study by Lee Ross, a Stanford University psychologist, obese people ate twice the number of cashews when the nuts were under bright lights than when the lights were dimmed, whereas normal weight people ate the same number of nuts regardless of how well they could see the food.

"Overweight people are not necessarily externally responsive, but those people who do respond to external eating cues are highly vulnerable to becoming obese," Dr. Rodin said in an interview. In a study of girls arriving at summer camp, she and a colleague, Joyce Slochower, were able to predict accurately on the basis of responses to external stimuli those who would gain weight when surrounded by the tempting edibles provided by the camp.

It takes 20 minutes for the signals of satiety to reach the brain. By then, most people have finished eating and, in the case of the obese, overeating. That is why many weight-control programs put so much emphasis on eating slowly □

📖 SELECTED READINGS

"Conspiring against fatness: obesity research at St. Luke's Hospital Center" edited by W. Stockton and T. Vanitallie. *Psychology Today,* October 1978.

"Do you have a cute, fat baby?" by G. Carro. *Ladies Home Journal,* October 1978.

The Pain of Obesity by Albert J. Stunkard. Hawthorn Books, 1976.

"Were you born to be fat?" by M. Schildkraut and A. Beller. *Good Housekeeping,* April 1978.

Newspaper Enterprise Association

ALCOHOL AND BIRTH DEFECTS

by Fritz P. Witti

THE more a pregnant woman drinks, the greater her risk of giving birth to an abnormal baby, according to top experts on alcohol and health.

Thousands of malformed and mentally defective babies, these experts say, are born yearly because their mothers drink too much alcohol during pregnancy. And, they suspect, thousands of other youngsters face learning and behavioral problems in childhood and youth because of brain dysfunction resulting from heavy drinking by their mothers during pregnancy.

FETAL ALCOHOL SYNDROME

The malady, suspected for centuries, was "discovered" and given a name—the Fetal Alcohol Syndrome—in the late 1960's. The symptoms shown by children suffering fetal alcohol syndrome may include slow growth before and after birth, small head, facial irregularities such as narrow eye slits and a sunken nasal bridge, defective heart and other organs, malformed arms and legs, genital abnormalities, and mental retardation. There are also behavioral problems, such as hyperactivity, extreme nervousness, and a poor attention span.

HOW MUCH? WHEN?

Although convinced that alcohol and birth defects are linked, scientists have been unable to pin down precisely the timing and degree of risk. Just how much beer, wine, or distilled spirits is it safe to drink during pregnancy? At what point in pregnancy is the risk to the unborn child greatest? They cannot answer these questions on the basis of present knowledge.

The answers are being sought through intensive clinical research and animal testing. In the meantime, the U.S. National Institute on Alcohol Abuse and Alcoholism (NIAAA) warns that there is a definite risk in drinking three ounces or more of alcohol a day—that's six drinks or more. Drinking one to three ounces of alcohol a day—two to six drinks—may be risky and caution is advised.

"The risk of the full fetal alcohol syndrome appears to start at three ounces of alcohol a day, but we are not certain that parts of the syndrome won't show up at consumption of from one to three ounces," says Dr. Ernest P. Noble, director of the Institute. "There is a possibility that symptoms short of the full syndrome could be caused by lesser doses of alcohol on a regular basis, or by a single high dose during one night or weekend of heavy drinking during a critical time in the development of the fetus."

He points to recent statistical evidence that suggests alcohol consumption during pregnancy may be significant in the development of more subtle but much more frequent abnormalities of attention, behavior, and learning called minimal brain dysfunction. It is estimated that minimal brain dysfunction affects 5,000,000 to 7,000,000 youngsters of the school-age population of the United States. There are indications that a substantial portion of those millions are affected because of the mother's consumption of alcohol during pregnancy.

CRITICAL PERIODS

Because of the uncertainty about how much alcohol is dangerous during pregnancy, the official notice on the subject issued by the NIAAA in June 1977 was labeled a "caution." But Dr. Noble says he personally would recommend that to be certain of their infants' safety, women should stay away from alcohol during pregnancy. That personal view is shared by Dr. Gerald L. Klerman, administrator of the Alcohol, Drug Abuse, and Mental Health Administration.

Early this year Dr. Klerman told a Senate Subcommittee on Alcoholism and Drug Abuse that there may be critical periods during pregnancy when a single episode of drinking may have as strong an effect as regular consumption of alcoholic beverages. Consequently, he said, damage could be done during the first month of pregnancy when many women are not yet aware that they are pregnant and when the fetus is especially delicate.

Some researchers have observed that mothers who drink an ounce or less of alcohol a day have a higher rate of stillbirths and

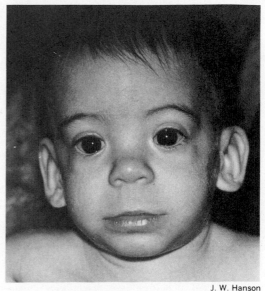

J. W. Hanson

The sunken nasal bridge and short nose are symptoms of fetal alcohol syndrome.

their babies weigh less. Two mixed drinks each containing one ounce of whiskey (distilled spirits) equals about one ounce of alcohol. So do two five-ounce glasses of still (not fortified) wine or two 12-ounce glasses of regular beer. The alcohol content in distilled spirits, such as whiskey, can be determined by dividing the "proof" number on the bottle label by two. One hundred proof whiskey, for example, is about 50 per cent alcohol, so two ounces of the whiskey contain about one ounce of alcohol.

COMMON PROBLEM

The NIAAA estimates that one or more of the symptoms of fetal alcohol syndrome may be present in more than 5,000 babies in the United States this year. A conservative estimate is that the syndrome affects one in every 2,000 babies born each year. Only two other birth defects that involve both mental and physical impairment occur more frequently. They are Down's syndrome, which affects one baby in 600, and spina bifida, which affects one in 1,000. Down's syndrome is a cause of mongoloidism and spina bifida is a malformation of the spine.

Social drinking is traditional and widespread in the United States so there is a great potential for alcohol-caused birth defects

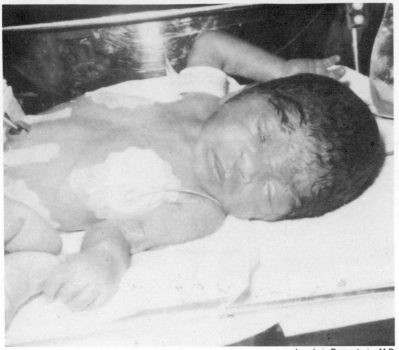

This victim of mother's drinking is permanently disfigured by a malformed nose and mouth, scarred lip, and a hairline down to the eyebrows.

Jose Luis Rementeria, M.D.

among the 48,000,000 women of childbearing age, generally considered to be from 15 to 44, who gave birth to more than 3,000,000 children in 1978.

CONCERN NOT NEW

Although it now has a name, there is nothing new about the concern of society for the effect of alcohol on unborn children. Warnings about alcohol consumption during pregnancy, and even at conception, date back to ancient times.

In the Book of Judges (13:3-5) an angel visits the wife of Manoah to tell her that she will bear a child but warns, "Now therefore beware, I pray thee, and drink no wine nor strong drink. . . ." She later gave birth to Samson, of great strength and long hair fame.

In a historical survey, Dr. Henry L. Rosett and researcher Rebecca H. Warner of Boston University found that Carthage and Sparta had laws prohibiting the use of alcohol by newly married couples to prevent conception during intoxication.

In the eighteenth century the College of Physicians in England called gin a "cause of weak, feeble and distempered children" and asked Parliament to control the distilling trade.

Throughout the nineteenth century there were reports of a high frequency of mental retardation, stillbirths, and deaths among the children of alcoholics. In 1899, a physician in a Liverpool prison observed that several alcoholic women who had borne infants with severe and often fatal complications gave birth to healthy children when, because of imprisonment, they were forced to abstain from alcohol during pregnancy.

AFTER-THE-FACT STUDIES

In the United States the fetal alcohol syndrome was first noted in 1972 by scientists at the University of Washington in Seattle. They found a pattern of symptoms which led them to review clinical records of infants born to chronic alcoholic mothers. They found that 11 of the 12 children born to alcoholic women exhibited a distinct pattern of abnormalities. A followup study of 12 offspring of alcoholic women found that all but one were in the borderline or retarded range of intelligence. By the spring of 1978, hundreds of cases had been reported from medical centers in the United States and elsewhere.

But scientists were troubled because many of the studies were retrospective, the syndrome being noted in newborn babies before the records of the drinking patterns of their mothers were investigated. Scientists prefer the evidence of prospective studies in which the pattern of drinking is noted first and detailed information on the outcome is obtained later. Three such studies are now

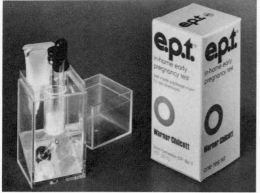

Warner/Chilcott

If a woman wonders if she is pregnant and if it is safe to have a drink, she can use an early-pregnancy test. The test is not 100% reliable though.

under way in the United States. Only preliminary information is now available, but some of the early data is highly significant.

ONGOING STUDIES

These findings confirm that babies born of women who consume between one and two ounces of absolute alcohol a day—that is, two to four drinks—can show abnormalities of growth, congenital malformations, and behavioral characteristics associated with alcohol consumption during pregnancy.

The studies are trying to determine the rate of fetal alcohol syndrome and similar symptoms in human populations; safe limits for alcohol consumption during pregnancy; and the role of episodic versus continuous drinking in the development of the syndrome. They are also studying the prospects of prevention efforts for pregnant women and women of child-bearing age and the possibility of using drugs to safeguard the fetus.

Still other questions being asked and examined include: What effect do different patterns of drinking have on the fetus at various times during pregnancy? What about the effects of different kinds of alcoholic beverages? And their interaction with caffeine, smoking, and other drugs? Or the general nutritional status of the mother?

DRUNK FETUS

In addition to the data being gathered on drinking mothers and their offspring, animal studies in which conditions can be con-

trolled are being stepped up. According to the NIAAA these studies already have shown that alcohol is the cause of a pattern of malformations.

The animals in these studies are not given massive doses of alcohol. Although animals can metabolize or "burn up" alcohol faster than humans, they must not be given an overdose because they, just as humans, will die if given too much. There always are reservations in applying the findings of animal studies to humans, but certain biological and chemical facts cannot be discounted.

For example, alcohol passes easily through membranes, in humans and animals. Therefore, alcohol consumed by a pregnant woman flows through her blood system to the placenta and then to the unborn child.

The alcohol courses through the bloodstream of the unborn child in the same concentration as in its mother's. If the mother is drunk, so is the baby. The problem for the fetus is complicated because its liver, the key organ for removing alcohol from the blood, is not fully developed.

The adult liver can metabolize (convert or eliminate) about a half ounce to an ounce of alcohol in an hour. If more is consumed within the hour, the liver-processing function becomes "overloaded" and the excess alco-

Dr. Henry L. Rosett is the director of the prenatal clinic at Boston City Hospital.

Ralph J. Shuman

Author Lucy Barry Robe, shown with daughter Parrish, has written *Just So It's Healthy,* a book about the effects of alcohol on the unborn fetus.

hol continues to circulate in the system, causing a rise in blood-alcohol content.

Because the undeveloped liver of the fetus works slowly, most of the alcohol that has reached it will be lost eventually by diffusion back across the placenta in a return to the mother's system. But that can't occur until the mother's blood alcohol goes down. Therefore, the fetus "holds" the alcohol until the concentration in its mother decreases.

TO BE SURE—DON'T DRINK

Fortunately, prevention of fetal alcohol syndrome, unlike Down's syndrome and certain other birth defects, requires no medical or scientific breakthroughs. The surest preventive, of course, is for a woman who is pregnant to avoid alcohol completely. Short of that, following the guideline of no more than two drinks per day and generally keeping aware of drinking patterns during pregnancy can help a mother to avoid potential harm to her unborn child.

For women who have a serious drinking problem, timely assistance from health professionals can be effective, according to Dr. Rosett of Boston University. He reports that in a survey of all patients registered at the Boston City Hospital Prenatal Clinic, nine per cent reported heavy drinking. He defined "heavy" as five to six drinks on some occasions and a minimum of 1½ drinks a day when monthly consumption is divided by 30.

Within a group of 42 of the clinic patients who said they drank heavily, 15 were able to abstain or reduce alcohol intake before the last three months of pregnancy. Rosett found that infants born to those 15 had fewer abnormalities than 27 infants whose mothers had continued heavy drinking.

Additional clinical experience supported the initial observation that "reduction of alcohol use during pregnancy benefits the baby," Rosett said.

Dr. Noble has placed the fetal alcohol syndrome high on the list of research priorities at the National Institute, which is committed to "aggressively seek out and study all aspects of life that may be adversely affected by alcohol."

Until the answers are in on the key questions of exactly how much or when alcohol is safe to drink during pregnancy, medical authorities agree that it is wise to be cautious □

SELECTED READINGS

Birth Defects and Drugs in Pregnancy, edited by O. P. Heronen and others. Public Science, 1977.

"Fetal alcohol syndrome," *Current Health,* September 1978.

Just So It's Healthy by Lucy Barry Robe. Comp Care Publications, Minneapolis, Minn. 1977.

"On popping pills and potions during pregnancy" by M. Newton. *Family Health,* May 1977.

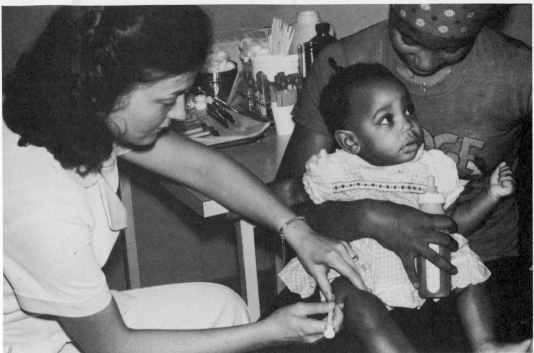

HEW

VACCINES

by Faye Peterson

THE average life expectancy for an American born in 1900 was 47 years. Today it is 72 years. The reason for the difference is not so much that more people today are living longer, but that fewer people are dying before they reach age 10. Vaccines against infectious diseases have played a major role in preventing illness and death at an early age.

There are vaccines available today for most of the so-called "childhood diseases" such as measles, mumps, polio, and diphtheria. Many communities now require that all children be given these vaccines before they enter public school.

MEASLES

Children who have not had measles or who have never been vaccinated should be immunized, preferably before they start school. Measles can lead to brain damage or mental retardation.

When administered at the proper age, one injection of measles vaccine confers long-term immunity. The U.S. Public Health Service says the ideal age for children to be vaccinated is about 15 months old, but a child can be vaccinated as early as 6 months if an outbreak of measles occurs. Children vaccinated before they are 12 months old should be revaccinated at age 15 months or older to assure full protection.

Vaccination of adults rarely is necessary since most of them are immune. However, high school and college age persons should be considered for immunization if a measles epidemic threatens. The vaccine usually can prevent measles if given within 2 days after exposure to the disease.

Immunization is particularly important among children with chronic illnesses, since they are prone to develop complications if they get measles.

The measles vaccine has a good record of safety. About 15 per cent of vaccinated children do experience fever, however, beginning about the sixth day after vaccination and lasting up to 5 days. Occasionally, a child will have a temporary rash following vaccination. More serious adverse reactions to the vaccine, such as encephalitis (inflammation of the brain), occur only once for every million doses given.

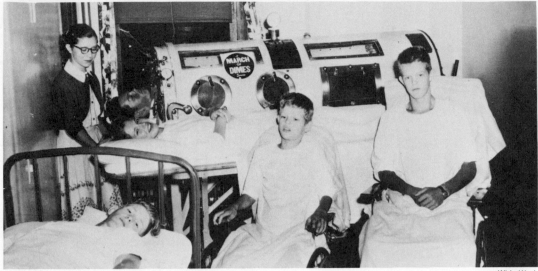

Since polio immunization started in 1955, most of that disease has been eradicated. But as late as 1956 six children of the Greeno family of Camp Douglas, Wisconsin, were stricken.

POLIO

All children should be immunized against polio. Introduction of polio vaccine in 1955 all but eradicated the disease in the United States. However, in recent years the number of unimmunized children has increased substantially. In 1976, about 38 per cent of children between the ages of 1 and 4 had not been properly vaccinated, and rates were even lower among children from poor families. Declining levels of immunization could lead to renewed outbreaks of polio.

Two types of polio vaccines are used in the United States: the Salk vaccine, an injectable, inactivated (killed) virus preparation, and the Sabin vaccine, a live-virus preparation taken orally. The live, oral vaccine is recommended by the Public Health Service because it is easy to administer and requires fewer periodic boosters as does the Salk vaccine.

The first dose of oral polio vaccine should be given to babies at 6 to 12 weeks of age, the second dose 8 weeks later, and the third should follow in 8 to 12 months. A booster dose should be given when the child enters kindergarten or first grade.

For Salk vaccine, a series of four doses should be given beginning at 6 to 12 weeks of age. The first three doses should be given at approximately 1- to 2-month intervals, and the fourth dose, 6 to 12 months after the third. Booster doses usually are given every 2 to 3 years.

Routine polio immunization of adults is not necessary, but unimmunized adults who plan to travel to an area where polio is common should be immunized.

In rare instances, oral polio vaccine has caused paralysis in recipients or in people who come in close contact with them. Of 193 million doses of vaccine distributed, 10 cases of paralysis were reported in otherwise healthy vaccine recipients. Thirty-four cases were reported in people who came in close contact with vaccine recipients. People who have taken oral polio vaccine "shed" live virus, which can infect unimmunized persons who come in close contact with them. It is for this reason that some doctors give unimmunized adults a series of Salk vaccine shots before a child in the same household is given oral polio vaccine.

No serious side effects from Salk polio vaccine are known to exist. It should not be given, however, to persons who are allergic to streptomycin or neomycin, because the vaccine contains trace amounts of these antibiotics.

RUBELLA—GERMAN MEASLES

Rubella is generally a mild disease in children. However, if a woman gets it early in pregnancy, it can affect the fetus, resulting in serious birth defects. Preventing birth defects is a major objective of rubella-immunization programs.

Because children who get rubella can spread it to pregnant women, the vaccine is recommended for all children over the age of 12 months. A combination rubella-measles vaccine is available. If the combination vaccine is used, it should be administered at about 15 months of age. Children should be immunized even if they are believed to have had rubella because other skin rashes often are mistakenly diagnosed as rubella. Therefore, a history of rubella is not a reliable indicator of immunity.

The Public Health Service emphasizes the importance of vaccinating unimmunized preteenage girls as well as susceptible adolescent and adult females. Adolescent and adult females should be immunized, however, only if they are not pregnant, and if they agree to make every effort to prevent pregnancy for 3 months after receiving the vaccine. When possible, they should be given blood tests to determine if they are susceptible to rubella. The Public Health Service recommends that state health departments perform premarital blood testing for rubella so that susceptible women can be immunized before their first pregnancy.

Under no circumstances should a pregnant woman be given the vaccine because of the theoretical risk that it could cause birth defects. If an unimmunized pregnant woman suspects she has been exposed to rubella, she should contact her physician or health department immediately. The rubella blood test can indicate whether she has contracted the disease during pregnancy or was immune before exposure.

Rubella-vaccine side effects, including rash and enlarged glands, occur occasionally in children. Pain in the joints occurs in 2 to 9 per cent of vaccine recipients and is more common and severe in women than in children. When pain in the joints occurs, it usually begins 2 to 10 weeks after immunization and lasts for 1 to 3 days.

Wide World

Dr. Jonas Salk developed a vaccine against polio that contains killed polio viruses.

DIPHTHERIA, TETANUS, WHOOPING COUGH

A combination preparation of diphtheria and tetanus toxoid and pertussis (whooping cough) vaccine (DTP) has been routinely used to immunize infants for about 30 years. Its use has led to a significant decrease in these three diseases during that time.

Children under 7 should receive five DTP injections, ideally beginning when the child is 2 to 3 months old. The first three injections should be separated by 4 to 8 weeks, followed by a fourth dose approximately a year after the third. A booster dose is needed when the child enters school—usually at age 5 or 6.

Because whooping cough is less severe and occurs less frequently as people grow older, children over age 7 and adults need only diphtheria and tetanus toxoid (Td). They should receive three doses, with the second dose 4 to 8 weeks after the first, and the third dose 6 months to 1 year after the second. Everyone should have a Td booster every 10 years. If taken more frequently, routine boosters can cause adverse side effects.

Despite the availability of tetanus toxoid, the disease remains a problem in the United States. In 1975, 102 cases of tetanus were reported. Tetanus is a dangerous disease, and immunization of all persons is important.

Even a minor cut or wound may call for some protection against tetanus. A physician usually is the best guide as to whether a tetanus shot is required for any wound. It is especially important that the physician know the patient's previous immunization record for tetanus.

MUMPS

Mumps occurs mostly in young school-age children. Although it seldom results in serious complications, it causes painfully swollen glands in the face and neck, fever, headache, and earache. It can lead to a condition called orchitis—painful swelling of the testes—when contracted by preteenage boys. Orchitis occurs in about 20 per cent of mumps cases in this age group and, although rare, can result in male sterility.

Mumps vaccine is recommended for all children over the age of 12 months. If given earlier, it may not be effective. Adolescents and adults who have not had mumps, particularly males, should be immunized. The vaccine is more than 90 per cent effective and one shot provides long lasting, possibly lifetime, immunity.

Swollen glands and other mild reactions, such as rash and itching, may occur following mumps immunization, but are rare. Mumps vaccine should not be given to pregnant women, because it has not been tested for its effects on the fetus.

INFLUENZA

Influenza viruses have a way of altering their makeup from time to time. For that reason, immunity to a flu virus that is prevalent in one year will not necessarily provide protection against a virus that is prevalent in the next year. When there is a drastic change in the virus, which occurs about every 10 years, most people will have no immunity to the new virus. It is under these circumstances that worldwide flu epidemics occur, resulting in thousands of deaths.

Influenza vaccines must be evaluated each year and, when necessary, reformulated to make them effective against a new virus. Unfortunately, scientists cannot always accurately predict which form of the virus will strike in time to prepare an effective vaccine against it.

The Public Health Service maintains influenza surveillance units throughout the

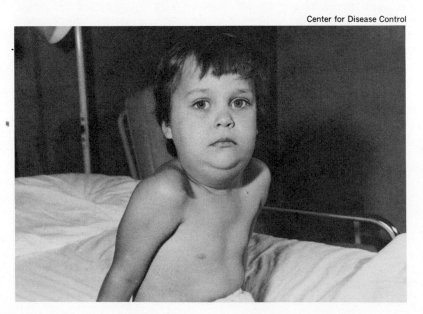

Mumps vaccine is recommended for all children over the age of 12 months. Adolescents and adults who have not had mumps should be immunized.

Rabies is caused by a virus that inhabits the saliva of many mammals, including dogs and cats. Any pet mammal can become a carrier for this deadly disease. The dog shown at right is rabid.

Center for Disease Control

world to detect the occurrence of new viruses. When a new virus is discovered in time to develop a vaccine for it, the vaccine is generally 70–90 per cent effective.

Annual vaccination against influenza is strongly recommended for those who may suffer serious consequences from the disease. This "high-risk" group includes adults and children of all ages who have chronic conditions such as heart disease, chronic bronchitis, tuberculosis, emphysema, kidney disease, and diabetes. Vaccination also is recommended for older persons, particularly those over age 65, because influenza can result in death among many people in this age group.

There is no evidence that flu vaccine is dangerous to pregnant women, but most physicians generally avoid prescribing unnecessary vaccines and drugs during pregnancy.

Reactions to flu vaccine, although infrequent, do occur. These include fever, chills, headache, muscle aches, and soreness at the injection site. These symptoms usually last 1 to 2 days. More severe reactions also can occur, but they are rare and usually are due to an allergy to egg protein (flu vaccine is produced in eggs).

RABIES

Immediate and thorough local treatment of all bites and scratches is perhaps the most effective rabies preventive. The wound should be cleansed immediately with soap and water. A physician should then be contacted. The physician will initiate tetanus immunization and determine whether to begin a series of 24 rabies vaccine injections.

The problem of whether and how to treat persons who have been bitten or scratched by animals or have been otherwise exposed to rabies (such as through contamination of an open wound by saliva from a potentially rabid animal) is complicated. One difficulty is that all available methods of treatment carry risks of adverse reactions. Antirabies treatments have in a few cases resulted in death or permanent disability. Another complicating factor is that the treatment—which involves a series of injections—must be started quickly because the longer it is postponed the less likely it is to be effective.

Thousands of people each year receive rabies treatment, mostly as a result of bites by dogs or cats. The Public Health Service recommends that every possible exposure to rabies be evaluated individually. The factors to be considered in determining whether to initiate antirabies treatment are:

• The species of the biting animal. Meat-eating (carnivorous) animals and bats are more likely than other animals to be infected. But the disease has become more prevalent in wildlife—especially among skunks, foxes, raccoons, and bats.

• The circumstances of the biting incident. An unprovoked attack by an animal is more likely to mean that it is rabid.

Wide World

By 1961 Dr. Albert Sabin had perfected an oral polio vaccine of weakened polio viruses.

PNEUMOCOCCAL PNEUMONIA

Despite the wide use of antibiotics, pneumonia today is the fifth leading cause of death in the United States, killing an estimated 25,000 Americans annually. When tested in people, the pneumoccal vaccine was about 80 per cent effective in preventing pneumococcal pneumonia, a type of bacterial pneumonia. But because information on its effectiveness in large groups of people still is limited, the Public Health Service has not established definite recommendations for its use. Instead, it has issued guidelines to help physicians determine which of their patients would benefit most from the vaccine.

The guidelines suggest that physicians consider giving the vaccine to patients for whom pneumococcal pneumonia would be particularly serious, including the elderly; people over the age of 2 years with serious chronic conditions such as diabetes, heart, respiratory, kidney, and liver disease; and persons with spleen dysfunctions including sickle cell anemia patients. Since pneumonia is more likely to occur under crowded conditions, the vaccine should also be considered for use in nursing homes and other institutions.

Pneumonia is not generally fatal in healthy young adults and children in the United States, and these groups are not considered prime targets for the vaccine. No serious reactions to the vaccine have been observed. A single injection of the vaccine appears to confer long-lasting immunity. Studies are under way to determine if booster doses will be necessary.

VIRAL HEPATITIS

"Viral hepatitis" is a term used to describe three different diseases. They are caused by different viruses known as hepatitis-A, hepatitis-B, and "other hepatitis viruses." It is extremely difficult to determine which of the three diseases a patient has. The physician's diagnosis is generally based on a history of the type of exposure as well as blood tests.

Immune serum globulin offers effective protection against hepatitis-A. This serum is recommended for persons living in the same household with someone who has hepatitis-A unless the uninfected person has had the disease before. It is also sometimes recommended for people traveling to tropical areas and developing countries. If travel to these areas is anticipated, a physician should be consulted about the advisability of administering this vaccine.

SMALLPOX

A worldwide eradication program has resulted in virtual elimination of small pox. No smallpox cases have been reported anywhere in the world since October 1977.

As a result of the decline in smallpox, the Public Health Service no longer recommends routine immunization of children. Smallpox vaccination is now necessary only for international travelers who are going to countries that require it, for those who have been in an infected country in the 2 weeks before returning to the United States, and for certain laboratory personnel □

SELECTED READINGS

"Dead or alive?" *Scientific American,* September 1977.

"Disease-free future for children." *Parents Magazine,* June 1978.

"Immunizing your children: the job of every parent" by J. Califano. *Parents Magazine,* November 1977.

"New hope for gonorrhea vaccine." *Science News,* July 9, 1977.

American Cancer Society

Vial containing 100 million units of interferon.

INTERFERON

by Romaine Bamford

AT LAST—A CURE FOR THE COMMON COLD!
NEW DRUG AGAINST VIRUSES
NEW CANCER-STOPPING DRUG

WHAT? Are these headlines talking about one and the same drug? Well . . . yes. Yes? But there are problems.

Some of the most interesting work in medical sciences at the moment concerns a substance that has a potential as a powerful antiviral drug and as a treatment for certain cancers. Its name—interferon.

WHAT IS IT?

Interferon was discovered in Great Britain in 1957 by two virologists, Alick Isaacs and Jean Lindenmann, who were studying the curious phenomenon that people are hardly ever infected by more than one virus at a time. While working with cultures of cells from chick embryos that had been infected with influenza virus, they discovered that the infected chick cells produced a substance that protected the healthy chick cells not only from influenza but also from other viruses. The substance was named interferon because it interfered with the viral-infection process.

Interferon is a protein that can be made by almost any cell in the vertebrate body that is under attack from a virus. Once the interferon is produced within a cell, it diffuses through the body fluids into other nearby healthy cells and protects them too. Although it has the advantage of being effective against all viruses, interferon is species specific. In other words, the interferon produced in one type of animal cell can only defend other cells of the same animal type against viral infection. Interferon produced in chicken cells cannot prevent infection in, say, monkey cells or human cells.

Ever since its discovery, interferon has held enormous promise as a potent virus fighter. Viral diseases are among the most widespread and devastating known to medical science. While there are many drugs that are extremely effective against bacteria, there are few that are effective against viruses. Furthermore, interferon seems to have most of the qualities of a "perfect" drug. It is active against all viruses, not just a few. And because it is a natural substance produced in the body, it seems unlikely that therapy with interferon would have the harmful and unpleasant side effects that often occur when other drugs are used.

Why is it, that after more than 20 years of research, scientists have not been able to make this "miracle drug" available?

ONLY MINUTE AMOUNTS

Interferon is extraordinarily difficult to recover from the cells where it is manufactured. Until very recently only minute amounts of human interferon have been available for study and research. Most of that has come from Finland where it is extracted from white-blood cells collected from Red Cross donors. The blood is first centrifuged and the thin layer of white blood cells is removed and purified. The white cells are suspended in a culture medium containing blood serum. A virus inducer is then added to the suspension and the mixture is incubated for 24 hours. The inducer stimulates the production of interferon by the white-blood cells. The suspension is then centrifuged again and the crude interferon is removed. Using this process, just one grain of human interferon costs nearly $3,500,000.

Animal interferon is available, but it is also difficult to isolate. And because of its species specificity, it is of limited use in studies affecting humans. Scientists are also investigating the possibility of synthesizing interferon in the laboratory.

HOW DOES IT WORK?

It has taken a long time for scientists to find out how interferon works in the cell, and they still don't know all the answers. First of all, interferon has to be induced—something has to stimulate its production. In the body the attacking virus is, of course, the inducer. In the laboratory, scientists have shown that one of the best inducers is a short segment of double-stranded RNA, or ribonucleic acid, a substance present in all cells involved in protein synthesis and the genetic material of most virus cells. Actual interferon production within the cell can be triggered in either of two ways.

In the first, RNA from a virus attaches itself to a receptor on the cell surface. It then either enters the cell or sends a message to the cell nucleus, which then initiates interferon production. In the second process, the entire virus attaches itself onto a cell-surface receptor and then enters the cell. There the virus makes new RNA that, in turn, induces interferon production. No matter by which process, once the inducer gets into the cell, it stimulates one of the chromosomes in the nucleus of the host cell to produce RNA that in turn directs the production of interferon.

ANTIVIRAL PROTEIN

The interferon then diffuses out of the cell and binds itself to another cell where it stimulates that cell to synthesize an antiviral protein. It is this protein that then protects the cell from attack by a virus. When a new virus tries to attack the cell, it can enter the cell but it cannot multiply and cause the cell's death. This is because the antiviral protein interferes with processes essential to the life of the virus.

Thus the antiviral agent is not interferon itself but is the antiviral protein that interferon stimulates. Interferon is, however, the vital substance in the process: no antiviral protein is produced without interferon. One molecule of interferon can trigger the synthesis of a great deal of antiviral protein. Thus very few interferon molecules are necessary to protect a cell. This explains how interferon is so biologically active and why it is such a powerful substance.

Because interferon alters protein synthesis in cells, it has an effect on host cells as well as on virus cells, but for some as yet unknown reason interferon's effect on virus cells is much greater and occurs much faster.

EXPENSIVE WAY TO TREAT A COLD

One of the most common virus infections is the common cold. In one study large doses of interferon were given to volunteers who had been infected with rhinovirus (just one of the many cold viruses). The volunteers' cold symptoms decreased significantly—and without drug side effects. But the cost of the treatment was expensive—about $700 for four days' worth of medicine.

GOOD AGAINST HEPATITIS

Interferon has proved extremely effective in studies of the treatment of chronic hepatitis. Chronic hepatitis is a common and often fatal disease of the liver that affects some 100,000,000 people throughout the world. Victims of chronic hepatitis are sub-

ject to repeated attacks of the active disease, each attack causing further damage to the liver. Patients treated with large initial doses of interferon showed a significant decrease in hepatitis indicators in the blood, and this improvement was thereafter maintained with smaller doses. These results were so encouraging that the study is being expanded to include tests on patients in the active phases of the disease as well.

FOR THOSE WITH INEFFECTIVE IMMUNE SYSTEMS

Many investigators believe that interferon could be very useful in treating people who are at a high risk from virus infections because their own immune systems are for some reason ineffective. This would include patients suffering from chronic immunological disorders as well as transplant patients taking drugs to suppress their immune systems. This would also include cancer patients and other patients whose immune systems are not functioning normally as a result of some kind of drug therapy.

INTERFERON AND CANCER

Interferon has also been used to treat some forms of bone cancer. In some patients with cancer of a limb bone, interferon treatment permitted removal of only the diseased portion of the limb and not amputation of the entire limb—the usual treatment for limb-bone cancer. Scientists do not, however, know how interferon works in cancer cases.

The drug appears to have some anti-tumor properties—a fact that has led some to have high hopes for interferon as an effective cancer weapon. But how does interferon fight tumors? Some cancers are thought to be caused by viruses and in these cases it could be interferon's antiviral properties that make it effective against tumors. However, it is also possible that interferon slows down tumor growth by interfering with nucleic-acid synthesis within these cells. And interferon's profound effects on the body's immune system may also result in tumor rejection.

Treating cancers with interferon is still, however, very much in the early stages of research. The decision to use it as a form of experimental therapy in the case of a particular cancer is often a shot in the dark, a decision taken only when there is no proven or even promising alternative treatment available. Prospects are bright, however. The American Cancer Society recently provided a grant of $2,000,000 to buy interferon and announced in November 1978 that interferon would be used in its first mass test in a number of medical centers throughout the United States.

A CURE ALL?

In 1960 a Flash Gordon comic strip showed interferon being used to combat a mysterious extra-terrestrial virus that was causing an epidemic among members of a spaceship crew. It may be some time before we find out if interferon is effective against such alien bugs but in the meantime there is at least serious hope that it may help eliminate some of our home grown health problems □

SELECTED READINGS

"Interferon: medicine for cancer and the common cold?" by A. Rosenfeld. *Saturday Review*, Nov. 25, 1978.

"Interferon: the unknown wonder drug" by J. R. Hixson. *Science Digest*, September 1978.

"Status of interferon" by D. C. Burke. *Scientific American*, April 1977.

Below: the scorpion's tail is tipped with a stinger whose poison can be fatal to children. Right: the black-widow spider is very poisonous and can produce paralysis.

John H. Gerard

Jacques Six

BUGS THAT BITE AND STING

by Claude A. Frazier, M.D.

FACE it: there is no escaping them. They are out there every spring and summer, waiting for you—mosquitoes, chiggers, black flies, ticks, spiders, scorpions, deer flies. In numbers alone, their advantage is staggering. One energetic soul with a computer cast of mind recently estimated that a single hectare of land can host some 1,000,000,000 "arthropods," as these creeping, crawling, flying creatures are called. With odds like that, you know they will leave their mark on you, whether you're a birdwatcher, a hiker, a fisherman, a hunter, or just a weekend picnicker. What you may not know, however, is that some insects can actually make some people quite ill.

As a physician, I have to deal with the problem of insect bites every summer. The sad part is that much of the carnage can be prevented. Potential allergic reactions to bee stings, chigger bites, and other frequently encountered nuisances can be spotted. Nonallergic people can console themselves with the fact that workaday stings, bites, and welts are treatable. What's more, many of these tiny creatures can be outsmarted.

AVOID, IF POSSIBLE

There are a few common sense rules for avoiding stings or bites: Don't wear extremely bright colors or sweet smells. Do wear light-colored clothing—khaki, light green, tan, or white. Don't go barefoot or wear sandals. In the presence of bees, don't flail your arms; retreat slowly.

If you do get stung by a winged pest, treatment is easy. Scrape out the stinger, if there is one, with a knife or fingernail. Do not try to pull it out, as this will squeeze the venom sac and pump more toxin into the wound. Wash the sting area well with soap and water. Apply ice or baking soda to sooth the pain, slow the absorption of venom into the body, and reduce swelling.

Beyond these general rules, there are some things you should know about specific pests.

MOSQUITOES

Studies have shown that a sweating, warm, dark-skinned individual who is breathing hard is exactly the meal the mosquito craves. This creature also seems to find healthy human beings more attractive targets than the ailing. Luckily, many of us can develop a certain amount of immunity to the bites and attendant itching inflicted by the mosquitoes living in our immediate vicinity.

Treatment, in any case, is simple. First, wash well with soap and water. Secondary infection is a real possibility, especially for children, so it's wise to keep the fingernails short during summer months to minimize chances of scratching bacteria into the lesions. Phenolated calamine lotion applied to the bites, or Temaril taken orally, helps relieve the itching. Very cold wet Epsom salt dressings reduce swelling. This type of dressing can be made by dissolving one tablespoon of Epsom salt in a quart of hot water and then chilling. For swollen bites around the eyes, cold compresses of bicarbonate of

Alexander B. Klots

This blood-filled mosquito (*culex pipiens*) has pulled its proboscis out of someone's arm, which may start to itch.

soda (one teaspoon to a glass of water) provide some relief.

Prevention is always a little uncertain, but some of the spray or rub-on repellents seem to work, especially those containing "deet" (diethyl-toluamide). Some outdoors people swear by oral thiamine choloride (vitamin B_1), which they claim makes their bodies unappetizing to mosquitoes.

BLACK FLIES

Worse by far than mosquitoes are the humpbacked black flies that swarm so viciously in some areas, or so it is said, that they can kill chickens or even mules. In Bullhead City, Arizona, the tiny things are so bad that they force residents to do the famed Bullhead Salute—a wild thrashing of arms. There are a number of species of this particular pest, and some of them can even bite through clothing. Apparently, the insect injects a bit of anesthesia with its bite, for the victim often doesn't know he's been bitten until the fly has dined and departed. Then the pain and itch begin. There are cases of severe allergic reaction on record, and even of deep shock. Treatment of ordinary reaction is the same as for mosquito bites.

Jacques Six

The horsefly has a heavy, stabbing proboscis. It's bite can be very painful. You may have seen them swarming around horses and cows.

BITING MIDGES

Biting midges are tiny flies that are sometimes called "no-see-ums." They are equally as vicious and as painful as black flies, and will descend upon their hapless victim at dawn and at dusk, particularly in the woods and in areas near water and marshy ground. Cloudy days also bring out swarms of these tiny Draculas, each one of which can raise a welt larger than that of the mosquito. Again, treat their bites the same as you would a mosquito bite.

CHIGGERS

Once aboard, the chigger scurries about until it comes to a clothing barrier, such as a belt or fairly tight seam. Here it settles down to dine, attaching itself firmly before secreting a digestive substance that liquifies the cells of the host's skin. The substance penetrates, forming a hollow tube that enables the chigger to suck up its dinner much like soda through a straw.

The host, meanwhile, is usually unaware that supper is being served—until the secretion penetrates deeper, and the itch begins. If allergic symptoms develop, or if signs of infection such as marked discoloration or swelling occur, you should see a doctor. Otherwise, phenolated calamine lotion, Caligesic ointment, oral Temaril, and starch baths may help relieve the itching. If the chigger is still present as a tiny red spot in the bite, it should be removed with a needle point.

TICKS

Ticks come in three familiar forms: the American dog tick; the Lone Star tick; and the Rocky Mountain tick, or wood tick, infamous for spreading Rocky Mountain spotted fever. All three have a habit of waiting patiently on vegetation beside roads, paths, and animal trails until something warm-blooded happens along. Once they find a host, they clamp on firmly with their curved teeth. Their grip is so strong that the body is often pulled free of the head and mouthparts. When this occurs in the human hide, infection may result, or a rather strange complication called tick bite granuloma may set in. In this granuloma, tumorlike growths occur at the site of tick bites. It is not known if these growths are the result of embedded tick mouthparts in the skin or of some substance in the tick's saliva. The resulting growths are frightening to look at, but they are harmless and often disappear in their own good time. The odd part is that the growths may appear days or even months after the tick has dined and departed.

The wood tick is a carrier of Rocky Mountain spotted fever, a serious disease.

John H. Gerard

The Tarantula's bite is especially effective against those insects it feeds on and is very painful to people.

Equally strange, but potentially far more serious, is tick paralysis. This condition usually develops from the bite of a blood-engorged female tick, in the region of the neck or close to the spine. The paralysis occasionally is fatal. Very small children are especially susceptible. It is important, therefore, to hold daily inspections during tick season. Prevention of tick paralysis is undramatic—simply remove the tick.

There is, however, a certain skill in removing the tick intact. One way is to grasp the tick between the thumb and index finger, then pull it out slowly and steadily. A drop of gasoline, kerosene, benzene, ether, or alcohol upon the animal's head or thereabouts is said to make the tick loosen its grip.

Once the tick is gone, the bite area should be thoroughly washed with soap and water, and then iodine or some other antiseptic should be applied. If infection or granuloma appears, consult a doctor.

How to discourage ticks from coming aboard in the first place? Slosh on plenty of insect repellent containing deet. And wear long pants and boots.

SPIDERS

Unless you're in the habit of sticking your hands and feet into dark places, you are unlikely to encounter the black widow and brown recluse spiders. Both of these venomous animals have a penchant for dark crevices, old rock piles, lumber stacks, trash, piles of long-unused clothing, and the like.

Initially, the black widow's bite is not much more than a pricking pain, but it soon becomes very painful, and the venom can make you very sick. Symptoms can be intense pain, a rigid, "boardlike" abdomen that mimics appendicitis, nausea, vomiting, convulsions, cold sweats, paralysis, breathing difficulties, discoloration of the skin, delirium, and shock.

The stiffened abdomen has almost been enough on occasion to land the victim of a black widow in surgery for an appendectomy. I had a call from a Georgia physician not long ago who nearly performed such an operation after being misled by the sudden illness of a man who had been working in his barn. The operation was called off after the patient happened to mention that he had observed a number of spiders in the barn.

Both the black widow and the brown recluse can kill people who are very young, very old, or infirm. The brown recluse makes a thoroughly gruesome-looking lesion.

The victim of either spider should be rushed to a physician or hospital and, if possible, the spider or its remains should be brought along for identification. Ice packs on the bite will slow absorption of the venom. There is an antivenom for black widow bite, and if given soon enough, it will bring quick relief to symptoms. I haven't heard of an antivenom to counter the brown recluse's toxin, but medical treatments are available.

SCORPIONS

Run-of-the-mill scorpions can inflict a painful sting with some accompanying discoloration and swelling, but the venom of the two potently toxic species (*Centruroides gertshii* and *Centruroides sculpturatus*) affects the nervous system. In the United States, this venomous duo is generally limited to the Southwest, especially southern Arizona. In this area, it does not pay to rummage under

The red-and-black velvet ants produce a painful sting. They are actually a type of wasp.

This honeybee is gathering nectar from a daisy from which it will make honey. Its sting is very painful and can be dangerous to those people who are allergic to the chemical that it injects.

Jacques Six

rocks, under the bark of trees, or in trash piles, unless you can see everything you touch. However, wet weather drives the pests out into the open.

Reaction to potent scorpion venom begins with a period of hypersensitivity, but then the victim becomes drowsy and numb. Soon, painful muscle spasms may begin, followed by convulsions. If the victim survives the first three hours, he is usually going to recover. Fatalities to scorpion stings most often occur in youngsters.

Treatment of a scorpion's sting must be immediate. Ice should be packed around the sting site, and the whole area should be immersed in ice water. The victim should be taken to a hospital quickly, for there is antivenom for scorpion toxins. A camper or hiker out in territory where scorpions abound should carry an ethyl chloride "bomb" among his first aid supplies. When sprayed on the sting area, it can cool and slow absorption of the venom almost as well as ice.

OTHER PESTS

There are many other beetles and bugs that occasionally run a collision course with humans. The puss caterpillar can inflict a very painful wound and can even kill a very young child. Sometimes called the "Italian asp," it possesses venom in hollow spines scattered among its hairs. Wheelbugs—those odd, large gray bugs that appear to carry half a cogged wheel as a crest—can inflict a painful bite if accidentally contacted.

Alexander B. Klots

The caterpillar of the flannel moth have stinging spines, which are very painful.

Blister beetles exude a powerful substance, cantharidin, that can raise large fluid-filled blisters on human skin. These beetles fly about at night and are attracted to lights. They may fall upon an unsuspecting person who will try to brush them off. The next morning, the result can be pretty horrifying, for wherever the beetle contacts the skin, it leaves a trail of unsightly blisters. Fortunately, they disappear within a few days.

young men from my home area went off on a Sunday fishing trip, about a week after one of them had suffered a severe reaction to a bee sting. Unfortunately, he was stung again kilometers from the nearest hospital or doctor. Within minutes, he was gasping for breath, and there was nothing his horrified friend could do. The young man died because he didn't have a sting kit.

Finally, it's wise for anyone who is allergic to insects—in fact to anything—to wear a medical warning tag or bracelet to alert an attending physician and save him precious time.

The sting of the vespula hornet, or yellowjacket, can cause internal bleeding because it makes the walls of the capillaries permeable.

Alexander B. Klots

A SPECIAL WARNING

In the United States, there are some 1,000,000 people who could suffer an allergic reaction to insect venom or saliva. These people must be the most concerned about encounters with pests. For them, only one or two stings or bites can cause fatal shock.

How to tell if you're allergic? You'll know from the symptoms when you're stung: severe swelling or widespread hives; itching about the eyes, mouth, and face or constriction in the chest and throat; maybe nausea, vomiting, and abdominal pain; perhaps dizziness, hoarseness, and thickened speech; weakness, confusion, and a sense of impending disaster; decreased blood pressure and purplish skin; unconsciousness.

If you have suffered even the mildest of these symptoms after being bitten or stung, you should consult a physician. Protective steps can be taken—including an insect sting kit your doctor can prescribe. This compact kit contains a dose of epinephrine (adrenalin) usually in a syringe. Without epinephrine, it's possible for severe allergic reaction to be fatal. Several years ago, two

NO CURE-ALL

Meantime, all of us will continue to fiddle with bug juices and various kinds of protective clothing, vainly looking for pest cure-alls. I know only one person who has an infallible solution. She's a patient of mine who carries within her body enough antibodies to make any mosquito that bites her drop dead. What's her secret? Apparently, her acquired resistance stems from a mysterious change in her internal chemistry, caused by a bout she had with malaria at the age of ten. And that's a higher price than most of us are willing to pay, even for immunity from the millions of little nuisances that await every time we step outdoors □

SELECTED READINGS

"How to avoid being stung" by R. A. Morse, *Conservationist*, April 1974.

"Insect sting: a biting question" by M. D. Valentine. *Family Health,* August 1978.

National Institutes of Health

Nobelist Dr. Daniel Gajdusek writes down medical histories of the Fore people in the New Hebrides during his study of the "trembling sickness."

SLOW VIRUSES

by Carol Kahn

IN the 1950's, in a remote corner of the earth, a group of 35,000 Stone Age cannibals known to modern people as the Fore, was dying. Barely ten years after their New Guinea jungle highlands were opened to civilization, a mysterious and terrifying disease threatened to end their existence.

The Fore called it "kuru"—the trembling sickness. Its victims were women and children. At the beginning, when kuru made its first insidious appearance in a victim, he or she would start to move a bit unsteadily and to experience barely noticeable tremors. Gradually, the trembling and shivering would increase, until the victims began a literal dance of death. Then, alone or in groups, they writhed uncontrollably in the throes of violent tremors. Sometimes they broke into grins, sometimes into shrieks of wild laughter. But as the dance went on, the smiles faded. Within a year, the kuru dancer no longer laughed, or walked, or stood, or sat, or swallowed. At the end of a year, the dance was over. The dancer was dead.

"It is so astonishing an illness that clinical description can only be read with skepticism, and I was highly skeptical until two days ago when I arrived and began to see cases on every side." So wrote Daniel Carleton Gajdusek, a medical anthropologist, when he walked into a Fore village in 1957 to seek the cause of the disease. He spent many months—and trekked more than 1,500 kilometers of dense jungle—before he had his answer. And a strange one it was.

CANNIBALISM CLUE

Kuru was spread among the Fore, Dr. Gajdusek concluded, "during their ritual cannibalistic consumption of their dead relatives as a rite of respect and mourning." Over and over, as the medical anthropologist watched, women and children performed "autopsies" on the bodies of their beloved dead. They removed brain tissue, squeezed it into a pulp, packed it and other tissues into bamboo cylinders, steamed it and ate it. Without washing their hands after such labor, they scratched insect bites, cleaned babies' noses and eyes, and wiped their hands on their own bodies and in their hair. They virtually inoculated themselves with contaminated brain tissues. Only adult men, who lived in separate houses and rarely took part in the ritual, were spared. Once the cause was known, the cure was obvious. The Government of New Guinea forbade cannibalism and enforced the ban. Within a short period, kuru virtually disappeared—and the Fore lived. Gajdusek received the 1976 Nobel Prize in Physiology or Medicine for his work.

AN UNUSUAL VIRUS

For modern man, the description of the Fore's deadly ritual held a grim fascination. For scientists, it held a mystery—and a revelation. Because the spread of kuru had reached such epidemic proportions, some transmissable, viruslike agent had to be considered a suspect. A virus is an infinitesimal creature consisting of only an outer protein shell and a bit of nucleic acid containing RNA (ribonucleic acid) or DNA (deoxyribonucleic acid), the genetic material of which all living cells are composed.

But usually when a virus causes a disease such as flu, smallpox, or the common cold, it spreads quickly from person to person. In each victim, it runs a short, intense course during which it either overwhelms the body's defenses and kills the host, or is itself overwhelmed, so that the patient recovers.

In kuru, however, all these familiar viral signs were lacking. The disease often failed to appear until years after the patient was contaminated. Once started, it ran a slow course of three months to a year. And there was no sign of the presence of a virus—or of the body's response to one—except that the kuru victim's brain showed spongelike changes.

SLOW INFECTION

Around the time Gajdusek was reporting on kuru in medical journals, an Icelandic researcher, Bjorn Sigruddson, was writing in veterinarian publications about a neurological sheep disease called scrapie. He concluded that the disease was due to a "slow infection" and listed a set of criteria for transmissable agents that cause disease long after they originally invade the victim. In 1959, William Hadlow, a U.S. veterinarian, noted striking similarities in the clinical symptoms and pathology of scrapie and kuru and suggested that kuru should be studied from the point of view of a slow infection.

"This report gave impetus to the whole effort to prove that kuru was a transmissable disease," says Clarence (Joe) Gibbs, Jr., a research microbiologist. Gibbs is a long-term collaborator with Gajdusek, who is now

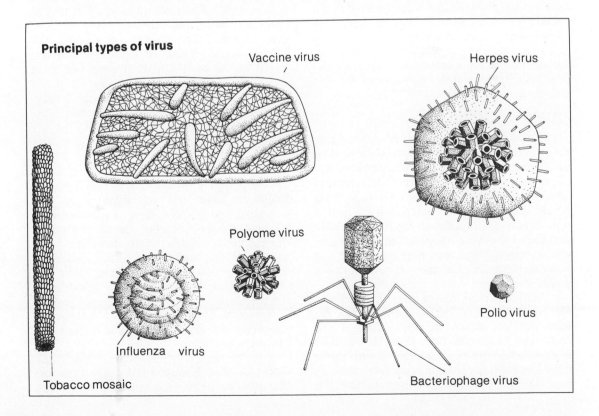

Principal types of virus

Vaccine virus

Herpes virus

Polyome virus

Influenza virus

Tobacco mosaic

Bacteriophage virus

Polio virus

Institute of Cancer Research, Fox Chase Cancer Center

Dr. Baruch S. Blumberg shared the 1976 Nobel Prize with Dr. Gajdusek for researching a test for hepatitis virus and a vaccine for it.

chief of the central-nervous-systems studies laboratory of the U.S. National Institute of Neurological and Communicative Disorders and Stroke, the world's leading center of research into slow viruses. It was there that chimpanzees inoculated with brain tissue from kuru patients developed the disease ten months to six years later. This experimental result finally proved the existence of the elusive slow kuru virus.

A TURNING POINT

The kuru virus discovery was a turning point in our knowledge of viruses. "The classical concepts of virology and infectious diseases were based on acute fulminating [intense] disease," explains Gibbs. "You would take infectious material and inject it into experimental animals or tissue culture and then if nothing happened in thirty days, you assumed there was nothing there. Nobody thought about holding animals for two, three, five years."

With the example of kuru in mind, the National Institutes of Health (NIH) researchers and others began looking at the dementias of people, both those that started in middle life and those associated with senility. New forms of transmission were considered—forms that ranged from eating the lightly grilled brains of sheep to fondling sick dogs. And outside of the nervous system, viruses connected with hepatitis and cancer were discovered to have unusual characteristics. The viruses thought to cause all these diseases have been lumped together under the name "slow viruses." But this is a misnomer, says Gibbs; "It is not the virus that is slow, but the infection." And slow infections can be caused by two completely unrelated kinds of viruses: conventional and unconventional.

Conventional viruses, such as those that cause measles and smallpox, have certain things in common. They stimulate inflammatory and immune responses in the bodies they infect. They can be seen under the electron microscope. They are inactivated by such chemical and physical agents as ultraviolet light, boiling water, or formaldehyde.

Unconventional viruses, such as the one that causes kuru, do none of these things. They are even smaller than the smallest conventional virus and as yet appear to have no nucleic acid. As one investigator puts it: "They have never been seen, smelled or heard from." Stealthy and secret, the unconventional virus multiplies rapidly in host cells, starting first in the spleen and the lymph nodes. Then, mysteriously unhampered by the body's protective antibodies, it makes its way into the gray matter of the brain, where it destroys certain nerve cells. Then and only then do the symptoms of disease begin to appear.

CREUTZFELD-JAKOB DISEASE

The unconventional virus's long incubation period and unique resistance to destruction have led to some horrifying accidents. Most of them have involved Creutzfeld-Jakob disease, the second disorder shown by Gibbs and his associates to be caused by a slow virus. Like kuru, this brain infection starts slowly. At first, there are vague psychic disturbances. In a few months the victim begins to experience jerking movements of the limbs. All intellectual functions deteriorate. In about a year, the patient is dead.

When the NIH researchers made their report on this disease, they warned doctors that persons dying of Creutzfeld-Jakob disease should not be allowed to donate tissues to other people. Nonetheless, the cornea of a man who died from Creutzfeld-Jakob disease was inadvertently transplanted into a woman. Eighteen months later, she developed the disease. In Switzerland, silver electrodes that had been used in treating a Creutzfeld-Jakob patient were used again— this time inserted into the brains of two young epileptics, a 17-year-old boy and a 23-year-old woman. Both came down with the incurable disease.

Incidents such as these have caused considerable anxiety among neurosurgeons, pathologists, and nurses who might come into contact with virus-contaminated objects. Some have begun to call the Creutzfeld-Jakob disease virus the "Andromeda strain." Gibbs insists this fear is unwarranted. A number of agents, including household Clorox and dry heat, will inactivate the virus. And the disease remains extraordinarily rare.

Apart from accidental transmission, almost nothing is known about how the Creutzfeld-Jakob virus gets into the body. There may be a genetic factor: 12 to 14 per cent of those with the disease have family members who are also victims. It is possible that scrapie, kuru, and Creutzfeld-Jakob disease, all of which involve spongelike changes in the brain, are caused by different strains of the same unconventional virus.

SENILITY? AGING ITSELF?

But fascinating as these diseases are, they affect only a tiny portion of the world's population. The circle widens dramatically when you include everyone suffering from familial Alzheimer's disease. This is a rare form of presenile dementia, the mental illness that accounts for up to 45 per cent of the residents in nursing homes and mental institutions in the United States. Familial Alzheimer's disease is now considered a possible variant of the Creutzfeld-Jakob disease virus, and a commoner form of presenile dementia, called sporadic Alzheimer's disease, is still under investigation for a slow-virus connection.

And what about other forms of mental deterioration? Senile dementia is one we tend to write off as an inevitable sign of aging. But could it be a result of an unconventional virus? "We know that the pathological lesions of both presenile and senile dementia are virtually the same," says Gibbs. "The old distinction between senile and presenile diseases, based on age, just doesn't hold." Now he and his colleagues are looking at the aging process itself, to see whether some aspects might not be due to a diminution of the immune system, resulting in a failure to combat invading organisms such as viruses.

ALL VIRUSES DEVIOUS

The discovery of the unconventional viruses has inspired new understanding of just how devious the conventional viruses can be. In certain circumstances they, too, can cause chronic, persistent, or latent infections such as the recurrent mouth blisters caused by the herpes-simplex virus. We now know that even normally acute diseases, such as rabies, can occur years after the person was bitten and treated.

The problem was, says Gibbs, that we often asked the wrong questions: " 'Why does one person get a disease and another person doesn't?' Now we realize that there are genetic factors involved, and that some people may manifest the disease, others may get subclinically infected and never manifest the disease, and still others may show the disease at a much later date."

Some of the slow infections caused by conventional viruses are finally beginning to reveal their secrets. We now know why we are witnessing a decline in the incidence of subacute sclerosing panencephalitis, a brain infection fatal to children and adolescents: it's because vaccination campaigns are pre-

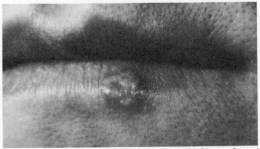

Center for Disease Control

The herpes-simplex virus (see figure on page 231) can cause recurring lip blisters.

venting the spread of the measles virus, the original source of infection.

MS AND DOGS

In still other diseases, slow infections from conventional viruses are strongly suspected, but not yet isolated. One of the most fascinating slow virus theories involves multiple sclerosis, a disease in which the myelin sheath that covers certain nerves and helps speed transmission of electrical impulses is broken down and replaced by thickened scar-tissue-like patches called scleroses. Stuart Cooke, chairman of neurosciences at the New Jersey College of Medicine and Dentistry, and his colleague Peter Dowling believe that in the same way that scrapie in sheep may turn out to be Creutzfeld-Jakob in people, multiple sclerosis may arise from dog distemper.

The New Jersey team's present detective work started a few years ago when they learned of a most unusual case in which three girls from the same family came down with multiple sclerosis in one year, while a fourth sister, who was living away from home, did not. What had happened, they wondered, in the interim between the time the fourth girl left home and the other three developed multiple sclerosis? It turned out that in that time the family dog had contracted a neurological illness. The animal recovered, but a year later the three girls were sick.

Because there are certain features of canine distemper that are similar to multiple sclerosis, Drs. Cooke and Dowling decided to probe further. In two epidemiological studies that they conducted among New Jersey multiple-sclerosis patients and matched controls, they found that the patients had a significantly higher number of small indoor dogs, the kind that are likely to be fondled. Moreover, the multiple sclerosis victims had more neurologically sick dogs during the five-year period preceding their own illness.

But the most striking piece of evidence linking the animal and human diseases comes from two sets of islands in the North Atlantic Ocean. The first is actually two groups—the Orkney and the Shetland islands—off the coast of Scotland. In these islands, which are believed to have the highest incidence of multiple sclerosis in the world, close contact with dogs is extremely common, and distemper is rampant among the canine population.

Some 350 kilometers away are the Faroe

Is Cancer a Slow Virus Infection?

The role of viruses in cancer is very complicated. In the sense that viruses have been shown to induce some malignancies in animals, and that the disease appears some time after exposure, certain forms of cancer could be considered a slow infection. But the case for virus in human cancer has yet to be nailed down, according to Carlos Lopez, head of the laboratory of herpes and slow virus infections at Memorial Sloan-Kettering Cancer Center in New York.

In some human cancers, such as Burkitt's lymphoma in Africa and nasopharyngeal cancer in certain groups of Chinese people, "We know that the virus is there but whether the virus caused the tumor, or is a passenger that is allowed because of the tumor, has not yet been established," says Lopez. Even if viruses are shown to cause cancer in people, most investigators, including Lopez, believe that they will not be the sole cause. Rather, it is likely that the virus interacts with a number of other factors, such as carcinogens in the environment, and genetic susceptibility in the host, to cause the disease.

But a vaccine that has the effect of preventing at least one form of cancer may soon be available. Developed by Baruch Blumberg and his colleagues at the Institute of Cancer Research of the Fox Chase Cancer Center in Philadelphia, Pennsylvania, the vaccine is designed to prevent hepatitis B infection. Dr. Blumberg, who shared the Nobel Prize in Physiology and Medicine with Dr. Daniel C. Gajdusek in 1976, found that the hepatitis B virus can result in different things in different people, ranging all the way from nothing (in persons who develop immunity against it) to acute hepatitis, chronic hepatitis, chronic infection without hepatitis, end-stage liver disease, and cancer of the liver.

"We have accumulated a considerable amount of evidence," he says, "that persistent infection with hepatitis B virus is required for primary cancer of the liver. If you can prevent the infection, it follows that you could prevent the development of cancer of the liver."

Are there other virus-induced cancers? "Just on the general logic that if one cancer happens this way, there may be others, we are looking for such things," he says. "That is where our major attention is directed."

Donna Fargo, a country-music star, was stricken in 1978 with multiple sclerosis, which may be caused by a slow virus. The virus breaks down the covering of certain nerves, which transmit electrical impulses.

Prima Donna Productions

islands, a Danish possession in which multiple sclerosis has been virtually nonexistent—except during one critical period. Between 1944 and 1960, there was an epidemic of 18 multiple sclerosis cases. John Kurtzke, a U.S. Veterans Administration neuroepidemiologist, and J. F. Hyllested, a Danish neurologist, studied this strange phenomenon and linked the cause of the outbreak to the British occupation of the islands during World War II.

Enter now Cooke and Dowling, who, with their dog hypothesis in mind, had a veterinarian check the records of dog distemper on the Faroe islands. He found that there was none prior to World War II. But shortly after the British troops arrived, there was a huge outbreak among the officers' dogs; in fact, 75 per cent of the animals died. Two or three years after this epidemic, the first cases of multiple sclerosis appeared in the Faroes. The last case of canine distemper was recorded in 1956, and that of human multiple sclerosis four years later.

Is this coincidence or cause and effect? Many experts are convinced it is coincidence, and are concerned that worried families might abandon or kill harmless pets out of unwarranted fear. The New Jersey neurologists concede that much work needs to be done before they can come to a firm conclusion. At the moment, they are carrying out a nationwide epidemiologic study sponsored by the U.S. National Academy of Science and the Veterans Administration, involving

thousands of multiple sclerosis patients. If multiple sclerosis does prove to be due, at least in part, to the canine virus, "It would be very exciting," says Cooke. "It offers the possibility of eliminating or greatly reducing the incidence of multiple sclerosis by vaccinating all dogs against distemper."

LAST UNEXPLORED AREA

Through studies such as these, workers in the field of slow infections hope first to identify the hidden culprit in a number of nervous diseases, and eventually to be able to nip the infectious process in the bud. "It's strangely interesting that the last of the unexplored areas of human disease has been that affecting man's most vital organ—his brain," says NIH virologist Gibbs. "It is really only in the last fifteen or twenty years that we have begun to re-examine the diseases affecting that part that even the philosophers of old called the 'seat of the soul.' It is as though we saved the best for last" □

SELECTED READINGS

"Multiple sclerosis: genetic link, viruses suspected" by T. H. Maugh, 2nd. *Science,* Feb. 18, 1977.
"1976 Nobel Prize—Physiology or Medicine" by R. F. Marsh. *Science,* Nov. 26, 1976.
"Slow virus finally identified; scrapie virus." *Science News,* Oct. 7, 1978.
"Viremia in experimental Creutzfeld-Jakob disease" by E. E. Manuelidis and others. *Science,* June 2, 1978.

Illustrations by Diana Coleman

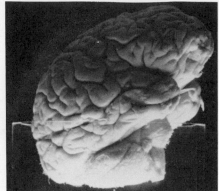

© Ted Spagna

The carbohydrate foods. Simple sugars like glucose are the building blocks of carbohydrates. They are made of carbon, oxygen, and hydrogen.

HOW DIET AFFECTS THE BRAIN

by Richard J. Wurtman

AT medical school, they told us that the brain occupied an exalted position among the body's parts. So grand was its role, they said, that its metabolic, or energy, needs always came first, before those of any other organ. In a crisis, if oxygen, glucose, or even heat failed to be present in adequate amounts within the bloodstream to supply all the body organs, then the brain could arrange to receive preferential treatment. Additional blood containing the scarce item, in just the right amount required to satisfy its appetites, would be pumped to the brain.

Unstated was that, under normal conditions, the amounts of circulating nutrients available to the brain at any moment were largely independent of their concentrations in the bloodstream. In other words, the brain knew what it needed and took it from the blood no matter what your metabolic state or what you ate for breakfast.

What I learned at medical school turns out to be only partly true. My associates and I at the Massachusetts Institute of Technology (MIT) have been surprised to discover that the brain is not an autonomous organ, independent of metabolic processes elsewhere in the body.

In fact, the ability of brain neurons, or nerve cells, to make and to release at least two of their own neurotransmitters depends directly on the composition of the blood. Neurotransmitters are compounds that neurons use to transmit signals to other cells. If your bloodstream does not contain certain nutrients these neurotransmitters are not available to do their jobs. Consequently, your brain depends on breakfast.

THE BRAIN AND FOOD CHANGES

We know that at least two neurotransmitters are affected by nutritional state. They are serotonin and acetylcholine.

Serotonin is formed, within some brain neurons, from tryptophan, an essential amino acid which the body cannot manufacture by itself. The brain obtains this amino acid from the bloodstream, which in turn gets it from the diet.

Other brain neurons create acetylcholine, the neurotransmitter released by all neurons whose axons leave the brain and spinal cord. Acetylcholine's immediate precursor, choline, is also an essential constituent of the diet. It cannot be made by neurons but must be obtained from the blood, which receives a small amount of it from the liver and the rest from lecithin in the diet. Lecithin is a choline-containing constituent of eggs, soybeans, liver and many prepared foods. Each meal, depending on its composition, raises or lowers brain tryptophan and choline levels. This, in turn, modifies the rates at which brain neurons produce serotonin and acetylcholine and release them into synapses, which are the tiny spaces through which neurons communicate.

Our research group initially discovered that one set of brain neurons—those releasing serotonin—were normally quite susceptible to the vagaries of food choices. More recently we found that cholinergic or acetylcholine-releasing neurons, which are located both within and outside the central nervous system, also are open to changes in food intake.

We are a long way from clearly understanding why evolution has allowed these brain neurons to be so vulnerable. Nevertheless our slim knowledge has not deterred a number of laboratories, including our own, from using what we now know about nutritional effects on the brain function to learn more about how the brain works under normal conditions. This might allow us to begin to treat some diseases thought to result from inadequate release of serotonin or acetylcholine.

THREE GROUPS

All of the known neurotransmitters synthesized in the neurons of mammals share certain chemical properties. All are low-molecular-weight, water-soluble compounds. All are made primarily in those parts of the neurons that form synaptic contacts with the cells to which the neuron transmits signals,

Foods and air enter the body, and then enter the bloodstream as oxygen, glucose, amino acids, and fats. Brain neurons use choline (an amino acid) to form acetylcholine and use tryptophan (another amino acid) to form serotonin.

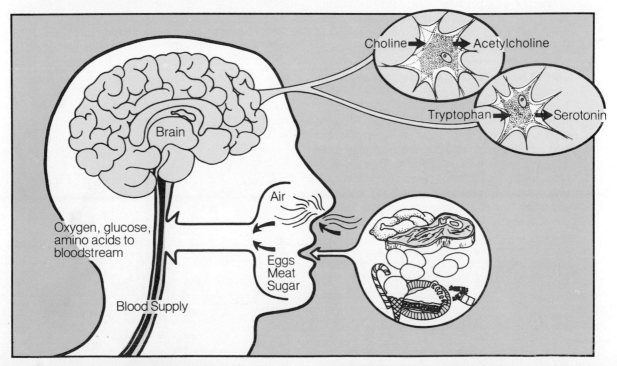

the so-called postsynaptic cells. All neurotransmitters are stored within the cell in characteristic organelles, called synaptic vesicles, or are bound to proteins within the cell prior to their release into a synapse.

At the present time, neuroscientists have identified in the mammalian nervous system about fifteen to twenty compounds which probably function as neurotransmitters. I suspect that these supposed transmitters can be classified as falling within three groups, depending on the mechanisms that control their syntheses. Only one of these three groups is likely to depend upon blood-plasma composition and food consumption.

SOME VERY DEPENDENT ON FOOD

The first group includes serotonin and acetylcholine and also histamine, dopamine, and norepinephrine. Histamine, apart from probably being a transmitter in the brain, also functions as a locally-acting hormone through the body, involved in many immunological reactions, and exerts important effects on blood circulation. Dopamine, a brain neurotransmitter, is involved in the coordination of movements and, possibly, in the antipsychotic actions of numerous drugs. Norepinephrine is a neurotransmitter in both the central and the peripheral nervous systems and is involved in controlling the heart and blood vessels.

These substances are produced from precursor compounds that neurons cannot make by themselves and must therefore be obtained from the bloodstream. Each of these neurotransmitters requires for its manufacture a specific enzyme whose activity is limited by the amount of precursor available.

OTHERS MORE INDEPENDENT

The second group includes various peptides that have been found in brain neurons and which are thought by many scientists to function as neurotransmitters. But, in contrast to the first group, these compounds almost certainly are not formed primarily by enzymes. Instead, they are synthesized by polyribosomes—strands of ribonucleic acid (RNA) attached to pairs of ribosomes in the cell. The amounts of their precursors—the circulating amino acids—needed to allow maximum rates of peptide synthesis are tiny.

Hence variations in blood amino-acid levels do not seem to have much effect on the production of these neurotransmitters, nor should food intake.

The third group includes three amino acids—glycine, glutamate, and aspartate—that can be synthesized by all cells, and a fourth amino acid, GABA (gamma-amino butyric acid) which is formed in some brain neurons from glutamate. Since all neurons are capable of synthesizing glycine, glutamate, and aspartate from glucose or any other energy source that happens to be available, it seems unlikely that the production of these compounds will normally vary to a great extent with food consumption or blood-plasma composition.

SEROTONIN STUDIES

The criteria to determine whether a particular neurotransmitter is subject to nutritional control and the proposed classification of neurotransmitters into the three groups—were arrived at rather slowly. Our first studies, started in 1971 with John Fernstrom, then a graduate student and now associate professor of physiology at MIT, were designed to determine whether the increase in brain serotonin observed in rats given a large dose of tryptophan might also occur following the consumption of meals that change plasma tryptophan levels.

Fernstrom took blood and brain sam-

John Fernstrom discovered that the synthesis of serotonin in a rat's brain increases after it ate food (such as fish) containing tryptophan.

Courtesy of John Fernstrom

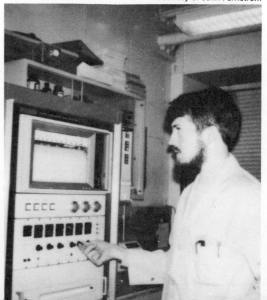

Proteins consist of amino acids, which are essential to body growth and repair.

ples from animals sacrificed at various times of day and night. He found that immediately after the onset of darkness—when rats began to eat the food he provided—parallel elevations occurred in blood tryptophan, brain tryptophan levels, and brain serotonin levels. This suggested that serotonin synthesis in brain neurons was normally affected by plasma tryptophan concentrations, which, in turn changed after food was consumed. Further evidence supporting this hypothetical relationship was obtained by giving rats very small doses of tryptophan at noontime when blood and brain tryptophan levels are normally relatively low. The increases in brain tryptophan induced by this treatment were also associated with increases in brain serotonin levels.

In later studies, Fernstrom found that when he injected insulin into the rat's bloodstream, it also caused parallel elevations in plasma tryptophan levels and in brain tryptophan and serotonin levels.

At this point, we decided to see whether the secretion of the animal's own insulin similarly affected brain serotonin synthesis. Following an overnight fast, the rats were allowed to eat a carbohydrate-containing meal which, we know, would elicit insulin secretion. As we had hoped, the blood tryptophan level and the concentrations of tryptophan and of serotonin in the brain were all raised after this one meal. We thus could confirm that eating had a demonstrable affect on the synthesis of a brain neurotransmitter.

PROTEIN DIET

But what happens when we add a large amount of protein to the meal? To our surprise both brain trytophan and serotonin levels fell. Since protein contains tryptophan and contributes some of its tryptophan molecules to the blood, why should the addition of protein to the meal depress brain tryptophan levels?

The answer lies in the system that transports tryptophan from the blood into the brain. This same system also transports numerous other amino acids found in protein—for example, tyrosine and leucine. When protein is consumed, it increases the concentrations of the other amino acids much more, proportionately, than that of tryptophan. What happens is that the more protein in the meal, the lower the ratio of the resulting bloodstream tryptophan concentration to that of its competitors. Thus also the more protein in a meal, the slower the uptake of tryptophan into the brain. Serotonin-containing neurons in the brain sense the ratio of amino acids in the blood. The more protein in each meal—and consequently the less the ratio of tryptophan to other neutral amino acids in the bloodstream—the less neurotransmitter is later produced and released.

These neurons probably provide the brain with information about the body's metabolic state. This information helps our brain to decide what and when we should eat, whether we should take a nap, and which hormones our organs should secrete.

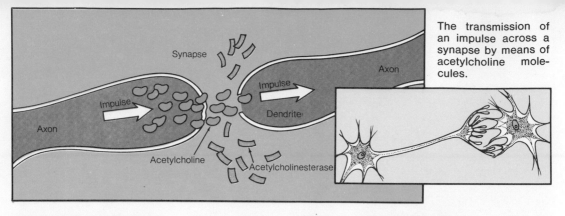

The transmission of an impulse across a synapse by means of acetylcholine molecules.

ACETYCHOLINE STUDIES

Edith Cohen, then an MIT graduate student, began to explore the relationships between choline levels in the blood and the manufacture of the neurotransmitter acetylcholine. To our knowledge, no one had ever before introduced choline into the bloodstream of animals to test what would happen to brain acetylcholine levels. The difficulty of performing such experiments lay in a problem inherent in the biology of the brain. Just a few seconds after death, much of the acetylcholine present in the brain is destroyed by an enzyme, acetylcholinesterase. Consequently, measurement of brain acetylcholine levels in post-mortem specimens tended to be useless. The same was true for our experimental subjects—rats. But, a newly devised technique in which the animal is killed by a focused microwave beam aimed at the brain which inactivates the brain's enzymes offered hope. Using the new method Cohen was able to show that elevations in blood choline levels produced by injecting choline, or by providing it in the diet, caused major elevations in the levels of choline and acetylcholine in the brain.

Subsequent studies by another MIT student, Madelyn Hirsch, showed that blood choline levels in humans and experimental animals normally vary with the amount of choline in the diet. She also showed that the effects of dietary choline provided as lecithin, the form in which it is usually ingested, are, if anything, far greater than those observed when choline itself is administered. She further demonstrated that the acetylcholine-forming enzyme is not subject to significant feedback control. She also showed that increases in acetylcholine levels are, in fact, associated with parallel changes in the amounts of the transmitter that are released into synapses to act on post-synaptic receptors.

MEDICAL USE OF CHOLINE

Within four months of the publication of our first article showing that choline administration elevates brain acetylcholine levels in rats, the first note appeared in a medical journal suggesting a clinical use for this effect. A letter to the editor of *The New England Journal of Medicine* (July 17, 1975), by Kenneth L. Davis, Philip A. Berger, and Leo E. Hollister, psychiatrists working at Stanford University in California, described marked improvement after choline administration in a patient suffering from tardive dyskinesia. Tardive dyskinesia is a neurological disease which causes uncontrolled movements of the tongue, mouth, face, and upper trunk. This disease is a common side effect associated with all of the antipsychotic drugs now marketed in the United States. In some patients, it persists long after treatment with the drug is stopped. Similar disorders have also been observed in aged patients with no history of having taken antipsychotic drugs.

Neurologists and psychiatrists had speculated for several years that tardive dyskinesia resulted from the release of inadequate amounts of acetylcholine in the b)rain. However, no drug was available to bring acetylcholine's production or actions in the brain to normal.

Since 1977, choline has been affirmed as a useful therapy for tardive dyskinesia in controlled studies, under the direction of John Growdon, an MIT colleague, who is also assistant professor of neurology at Tufts University Medical School. Growdon, Hirsch, and William Weiner of the Medfield State Hospital in Massachusetts, and I treated twenty patients suffering from chronic tardive dyskinesia for two weeks each with choline and with a placebo. Nine patients showed major improvement after choline: none showed any response to the placebo. To our knowledge, no other treatment has ever been shown in a controlled study to benefit patients with this disease.

We are now trying to determine whether choline continues to be effective when used as a drug for long periods, and whether lecithin, the natural choline source, might be even more effective therapeutically than choline itself. Even though choline administration apparently suppresses a major side effect of antipsychotic drugs, we were delighted to find no evidence that its administration in any way interferes with the therapeutic actions of the drugs. Ultimately these findings may have important implications for helping us to identify what parts of the brain are involved in causing psychosis.

Similar studies are now under way at MIT and numerous other laboratories on the possible uses of choline (or lecithin) to treat an array of other diseases that are thought to involve related brain neuron function. These diseases include both brain diseases such as mania and memory loss, and peripheral disorders, such as the myasthenic syndromes. Another MIT graduate student, Larry Botticelli, has observed that choline administration can cause a dose-related blockade of some effects of morphine on pain sensitivity. This sort of observation could—with luck—provide the basis for developing a drug that might mimic the analgesic effects of morphine.

OTHER CLINICAL POSSIBILITIES

Future studies may show that the production of the neurotransmitters dopamine and norepinephrine can also, under some circumstances, be modulated by treatments that change the brain levels of tyrosine, their amino-acid precursor. If so, this relationship could have an even greater impact on clinical problems. Norepinephrine-releasing neurons are involved in a very large number of physiological mechanisms, both inside and outside the brain, while dopamine-releasing neurons have clearly been implicated in Parkinson's disease, schizophrenia, and in the control of hormone secretion from the pituitary gland.

WHY? MOTHER NATURE

But we shouldn't allow our expectations to run too high. We must remember that only a very few years ago it seemed highly im-

Fruits and vegetables are considered as the food group that contain vitamin A and C. Every body function requires one vitamin or another.

probable that the synthesis of any transmitter would normally be susceptible to nutritional influences. We must recall that no member of that other great class of biologic signals—the hormones—normally has its synthesis rate coupled to the availability of specific-needed nutrients and that most neurotransmitters apparently are exempted from such control. We should be grateful indeed that nature has given us this simple and even natural way of varying brain function and continue to ponder why □

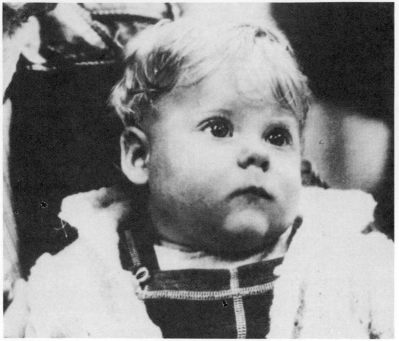

Louise Brown, a beautiful and healthy test-tube baby.

Wide World

"TEST-TUBE BABIES"

by Walter Sullivan

IN ALL respects the birth of Louise Brown in Oldham and District Hospital in England the night of July 25–26, 1978, was a landmark event. It was the first birth of a person conceived outside the human body. It was the sensational culmination of decades of research on human reproduction. It told thousands—even millions—of women throughout the world who shared a specific type of infertility with Louise's mother, Lesley Brown, that there was yet hope.

Nevertheless, it sharpened as never before the ethical and social issues being raised as scientists become ever more adept at exercising control over all aspects of the life process. Such control ranges from various forms of birth control and genetic engineering to mood control and prolongation of bodily life when the mind has ceased to function.

DEFECTIVE OVIDUCTS

Louise was not really a "test-tube" baby, as widely reported. She did not develop in a test tube. The egg from which she developed was not even fertilized in a test

tube but in a special laboratory dish. Nor did she, as depicted in Aldous Huxley's 1932 novel, *Brave New World,* develop in a baby factory. Except for the first few days after laboratory fertilization of an egg cell, she developed in the uterus of her mother as in any normal pregnancy. There had been at least two earlier reports of laboratory fertilization of human-egg cells, but in neither instance was validity of the claim generally accepted by the medical profession.

In normal reproduction the ovaries of a fertile woman produce one mature egg cell each month. This egg descends to the uterus through the oviducts, or Fallopian tubes. It is during this descent that the egg is fertilized by a sperm cell that has made its way up into that duct. By the time a fertilized egg reaches the uterus it has already subdivided a number of times. Although barely visible to the unaided eye, it is already a developing embryo. Within a few days, it attaches, or implants, itself into the wall of the uterus.

As with millions of other women, Mrs. Brown had been unable to bear children be-

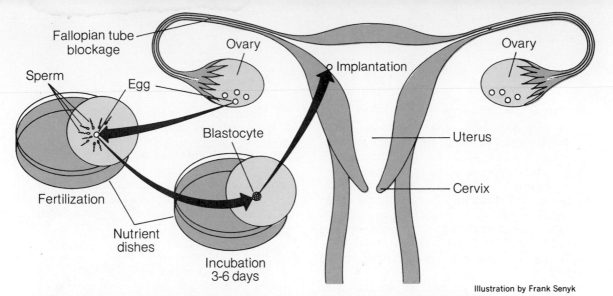

Illustration by Frank Senyk

If there is a blockage in the Fallopian tube, a sperm cannot reach and fertilize an egg. Edwards and Steptoe devised a method in which fertilization takes place outside the female body.

cause of defective oviducts. Defective oviducts may occur because of inheritance or disease. In many cases, repeated or untreated infection, often of gonorrheal origin, is responsible for the defective oviducts. Some can be corrected by surgery and this had been attempted on Mrs. Brown without success. In Mrs. Brown's case, the tubes were removed to facilitate the procedure that finally triumphed in Louise's conception and birth.

The two men responsible for this achievement were Dr. Robert G. Edwards, a specialist in reproductive physiology at the University of Cambridge, and Dr. Patrick C. Steptoe, a gynecologist recently retired from the British national health service. They had been working together on the problem for at least a dozen years. Dr. Edwards concentrated on the use of chemical controls, or hormones, to provide Dr. Steptoe with a mature egg cell at a predictable time when he could remove it surgically.

Dr. Steptoe was internationally known for his role in the development of laparoscopy, the technique used to remove the egg from an ovary with a minimum of cutting. An instrument is inserted into the abdomen through a small incision. Light is directed through this instrument via a bundle of glass fibers, illuminating the area of the ovary. Through additional fibers the physician can observe the lighted area, select the mature egg within its capsule, or follicle, and draw it out.

LABORATORY FERTILIZATION

The egg cell is then placed in a dish of the type used routinely for cell cultures, and known as a Petri dish. There it is immersed in a preparation known to promote fertilization and sperm from the husband are then added. Once microscopic examination shows that fertilization has occurred—that a sperm cell has successfully penetrated and fertilized the egg—the egg is transferred to a special preparation that encurges its subdivision into two cells, then four, eight, sixteen cells, and so on.

Close to the stage when a developing embryo would normally complete its passage through the oviduct and enter and attach itself to the wall of the uterus, the laboratory-fertilized egg is blown into the mother's uterus. A tiny tube is inserted into the vagina, and the egg is blown through the tight passage of the cervix into the uterus.

If all goes well, the blown-in embryo attaches itself to the wall of the uterus. Then, as in a normally fertilized egg, some of the embryo's cells develop into the placenta and umbilical cord, which derive nourishment from the mother's bloodstream. Other cells begin developing into a fetus.

Steptoe and Edwards appear to have made at least 100 attempts before achieving success. Other clinics are attempting the procedure (or preparing to do so) in Britain, Australia, the United States, and possibly elsewhere. In some cases a modification of the Steptoe-Edwards method is being used.

ETHICAL PROBLEMS

The birth of Louise Brown has raised troublesome questions. As conceded by the two men who made it possible, the method, like many other modern capabilities, could be abused. Women seeking to avoid the discomforts of pregnancy and childbirth could relegate gestation of their children to others. Couples seeking only sons or daughters could specify that, after laboratory conception, only embryos of the preferred sex be used.

Some critics of the Steptoe-Edwards method view it as degrading the sanctity of life. They regard procreation as sacred. Others argue that in a world beset by overpopulation, adding to the problem in this way is a disservice. The two men reply that a physician's task is to relieve suffering and that their patients are deeply troubled by their infertility. This was evidenced by their willingness to undergo a difficult, costly, and painful procedure.

As it is, an essential part of the Steptoe-Edwards procedure is that only normal-appearing embryos be used. The embryos are monitored microscopically during their early development in the Petri dish, and those appearing abnormal are rejected. It has been reported that women undertaking the procedure must agree to the abortion of any seemingly defective embryo.

Defenders of this practice argue that it only mimics what nature does in the uterus. It is suspected that a considerable percentage of conceptions are naturally aborted at a very early stage because the reproductive system recognizes them as defective. They are swept out unobserved during the menstrual discharge, the tiny embryo having failed to give the chemical signal that turns off the monthly cycle. Or they are swept out in what a woman may think of as simply a late, or overdue, period.

Despite such arguments Dr. Edwards recognized possible dangers in his method. In normal reproduction an army of several hundred million sperm must enter the female reproductive system for one finally to make its way to the egg and fertilize it. This may weed out weak or defective sperm, whereas in the Petri dish there is no such screening.

Nevertheless it is the willful destruction of some embryos, tiny as they are, that has raised questions similar to those of the much-debated abortion issue. Early in his research effort Dr. Edwards became so concerned at the ethical problems it raised that he took a year off to examine them. Some scientists were questioning the propriety of such work.

AN ADDED BENEFIT

The procedure has added benefit: it has proved valuable in coping with a certain form of male infertility in which the number of highly motile sperm produced is meager. In these cases the limited number of sperm have a better chance of success—of fertilizing the egg—in the Petri dish than in the normal manner. If necessary, the sperm can also be frozen and stockpiled until numerous enough.

One application of the method discussed by Steptoe and Edwards would enable a couple to derive their entire family through a single surgical procedure. The woman would be stimulated, by a hormone, to "superovulate"—that is, produce a number of mature eggs at once. The eggs would be fertilized, providing a number of embryos to choose from. One embryo—of the desired sex, for example—would be cultured and implanted, and the remaining would be frozen for implantation at intervals of a year or more.

Embryo freezing for storage or shipment has become routine with some forms of livestock, and defective births do not seem to occur any more often than with normal reproduction. But to date no attempts at freezing and thawing of human embryos have been reported.

The editors of this book take no position on the moral and ethical questions involved in *in vitro,* or out-of-the-body, fertilization of humans. The birth of the first *in vitro* fertilized baby is, however, a major scientific happening and one that cannot be ignored. This article simply describes the physical and medical facts involved in the birth of the first "test-tube baby," mentions some of the possibilities of the new treatment, and cites some of the ethical questions widely discussed in connection with the procedure □

George Holton/Photo Researchers

*Papuans in war canoe. The Papuans live on the eastern half of New Guinea, a large island north of Austra-
lia. About 700 languages are spoken there so there is only slight tribal unity.*

MAN & HIS WORLD

FAO Photo

Nomads of the nations in the southern edge of Africa's Sahara were struck by a crippling drought, which killed most of their herds of sheep, goats, cattle, and camels. Sorghum from the United States and powdered milk from the Federal Republic of Germany were sent to their aid.

These bones are from *Aegyptopithecus*, which Elwyn L. Simons of Duke University calls the "dawn ape." In 1965, working an anthropological dig 80 kilometers southwest of Cairo, Egypt, he discovered the three jawbones. Recently Simons came upon a fragment of the upper arm and elbow (right of quarter). He believes that the species *Aegyptopithecus* can be thought of as a connecting link between the primitive primates (lemurs and howling monkeys) and the later apes.

Jimmy Wallace, Duke University

Population and Food. Once again in 1977/78 world grain production increased faster than population growth. Production for the first time surpassed 1,500,000,000 metric tons. Nearly 90 per cent of this grain is consumed in the countries where it is grown. Some 160,000,000 metric tons were traded, more than one half of that coming from the "North American breadbasket." At the same time, the population-growth rate began to level off, even in some of the less developed countries.

The World Food Council met in Mexico City during the year and adopted a Mexico Declaration, which described the world food situation in stark terms. It reported that despite steadily increasing world-food production, the poor countries, where the food is needed most, continue to lag. Distribution of food is simply not improving the nutritional status of the poor.

Long-range food forecasts also continue to be alarming. International Food Policy Research Institute data suggest that developing countries will need to triple their grain imports by 1990 unless there is a fundamental improvement in their capacity to produce it. Worldwide demand for grain is projected to increase by about 700,000,000 metric tons by 1990, or nearly half of last-year's total production. Unless the patterns of production change significantly, about 100,000,000 of these additional tons will have to be met by North American exports. Such an increase in exports would also affect the consumer price of grain products, but it is difficult to predict the impact.

The problem of how to increase food production in the developing countries was a major concern of several international forums that met during the year. The growing world imbalance in food production and food consumption that has emerged in the last few decades must be reversed. Meetings preparatory to the July 1979 World Conference on Agrarian Reform and Rural Development in Rome, Italy, were held in all the major developing regions. They did not, however, result in strong commitments to the kinds of land-reform measures that benefit the small farmer and the landless laborer and that may be prerequisites for lasting and meaningful rural development and increased food production in many countries. It remains to be seen to what extent the recommendations of the Rome conference will be followed.

The major step in U.S. policy and action on world hunger in 1978 was the establishment of the Presidential Commission on World Hunger. President Carter named Sol M. Linowitz to head the 20-person group of distinguished academies, public figures, members of Congress, and entertainers. After the Commission reports to the President in June 1979, it will spend a year following up its recommendations.

Despite government limitations on the amount of land cultivated, U.S. grain production increased in 1977/78. Food prices also increased. Nevertheless many U.S. farmers, who had over-invested in the hopeful days of the early 1970's, said that they were still losing money—or breaking even at best—on their farm operations. At the beginning of 1979, as in 1978, farmers—with their tractors—rolled into Washington, D.C. to protest the Carter Administration's agricultural policies. After a month of the bitterest weather and heaviest snow in 60 years, they headed home, uncertain of having achieved any of their goals.

Martin McLaughlin

Anthropology and Archaeology. The year 1978 witnessed the loss of a giant in anthropology, new discoveries about our human ancestors, continuing debate on sociobiology, and some new information about chimpanzee behavior.

The death of Margaret Mead, a pioneering researcher in cultural anthropology for over 50 years, on November 15, 1978 at the age of 76, was mourned by people far removed from anthropology. More than any other anthropologist, she embodied the discipline and its perspective to the public eye. See "In Memoriam" on page 274.

Archaeological discoveries in 1978 shed more light on human evolutionary behavior. In Tanzania, Dr. Mary D. Leakey announced the discovery of a series of footprints made over 3,500,000 years ago at the site of Laetoli. The prints have been preserved in volcanic ash, covered by a layer of lava. These tracks can provide information on the height and gait of our supposed ancestors. As interpreted by scientists they give the picture of a creature about four feet tall with broad feet, who, although bipedal, took short, slow, rolling steps. Other footprints announced later in the year leave no doubt that by 3,500,000 years ago East Africa was the home of a fully erect, bipedal walking hominid. ■ In another archaeological find, Dr. D. Johanson discovered the remains of a population of hominids from over 3,500,000 years ago in the Afar Triangle region of Ethiopia. Remarkable for their completeness and the large number of individuals represented, these hominids have been named *Australopithecus afarensis* and have been claimed as the ancestor of later *Australopithecus africanus* and specimens that may fall in our own *Homo* genus. The interpretation of these findings is, however, controversial. For a more complete discussion, see the article *"Australopithecus afarensis"* on page 248.

Using refined dating techniques, scientists have been able to date teeth found in China and identified as coming from *Homo erectus* at 1,700,000 years old. This finding indicates that humans spread from Africa to other parts of the world earlier and more rapidly than has hitherto been thought.

There were also discoveries concerning later human prehistory. Archaeologists described the 13,500-year-old tools of the earliest big game hunters in the Americas, the El Jobo culture of Venezuela. ■ Others found new evidence that prehistoric human groups in the New World may have been responsible for the extinction of several groups of large animals, such as mammoths. ■ Scientists also discovered shell eyes made for the giant stone statues of Easter Island and debated the reasons for Aztec cannibalism.

Sociobiology, the theory that animal (and human) behavior evolved biologically and is genetically transmitted, continued to be a topic of interest. There was continued debate between anthropologists who believe that their discipline can account for social systems by cultural transmission and sociobiologists, such as Dr. E. O. Wilson, who believe that some important aspects of human behavior are better explained as a result of innate patterns developed through evolutionary processes.

For many years anthropologists have been studying the behavior of our primate relatives for clues to the behavior of our early ancestors. In 1978 Dr. Jane Goodall observed behavior among chimpanzees that had been thought to be a peculiarly human phenomenon: the gradual extermination of a social group by a stronger neighboring group. While she could offer no explanation for the vicious attacks and killings among the animals, she said that they "show chimps are even closer to humans than I thought."

Arthur Bankoff

Volker Zinser

At Fajada Butte of Chaco Canyon in northwestern New Mexico are three upright slabs of rock. Around noon light strikes a rock surface behind the slab that has a spiral carved on it. At noon on summer solstice, a streak of light appears at the center of the spiral. Some ancient inhabitant of Chaco Canyon must have been aware of the summer solstice and perhaps other astronomical events to have carved the spiral where he or she did.

The Venus of Willendorf is an example of Stone Age/Ice Age art. For reasons that anthropologists are trying to comprehend, the early artists created human figures less realistic than the animals they drew and carved.

The Bettmann Archive

AUSTRALOPITHECUS AFARENSIS

by Boyce Rensberger

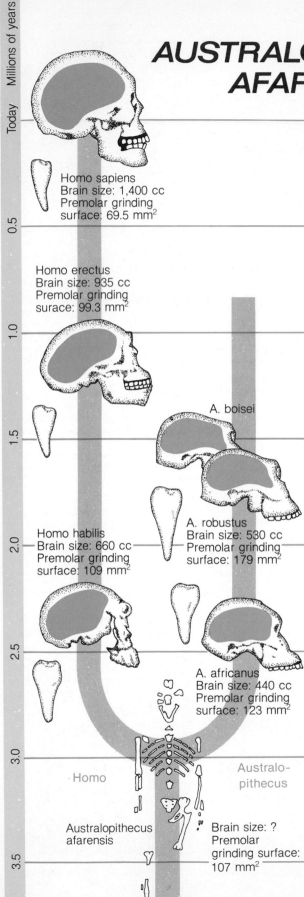

Homo sapiens
Brain size: 1,400 cc
Premolar grinding
surface: 69.5 mm^2

Homo erectus
Brain size: 935 cc
Premolar grinding
surace: 99.3 mm^2

A. boisei

Homo habilis
Brain size: 660 cc
Premolar grinding
surface: 109 mm^2

A. robustus
Brain size: 530 cc
Premolar grinding
surface: 179 mm^2

A. africanus
Brain size: 440 cc
Premolar grinding
surface: 123 mm^2

Homo

Australo-
pithecus

Australopithecus
afarensis

Brain size: ?
Premolar
grinding surface:
107 mm^2

Millions of years

Today

0.5

1.0

1.5

2.0

2.5

3.0

3.5

"WHERE did I come from?" Long after we learn the answer as it applies to individuals, many of us continue to wonder about the human species as a whole.

What were our earliest ancestors like? Did they resemble apes? How did we come to walk on two legs? What caused the human brain to become so large in proportion to the body?

A major new attempt to answer some of these questions in January 1979 with the announcement that anthropologists had identified a previously unknown form of human ancestor that lived in Africa between 3,000,000 and 4,000,000 years ago. Fossil remains of the species have been found in Ethiopia and Tanzania.

The "new" species had an unexpected combination of a small, apelike head and a fully erect, virtually human body. It was named *Australopithecus afarensis* by its discoverers, Dr. Donald C. Johanson of the Cleveland Museum of Natural History and Dr. Tim White of the University of California at Berkeley. A knee joint believed to come from the same species established that the creature walked exactly as do modern human beings, although it stood only 107 to 122 centimeters tall. The two anthropologists believe that the species was the common ancestor of all later forms of human and humanlike creatures—a family of several species that are all called hominids.

The naming of a new species—the first new human ancestor to be named in 15 years—has sparked a controversy with challenges from well-known Kenyan anthropologist Richard Leakey and his mother, archaeologist Dr. Mary Leakey.

Analysis of the new discoveries has reopened the question of why a creature with a head almost resembling that of a chimpanzee, and apparently incapable of making stone tools, would have begun to walk on two legs. To appreciate the new interpretation and the controversy, it is necessary to recall earlier views of human evolution.

Illustration by Frank Senyk

A TWO-TRUNK TREE

Until about the mid-1960's most anthropologists thought of human evolution as a kind of single-file progression. The progression began with an apelike creature that gradually evolved into more and more human form. Fossil bones that might reveal posture were then unknown. Therefore anthropologists assumed that as the brain size (evident from fossil skulls) gradually enlarged, posture changed gradually as well. From a four-footed stance, posture was thought to have passed through an intermediate stage of creatures with a stooped, shuffling, two-legged gait. A fully human, striding bipedalism did not emerge, most experts used to think, until the skull shape and brain size had reached virtually human proportions.

In recent years part of this view has changed. Largely because of fossils found by the Leakeys in Kenya and Tanzania, it has become apparent that there was more than one evolving lineage of hominid. It became clear that the single-file progression had branched at least once and probably twice. The branching produced two or three lineages, which developed at the same time, but only one of which survives today.

One lineage of small-brained creatures was named *Australopithecus*. It is thought to have branched again, producing a larger, more robust version and a smaller, lighter-boned version, both with small brains. The other lineage was *Homo,* the genus whose members evolved progressively larger brains and to which all modern human beings belong.

It was assumed that the two lineages had a common ancestor, and most anthropologists suspected that it was an early form of *Australopithecus.* The Leakeys, however, have long speculated that the *Homo* lineage had not descended from any form of *Australopithecus* but, rather, from some still unknown species.

HOW OLD IS HOMO?

How far back did *Homo* begin? The oldest date so far put forth was announced by Mary Leakey in 1975. She found a collection of jaw and teeth fossils in Tanzania at a place called Laetoli. The fossils were in deposits measured at 3,750,000 years of age, and Leakey pronounced them to be *Homo*. At a stroke, this discovery appeared to extend the known age of *Homo* by nearly 2,000,000 years.

If the Laetoli fossils were truly *Homo,* as Mary Leakey insisted, anthropologists would be left with no known ancestor of the human race. The reason for this interpretation is that all known remains of other hominids lived after the time of the Laetoli hominids.

ETHIOPIA FINDS

While Mary Leakey was working in Tanzania, Dr. Johanson, working in the Afar region of Ethiopia, was finding hominid fossils that were a little over 3,000,000 years of age. Initially he thought that some of the specimens looked like *Australopithecus* and others like *Homo*. Later, after conferring with Dr. White, who had been studying the Laetoli hominids in detail, the two concluded that all the fossils—the Laetoli fossils and the Ethiopian fossils—were from the same species. These fossils appear to be from a relatively primitive species at that, but one with some modern-looking traits mixed in.

The present great anthropological debate is between Donald C. Johanson (left) and Richard Leakey of Kenya, Africa.

After many months of analysis, Dr. Johanson and Dr. White decided that they were dealing with a previously unrecognized species that had a mixture of primitive and modern features. As such, and given an age greater than that of all other known hominids, the anthropologists suggested that their species, *A. afarensis,* was the common ancestor of the two main lineages recognized previously—namely *Australopithecus* and *Homo.* The *Australopithecus* lineage includes previously known forms such as *A. africanus* and *A. robustus.* The *Homo* lineage gave rise to forms already recognized as *H. habilis, H. erectus,* and *H. sapiens.*

The Johanson-White interpretation, which would disqualify the Laetoli hominids from *Homo* status, leaves the oldest known form of *Homo* as the so-called "1470 man," discovered by Richard Leakey in Kenya. This individual, with a brain nearly twice the size of a chimpanzee's brain, lived about 2,000,000 years ago.

ONE SPECIES OR TWO?

Richard Leakey's objections to the Johanson-White interpretation turns largely on two points. One is his feeling that the Laetoli and Afar fossils cannot all be lumped into a single species. He perceives two distinct species—one *Australopithecus* and one *Homo.* If there are indeed two species represented in the collection, it would mean that the common ancestor had to have lived even further back in time. Almost nothing is known of hominids that lived before those of Laetoli—some 3,750,000 years ago.

Dr. Johanson concedes that there are two groups of hominids that can be distinguished in the collection. But he claims that the two groups represent the males and females of a single species. It is known that in many primates there can be striking differences between the sexes. Supporting the idea of a single species is the fact that representatives of both groups were found at a remarkable site. The site contained the remains of at least 13 individuals, including adults and children all found together.

Dr. Johanson believes it is likely that the group was a family, with males and females, rather than a party of two distinct hominid species. Mr. Leakey argues that the differences between the two groups are too large to attribute to sex differences.

IS THERE A THIRD?

The second point on which Richard Leakey challenges the new view involves his discovery in Kenya of eight isolated hominid teeth. They were found in deposits of an age comparable to those of the Afar and Laetoli finds—that is, over 3,000,000 years of age. But the eight teeth do not resemble the teeth from these sites. If the teeth really do represent a third and different hominid, they could invalidate Dr. Johanson's theory that *A. afarensis* was the common ancestor of all later hominids.

Mr. Leakey concedes that isolated teeth are difficult to interpret and constitute slim evidence upon which to draw conclusions. But he argues that they are enough to raise a challenge. A detailed analysis of the teeth has not as yet been made.

BUT SOME AGREEMENT

Despite the controversy, there is one area of agreement on both sides. In at least one species of hominid a fully human method of walking on two legs had evolved by 3,750,000 years ago in a creature with a chimp-sized brain.

It appears that our ancestors did not become human at a rate that was uniform over the entire body. From the neck down, they were virtually fully human. While from the neck up, they were, at least by appearances, barely more than apes. It appears that bipedalism did not arise as an adjunct to growing intelligence, as was for so long thought. Although anthropologists are working to develop new theories on the origin of bipedalism, little hard evidence is available to them.

Where did we come from? Anthropologists are not able to answer the question fully. But they suggest that walking on two legs developed fully before the first hint of progress in another distinctive human characteristic—the large brain □

 SELECTED READINGS

"Finding Eve's cousin" by P. Gwynne and S. Begley. *Newsweek,* January 28, 1979.

"New species of man: ancestors from "afar." *Science News,* January 20, 1979.

"Hominids of East Turkana" by A. Walker and R. Leakey. *Scientific American,* August 1978.

"Systematic assessment of early African hominids." *Science,* January 26, 1979.

© Pressens Bild AB/Photoreporters Inc.

For the Nobel prizes the Royal Academy of Science in Stockholm, Sweden, chooses the winners for physics and chemistry; the Caroline Institute of Stockholm chooses the prize for medicine.

WHO GETS THE PRIZE?

by Nicholas Wade

OCTOBER is Nobel prize season, a time when those with an itch to wear the old dynamite-maker's laurel crown feel their pulses involuntarily quicken at every phone call and mailman's knock. "This is it!" Edmund Wilson cried up to his wife one day when he received a special delivery letter from Stockholm, but it was an appeal for funds from a missionary society.

Wilson's consolation in missing the Nobel prize for literature was that so did writers such as Ibsen, Kafka, Lorca, Proust, and Tolstoy. Science being less a matter of opinion, the three science Nobel committees have had a less erratic batting average. It's too bad that figures such as Dimitri Mendeleyev, who formulated the periodic table of elements, Willard Gibbs, who did outstanding work in vector analysis, electromagnetic radiation theory, and thermodynamics, and Oswald Avery, who discovered that DNA is the hereditary material, never made the grade. But conversely, the selection committees have committed only a few obvious lulus, such as the 1926 award to Johannes Fibiger for what turned out to be a false discovery about the propagation of malignant tumors in the stomach of rats to which he had fed parasitic worms.

At $165,000, a Nobel prize or even a third-part share in one is not a bad thing to pull down, particularly as it does not seem to be *de rigueur* to spend it on research as the founder had in mind. But if for yet another year the invitation to Stockholm somehow fails to arrive, a scientist should not be downhearted. Here are seven reasons for comfort.

Mendeleyev used the regularities of the properties of elements to bring order to a mass of chemical facts.

NOT THEIR BEST WORK

First, if he or she had received the Nobel, their productivity would have suffered. Laureates on average produce six papers a year in the five years before being ennobeled, but only about four a year in the five-year period thereafter. A control set of scientists produced about two papers annually in the same two periods, reports Columbia University sociologist of science Harriet Zuckerman.

Second, there is a fifty-fifty chance that he or she would have been terribly vexed by the particular aspect of their work cited by the judges. "Nearly half of the laureates who were interviewed thought that the research earmarked for the Prize was not their best work," Zuckerman reports.

Third, since the scientist merited the prize for so long, many of his or her colleagues probably assume they have it anyway. It is widely believed, for example, that Sam Goudsmit and George Uhlenbeck won the prize for their discovery of the electron's spin. "This is all very flattering but it does not supplement my . . . pension," Goudsmit has written.

UNPRIZABLE WORK

Fourth, although his or her work is of prize quality it may be unprizable through no fault of their own. The Nobel is restricted to three disciplines—physics, chemistry, and medicine—which leaves many subjects out in the cold. In addition, each prize can be split only three ways, which may rule out the discoveries made by four or more collaborators. Cases where priority is disputed may also be avoided by the Nobel committees, since it is not clear that they possess the expertise to sort out tangled claims.

Some believe that the design of the Nobel prizes no longer conforms to the way science is done. "The great changes that have occurred [since 1901] contribute to the apparently growing conviction among scientists that the prizes have become increasingly parochial and governed by a set of rules no longer adequately meshed with the realities of modern science," Zuckerman has noted, after a study based on interviews with most of the Nobel prizewinners in the United States.

TOO YOUNG, TOO POOR

Fifth, the scientist may just be too young. The potent story of Evariste Galois scribbling out his revolutionary discoveries on the last night of his 20-year-old life may hold a general truth for mathematicians, but it is a myth that scientists do their best work when young. Avery was 67 when he showed that DNA was the hereditary material. Zuckerman has ascertained that the mean age of Nobel laureates when they do their prizewinning work is 36 for physicists, 39 for chemists, and 41 for laureates in medicine and physiology. Add onto that the habitual decade or more which the Nobel committees like to leave between an achievement and their cognizance of it, and it is clear that being over 45 constitutes grounds for hope.

Sixth, the fates may have endowed the scientist with genius but the wrong sociological profile. Genius, no doubt, is randomly distributed among classes and nations. Yet even in a system as eminently based on merit as U.S. science the ultra-elite, Zuckerman concludes, "continue to come largely from the middle and upper middle strata. What-

Avery showed that DNA is the material that determines inherited traits. He used pneumococcus bacteria in this work.

ever the explanation of this fact—one aspect of the fact itself is clear: the social origins of Nobel laureates remain highly concentrated in families that can provide their offspring with a head start in access to system-recognized opportunities."

NO FANS

Seventh, the scientist may not have the right patrons, or those he or she has may not be rooting hard enough for them. Zuckerman has documented an intriguing set of master-apprentice lineages among Nobelists. Nobel laureate J. J. Thomson had six Nobelists among his pupils, one of whom, Ernest B. Rutherford, saw 11 Nobel prizes come to his apprentices, one of whom, Niels Bohr, had seven laureates among his pupils and so forth. More than half of the 92 laureates who did their prizewinning work in the United States were apprenticed in one form or another to older Nobelists. The apprentices were not the mere creations of their masters; many sought out their masters before the Nobel prize committees did.

Between two equally deserving researchers, could an advantage lie with the one who has a Nobelist master? Nobel winners get the chance to nominate candidates each year, which could give their students an edge at least in reaching the committees' attention, and some laureates, such as Rutherford, have lobbied vigorously for their apprentices. Politicking for or against worthy candidates is a "potentially effective strategy," but only the members of Nobel committees can know if such campaigns are effective in practice, Zuckerman observes.

CRÈME DE LA CRÈME

No system of recognizing merit is perfect, as witnessed by the fact that two of the most elaborate mechanisms for doing so, those of the U.S. National Academy of Sciences and the Nobel committees, often fail to select the same people. The Academy, to be sure, has a harder problem with marginal choices. It is aiming for the cream while the Nobel committees have the easier target of finding the *crème de la crème*. Even so, the Academy has managed to identify only four fifths of the U.S. laureates before they went to Stockholm, an oversight that some observers attribute to local politics.

CITATION ANALYSIS

A far more objective system of recognizing scientific influence, although it may have other defects, is that of citation analysis. Resting on the seemingly simpleminded notion of counting the number of times an author's papers are cited by others, citation analysis nevertheless produces some remarkably evocative lists of names.

In 1977 Eugene Garfield, founder of the Institute for Scientific Information, published a list of the 250 most-cited authors. The list had a major systematic defect, in that it credited a citation only to the first-listed author of a paper. Nevertheless, out of the teeming sea of about 1,000,000 publishing scientists, Garfield's list of the 250 most-cited authors netted no less than 42 of the 320 Nobel prize winners and 110 members of the National Academy of Sciences.

AIP Niels Bohr Library

Rutherford discovered transmutation of elements from Becquerel's work on radioactivity. He showed that thorium transmutes into a different element. He predicted the atomic nucleus.

Citedness is a quality that requires great care in interpretation. A researcher with few citations may just come from a small field, like astronomy or botany, while a scientist who is heavily cited may only have developed a refinement of a widely used method. Nevertheless, citedness does seem to correlate strongly with conventional measures of distinction, at least in the aggregate.

Garfield recently set his computer running day and night for a month to produce a citation list that would credit all authors of the paper cited, not just the first. The new compilation, containing the 300 most-cited authors, also differs from the old in that it samples a more recent body of literature. It is based on citations only to journal articles published between 1961 and 1975, whereas the earlier list of 250 included citations to papers published earlier.

Perhaps in part for this reason, the 300 list picks up only 26 Nobelists, although it captures slightly more—115—members of the National Academy of Sciences. Earlier lists have contained the names of several laureates-to-be and the 300 list may do likewise.

TO BE CONSIDERED

Should prize committees test the validity of their own selections against Garfield's objectively derived list? "What I am saying is that no one on that list necessarily deserves a prize, or to be elected to an academy, but everyone certainly deserves at least to be considered," Garfield suggests.

Those not on Garfield's chosen 300 should take solace from the minuteness of his sample which, after all, contains fewer names than the entire Nobel roster. Garfield promises to extend his list in the near future.

DON'T PUSH

As for prize, here are such tips as could be gleaned from Zuckerman. One reliable way of getting in line for a prize, she believes, is to have someone write you a good nomination. The Nobel prize committees request nominations from about a thousand people for each prize. Hard work, and a lot more than listing a candidate's published papers, are required if the nomination is to make an impression.

Among U.S. scientists it is widely believed that decorous behavior both in one's private and public life is also necessary if one is not to forfeit the Nobel committee's approval. Zuckerman does not know if the belief is well founded or not, but one thing that is terribly important is "not to seem to be pushing" should a Nobel committee delegation come touring a scientist's laboratory □

SELECTED READINGS

"Faded laurel crown" by C. Hitchen. *Harpers,* November 1977.

"Laurels and limits on Nobel prizes." *Science News,* May 6, 1978.

Nobel experience by E. Warner. *Horizon,* May 1977.

"Nobel prize: a mixed blessing." *BioScience,* August 1978.

"Re Sociology of the Nobel Prize" by Harriet Zuckerman. *American Scientist,* July-August 1978.

For the members of an experimental Iron Age community, gathering up wood and cooking took much of their time.

Mike Wells

TRYING THE IRON AGE

by Timothy Green

TWO women out gathering primroses in the woods of southern England in the spring of 1977 were startled to be confronted by a wild-looking man with a beard, clad only in a rough woolen tunic and wielding a primitive billhook. The woods were private, the stranger told them, so would they please go away and tell no one what they had seen. About the same time, woodsmen were encountering long-haired people busy setting traps for squirrels or chasing rabbits with swift-running ferrets.

These strange goings-on suggested that some long-lost band of Celts, the inhabitants of these rolling downlands about 300 B.C., had somehow survived in rural tranquility into the twentieth century. Well, not exactly.

In 1978 word went round the little village of Berwick St. John that it was all right now for locals to go calling on the bearded strangers. For this "Iron Age" community was simply the brainchild of a British Broadcasting Corporation (BBC) producer (and archaeology buff) named John Percival. Fed up with archaeology shows on television that "consisted of backsides of diggers and chattering archaeologists," he conceived a secret project to create an Iron Age village. He hoped to give people a better understanding of what that life was really like then.

VOLUNTEERS SET OUT

From a thousand volunteers who responded to discreet newspaper advertisements, Percival chose six couples and three children to spend a year living in a careful reconstruction of an Iron Age settlement. To create the right environment, he found an obliging estate owner, who was prepared to rent 14 hectares of woods and six hectares of fields down a dead-end lane to these budding ancient Britons. There they would be relatively cut off from all contact with the outside world. The only concession the BBC would make to the twentieth century was to allow the settlers medical supplies and emergency visits by a doctor, plus some regulations dictated by bureaucrats: schoolbooks for the children and four exits from the hand-built round house to satisfy fire laws. And, of course, John Percival and his television crew came jolting through the woods in Land Rovers twice a week to film what was going on for a 12-part British television series.

So one chilly March day in 1977, a bold band comprising three schoolteachers, a hairdresser, a nurse, a doctor, a social worker, a builder, a mathematician, a National Farmers Union official, two students, and three children aged seven, five, and

A wattle fence atop an earth mound encloses the Iron Age wattle and thatch structures.

three, took off their modern jeans and sweaters, donned woolen shirts, and set up tents. The tents were needed because all the BBC had done in advance was to clear a site in the woods, bulldoze a boundary wall of earth, and hand out a few metal tools. Water had also been piped into a "well," because the water table was 60 meters down. For company they had a mongrel dog named Sirius and an Old English sheepdog retriever called Emer, three cows, four pigs, nine goats, 25 sheep, 40 chickens, and some bees.

Once the twentieth-century vehicles drove away, an Iron Age calm settled over the woods. The volunteers went to work to build a home and create such comforts as they could. Admittedly they were not entirely unprepared. They had taken evening classes in potting, metalworking, and weaving and had been advised by "survival" experts on what could safely be eaten in the woods.

Happily, they survived. British archaeologists differ over whether they have lived as Iron Age people. But without question they have existed much closer to the life of 2,300 years ago than of today, as I discovered during a visit just before their sojourn ended.

WELCOME SIGN OUT

The muddy track threatened to engulf my car long before I reached the Iron Age village, so I abandoned it and set out on foot. After about one and one-half kilometers there was a whiff of woodsmoke, and presently a clearing opened out. A few goats were straying about, and a rather ragged figure in a woolen jerkin and trousers, with a huge basket of logs on his back, was staggering toward a compound in the middle, which was surrounded by an earth wall topped by a wattle fence. Over the palisade gate a sheep's head presided, an Iron Age sign of welcome. Within was a yard, ankle-deep in mud, through which a cheerful, round-faced woman with bare feet was lugging a bucket of water from the well.

A young fellow, who looked like some prehistoric Daniel Boone, with a squirrel cap and calf-leather moccasins, was perched on a log, twisting and bending strips of hazel into a basket. Their roundhouse dominated the scene. Before its deerskin door a small two-faced stone head, perched on a stick, leered at the outside world to ward off evil spirits, while at the same time smiling benevolently toward the interior to bless those living within.

Stooping slightly to enter, I was at first confused by the darkness and smoke. Apart from the small doors, the only light came from the log fire blazing in a shallow depression in the center from which the smoke drifted upward to escape through the thatch. A big black cauldron was suspended over the flames.

The barefooted woman, whose name was Kate Rossetti, set down her water bucket and started stirring the cauldron. She was preparing a beef stew from part of a cow killed a few days before, flavoring it with parsnips, tickbeans, wild garlic, and thyme. Nearby in a clay oven, the day's bread was baking. Her husband, John, eased the basket of logs off his back and began stacking them by the fire. "We never allow it to go out," he explained, "and it eats up wood—a ton every five days. Actually we have succeeded in making fire by rubbing two pieces of softwood together—not hardwood against softwood, as most experts recommend—but we aren't expert."

ROUNDHOUSE

As my eyes grew accustomed to the gloom, I remarked how spacious the roundhouse was. "It's about 15 meters across and nearly nine meters high," said John, "but it took us much longer to build than we expected. We spent six weeks making the basic structure, and eight weeks thatching. We worked all day, every day, on it." Wattle screens and straw blinds divided the house into 13 "rooms" around the low walls, thus ensuring each couple the modern luxury of some privacy. They slept between animal skins on low wooden beds.

The roundhouse proved surprisingly warm and comfortable. Indeed, the Iron Agers endured one of Britain's coldest winters in years without the inconvenience suffered by most citizens troubled by power cuts. When 60 centimeters of snow fell, they just stayed in the roundhouse with plenty of food and logs and got on with the weaving and wood carving. The place was so cozy that Jill Grainger, a 30-year-old teacher, told me she had never closed the straw windows of her room.

AROUND THE HEARTH

The central hearth was always the focal point of the community. Here everyone sat round in the long winter evenings, each telling his or her life story to while away the time, or picking out a tune on a six-stringed lyre. Once in a while they sang. "We usually sang hymns," confided Sharon Preston, "simply because everyone knew the words." And they cheered themselves with such homemade brews as mead, elderberry wine, and beer. "Our mead was the most successful," recalled John Rossetti. "All we had to do was mix honey and water with the dregs of some elderberry wine to make it ferment. It was ready for drinking in three or four weeks and was very strong. We made 23 gallons, and it's all gone."

Iron Agers show off their home-made woolen clothing while ankle-deep in mud.

Mike Wells

There was no vacation from taking care of teeth and bathing for the three children of the Iron Age community.

BBC Copyright

Each couple also took their bath in a big tub beside the fire, warming it up by plunging pieces of heated metal into the water. "It was a luxurious way to bathe," John Rossetti said, "sitting there by the fire in the midst of the conversation. If the water cooled, you just popped in another piece of hot iron." Hard scrubbing was necessary because their experiments at making soap out of animal fats was not successful. Eventually, most of them became resigned to being a bit grubby most of the time. And in the absence of good soap, the women took to "shampooing" their hair with clay. "The clay picks up the grease," said Jill Grainger, "but you have to rinse it a lot." Clay can also be used for scrubbing greasy pots.

SLOWER PACE

Bathing, like most things, was done in leisurely fashion, for they swiftly forgot the pace of modern life and lapsed into the slower rhythms of the countryman. No one had a watch, and although they built a sundial, they soon destroyed it because they found it tended to impose a schedule on them. "You'd look at it and think 'it's time for lunch,'" said Sharon Preston, "but you might be busy and lunch might not be ready." Sunrise and sunset determined the shape of the day, especially in winter. "Life slowed down then," said John Rockcliff, who had once been a builder. "We almost hibernated, and felt tired without 12 hours' sleep."

But their achievements suggest they cannot have spent too much time lying around. While the beef stew grew tender in the cauldron, John and Kate Rossetti took me on a tour of their domain. Around the compound were thatched farm buildings. First we looked at the pigsty. Despite the fertility rattle on top, Kate said, they had experienced great difficulty in getting the pigs to breed. But the pigs had made excellent bacon, and their fearsome teeth had been fashioned into primitive jewelry, capped with little bronze holders, that several of the Iron Agers wore around their necks.

The nine goats, stabled in their own miniature roundhouse nearby, had been more obliging. They had produced 16 kids during the year, including two born that very morning. "We've really been very successful," said Kate, "because our sheep also had 13 lambs, and we've reared four calves." But the chickens strutting all over the place had been less amenable. The BBC had thoughtfully provided a handsome Old English breed, including some splendid black and gold cocks, but the Iron Agers found that these hens laid eggs only in the spring.

The meat available from their domestic animals was supplemented by rabbits, squirrels, an occasional deer, and even the odd rat, which was spit-roasted. The only trouble with rats, someone confided later, was that there was so little meat on them it was scarcely worth the trouble.

Having formed the four sections of a wooden wheel with an adze, the fourth section is being readied for joining.

APPEASING THE GODS

Beyond the woods, the Iron Agers worked on four hectares of pasture and two of cultivated land. They grew wheat, barley, oats, peas, and tickbeans, all without benefit of modern pesticides or fertilizers. But they made sure of appeasing the gods. On August first, they duly celebrated the Celtic festival of Luġnasad to ensure a good crop. As everyone danced round decked out in body paint made from clay mixed with pig fat and tinted with vegetable dyes, Iron Ager Brian Ackroyd, smeared from head to foot in white wood ash to represent the Spirit of Goodness, ceremonially buried an ear of corn. The gods were content. The resulting harvest was so bountiful that reaping it all became a real chore.

It took them several days to develop a good swing with their long-handled reaping hooks, and they found it frustrating to stop every two or three minutes to sharpen the soft iron blades. Yet in four weeks they cut, dried, and carried almost a kilometer back to their village three and one-half tons of hay, which they fashioned into six stacks that provided some of the feed for their animals through the winter.

They concluded, however, that a true ancient settlement would have needed more land and larger flocks. As Jill Grainger told me, "We had 25 sheep and that's not enough

to clothe us. We estimate that at least 60 sheep would be necessary for a community of our size." Even so, they were all wearing garments made from wool cut from their sheep with sharp flints. The wool was coarse and slightly greasy, but kept them warm and resisted the rain.

Indeed, their real worry was not clothes, but shoes. "The 20th-century thing we miss the most is footwear," said Jill, wriggling mud-caked bare feet before the roundhouse fire to thaw them out. "The Wellington boot was the most fantastic invention. Going barefoot in winter mud is cripplingly cold. I think the Celts must have had shoes." At the beginning, the Iron Agers, following the advice of archaeologists, made shoes out of cowhide, pigskin, and sheepskin. But they were not waterproof and wore out in a few days. Martin Elphick came up with the best solution: he made himself clogs from two strips of wood, each 12 millimeters thick, between which he fixed a strip of calf leather and then added leather uppers. They lasted well and elevated his feet out of at least some puddles.

The houses were built with a wood frame, and branches of the fast-growing black wattle tree (acacia) were woven around the frame. Clay was then daubed onto the woven branches; hence the construction is called wattle-and-dab.

TRIAL AND ERROR

Inventing footwear was but one example of the volunteers' experiments by trial and error to see how their Iron Age ancestors might have coped. "The most frustrating thing," said Peter Little, who proved one of the most dexterous craftsmen of the group, "was not being able to do things as well as the Celts. We could probably equal their skills in ten years, but not in one year."

Weeks were wasted, for instance, trying to make pottery because they not only had to build their own kiln, but had to learn exactly the right amount of groundup stone or "grog" to put with the clay to make it bind correctly. The first pots crumbled to dust.

The Iron Agers proved more skillful at metalwork: they constructed a "forge" in which they swiftly found they could shape and weld iron. The real secret, John Rockcliff revealed, was a good pair of bellows, as he displayed what looked like a dirty old carpetbag. "We have been able to build up a heat of 1,500 degrees Celsius," John said proudly, "so that we can do almost anything on the forge. Unfortunately, we have not cracked the smelting side."

BARTERING

The latter-day Iron Agers found that barter was essential to their whole survival. So they traded with the BBC team. Goat kids, a calf, pots, and baskets made from hazel twigs were swapped for salt, eggs, cheese, and honey. The volunteers had expected to be self-sufficient in honey (they ate almost one-half a kilogram a day), but their modern bees did not take kindly to clay and straw hives and showed their displeasure by buzzing off to swarm in nearby trees. The honey harvest yielded scarcely 18 kilograms, so there was no option but to trade. The art of cheese making also took a while to master; it was not until they killed a calf and took rennet from its stomach that they were able to make hard cheeses. Despite the need to buy, they ended the year as creditors to John Percival and his crew.

NO WASTE

Even with swapping, however, the viability of their community depended on their using everything a dead animal had to offer. "We use the heart, the brains, the tongue, the skin, even the hooves for glue," explained

John Rockcliff, "and we keep the blood to make blood pudding, which has been a staple of our diet." Without the benefits of refrigeration, some of their meat rotted, but they soon discovered that if the meat was hung in the smoke from the perpetual fire, the flies usually stayed away. The meat often tasted high, but at least was not maggoty.

Meat formed a large portion of their diet, which did not make eating easy for a few of the volunteers who were vegetarians. Indeed, the lack of much alternative to meat caused considerable tension. Lindsay Ainsworth and her husband, for instance, loathed meat, and on her days as cook she prepared only a vegetable menu. This led to friction between Lindsay and the rest of the group. The Ainsworths stayed on, but were forced to quit the village in December when their five-year-old son Nicholas became ill.

SENSE OF SATISFACTION

Although the Ainsworths' three children now look back on their Iron Age experiences as the "silly time," they adapted readily to the freedom of the village life while they were there. Peter, the oldest, spent long hours wandering through the woods trying to trap animals, and with his brother Nicholas even tried his hand at welding in the camp fire. "Nicholas would take over the bellows at the forge and keep them going for hours," recalled Martin Elphick. "I am sure that in a real Iron Age village he would have been a fully fledged blacksmith by the age of ten."

The satisfaction of becoming more dexterous seems to have been a real reward, not just for the children but for everyone. "I've learned loads of practical things—looking after animals, weaving, even making my own home," said Jill Grainger, "and above all I've enjoyed living in a community and seeing myself and others in terms of a group of people."

SORRY TO LEAVE

They had settled so well into the Iron Age that I found they had a sense of real regret at the prospect of having to travel 2,300 years forward in time.

"We'd all have been ready to do it for another year if the money had been available," said Peter Little. The only concession they would have demanded for a longer stay would have been some contact with family and friends. The BBC took them on a three-day outing to the sea during the summer, when they camped on the beach in a rough shelter, but otherwise their horizon was limited by their woods. Relatives were barred.

The essence of the experiment would have been ruined if there had been weekends off at home to bathe, wear normal clothes, and sleep in soft beds. Actually, Martin Elphick, a junior hospital doctor before he went Iron Age, did sneak off to an unauth-

Milking a goat requires a great amount of friendly persuasion and persistence.

Mike Wells

Using soft-iron tools to fell trees and to hew them into building materials was a time-consuming task.

Mike Wells

orized two-day break on his own during the summer. He dug up a pound note buried carefully in advance and hitchhiked to the seaside town of Bournemouth where, still in Iron Age garb, he slept on the beach and treated himself to fish and chips. No one knew where he had gone, but after two days he was ready to return.

LIVING A DREAM

Claustrophobia was intense during the first few months as the villagers adjusted to the slow, pastoral existence of the Iron Age community. But after 12 months in the wild, I sensed, their new way of life had become their normal one.

British television viewers have sometimes found it very recognizable, also. As one newspaper columnist complained, "The odd thing about the series was that it *didn't* seem odd. You could run into those glowing women in homespun frocks round Hampstead or Chelsea any day, explaining the virtues of naturalness, breast-feeding and whole grains. . . . The moment when they all emerged from their lake fishing with innocently gleaming bare bottoms (and fronts) could have been yet one more remake of *Hair;* . . . What they were really enacting was our own myth: a dream of simple communal living."

BUT AS AN EXPERIMENT?

What the Iron Agers were really up to has been debated by archaeologists. "As a serious scientific project, I have grave doubts," said Dr. John Coles, lecturer in archaeology at Cambridge University and author of *Archaeology by Experiment.* "If you think this is really like living in the Iron Age, the heck it is." But Oxford University's Professor Barry Cunliffe is prepared to be much more generous. "All right, it is *not* an experiment," he said. "They have simply been trying to live out some of our guesses. When I visited the site, I was very intrigued by walking around and examining the effect that these villagers had had on their environment. Just looking at their rubbbish heaps, the paths they had worn, the effect on the soil, told me a lot about Iron Age sites that I have dug."

One long-standing mystery was solved for Cunliffe when he noticed just inside the door of the round house a shallow depression of scooped-out earth. He remembered that he had found this at every Iron Age site he had ever excavated. Archaeologists had always questioned whether some religious significance should be attached to this strange hollow in the ground. Cunliffe asked the villagers how their depression came into being. Oh, they replied casually, whenever the chickens strutted in out of the rain, they took a dust bath just inside the door. They had worn away quite an interesting-looking hollow, hadn't they? □

SELECTED READINGS

"From bronze to steel." *Scientific American,* May 1977.

"How the Iron Age began" by R. Madden and others. *Scientific American,* October 1977.

"Reliving the Iron Age in Britain." *Time,* March 13, 1978.

Van Bucher/Photo Researchers

Javanese workers transplant rice seedlings in the volcanic soil of a flooded paddy.

THE GREENING OF JAVA

by Barry Newman

THE rice-paddy land surrounding the old city of Solo in Indonesia is a brilliant green, rising in flooded terraces on the slopes of the extinct volcano Lawu. Peasants bend in the fields and throng the roads, carrying full baskets to the mills. Everywhere, it seems, there is rice.

A picture of abundance, and one that ought to be expected on the island of Java. This is one of the most fertile places on earth—far more fertile than Indonesia's many outer islands. It is a place where the Green Revolution worked. It is a place where since the mid-1960's rice crops have multiplied, and the birth rate has dropped. And it is part of a country that is rich in oil. What is the problem?

If there is a spot in the Third World in a position to escape the tortures of underdevelopment, this is it. And yet, Java seems destined to join the likes of Bangladesh and the Sahel in human and ecological surrender.

Java's experience is a chilling reminder that a world food crisis is still with us. It is also a sobering example of the social, economic, and political hurdles that Third World nations face in dealing with their problems.

OF RICE AND FIREWOOD

The Green Revolution did produce more rice on Java, but the poor here can scarcely afford it. Indonesia's oil revenues, which were over $6,000,000,000 in 1977, produced foreign-exchange reserves, but they didn't solve the country's real energy crisis—the dwindling supply of firewood.

As the landless are driven into the mountains in search of food and fuel, deforestation leads to erosion, and erosion results in floods and droughts that eventually will take their toll in the rice land below and drive still more people into the mountains.

A respected Dutch ecologist, J. P. Thysse, has said publicly that Java could be a desert in 30 years. Others don't go as far, but that is little reason for comfort. "What you could have is bare mountains and savanna country at the foot of them," says an expert. "They should be bloody well scared."

The other face of Java comes into view when a traveler turns off the main market road and begins the trek along grassy tracks to the steeper heights of Lawu. Soon the lush terraces disappear. Rice is replaced by cassava, a poor man's root crop planted pre-

Vail/Maryknoll
Finding enough firewood is a problem in Java.

cariously in the clay. Deep gullies scar the land. In places, the soil has a dusting of sand. Whole hillsides have collapsed. The streams run red with mud.

POPULATION PROBLEM

And along the route is a steady procession of men and women, young and old, shouldering heavy bundles of wood poached from the national forest near the volcano's peak.

"What has happened to the land?" one of them is asked.

"It has not been maintained," he says.

Population is at the root of Java's problems. This is the most densely populated farmland in the world. Some 85,000,000 people live here, in a space no bigger than Arkansas. Indonesia's birth-control efforts have been as effective as any, but that means the country's total population of 140,000,000 will double in the next 35 years instead of the next 30 years. The immediate question isn't how to reduce the population, but how to feed it.

STILL A FOOD CRISIS

That was what the Green Revolution, with its high-yielding rice strains and its high-technology irrigation systems and fertilizers, was supposed to do. Its success in Indonesia was spectacular. Since the mid-1960's, rice production in Indonesia has jumped by

50 per cent. Rice yields are still 36 per cent higher than the average of all other rice producers in southern Asia. Per-capita rice consumption has gone from 90 kilograms a year to 115. This would be cause for rapture, except for one thing: Indonesia is still facing a food crisis.

REVOLUTION TURNED AGAINST ITSELF

There isn't anything left in the Green Revolution's bag of tricks. The revolution, in fact, has turned against itself. Now that Java's paddies are supporting two or three crops a year, rice-ravaging pests can feast full time. The only deterrents are insect-resistant seeds, but the insects seem to get used to these seeds as fast as the scientists can fashion them. The new insect-resistant seed varieties are also more vulnerable to the droughts and floods that intensify on Java as erosion gets worse.

In 1976 and 1977, rice production in Indonesia actually dropped, from nearly 16,-000,000 tons a year to perhaps as low as 15,000,000 tons. The government took up the slack in 1977 by importing nearly 2,000,000 tons, at a cost of over $500,000,000. That made Indonesia the world's largest rice importer, taking almost one third of the available supplies.

Government advisers think these imports are dangerously high. In a year when bad weather cuts supplies, Indonesian demand alone could more than double the rice price, draining away a large share of the country's oil revenue. "It would be a major shock to this economy," one expert says.

Ominous as this may be for the economy, Indonesia's millions can still thank the Green Revolution for giving them more to eat. Or can they? "Solving a production problem isn't necessarily solving a hunger problem," one of Indonesia's few agricultural economists says. "It isn't a problem of supply. It's a problem of purchasing power."

MONEY FOR RICE

It is true that Indonesians in general are eating more rice, but not all Indonesians—only those with the money to buy it. This was driven home in 1977 when a particularly bad pest attack left thousands hungry. Indonesians with rice money are most often farmers

Left: the rich soil of Java produces a large variety and quantity of fruits and vegetables. Below: these stacks of rice are drying before they go to the mill.

Vail/Maryknoll

Georg Gerster, Rapho/Photo Researchers

who were lucky enough to profit from the new rice technology.

With more rice to sell and more money coming in, many of these better-off farmers (who were generally better off to begin with) have been investing in labor-saving mechanical weeders, hulling machines, and even small tractors. Some farmers have even begun hiring contract labor and abandoning the tradition of allowing landless peasants to help in the harvest for a share of the crop.

Probably one-half of Java's population is landless, and another quarter nearly so. For them, the trend means less work and less to eat. The farmer whose high-yielding crop is killed by the weather or the bugs isn't any better off. When he defaults on his fertilizer loan, the government cuts off his supply. Without fertilizer, his prospects for recovering in the next season are dim. Faced with mortgage payments and taxes, he probably will sell out and join the landless himself.

"Their lives are squeezed," an Indonesian academic says of Java's landless population, as quoted by a Jakarta newspaper. "Employment opportunities are narrow, and they don't have the money to buy rice."

ESCAPE TO MOUNTAINS

Short of a very unlikely realignment of power in the villages, the most practical recourse is an escape to the mountains to grow corn and cassava, sweet potatoes and soybeans. This may be the best solution.

After a decade of pushing rice production, some advisers are now telling the government it has to promote a switch to other foods—namely, the crops currently clinging to the mountainsides. By teaching the upland squatters how to cultivate these plants correctly, the pressure on rice might be relaxed and erosion reduced.

Unfortunately, accomplishing this requires more than logic. Rice is a political commodity in Indonesia. Indonesians like rice, and they like it cheap. To encourage the consumption of other foods, the government would have to let the price of rice rise. This would be risky. So rice imports continue, and so does erosion.

"Some of the loveliest soil in all of Asia is being washed into the sea," says a forestry expert in Jakarta. From an airplane above the north coast of Java, you can see it: great plumes of red mud spilling from river

Left: these terraced paddies show that no land is wasted. Right: better land management would end erosion and supply more food to the Javanese.

mouths. One storm can sweep 185 tons of topsoil from a single hectare. For all of Java, this translates into as much as 80,000,000 tons a year.

HIGHER AND HIGHER

The process generates its own momentum. As erosion wastes one swatch of land, the farmers give up and move higher. As trees are pulled down to make way for cultivation, the search for firewood moves higher, too. Without trees to help absorb the water, the rain—250 centimeters a year—washes down the mountains, floods the rice fields, and silts up the irrigation canals. In the dry season, the canals are clogged and the wells are empty.

The government is taking a stab at slowing the consumption of firewood by subsidizing the price of kerosene. But as long as firewood can be taken free, it will be preferable to kerosene no matter how heavy the subsidy. Without adequate truck routes, most parts of the island don't have access to kerosene anyway.

The government is also trying to do something about erosion by planting trees— lines of them on more than 800,000 hectares of land. It is asking farmers to plant their crops between the rows of trees, but it is barely trying to teach the farmers how to build erosion-resistant terraces on dry land. For 2,000 years the Javanese have been building fine terraces for rice, but they do not build terraces for crops that don't have to be flooded.

The government's trees, meanwhile, cast shadows over the fields, stunting the cassava

plants. So the farmers are cutting the trees down. From 1975 to 1978, Indonesia spent $180,000,000 planting these trees. The experts say most of it has been wasted.

"GREENING" GONE AWRY

Near the village of Genegan on the slopes of Lawu, there is a field of cassava that has been "greened" by the government. The cassava, without proper terraces, is scrawny and sparse. The files of government-planted trees have been reduced to stumps, the clay is turning to sand, and the gullies into gorges.

A hectare of this land produces in one season about two-and-one-half tons of cassava. A hectare fertilized and protected from erosion would produce a hundred times that. But there isn't any fertilizer for the farmers of Genegan. They grow cassava, and the focus of the Green Revolution has been on rice. And even if the farmers knew how, chances are they wouldn't build the terraces they need. The price of their crop is too low to make the effort worthwhile. So when the land is exhausted, the people will move higher. Until then, they are doing what they can to stop the earth from washing away.

Across a deep gully in a field just outside the village, the farmers have built a crude bamboo dam. When it rains, the water rushes over the dam, but some of the silt remains. Then, like Sisyphus, the farmers haul it up the mountain again.

"Every day we dig the mud and put it back on the land," says a small, muscular farmer. "But the flood is very big and the land is loose. The water digs deeper every year" □

KING TUT

by Jenny Tesar

TUTANKHAMUN was a 9-year-old boy when he became king of Egypt in 1334 B.C. Less than a decade later, when only 18 or 19 years old, he died. His brief reign was relatively uneventful and, in the normal course of events, his name would now be known only to historians. But in 1922, a British archeologist discovered the tomb in which Tutankhamun was buried. Unlike the other royal tombs found in Egypt's Valley of the Kings, Tutankhamun's tomb had largely escaped being plundered and despoiled by robbers. Its contents were virtually intact—unchanged and unseen for more than 3,300 years.

The tomb contained four rooms. Each was filled with a wealth of artifacts: furniture, weapons, toys, musical instruments, jewelry. And, in the burial chamber, there was a solid gold coffin containing the embalmed body, or mummy, of the young king.

Why was the tomb built? Why was it filled with so many treasures? Why was the body of the king mummified?

A LIFE EVERLASTING

The people of ancient Egypt believed in life after death. Of course they weren't certain what the afterlife was actually like. Some thought the dead person continued to live in the tomb. Others believed that the spirit, or soul, of the dead person journeyed to another world, a blessed place inhabited by gods. Even if such a journey was made, however, the spirit needed an earthly resting place. This was provided by the mummy.

The ancient Egyptians believed that immortality was guaranteed as long as the body was preserved. If the body began to decay, then the spirit of the person also lost part of itself. The complete decay or destruction of the body meant that the spirit also would be completely destroyed.

The tomb, which housed the body, was thought of as a "house of eternity." As such, it was filled with items that the king might need during his afterlife—food, a headrest, chairs, writing implements, chariots, and so

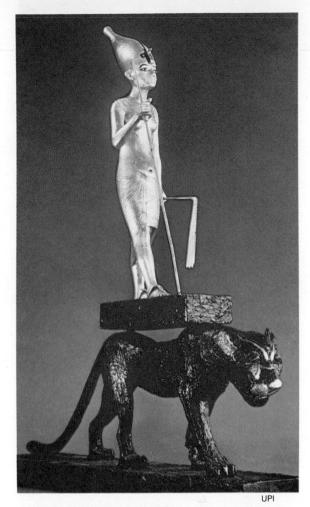

A golden deified Tutankhamun.

on. There were belongings he had used during his life, including several board games that resemble backgammon.

PRESERVING THE BODY

The purpose of mummification was to preserve the body. But embalming, in addition to being a highly skilled profession, was a religious ritual. Various steps of the procedure were accompanied by prayers and incantations.

The embalming of Tutankhamun probably was done at his palace at Thebes (Luxor). The hair was shaved from the corpse. The brain was removed bit by bit, by drawing it out through the nostrils. Iron hooks and probes were used to do this. Presumably the brain fragments were discarded since no evidence of them was found in the tomb.

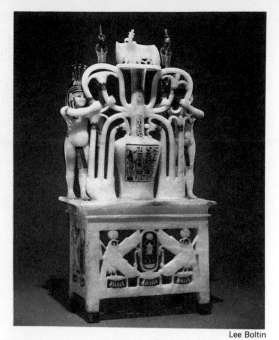

An alabaster unguent jar from Tut's tomb.

The heart was left in place, for it would be needed by the body when it faced Osiris, the god of the dead and ruler of the underworld. The intestines, liver, stomach, and lungs were treated with spices and other preservatives, bandaged, and placed in four miniature gold coffins. These in turn were placed in an alabaster chest which is known as the canopic chest.

After the empty body cavity was washed out, the body was packed and covered in a dehydrating agent called natron. This mineral is mined in Egypt, and is a mixture of sodium carbonate and sodium bicarbonate.

The body was left in the natron for 70 days. At the end of this time, the natron had absorbed all the moisture in the body, leaving it dry and shriveled.

The body was washed. Then it was completely wrapped in layer after layer of linen. Each limb was wrapped separately. So were each of the fingers and toes. The body cavity was stuffed with linen soaked in ointments. Then linen padding was placed around the shrunken tissues in an effort to maintain the body's original shape.

About 20 layers of linen were used. Between every few layers, a coating of various oils, resins, and gums was applied. The coatings served as preservatives and binding agents. Jewelry also was placed within the wrappings. A total of 143 gold objects, including sandals, daggers, armbands, neck pieces, and 13 rings, were found on the body or within its wrappings.

Perfumed oils were poured over the wrappings. Then a magnificent gold burial mask was placed over the head and shoulders of the mummy. The mask, believed to be a portrait of the young king, weighed almost 10 kilograms. Hands of gold, holding the royal crook and flail, were attached to the wrappings.

The mummy was placed in three coffins, one sitting within another. All three were carved with the same motif used on the burial mask. The innermost coffin was solid gold inlaid with semiprecious stones.

A funeral procession accompanied the mummy and the canopic chest containing the internal organs as they were carried from Tutankhamun's palace to the Valley of the Kings. The coffins were carried along a tunnel in the pyramid that led to the tomb chamber. Then they were lowered into the quartzite sarcophagus. Four shrines, one encasing the other, were placed around the sarcophagus.

The canopic chest was enclosed in a gilt shrine. Statues of the goddesses Selket, Isis, Nephthys, and Neith stood on the four sides of the shrine. Each goddess guarded one of the organs: Selket the intestines, Isis the liver, Nephythys the lungs, and Neith the stomach.

Finally, the various treasures and other artifacts were placed in the tomb. And then the entrance to the tomb was closed. Tutankhamun was left to begin his journey to the next world.

DID MUMMIFICATION WORK?

Tutankhamun's tomb was discovered on November 4, 1922, by Howard Carter. He cabled his sponsor, Lord Carnarvon, who hurried to Egypt from his home in England. Twenty-three days later the two men opened and entered the tomb. Over the next 10 years, Carter and his staff recorded and removed from the tomb the artifacts.

It wasn't until November 11, 1925, that Carter and his associates began to examine the mummy. The examination had to take place in the coffin. Humidity, locked into the coffin, had reacted with the oils that had been poured over the mummy. The result

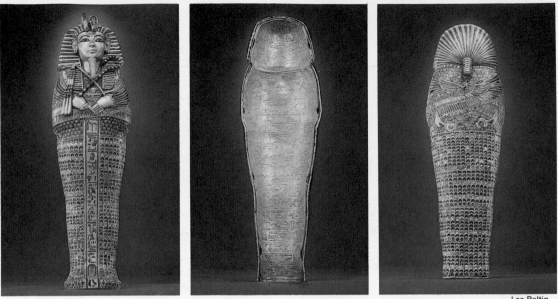

Sarcophagus (*left*) front; (*middle*) inside; (*right*) rear.

was a thick, gluey substance that firmly attached the mummy to the bottom of the coffin.

A communiqué from Carter's group stated: "The outer surfaces of the mummy's wrapping, which were in a most fragile condition, were first strengthened by means of a thin coating of paraffin wax, after which Professor Derry [Professor of Anatomy, Egyptian University] made a longitudinal incision extending from mask to feet.

"The outer coverings being turned back, exposed the next layers of wrappings, which proved to be equally carbonized and decayed. In these circumstances any orderly unwrapping was manifestly impossible."

The unwrapping of the mummy took seven days. It was necessary to remove the linen in small pieces, many not much bigger than a band-aid. Special brushes were used to remove tiny fragments and powder.

When people finally gazed at the mummy, they saw a very emaciated and blackened body. The head was the best preserved portion, since it had not been saturated with unguents. "The face," wrote Carter, "was refined and cultured, the features well formed, especially the clearly marked lips. . . ."

The chemicals formed over the centuries had caused the mummy's skin and underlying tissues to become extremely thin and brittle. In places, some of the joints were exposed. This enabled doctors to estimate Tut-

ankhamun's age at death as about 18. This was done by taking measurements of the bones in the feet and by determining the extent of calcification of the bones. The king's height was estimated at 5 feet, 6 inches.

A careful application of heat and chemicals softened the gluey mass and enabled Carter to separate the body from the coffin. Carter rewrapped the mummy in fresh linen and placed it into its outermost, wooden coffin. This was placed into the sarcophagus. The original cover of the sarcophagus, a massive piece of stone weighing 1¼ tons, was not replaced. Instead, the sarcophagus was covered with thick glass so that visitors to the site could see the mummy.

Certainly Tutankhamun is very much alive in the twentieth century. The treasures he brought with him to our modern world have thrilled all who have viewed them. And the knowledge imparted by the treasures and by his mummy have given us a detailed picture of life in the land he once ruled □

 SELECTED READINGS

"There's much more in Cairo at the Egyptian Museum" by R. Ahrens. *Horizon,* October 1978.

The Untold Story by Thomas Hoving. Simon and Schuster, 1978.

"What Tut has wrought" by S. Weisman. *Horizon,* October 1978.

Wonderful Things: The Discovery of Tutankhamun's Tomb by Howard Carter, et al. Metropolitan Museum of Art.

Otis Imboden/Courtesy of Earthwatch

Volunteer researchers study the artifacts of early people on the island of Majorca.

EARTHWATCH

by Mary Carpenter

HELP is on the way for the beleaguered scientists who chronically experience problems in staffing and financing digs, dives, and sundry other expeditions that will further their work and advance scientific knowledge.

The help—actually it's been flowing since 1972—is in the form of volunteer amateurs who sign on to work under a scientist's direction in some field that interests them. And anyone—male, female, young, old— "with enthusiasm and interest" is being urged by the project's sponsor to "come, share costs, and work" with research teams.

The sponsor is Earthwatch, a non-profit organization based near Cambridge, Massachusetts. It is a clearinghouse coordinating interested applicants and scientists who need support teams for their research and also funding assistance.

IMPORTANT DISCOVERIES

Some Earthwatch expeditions have already led to important discoveries. Among these are:

• One group discovered a polluted reef among the Grenadine Corals that was dying for no apparent cause. The Lesser Antilles actually is the healthiest reef system in the world. The team, under Dr. Melvin Goodwin of Toronto, Canada, returned to investigate why this reef is so badly affected.

• On the last day of an expedition exploring Mediterranean shipwrecks in the Balearic Islands, off the east coast of Spain, a group under Dr. Dominick Ruegg of St. Mary's College in California discovered the wreck of an ancient ship off the coast of Majorca. It is believed to have been a carrier of oils once used for bathing and cooking.

• In the summer of 1977 an Earthwatch team uncovered the first *in situ* (undisturbed) evidence of early human habitation in Connecticut.

WORKING MEMBERS

"Previously, scientists worked laboriously on field research, with little assistance, if any. Then they published results that were rarely read and were, in any case, often too technical to be informative to the general public," says the Earthwatch president, Brian Rosborough.

Now, people who always have felt a curiosity are able to participate—they are treated as "working members"—with research scientists from the Smithsonian Institution and universities around the world including Harvard University in Massachusetts, Cambridge University in England, and Ben-Gurion University of the Negev in Israel, as well as museums and environmental projects such as the Massachusetts Audubon Society.

Founded in 1971 by Robert Citron of the Smithsonian Institution, the original idea behind Earthwatch was to improve the communication gap between scientists and the public. Mr. Rosborough, who was a lawyer in New York at the time, began by consulting for Earthwatch and became president in its second year.

The idea has grown from 32 volunteers in 1971 to 1000 in 1978, who worked on research projects in 13 states and 17 foreign countries.

Each Earthwatch group has 6 to 10 volunteers whose ages vary from 16 to 75. Adults usually outnumber the teenagers 3 to 1; and the groups represent a "good balance" of men and women.

EXERCISE IN PATIENCE

After a scientist sends in a funding proposal and it has been accepted, he or she receives a profile of the applicants. The scientist is then responsible for giving the volunteers job assignments. These may involve anything from mapping or excavating to cooking.

Useful skills of the applicants can include video-taping and electronics for research on animals in Massachusetts zoos, but the one most often mentioned is patience.

Betty Dunlop, an artist from Maryland, participated in a study of social wasps in Costa Rica. Each day for scheduled periods lasting one and a half hours each, she stood with her face only about ten centimeters from the entrance to a wasp's nest and called out the number of colored dots on the thorax of each wasp as it left the nest and returned.

Another volunteer recorded the data, which included what each wasp was carrying when it returned. More than 350 wasps could fly in and out of the nest each hour. "I had no formal training in biology," says Ms. Dunlop, "but an alert person with a varied background can generally apply it to the project."

Jeff Eaton, a chemist for the Polaroid Corporation in Cambridge, Massachusetts, points out that, though he is trained as a scientist, his group worked well together because they were all non-archaeologists.

The graduate students on the scientist's research team were the ones who trained the volunteers, says Mr. Eaton, "but archaeology is mainly an exercise in patience, and the skills involved are mostly trowelling and pick

and shovel work." Mr. Eaton has made two Earthwatch trips, both to study recumbent stone circles, the Berrybrae Stone Circle in Scotland and the Stone Monuments of Cashelkeelty in Ireland.

However, for him and others, the main interest in Earthwatch stems from their desire to do something on their vacation other

Jack Kirkham/Courtesy of Earthwatch

Perhaps the most time-consuming activity in archaeology is sifting piles of rubble.

Courtesy of Earthwatch

than "putting a camera around my neck and being Joe Tourist," as Mr. Eaton puts it.

"Earthwatch engages your mind," he observes, "while providing opportunities to get to know the local people."

Shopping in the towns, singing in the pubs, and dealing with the farmers whose property they crossed gave the groups daily contact with local people.

Although most people describe their Earthwatch experiences as "super" and "tremendously interesting," Jean Lundquist, a science teacher from Lake Elmo, Minnesota, said her trip to the Ozarks was "also kind of miserable."

"We had more rain in a week and a half than that part of Missouri usually has in a whole year. We spent a good deal of the time mopping up the mud."

Ms. Lundquist notes that her group "got along well" considering those circumstances and a wide age range within her group. And they found many bones of giant sloths, mastodons, mammoths, and buffalo, which were "amazingly" well-preserved. "You could almost see the parts of the animals," she says. "This was more than a school field trip."

FREQUENT REPEATERS

Mr. Eaton would like to try a trip to the Galapagos Islands next, and Ms. Lundquist joined the mammoth excavations in South Dakota in 1978. Many volunteers return year after year and sometimes repeat the same trips. This becomes an advantage for scientists who do not need to train repeaters. In frequent cases, entire families go together.

Dr. Larry Agenbrod, of Chadron State College in Nebraska, taking groups to excavate a graveyard of mammoths—extinct elephants—in the Black Hills of South Dakota for three years, has frequent repeaters. In addition to excavating, his team is involved in mapping, photographing, transit surveying, and analysis.

So far, this location has yielded 22 mammoth as well as bears, coyotes, camels, peccaries, and unidentified vulture-like birds, all trapped in a limestone sink or cavern when it collapsed 22,000 years ago.

Dr. Agenbrod's recent book, *The Bison Kill,* describes the site and some findings. An important finding was that of a pointed weapon that may indicate the presence, at one time, of a sophisticated human society.

"Some volunteers are almost inherently proficient," Dr. Agenbrod notes. "Others learn, and others—very few—find out that they don't really like the work after all."

But many enjoy their experience enough to follow it up when the trip is over. After learning to operate metal detectors and other devices used to explore shipwrecks off the coast of Plymouth, England, David Krause of Chicago joined an archaeological society. One woman, after four Earthwatch expeditions, returned to school in her middle years to earn a degree in archaeology.

Occasionally, the planned adventure is augmented. A group surveying the volcanic crust on Mt. Arsenal in Costa Rica, for example, was able to collect especially good data because the volcano erupted while they were there. Another team, in Guatemala during an earthquake, was recruited to help.

Helen Paulson, a Miami Beach nurse, was able to learn something about her team's work from the Samoan family she was staying with. Her medical team was studying obesity and aging in western Samoa. After sitting on the floor to share meals of boiled green bananas and taro, Ms. Paulson comments, "No wonder it's better to be fat in Samoa: more padding for sitting cross-legged."

Researchers measure the impression of tire tracks on a sand dune on Fire Island, N.Y.
Courtesy of Earthwatch

Courtesy of Earthwatch

Inscriptions on a megalith in Great Britain are being studied by Earthwatch researchers.

MANY DIFFERENT PROJECTS

In addition to the projects already referred to, some other recent trips included: a study of the impact of rapid industrialization in Pakistan, at the invitation of the Pakistani government; a study of public health in Kenya with an African research team; and a study of the potential for maintaining park services on the Boston harbor islands.

The expeditions, which run from a week to three weeks in order to coincide with vacation schedules of working adults, are arranged throughout the year. Pre-trip information for volunteers includes 30 or 40 pages of background materials, encompassing the scientist's proposal, plus a reading list. At this stage, the volunteer is urged to prepare for any strenuous activity that may be ahead. An extreme example: one trip to study the lakes of Lapland in Abisko Ostra, Sweden, is "open to all who can hike to the base camp: six miles in the mountains carrying a 50-pound backpack."

Applicants must be able to make a contribution (tax-deductible) to subsidize an expedition (from $550 to $950, depending on the trip) and pay their own way to and from the site □

Volunteers Unearth Evidence of Early Man

An Earthwatch expedition under Dr. Roger Moeller of the American Indian Archeological Institute discovered a five-centimeter fluted spear point in northwestern Connecticut. The carbon-14 date of 10,190 years ago places man in New England more than 5,000 years earlier than previous evidence.

Earthwatch volunteers Andy Postman and Maggie Tolladay each discovered one of the separated halves of the point, lying less than 15 centimeters apart. Mr. Postman discovered the first half when his trowel made what Dr. Moeller had just described to the group as the "distinctive ringing sound of metal against the flint of the spearhead."

Although other points had been found previously in Connecticut, this point was the first to be discovered more than one meter below the ground surface in an undisturbed context (in situ). Dr. Moeller comments that, "For the first time in this state, we will have the opportunity to analyze a Paleo-Indian camp site: How large was it in area? How many people lived there?"

The site was chosen because of the large number of Indian artifacts that farmers had been finding there. Additionally, certain indications suggested that the field was once the confluence of a brook and the Shepaug River, a natural campsite even for present-day campers.

In addition to the point, the team also discovered flint chips and other artifacts, including a miniature of an arrowhead. The function of this object is "mysterious," according to Dr. Moeller, because, as compared to other artifacts from that period, it had no practical use.

The quantity and variety of tools found at the site can offer clues to the reason for the encampment and to predict sites for future excavations, Dr. Moeller observes. He sees it also as a challenge to the long-held theory that Indians in the area traveled to the Hudson River for flint for their weapons.

SELECTED READINGS

Earthwatch, a publication of Earthwatch, Box 127, Juniper Road, Belmont, Massachusetts 02178.

University of Toronto

Charles H. Best

IN MEMORIAM

by Barbara Tchabovsky

SEVERAL people important in science and technology died during 1978 and early 1979. Among them were Charles H. Best, the codiscoverer of insulin; Vincent du Vigneaud, a Nobel Prize winning chemist famed for his work on hormones; Dennis Gabor, Nobel Prize winning physicist, who invented holography; Samuel Goudsmit, the codiscoverer of electron spin; and Margaret Mead, anthropologist and social critic.

CHARLES H. BEST

Charles Herbert Best, the codiscoverer of insulin, was born in West Pembroke, Maine, on February 27, 1899, the son of a Canadian-born physician. His study of the arts at the University of Toronto was interrupted by military service during World War I. After the war, he returned to Toronto to study physiology and biochemistry. At the age of 21, while still an undergraduate, he was asked by physician Frederick Banting to join him in investigating diabetes mellitus. Having obtained the reluctant permission of J. R. MacLeod, head of the University of Toronto's physiology department, to use the department's laboratory, the two began their work, at their own expense, in the summer of 1921.

Aware that a substance from the pan-creas had already been shown to be involved in sugar metabolism, they set out to isolate the substance. They succeeded in isolating the hormone—insulin—and found that when they gave it to diabetic dogs, the dogs were restored to health. They announced their findings in late 1921, and in early 1922 insulin was first given to a human diabetic. It proved to be a successful treatment and subsequently became one of the greatest tools ever provided medicine—one that has saved or lengthened the lives of many millions of diabetes sufferers throughout the world.

Banting and MacLeod were awarded the 1923 Nobel Prize in Physiology or Medicine for the discovery of insulin. Banting, angered that Best had not been honored, shared his prize money with Best.

After the discovery of insulin, Best went on to develop the antiallergic enzyme known as histaminase and to do important work on the anticoagulant heparin. Best died in Toronto, Canada, on March 31, 1978, as a result of a ruptured blood vessel suffered several days earlier after hearing that his 46-year-old son had died suddenly.

VINCENT DU VIGNEAUD

Vincent Du Vigneaud, Nobel laureate for his work on hormones, was born in Chicago, Illinois, on May 18, 1901. In 1938, he became professor and head of the department of biochemistry at Cornell University Medical School in New York City. Under Du Vigneaud the biochemistry laboratories at Cornell became centers for many important discoveries.

After early work on the isolation and chemical structure of the vitamin biotin, Du Vigneaud participated in efforts to synthesize penicillin. The final experiments, carried out in the Cornell laboratories under Du Vigneaud and others, led to the synthesis of penicillin and to prove that the synthetic was identical to the natural penicillin.

It was, however, Du Vigneaud's work with hormones that led to his 1955 Nobel Prize in Chemistry. He and his associates isolated the hormone oxytocin from the posterior part of the pituitary gland. Oxytocin is the main uterus-contracting agent during labor and milk-secreting agent after childbirth. They then studied its chemical structure and in 1953 succeeded in synthesizing it in the laboratory.

From 1967 to 1975 Du Vigneaud was a professor of chemistry at Cornell University in Ithaca, New York. He died in White Plains, New York, on December 11, 1978.

DENNIS GABOR

Dennis Gabor, the inventor of holography, was born in Hungary in 1900. He was educated as a theoretical physicist and was professor of applied electronic physics at Imperial College in London until his death in London on February 8, 1979. His main interest, however, was invention. He was awarded more than 100 patents during his lifetime.

Holography is a photographic technique by which a three-dimensional image is presented from a flat photographic print. The print itself is merely a jumble of curved lines, but when it is viewed in light, the observer sees a three-dimensional image that is a perfect likeness of the original. Holography does not use lenses but rather relies on beams of light. Today the light beams normally used are lasers, but in 1947, when Gabor invented the idea of holography, lasers had not yet been invented. He used the light of a mercury arc.

An invention far ahead of its time, holography took, according to one of Gabor's colleagues, an "intellectual leap" and was "an amazing accomplishment" for its time.

Vincent du Vigneaud

Samuel Goudsmit

Aware that it was highly unusual for an inventor like him to be honored with a Nobel Prize, Gabor said, shortly after winning the 1971 Physics prize, "Most people get the prize for one thing they spend a long life in science to accomplish. I'm an outsider. I've worked in industrial laboratories most of my life, and industrial workers rarely get Nobel prizes. I consider it an invention."

SAMUEL GOUDSMIT

Samuel Abraham Goudsmit, the codiscoverer of electron spin, was born in The Hague, the Netherlands, on July 11, 1902. He displayed an early interest in physics, did experimental work at the University of Amsterdam, and studied theoretical physics at the University of Leiden, receiving his Ph.D. in 1927.

While still a graduate student at the university of Leiden, Goudsmit and fellow student George E. Uhlenbeck made a momentous discovery. The two studied the spectral lines emitted by atoms, knowing that none of the then-current theories explained the number of spectral lines. They proposed that electrons were not merely charged points but were spinning particles. They theorized that electrons spin on their own axes, creating spinning spheres of negative electricity. This theory accounted for spectral and magnetic properties of atoms that could not previously be explained. For their discovery, Goudsmit and Uhlenbeck received Research Corporation Awards in 1953, Max Planck Medals in 1964, and National Medals

Margaret Mead

Ken Heyman

of Science in 1977, but, to the surprise of many, they were never awarded the Nobel Prize in Physics.

During World War II he worked on radar projects at the Massachusetts Institute of Technology and then became scientific director of a secret effort to determine if Germany was building an atomic bomb. In recent years Goudsmit lectured and served as a visiting professor at numerous universities, including the University of Nevada in Reno, where he died on December 4, 1978.

MARGARET MEAD

Margaret Mead, well-known anthropologist, social critic, author, and lecturer, was born in Philadelphia, Pennsylvania, on December 16, 1901. She was educated at Barnard College and Columbia University, receiving her Ph.D. in anthropology in 1929.

The American Museum of Natural History in New York City was her home base, so to speak. From 1926 until her death she served in various posts in the department of ethology and anthropology, the last being curator emeritus of the department of anthropology. She was also adjunct professor of anthropology at Columbia University and taught at several other universities.

It was her trips and her writings and lectures about them that made Margaret Mead famous. They also made anthropology known to the general public, taking it out of dusty academe and placing it in front of the public, often as a mirror in which to view contemporary life. At the same time Margaret Mead's work contributed to the development of anthropology as a science. Not content to restrict her observations of a culture to behavior that could be statistically analyzed, she advocated a broad base of observation, drawing upon psychology, economics, ecology, nutrition, physiology, and other disciplines before making her conclusions. Her frank, vehement, sometimes acerbic way of expressing herself alienated some of her colleagues, but she won the respect of most.

Her first trip—to Samoa—resulted in *Coming of Age in Samoa* (1929), perhaps her most famous book. In it she described adolescence in Samoa, an adolescence free of the emotional crises considered so much a part of adolescence in many Western cultures.

Among her other anthropological trips were expeditions to Manus in the Admiralty Islands (1928–29, 1953), New Guinea (1931–33, 1938), and Bali (1936–39). Her work in Bali, with then-husband Gregory Bateson, a fellow anthropologist, included some 25,000 photographs, an important contribution to anthropology. She described her findings in a number of books, including *Growing Up in New Guinea* (1930), and *Sex and Temperament in Three Primitive Societies* (1935).

A widely recognized figure—a robust, open-faced woman, brandishing a forked walking stick—Margaret Mead was criticized, loved, and admired by those within and outside her profession. Her influence and power cannot be denied and was perhaps exemplified by her election at the age of 72 to the presidency of the American Association for the Advancement of Science. She died of cancer in New York City on November 16, 1978. Her best tribute was perhaps that given by a young anthropologist: "Anthropology without Margaret Mead—unthinkable" □

Science Books of the Year

Many books on science and technology are published every year. The titles below were selected for review by the editors because they seemed of particular significance, interest, or usefulness. The choice was not restricted to books appearing within the last year, since this does not affect the value of their contents. The titles that were chosen represent the range of subjects that is provided within the various sections of this annual.

Your Genes and Your Destiny *by Augusta Greenblatt and I. J. Greenblatt. Bobbs-Merrill, 1979. 226 pp., $8.95.*

The subtitle of this book: "a new look at a longer life when heart disease, high blood pressure, diabetes, or obesity is a family affair" explains the theme. What the Greenblatts have done is to describe the research that indicates that these diseases can be inherited. Then they review the latest research on their prevention. Medical researchers now realize that your genes do not have to be your destiny. And with this realization, they are now treating these genetic disorders in children rather than waiting until the coronary strikes, the high bood pressure has done its damage, the blood sugar is not metabolized, or obesity has taken its toll. Some diseases are now diagnosed while the fetus is in the uterus, and sometimes the disorder can be rectified. Usually something can be done to help the victim and the parents. As research zeros in on such disorders, it traces them back to their genetic beginnings. For example, certain genes control blood pressure. Environmental factors such as weight, smoking, drinking, stress, use of salt, and others then determine whether the defective gene(s) will actually cause high blood pressure.

Wildly Successful Plants *by Lawrence J. Crockett. Collier Books, a division of Macmillan Co., 1977. 268 pp., illus., $6.95.*

Mr. Crockett observes that, "There are no weeds in nature, just as there are no peasants. Cultivation and civilization have created both." Although weeds are not biologically related, they do have much in common: they all have an aggressive and competitive growth habit, and of course, they are unwanted by people—like many insects. Some are useful and/or beautiful, such as the black-eyed Suzan and the wild strawberry. Others, like poison ivy and nettles, are a plague. This book describes the botanical characteristics and the historical and useful aspects of about a hundred weeds. Before the author describes the individual plants, he lays a clear and simple botanical groundwork so that his descriptions will be meaningful to the novice. He also presents an easy-to-use key for identifying the weeds in this book. For every weed described there is a full-page illustration of that weed and its parts along with a whimsical human figure to give the reader, at a glance, its size and growth habits.

The One-Straw Revolution *by Masanobu Fukuoka. Rodale Press, 1978. 184 pp., illus., $7.95.*

This book is about a naturalistic life style as well as about farming. The author's insights about nature and how to adjust to it instead of forcing it to adjust has become a philosophic theme. For centuries Japanese farmers have composted their shredded straw in piles all winter so that it will be decomposed by spring. Then they flood their fields, add the compost, and plow it into a pea-soup consistency. But along comes Mr. Fukuoka with a revolutionary farming practice: don't compost your straw in piles, and don't plow. He lets nature establish a balance between the insect communities, so that he uses no insecticides. His work schedule is as follows: In October, winter wheat or barley, clover, and rice seeds are broadcast in fields where rice is still standing. (The rice seeds will lie dormant until spring.) A few weeks later the standing rice is harvested, and its straw is spread over the fields on top of the newly sewn seeds. In May, the barley or wheat are harvested, and their straw is spread over the fields. Monsoon rains flood the fields in June, weakening the clover and weeds and giving the rice seeds a chance to grow through the all-important ground cover of straw. When the field dries, the clover recovers and grows beneath the rice plants, enriching the soil with nitrates.

Beginner's Guide to Home Computers by *Marvin Grosswirth. Doubleday & Company (Dolphin), 1978. 128 pp., illus., $3.95.*

If all you want to do is stick your toe in the water, do it with the help of this book. It is a warmly written intoduction to microcomputers, covering everything from the binary system to BASIC. Grosswirth also discusses some of the many uses for home computers and whether or not you should consider building from a kit instead of buying outright. Readers will also find the appendix of dealers and computer societies very useful.

The Rand McNally Atlas of the Oceans *edited by Martyn Bramwell. Rand McNally, 1977. 208 pp., illus., $29.95.*

Like a beautifully presented documentary film, this book illustrates and explains the components of the ocean—its origins, its life, its movements, its resources, its many geographical parts, and the ongoing research that is revealing its secrets. There are six sections, which you can explore and admire without the background of a preceding section. The sections are made up of many topics, each of which occupies only two facing pages. In this way, you get a summarized panorama of one topic at a time. And each panorama delights the eye with large, colorful photographs, maps, and diagrams. One usually thinks of an atlas as being a large-size book containing maps. This atlas is indeed a large-size book (16″ x 12″). The section entitled "The Face of the Deep" is the section where most of the maps are found. For each ocean there are maps to show their bottom contours, their water and air circulation, their structural geology, and their resources. In the other five sections are such topics as changing coastlines, currents and tides, submersible craft, plankton: the basis of life, marine life, farming the ocean, tapping the bottom for oil, and the problem of pollution. The sixth section is an abbreviated encyclopedia of marine life.

The Picture of Health: Environmental Sources of Disease by *Erik P. Eckholm. W. W. Norton, 1977. 256 pp. $3.95.*

This book is about environmental diseases and their causes. That is a large order because "environment" includes about everything. Eckholm describes the picture of health throughout the world. In the developing countries, where disease is "rooted in the ecology of poverty," infectious diseases and childhood death are rampant because the environmental and economic conditions bring about filth and undernutrition. Modern medicine cannot work health miracles where hunger and filth are pervasive. But in the developed countries, overeating, sedentary living, smoking, and tension—all part of the environment—take their toll in diabetes, cardiovascular diseases, and cancer. Eck-

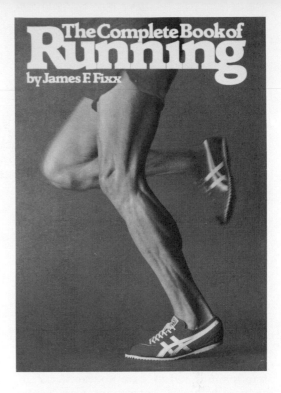

holm guides the reader through undernutrition and its opposite—the affluent diet. He also covers cancer: a social disease, the tobacco diseases, air pollutants, occupational diseases, schistosomiasis, and family planning. In his final chapter, "Creating Better Health" he warns us that "the surest way to avoid vicious environmental repercussions is to slow down the pace at which the ecosystem is being altered and to keep human intervention within the boundaries of human understanding." This fine book makes the reader understand that the picture of health is, ultimately, a reflected image of habitat and habit—in sum, of society.

Everything You Always Wanted to Know About Nutrition by David Reuben, M.D. Simon and Schuster, 1978. 288 pp. $9.95.

At a time when food prices and medical-dental fees are soaring, this book appears as a ray of hope. It explains the fundamentals of a healthy diet free of overprocessed "junk food." The book is a confirmation of what millions of us have suspected all along: that our forefathers ate more nutritious food and suffered less heart attack and cancer; that 500,000,000 Hindus live healthy lives without ever eating meat. The main point that Dr. Reuben hits the reader with so often is that every vitamin, every mineral, every substance required for perfect health can be obtained from easily available food if you can get it before the food processors ruin it. Reuben's advice will be applauded by the people who already understand the benefits of unprocessed food, such as whole wheat and unrefined sugar. His book will come as a revelation to those who try to live on "junk food" or those who think they must consume vitamin pills. But his advice will be damned by the food processors. For these, Reuben has included a "Special Note to the Food Industry" as well as one for the Food and Drug Administration, who "tinker with our nutrition in a way that is convenient for the food processors—but not for us." You will find throughout this excellent book many hard-hitting statements such as: ". . . the trouble with the truth is that it doesn't sell (vitamin) pills."

The Complete Book of Running by James E. Fixx. Random House, 1977. 314 pp., illus., $10.00.

Long hair and blue jeans are superficial aspects of a modern lifestyle, but running, not-smoking, careful eating, and environmental caring are its more basic ones. Undoubtedly, running is a fad for many people, just as it is a way of life for many more. For psychological reasons, it has become a symbol for some, an exhausting challenge for others, and a lot of fun for still others. For the latter, Mr. Fixx sums it up this way: "Running is a vacation from everyday chores—a special treat for your mind and body. If you concentrate on the fun, the fitness and style will take care of themselves." If it *is* fun, you will keep on running and benefit by the fitness, which can be a matter of life and death. The most important indication of fitness, or adult health, is cardiovascular endurance. And that is exactly what running develops. Also, something happens to your mind when you run. You become mentally relaxed because running seems to break the shackles of routine—it's freedom. This readable book includes everything you would want to know about jogging and long-distance running. Perhaps the most valuable chapter for beginners is "What You Need to Know as You Take Your First Steps."

Consultation With a Plastic Surgeon *by Ralph Dicker, M.D., and Victor Syracuse, M.D. Warner Books, 1975. pp. 320, illus., $2.50.*

Modern plastic surgery sprung out of the mutilated bodies of World War I and was maintained by our love affair with automobiles and speed. By the time World War II came, the importance of plastic surgery was recognized, and military surgeons were taught its techniques. Such surgery became increasingly successful for two reasons: (1) Sulfa drugs and penicillin helped prevent infection. (2) Skin grafting was made possible with evenly cut sheets of skin made available by the new dermatone. The present-day facial surgeon is a specialist in head and neck surgery with additional training in cosmetic surgery. His or her goal is to correct physical abnormalities and to leave no trace (scar) of the manner the correction was made. Through the question-and-answer format, the reader will learn about face lift, nasal reconstruction, breast augmentation and reduction, dermal abrasion of acne scars, fat-tissue removal, and other procedures. The diagrams illustrating these procedures are instructive, but the before-and-after photographs are poor—even for a paperback.

The Photography Catalog *edited by Norman Snyder. Harper and Row, 1976. 256 pp., illus., $7.95.*

The Photography Catalog reflects care throughout—excellent writing and superior editorial craftsmanship. The encyclopedic coverage fairly boggles the mind. You'll find out where to get a now-rare Tessina mini-camera, the kind that the Watergate burglars used; where to get a precision tool for cutting mattes—"... with it a gorilla could cut perfect mattes"; who to go to—the professional's professional, Mary Forscher—to get your camera repaired. More than just a catalog, the book is full of crisp instructions on every aspect of photography from cameras to film to printing to display to sale. In short, *The Photography Catalog* is just about the best bargain available today in photography books.

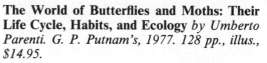

The World of Butterflies and Moths: Their Life Cycle, Habits, and Ecology *by Umberto Parenti. G. P. Putnam's, 1977. 128 pp., illus., $14.95.*

Have you ever wondered how you could attract butterflies to your garden? In this beautiful book for the beginning lepidopterist, you will discover that the butterfly bush, in particular *Buddleia davidii*, will attract many of the butterflies of the northern hemisphere, such as the Red Admiral, Painted Lady, and Peacock. And don't get rid of your stinging nettles, as the caterpillars of some of the above butterflies live in and on them. You can attract moths by boiling equal parts of brown sugar and molasses and then daubing this home-made nectar on tree trunks. Then go out at night in late summer with a red light to inspect your night visitors. But once you have attracted the butterflies and moths, how are you going to identify them—if you really want to go that far? The book does not include an identification key—so you will have to go to a library. To the non-lepidopterist the chapter entitled "Friend and Enemy of Man" is the most interesting, even though it is European oriented. Throughout the book the large—even enormous—full-colored photographs are superb.

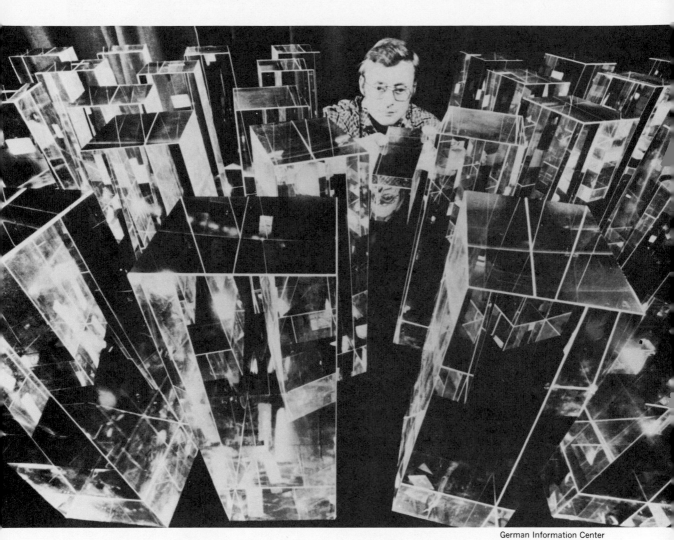

German Information Center

These 2,600 blocks of leaded glass form part of the detector system for elementary particles, which will be produced by West Germany's electron-positron collision machine called PETRA.

PHYSICAL SCIENCES

PHYSICAL SCIENCES
REVIEW OF THE YEAR

Richard N. Levine

This research balloon carried a gamma-ray telescope over Australia to detect gamma-ray spectral features from our galactic center and other astronomical objects. The accompanying apparatus plotted the number of gamma-ray photons versus their energy. The researchers had also previously reported detection of positrons at the center of the Milky Way.

Physics. There were promising findings in several fields of physics during 1978. Among these were some successes in fusion-energy research. A major problem has been ion confinement, or the keeping of the very energetic, or "hot," ions of the plasma fuels close enough for long enough that collisions and subsequent fusion that releases energy can take place. Scientists at Princeton University's fusion research facility, known as Princeton's Large Torus (tokamak), were able to triple the ion temperature in the plasma, thus making the ions more energetic. At the same time scientists working with the Livermore Magnetic Mirror system found that controlled injection of ions reduced the instabilities that have plagued various fusion research projects. This progress in increasing both the plasma density and its confinement time may make possible a theoretical break-even point where the amount of energy produced is about equal to that needed to start and maintain the reaction. From there, research on ways to increase the net energy output can continue. See the article "Fusion Research," which starts on page 296.

The atomic nucleus continued to be studied in detail. Recent experiments have shown that the two main nuclear particles—protons and neutrons—may not be completely intermingled in the nucleus as has long been thought but rather may each have specific distribution patterns with different radii. ■ Another nuclear particle—the elusive neutrino—was better identified and studied during the year thanks to acoustic-detection methods by which the neutrinos were detected in large volumes of deep ocean water. ■ Efforts to fit the hypothetical quarks into the existing model of the atomic nucleus continued even though no quark has ever been observed and the whole quark hypothesis has recently been thrown into doubt by the discovery of new particles and presumably more—too many—quarks. For a complete discussion of this problem, see the article "Quarks," which starts on page 289.

The 1978 Nobel Prize in Physics was awarded to Soviet scientist Peter L. Kapitza for his work in low temperatures and particularly liquid helium and jointly to U.S. radio astronomers Arno A. Penzias and Robert W. Wilson of Bell Labs for their discovery of residual "background radiation" from the theorized initial "big bang" explosion that created the universe. However, recent studies of cosmic rays originating in novae and supernovae indicate that there is probably a year-long interval between the initial acceleration of the cosmic-ray particles and nucleo-synthesis, or the production of elements. This disagrees somewhat with the implications of the big-bang theory. ■ Also in the astrophysics field, radio-astronomy measurements made during the year indicated a major gamma-ray emission apparently coming from the center of the galaxy. The particular emission frequency would be that expected as a result of possible annihilation collisions between electrons and positrons (anti-electrons) and would thus indicate that anti-matter could possibly exist in the galaxy.

Use of the Doppler effect now permits a researcher to measure high-speed fluid velocity within an operating internal-combustion engine or gas turbine. This laser-Doppler anemometer will help engineers to design more efficient internal-combustion engines.

Rodney Rask

Some other advances in physics may have some immediate usefulness. It was found that measurements of the Doppler shift in laser light reflected from small particles suspended in a moving fluid can provide a way of indicating fluid motion inside the cylinders of an internal-combustion engine. Such knowledge could be a first step toward improving engine efficiency. ■ Scientists at General Motor's Research Labs found that as early as the first one per cent of a metal's useful lifetime, small cracks may reveal changes in the photoelectric work function of the interior metal and thus early stages of metal fatigue.

Hugh F. Henry

Chemistry. The search for clues to how life began on earth continued to interest chemists during the year. Most attempts to recreate the earliest precursors of life are aimed at simulating the early earth conditions that spawned the amino acids, peptides, proteins, and other building blocks of life. In one of the most recent attempts, Noam Lahav of the University of Jerusalem, David White of the University of Santa Clara, and Sherwood Chang of NASA's Ames Research Center tested the role of clay in the process. The researchers postulated that single amino acids formed into longer chains called peptides on the surface of clay particles with the clay acting as a catalyst while fluctuations in earth temperature and water content acted as strong physical forces favoring peptide formation. To test their hypothesis, they added a small amount of the amino acid glycine in solution to various clay minerals and then exposed the mixture to changes in temperature and wet-dry conditions. The main finding was that longer amino acid chains were produced at a given temperature more easily when clay was present and that productivity was greater when moisture conditions as well as temperature changed. They theorize that fluctuations in temperature and wet-dry conditions on the early earth created repeated redistributions of different amino acids on clay surfaces and that this favored the formation of more and more complex peptide chains and ultimately protein molecules. ■ Chemists have also given us a look at an even earlier time on earth. Dr. R. Ganapathy of J. T. Baker Chemical Company and colleagues found, using neutron activation and other analytical techniques, that tiny spherical-shaped objects found buried in Pacific Ocean bottom sediment are very probably remnants of space debris that probably formed at about the same time our solar system did.

Lasers continue in their seemingly endless uses. Sidney Benson of the University of Southern California has developed a laser that can separate the heavy isotopic form of hydrogen, called deuterium, from the ordinary form of the gas. Benson uses a frequency-doubled carbon dioxide laser and tunes it to a wavelength that is absorbed only by molecules containing deuterium. He also proposes a new source for deuterium: the plastics industry, where deuterium-containing substances are used in the manufacture of polyvinyl chloride. Using the new technique, Benson believes that deuterium in the form of heavy water can be produced cheaply enough and on a large enough scale to be a boon to the nuclear industry. Deuterium acts as a moderator in a nuclear reactor and facilitates the splitting of uranium atoms. If it were to become easily available and economical, it could be used in U.S. nuclear facilities and might reduce the overall cost of nuclear energy. ■ Dr. Robert L. Byer and graduate student Richard Baumgartener of Stanford University have developed a continuously tunable laser, based on lithium niobate crystals, that can monitor air pollutants up to 13 kilometers away. The laser can also measure atmospheric temperature and humidity and could be used to locate oil fields by detecting methane, a common marker for an underlying oil deposit.

We can now look at single atoms—in color. In October 1978 Drs. Albert Crewe and Michael Isaacson of the University of Chicago reported that they have produced color motion pictures of the activity of single atoms of a number of heavy metals. Using a home-made version of a scanning transmission electron miscrscope and converting the brightness of colorless atoms into images of different hues, they have observed entirely unexpected atom behavior. They hope to figure out why the atoms act as they do and apply the information to many fields of chemistry.

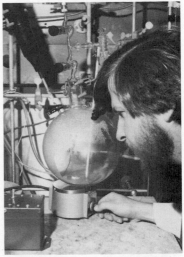

James Lawless

Dr. James Lawless at the University of Santa Clara, California, inspects a flask containing the amino acid glycine and a solution of clay particles. His group has discovered that longer peptide molecules are formed at given temperatures when clay was present than without clay.

Tiny iron, spherical objects of microscopic size are being discovered in the bottom of the Pacific Ocean. They may be space debris from the formation of the solar system.

J. T. Baker Chemical Co.

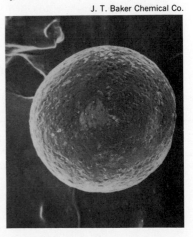

ALBERT EINSTEIN

by Sara Lazaroff

WHEN in 1919 Albert Einstein received word that the first experimental test of his revolutionary theory of general relativity had been successful and the results had borne him out, he remained visibly unmoved. "But I knew that the theory was correct," he explained. And when asked how he would have felt if instead the experimental data had gone against his ideas, Einstein replied, "Then I would have been sorry for the dear Lord— the theory is correct."

One hundred years ago—on March 14, 1879—the man acclaimed as the greatest genius of our time, a modern-day Newton, was born. It seems appropriate to ask in his centennial year—how well have Einstein and his work endured?

Today, almost a quarter of a century after his death, Einstein's most important work on general relativity remains the driving force behind active research in the forefronts of astronomy, astrophysics, and theoretical physics. Interest in Einstein's theory is in the midst of a great revival now that some of the sophisticated technologies needed to test it—like giant radio antennas, atomic clocks, and orbiting X-ray telescopes—are finally available.

"Black holes," for example, those incredibly dense celestial objects, which create such strong gravitational fields around themselves that all nearby matter is sucked into their depths, are a direct prediction of relativity theory. Other puzzling celestial phenomena, like quasars, pulsars, or the concept of an eternally expanding universe, are all major areas of astronomical research and all can be explained by the theory of general relativity.

CENTENNIAL CEREMONIES

As for Einstein the man, how he has survived—the year's events speak for themselves. To mark the centennial, ceremonies honoring Einstein were planned worldwide. At Princeton University, where Einstein spent the last 22 years of his life, a six-day symposium was held with the world's leading scientists in attendance. About 30 Nobel laureates in physics discussed current, unsolved aspects of Einstein's work. At Hebrew University in Jerusalem, internationally known scholars gathered to examine Einstein's influence on twentieth-century thought in such diverse fields as psychology, economics, and Jewish studies. Throughout the United States, as well as in France, India, Switzerland, East Germany, West Germany, and elsewhere, Einstein festivals were held.

The United States and West Germany issued commemorative Einstein stamps. Numerous Einstein television specials were shown. At Princeton, work has begun on a 15-20 year project to publish a 20-volume set of Einstein's complete writings, including never-before published material, such as letters of Mahatma Gandhi and Sigmund Freud.

Why is Albert Einstein, a scientist, the subject of all this international attention? And how would he react to so much commotion in his honor? Many, like John Stachel, editor of the planned compendium of Einstein's complete writings, feel he "would have been horrified." The explanation is Einstein's own: "Decorations, titles, or distinctions mean nothing to me. I do not crave praise. . . ." Or, as Einstein biographer and fellow physicist Banesh Hoffmann has written, "Vanity was no part of him."

EARLY YEARS

Born in Ulm, Germany, to Jewish parents, Einstein did not learn to talk until he was three. He was a loner, a daydreamer, showing little interest in sports or other group activities. He had a strong repulsion for the military, drill-like emphasis of the German educational system, and was not a good student.

Two childhood events left strong scientific, almost religious, impressions upon him. Described in his own "Autobiographical Notes," the first occurred when he was about five and sick in bed. To cheer his son up, Einstein's father brought home a compass. That the magnetic needle in the box responded to some unseen law of nature amazed and awed the young boy. He later wrote of the experience, ". . . Something deeply hidden had to be behind things."

The second event, at around age 12, was the discovery of Euclidean geometry. In a book given to him by his Uncle Jakob, later referred to as the "holy geometry booklet," Einstein discovered the simple and beautiful world of pure mathematical reasoning and logic. Whereas before this event Einstein had been religious in a strict, biblical sense (although his parents were not religious at all), his faith was now transferred to science. "Through the reading of popular scientific books I soon reached the conviction that much in the stories of the Bible could not be true." In later years when asked whether he believed in God, Einstein would reply, "I believe in Spinoza's God, who reveals himself in the orderly harmony of all that exists. . . ."

When the family business failed in 1894, the Einsteins moved to northern Italy. Einstein, then 15, stayed behind to finish his studies at the Munich Gymnasium (high school). After six unhappy months, he dropped out of school, renounced his German citizenship, and left to rejoin his family. From age 15 through 21, when he became a Swiss citizen, Einstein was stateless.

FRAMING THE RIGHT QUESTION

Around this time, Einstein asked himself a profound question that would take 10 years of persistent thought to answer. The question—"What would a light wave look

National Archives

Here Albert Einstein receives an honorary degree at Harvard University in 1935.

like to an observer traveling alongside it at the same speed?"—would form the basis for his 1905 theory of special relativity. The question is an example of the visual "thought problems" Einstein's mind conceptualized and pursued with extreme patience and determination. It has been said that true genius lies in knowing how to frame the right question much more than in solving one already framed.

In 1900, Einstein graduated from Zurich Polytechnic, in Switzerland, with only an average record, and had no luck whatsoever in obtaining an academic post. Finally, after two desperate years, he took a low-paying position as a clerk in the Swiss Patent Office in Bern. For most scientists this sort of non-academic job would have been intellectually stifling for two reasons. They would have been isolated from their scientific peers, and they would have had no access to recent advances reported in the professional literature. Einstein, however, found in that job just the calm climate he needed to nurture his fertile thoughts. He later claimed he never actually met a theoretical physicist until he was 30.

It has been argued that the patent-office job helped to further refine Einstein's extremely keen intuition. He had to learn to scent out quickly from the thick stack of patent applications, which routinely crossed his desk, those few that held promise. Einstein

California Institute of Technology

would finish his patent work fast enough to steal time for his own studies. Even in his later years, he still experienced twinges of conscience for having done his own, private work on company time. He recalled that each time footsteps approached, he would quickly stuff his calculations into his desk drawer.

During his patent-office days, Einstein married Mileva Maric, his former classmate at Zurich Polytechnic. It is hard to find any detailed information on Einstein's homelife and his personal relationships. One reads that the marriage "was not a happy one," but never learns precisely why. Perhaps an introspective quote of Einstein's provides a clue. "I am truly a 'lone traveller' and have never belonged to my country, my home, my friends, or even my immediate family with my whole heart." The marriage produced two sons, Hans Albert and Eduard, and ended in divorce.

Einstein's second wife, Elsa, is described by physicist-author Jeremy Bernstein as "a woman of friendly, maternal temperament . . . interested in creating a pleasant home." Rather like the quiet patent office, his second marriage provided Einstein with a serene atmosphere for pursuing his true love, science. ". . . I sold myself body and soul to science," he once admitted. "It is the most precious thing we have."

LIKE AN OLD-FASHIONED WATCHMAKER

That Einstein was not especially concerned with the ordinary affairs of people was well portrayed by his personal appearance—his wildly radiating white hair, his baggy pants, sweatshirt and sandals. ". . . Neckties and cuffs exist for me only as remote memories," he once remarked in a letter. C. P. Snow, upon meeting Einstein for the first time, described him thus: ". . . he looked like a reliable old-fashioned watchmaker in a small town who perhaps collected butterflies on a Sunday." Einstein never owned an automobile.

Although he was a major world figure for most of his life, and well aware of his overwhelming popularity, Einstein neither understood nor liked it. "With me," he once said, "every peep becomes a trumpet solo." At times he was treated more like a movie star than a serious scientist. When Charlie Chaplin took him to the opening night of "City Lights," the crowds tried just as hard to catch a glimpse of their hero Einstein as of their matinee idol Chaplin.

So hounded was Einstein by the press and public, that he adopted a formal policy for signing autographs, a custom he considered almost cannibalistic. He would send printed cards to autograph seekers explaining that if they would first send "a small contribution" to a worthy charity he designated, and return the stamped receipt to him, he would then grant their requests.

Not only did Einstein not seek fame, he actively avoided it. His last wish upon his death was to be cremated without any ceremony and to have his ashes scattered in an undisclosed spot so that his resting place could never become a shrine.

"NEWTON, FORGIVE ME"

"The non-mathematician is seized by a mysterious shuddering when he hears of 'four-dimensional' things . . ." Einstein observed, referring to the public's awe and lack of comprehension of his theory of general relativity in which "time" is declared the fourth dimension. Published in 1916, during World War I, relativity provided a mathematical explanation for gravity—nature's weakest, yet most omnipresent force.

On earth, where gravitational effects are

minimal, classical Newtonian physics works very well. But for more massive bodies, like stars or galaxies, which create tremendously strong gravitational fields around themselves, new sorts of phenomena occur that cannot be explained by Newton's laws. One such phenomenon, long observed but never understood, was that Mercury's orbit was a bit more curved than was expected. Einstein's new theory explained this discrepancy precisely, and went on to predict other, non-Newtonian, phenomena that could be looked for experimentally. These include the bending of starlight by intense gravitational fields, and the relationship between mass and energy described in the famous equation, $E=mc^2$. Solar-eclipse observations have substantiated the former prediction, while the awesome power of the atom bomb is frightening proof of the latter.

Years later, while writing of the failures of classical physics that prompted him to search for a better explanation, Einstein suddenly breaks off his discourse, turns to his predecessor, and pleads, "Newton, forgive me."

A GURULIKE PERSONALITY

Einstein, a simple, reclusive man, became a celebrity overnight when results from the first experimental test of general relativity proved him right. He captured the hearts of a public, who could not even understand his theories.

Perhaps the timing was critical. World War I was tremendously grueling, brutal, and destructive. Thoughts about Einstein, locked away in his own world of wizardly calculations, provided a much-needed avenue of fantasy and escape from the bloody reality of everyday lives. And perhaps the theory itself provided a sense of well-being and faith at a time of uproar.

Even if most people could not understand relativity, they could understand that it offered hope of an underlying harmony and unity in the universe at a time when faith in human nature was low. Furthermore, a mystique surrounding the esoteric nature of the theory developed. It was rumored that there were only six persons in the world who understood it. This may have added a magical attraction for the genius who created it.

Ernst Haas/Magnum

Einstein himself seemed a unique, almost gurulike personality. Even though he moved in the highest of social circles (one of his closest, lifelong friends was Queen Elizabeth of Belgium), fame did not affect his humble nature. There is often a saintly appeal of those who seem above the earthly needs and wants of people.

THE PACIFIST

Yet Einstein's moral conscience was strong and outspoken. Repeatedly during his later years in America (he became a U.S. citizen in 1940), he used his public image to add momentum to causes he believed in. Shortly before his death, Einstein along with Bertrand Russell drafted an anti-war statement. "Shall we put an end to the human race; or shall mankind renounce war?" the lifelong pacifist asked. Similarly, Einstein spoke up bravely against McCarthyism, calling the senator "an enemy of America."

A strong Zionist, Einstein was instrumental in founding the State of Israel. When Israeli President Chiam Weizmann died in 1952, the presidency was offered to 73-year-old Einstein. With characteristic modesty, Einstein declined saying, "I know a little about nature, and hardly anything about men."

Along with his political and humanitarian activities, Einstein was devoted to science

Appearing with Mrs. Casadesus for a performance benefiting the American Friends Service.

for the whole of his life. "The fascinating magic of that work will continue to my last breath," he correctly predicted. For 35 years Einstein searched without success for a "unified-field theory," which could explain the simple, underlying unity connecting all forces in nature. This quest, he said, would reveal "the secret of the Old One."

GOD DOES NOT PLAY DICE

Einstein categorically rejected the new quantum mechanics, even though years earlier he had been the first to suggest the quantum nature of light. For three decades Nobel physicist Niels Bohr persistently tried to convince Einstein of quantum mechanic's merits. Bohr met with no success; once again, Einstein was certain he was right.

Quantum theory states that many processes in nature cannot be described in definite, absolute terms, but only by their statistical probabilities of happening. This uncertainty Einstein could not accept. "God does not play dice with the world," he reprimanded. Having withstood 30-odd years of Einstein's critical attacks, the foundations of quantum mechanics seem all the more solid today.

GENERAL RELATIVITY UPHELD

One hundred years after Einstein's birth and 63 years after the publishing of his theory of general relativity, both the man and his ideas are still very much with us. Relativity has weathered many lines of theoretical and experimental attack extremely well. An X-ray telescope orbiting in space, which has been nicknamed "Einstein," is sending back images of possible black holes. An experiment to see whether the sun's gravity slows down radio waves passing nearby, as general relativity predicts, has been done and the theory works. Within the last year indirect evidence of "gravity waves," another key prediction of the theory, has been found.

One possible crack in Einstein's theory is the recent, still controversial, radio-telescope observations of objects that move at rates five to eight times the speed of light. If this observation holds, these objects violate the cardinal assumption of relativity: namely, that nothing can travel faster than the speed of light. Already, scientists are trying to devise explanations for how objects could "appear" to be moving faster than light without actually doing so.

At present the amount of evidence in favor of relativity greatly outweighs any against. Still the tests continue relentlessly. At one hundred years of age, Einstein's legacy is surviving splendidly. Whether someday another genius will be forced to look back and say, "Forgive me, Einstein"—only time will tell □

SELECTED READINGS

"Celebrating Einstein" by William Stockton. *New York Times Magazine,* February 18, 1979.

"The year of Dr. Einstein" by Frederick Golden. *Time,* February 19, 1979.

Einstein by Jeremy Bernstein. Viking Press, New York, 1973.

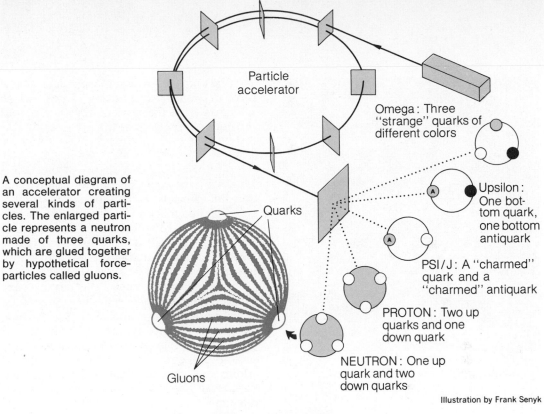

A conceptual diagram of an accelerator creating several kinds of particles. The enlarged particle represents a neutron made of three quarks, which are glued together by hypothetical force-particles called gluons.

Particle accelerator

Omega: Three "strange" quarks of different colors

Upsilon: One bottom quark, one bottom antiquark

Quarks

PSI/J: A "charmed" quark and a "charmed" antiquark

PROTON: Two up quarks and one down quark

NEUTRON: One up quark and two down quarks

Gluons

Illustration by Frank Senyk

QUARKS

by James S. Trefil

THERE is a dream that physical scientists have cherished for centuries. It is a dream whose main ingredient is the idea that the world is really simple in spite of the enormous complexity that we observe around us. Those who share this dream have believed that if only we looked at things in the right way, if we could just penetrate deeply enough into nature, we would find that the complexity would fall away. And we would have a beautiful and simple understanding of the world.

There are many examples of how this dream has been fulfilled in the past. For example, Isaac Newton summarized all the complex data on the motion of the different members of the solar system and all the complex data on the motion of objects on the surface of the Earth into just three laws of motion and one law of gravitation. These laws (literally) can be written on the back of an envelope, but they describe a range of natural phenomena—as diverse as the structure of a galaxy, the forces on a bridge, and the flow of blood through an artery. That

they do, in fact, represent a triumph of the idea of the simplicity of nature.

A more striking triumph of the idea of simplicity occurred in the early part of the twentieth century, when investigations of atomic structure showed that all the chemical elements were built from just three basic constituents. These were the proton, a heavy particle with a positive electrical charge; the neutron, a heavy particle with no electrical charge; and the electron, a light particle with a negative electrical charge. In terms of these constituents, each atom consists of a positively charged nucleus made up of protons and neutrons, and the electrons circle this nucleus in a manner similar to the way the planets circle the sun. This picture of the atom has become so commonplace that we tend to forget what a tremendous simplification it brings to our picture of matter. This model says that the ultimate pieces of matter are merely three in number. That would mean that all of the physical world is the result of different arrangements of these three particles.

Warman/Columbia University

Nobel laureates Hideki Yukawa, left, and I. I. Rabi at Columbia University. Yukawa predicted the meson.

THE ASSUMPTION OF SIMPLICITY

The successes of Newton's laws and the nuclear atom have strengthened an assumption about the way physics will proceed in the future, an assumption that is only now being called into question. Stated in its most extreme form, the "Assumption of Maximum Simplicity" can be stated as follows: all matter is ultimately composed of a small number of fundamental particles, and these particles obey simple physical laws.

That this assumption held true in the development of the modern idea of the atom is clear so far as the number of fundamental particles is concerned. But when the second part of the assumption—the part dealing with the laws governing the behavior of fundamental particles—was subjected to investigation, the picture darkened rapidly. The reason for this is not hard to see. One of the basic laws of electricity is that like charges tend to repel one another. If we think about the nucleus, we realize that all of the positively charged protons in it will repel each other, and that in the absence of some other force the nucleus would simply fly apart.

This fact led physicists to postulate a new force in nature—the "strong" force—which served to hold the nucleus together against the mutual repulsion of the protons.

FOURTH PARTICLE NEEDED

In 1935, Hideki Yukawa of the Osaka Imperial University in Japan pointed out that this cohesive force—the strong force—could be understood if a fourth kind of particle were added to the list of fundamental particles. He called the new particle a "meson" because it was supposed to be intermediate in mass between the proton and electron. He showed that if this particle were to be exchanged between the protons and neutrons inside of a nucleus, a force would be generated which would be strong enough to overcome the electrical repulsion of the protons for one another. So at the cost of adding one extra fundamental particle, Yukawa was able to suggest a solution to a dilemma.

But of course, no physicist would be content with having such an important particle remain in the hypothetical realm. If the mesons really exist inside of the nucleus, the thinking ran, then we ought to be able to see them in the debris of collisions of high-energy particles with nuclei. In the late 1930's, no machines like modern particle accelerators were in existence, so experimenters had to look to nature to provide the necessary high energies. The first attempts to find the meson involved putting out detectors to see if anything other than protons, neutrons, and electrons could be seen in the spray of particles which resulted when high-energy cosmic rays hit a nucleus in the atmosphere. And sure enough, a particle whose mass was about two hundred times that of the electron was seen.

"WHO ORDERED THIS?"

The new particle was designated by the Greek letter μ and called the mu meson or muon. The excitement of the discovery quickly turned to dismay, however, when further study showed that the new particle could not possibly be the one Yukawa had talked about, since it was incapable of generating the strong force. Nobel laureate Isidor I. Rabi summarized the reaction of

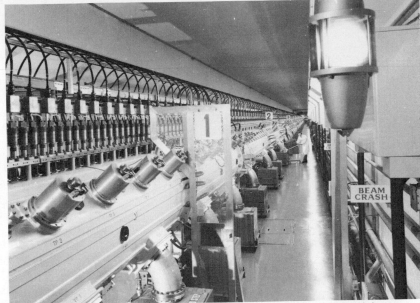

Accelerators speed up beams of particles to extremely high levels and smash them into other particles in an attempt to discover what the bits and pieces are.

Brookhaven National Laboratory

the physics community to this realization with the comment, "Who ordered this?"

So with the list of fundamental particles increased to four, the search continued, and to make a long story short, the "right" particle eventually turned up. It was denoted by the Greek letter π, and was called the pi meson, or pion. Slightly heavier than the muon, it had all of the properties necessary to provide the binding force in the nucleus. The reason that pions had not been seen first was that they exist for only about 10^{-8} seconds, and then decay into other particles.

So by the late 1940's, the Assumption of Simplicity was slightly battered, but still serviceable. After all, it is still reasonable to call five fundamental particles a "small" number, and the existence of the muon, while puzzling, was certainly not enough to shake belief in the principle.

STRANGE PARTICLES

But this state of affairs was too fragile to endure. Improved detection techniques soon began turning up new kinds of particles—hitherto unexpected—in the cosmic-ray interactions. Some of these particles were even more massive than the proton, but their most striking characteristic was the time that elapsed between their production and their decay. They lived much longer than expected. A "normal" nuclear particle ought to exist for only about 10^{-24} seconds, while these new discoveries would exist for as much as 10^{-12} seconds before they decayed into other particles. The "naturalness" of 10^{-24} seconds

is related to the fact that this is roughly the time it takes for light to cross a nucleus. So puzzling was the long life of the new particles to physicists at the time that these objects were given the collective name of "strange particles."

MORE AND MORE PARTICLES

By this time, of course, the Assumption of Simplicity was in trouble, and in the early 1950's a new technology became widely available which seemed to administer the *coup de grâce* to the assumption. Particle accelerators were built which allowed physicists to take ordinary protons and give them enough energy so that they could be used to produce the new particles in nuclear collisions. Not only were the mesons and strange particles of the cosmic-ray experiments reproduced, but a whole new class of particles was seen, particles which decayed in the expected 10^{-24} seconds. The number of particles created in this way grew very quickly. No one is counting any more, but the number of "elementary" particles that have been discovered since the mu meson is well into the hundreds by now.

NO WAY OUT?

These developments seemed to lead to a direct contradiction of the Assumption of Simplicity. It makes no more sense to call all of the newly discovered particles fundamental than it does to give each chemical element that title.

Then, in 1964, Nobel laureate Murray

Caltech

Murray Gell-Mann theorized that with three more particles, all matter could be explained.

Gell-Mann at the California Institute of Technology (Caltech) and George Zweig, then at the particle accelerator facility CERN in Switzerland showed a way out of the dilemma. They showed that all of the properties of the elementary particles could be understood if we thought of these particles as being built up from other, still more elementary, objects. In the original theory, there were to be three such objects, and they have come to be called "quarks" (from a line in James Joyce's *Finnegan's Wake:* "Three quarks for Muster Mark").

From a logical point of view, the quark hypothesis is equivalent to the development of the modern atomic theory. Instead of a large unordered array of particles, we can now talk once more about a small number of fundamental pieces of nature.

LEPTONS AND HADRONS

Perhaps it would be worthwhile to go into a few details of how this new picture of the world works. Certain particles do not participate in generating the strong nuclear force. They are called leptons and are not thought to be composed of quarks. The mu meson, the electron, and a small number of other particles are classified as leptons.

Particles which do participate in the strong interaction are called hadrons, and these particles—the ones that no one is counting anymore—are thought to be composed of quarks.

A large sub-group of hadrons is the class of particles known as baryons. These include the proton and all heavier particles that ultimately decay into a proton and anything

else. Each baryon is composed of exactly three quarks; different baryons either have different types of quarks in them or have the same quarks in different arrangements.

UP, DOWN, AND STRANGE

In current terminology, the three quarks are called the u, d, and s quarks. The letters stand for "up," "down," and "strange." The "up" and "down" refer to directions in a space whose coordinates are related to the electrical properties of the quarks. "Strange" refers to that same property that was attributed to the elementary particles that decay more slowly than expected.

The up quark has an electrical charge which is positive and equal to two-thirds of the charge on the proton. The down and strange quarks have charges which are negative and equal to one-third of the charge on the electron. The fractional charge on quarks makes them unique among particles in nature, since every other known particle has a charge equal to a whole number.

The proton, then, is made up of two up quarks and one down quark. The total electrical charge it possesses is $\frac{2}{3} + \frac{2}{3} - \frac{1}{3} = 1$. The neutron has (two down quarks and one up quark) and thus has a charge $-\frac{1}{3} -\frac{1}{3} +\frac{2}{3} = 0$. All the properties of the elementary particles are thus related in a simple way to the properties of the quarks.

Even the rate of decay of the particles can be explained when we add in the strange quark. You will recall that by definition all baryons must have a proton in their decay products. This statement is equivalent to saying that when we add up all the quarks among the final decay products, the net sum must contain only up and down quarks, but no strange quarks since protons contain only up and down quarks. For baryons composed entirely of up and down quarks, all that would be required would be a rearrangement of the quarks already present. Suppose, however, that a particular baryon contained one strange quark. In order for such a baryon to decay and produce a proton, the strange quark would have to be converted into an up or a down quark. It does not seem unreasonable to say that such a conversion would slow the decay time. Thus the descriptive label of

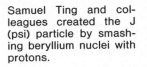

Samuel Ting and colleagues created the J (psi) particle by smashing beryllium nuclei with protons.

strangeness for particles that exist longer than expected is converted into a real physical property at the level of quarks.

BUT STILL PROBLEMS

It would seem, then, that the introduction of quarks would provide the final justification of the Assumption of Simplicity. Events in the last few years, however, have started to cast doubt on that conclusion. There are two major problems with the quark model: the problem of quark confinement and the problem of quark proliferation.

QUARK CONFINEMENT

As soon as the quark model was put forward extensive attempts were made to "bring one back alive"—to find an isolated quark in nature. In spite of the importance of the question and the extreme ingenuity of the experiments involved, there has been no generally accepted claim for the discovery of the quark. In view of the time which has elapsed since the searches began, this raises very real questions about what it means to say that quarks "exist."

Most quark theories now take as given the fact that although quarks may exist inside of particles, they cannot be seen in isolation. This is referred to as "quark confinement." Let's look at two simple pictures which illustrate how quarks may be said to "exist" and still be confined to the interior of particles.

Suppose that the ultimate matter inside of particles is analogous to an elastic string, and what we identify as a quark is actually the end of such a string. If we were to reach inside of the particle and try to pull a quark out, we could probably snap the string if we

pulled hard enough. But then we would have extracted a shorter piece of string which had two ends. A little reflection will convince you that in such a situation it is logically impossible to see one end of a string by itself.

Another example of the same effect was cited recently by Sidney Drell of Stanford University. We know that an ordinary bar magnet always has a north and a south pole. If we saw the magnet in half, however, we do not wind up with isolated north and south poles, but with two shorter magnets, each of which has two poles. If we continued this cutting process down to the atomic level, we would find that each atom of iron can be thought of as a tiny magnet with two poles. In this sense, we could say that magnets "exist" inside of the piece of iron: we can actually pull a small magnet out and point to it.

If we continue the cutting process beyond the atomic level, however, the picture changes. If we take an atom apart and lay the constituent protons, neutron, and electrons out, there is nothing we can point to and say that it is a magnet. The reason for this is that the atom looks like a magnet because of the arrangement of its constituents, rather than because any single constituent may be a magnet in and of itself.

In the same way, elementary particles may appear to be composed of quarks, but these quarks may be the result of the arrangement of matter inside of the particles, rather than distinct entities which can have a life of their own. Because of arguments like this most physicists today would probably not accept the failure of quark search experiments as strong evidence against the quark model, but there is an underlying uneasiness about the whole business.

Stanford University News Service

Burton Richter created J (psi) particles by colliding electrons with positrons.

QUARK PROLIFERATION

In the fall of 1974, two Nobel Prize winners, Burton Richter, working at the Stanford Linear Accelerator Laboratory in California, and Massachusetts Institute of Technology physicist Samuel Ting, working at Brookhaven National Laboratory on Long Island, New York, simultaneously announced the discovery of a new kind of particle. The Stanford experiment involved producing the particle from the collision of an electron and a positron, while the MIT-Brookhaven experiment produced the same particle from the collision of a proton with a beryllium nucleus, so there was no serious doubt about the particle's existence. It was called the ψ (psi) particle on the West Coast and the J particle on the East Coast. Its dual discovery is reflected in the current usage, which is to refer to it as the J/ψ. The particle was not strange, but it decayed slowly. This can mean only one thing: there must be a fourth kind of quark in nature.

ENTER CHARM

The new property associated with the particle is given the name "charm," and the quark which carries this property is called the charmed, or c quark. The J/ψ particle itself is now known not to possess charm in the sense that we have been using the term, but a recent experiment has turned up particles that exhibit charm explicitly. These particles decay slowly because of the need to convert the charmed quark to an up or a down quark.

By itself, the addition of a fourth quark to the subnuclear zoo does not seem to have much significance for the Assumption of Simplicity. After all, we can interpret four quarks as being "few" as well as we can interpret three. The real problem comes from the fact that theorists have suggested that there might be two more kinds of quarks, called the t and b (for top and bottom, or truth and beauty). And there is already evidence in an experiment carried out by Leon Lederman at the Fermi National Accelerator Laboratory in Illinois that a particle containing one of them has been seen. So if we take this suggestion seriously, we now find that the number of quarks has proliferated from three to six in the last few years.

EACH IS THREE

And if this were not enough, most quark theorists now assume that each type of quark that we have discussed so far is actually three quarks which are indistinguishable to us, but which are in fact different from each other.

Properties and Quark Compositions of Some Particles

Greek Symbol	Common Name	Mass (Proton=1)	Quark Composition	Charm	Strangeness
π^+	pi-plus	0.149	ud	0	0
K^+	K-plus	0.526	us	0	1
K^0	K-zero-bar	0.530	sd	0	−1
η	eta	0.585	ss	0	0
p	proton	1	uud	0	0
n	neutron	1.001	udd	0	0
Ω^-	omega-minus	1.783	sss	0	−3
D^0	D-zero	1.986	cu	1	0
D^+	D-plus	1.991	cd	1	0
F^+	F-plus	2.164	cs	1	1
ψ	psi	3.299	cc	0	0

From *The New World* (Harper & Row). © 1965 Saul Steinberg.

The reason for this assumption is that without it the quarks would have to violate the Pauli exclusion principle—the principle which says that no two particles like the quarks can exist in the same state.

If two of the same kind of quarks are put into one particle, the quality known as spin can distinguish them. There are only two spin states that these quarks can occupy, which we could call spin "up" and spin "down" (not to be confused with "up" and "down" quarks). The problem arises when the third quark is put in. It is bound to have up spin or down spin, or in other words, to be the same as one of the other two. The Pauli exclusion principle will not allow this.

The key to solving this dilemma is in the phrase "of the same type." Up to now, we would say that any number of down quarks, for example, were of the same type, except for spin. But what if some subnuclear gremlin had gone around and painted the quarks in three different colors? What if three objects we label as "down quarks" were actually down quarks of three different colors? Then they wouldn't be "of the same type," and there's no reason why they couldn't exist together in the same particle.

BUT EIGHTEEN?

And that's where things stand right now. We know of five types of quarks from experiments, and suspect a sixth will turn up soon. Each of these types of quarks (or "flavor" of quark in the current terminology) comes in three "colors" for a total of eighteen quarks.

The proliferation of quarks is so similar to the proliferation of the elementary particles that started the quark search that it can scarcely be ignored. It is completely within the realm of possibility that some future physicist, trying to reestablish the Assumption of Simplicity, will introduce a new "fundamental" entity, the sub-quark (although he or she will undoubtedly come up with a better name that that). And if the past is any guide we can probably expect the sub-quarks to start proliferating, leading to sub-sub-quarks, and so on *ad infinitum*.

SUB, SUB-QUARKS . . . AND SO . . .

This possibility raises a question in my mind—a question which is almost heretical for someone like myself who was trained in elementary particle physics—about how far and how fast we want to pursue the quest for ultimate simplicity. At what level do we decide that the knowledge to be gained by penetrating to a new level can justify the drain on our limited basic research resources? □

SELECTED READINGS

"Elusive quarks: hints of two from a Stanford experiment" by W. D. Metz. *Science,* May 13, 1977.

"High-energy physics: a proliferation of quarks and leptons" by A. L. Robinson. *Science* Nov. 4, 1977.

"New physics: quarks, leptons, and quantum field theories" by A. L. Robinson. *Science* Nov. 17, 1978.

"New quarks stir debate on basic laws of nature" by Walter Sullivan, *New York Times,* February 13, 1978.

"Quarks: merely Joycean or the ultimate McCoy?" by M. Guillen. *Science Digest,* March 1977.

"Scientists speak with quarked tongue" by L. Nathan and W. J. Brandt. *Bulletin of the Atomic Scientist,* April 1978.

"What is smaller than . . . ?" by John O'Reilly. *Chemistry,* January 1979.

The Princeton Large Torus in center with four neutral-beam-heating units.

FUSION RESEARCH

By Edward Edelson

IT'S an ordinary day at the Princeton Large Torus (PLT), in New Jersey, one of the world's leading fusion-energy research centers. (Torus means doughnut-shaped.) I'm in the control room, watching red numbers on a digital counter click backward in a countdown. At zero, images on video monitors bulge outward for an instant, as if to register the violence of the fusion reaction taking place in the PLT. It's a scene I've witnessed often in some 15 years of reporting the great effort to harness fusion energy for peaceful purposes.

BREAK-EVEN FUSION

I leave the PLT control room and stroll across a field to watch workmen in an excavation about 100 meters square. Right now, there's nothing in the excavation but a huge, oddly-shaped concrete foundation. But this is the site of the Tokamak Fusion Test Reactor, the next generation of fusion-research machines. And this construction site is the start of a scientific dream come true—a dream that could haul humanity into a new era of energy riches.

For some 30 years, physicists have been trying to achieve break-even fusion energy—to get out more energy than they put in. The Tokamak seems likely to reach that goal in the early 1980s. When that happens, scientists will have proved that fusion power is scientifically feasible. The next step will be to construct a fusion reactor that generates electricity.

But there are still major problems to be overcome before our homes are lighted by fusion power. These are problems of politics, economics, and engineering, however—not of basic science. For the first time, the almost infinite power source of the stars seems to be within our grasp.

FISSION AND FUSION

Using that power source is simple in principle but astoundingly difficult in practice. It starts with the familiar Einstein equation $E = mc^2$. This equation means that a little matter can be transformed into an enormous amount of energy. One energy-releasing process involves fission, splitting very heavy atoms—the energy source in today's nuclear reactors. A more effective method is fusion, squeezing together light atoms to release even more energy.

Fission energy became practical first because very heavy atoms, such as uranium-235, split spontaneously. By contrast, light atoms such as hydrogen resist being fused. In nature, hydrogen atoms fuse only in the extreme temperatures and densities that exist in the cores of stars. On earth, we have fused hydrogen atoms only by using a fission bomb to set off the uncontrolled fusion reactions of the hydrogen bomb.

HOLDING IN THE PLASMA

To build a fusion reactor, physicists must first strip away the electrons of hydrogen atoms to produce the hot, seething gas called plasma. Then they must heat that plasma and contain it long enough for fusion to occur. For this they must achieve a temperature of about 100 million degrees Celsius in a plasma about 10,000 times thinner than air. This must be done for a time span between a tenth of a second and a full second. Physicists call this combination of density, temperature, and confinement time the "Lawson criterion."

Fusion energy is a glittering prize because it could be both safe and inexhaustible.

Fuel is no problem. A fusion reactor probably will use deuterium, a hydrogen isotope with one proton and one neutron, and tritium, which has one proton and two neutrons.

The oceans contain enough deuterium to meet humanity's needs for thousands of centuries. A fusion reactor could easily be engineered to breed more tritium than it uses. As for safety, plasma in a fusion reactor would cool down automatically if the magnetic-confinement system failed. The nuclear reaction would then stop.

Containing a plasma is more difficult than physicists originally thought. You can't hold plasma in anything solid, because it cools instantly when it touches a wall. The major effort in fusion research has been to build a magnetic "bottle" that will hold the plasma.

I saw how tough that challenge can be when I visited Princeton five years ago. Workmen were just building the Princeton Large Torus, fabricating 18 huge coils, each weighing 500 kilograms, to produce the main magnetic field. Two other sets of coils produce other magnetic fields. All this magnetic

(Top): Fission releases stored energy from the nuclei of uranium atoms when they are bombarded by speeding neutrons. (Bottom): Fusion releases the stored energy of the nuclei of hydrogen isotopes, deuterium and tritium, when they smash into each other at great speeds and high temperatures.

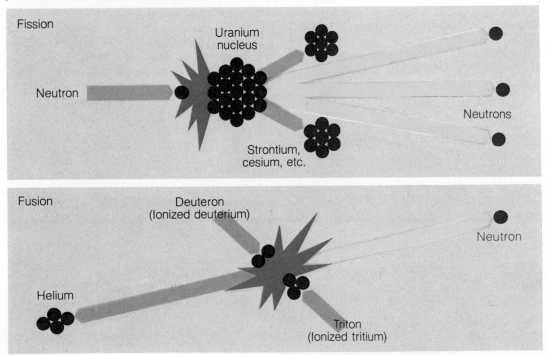

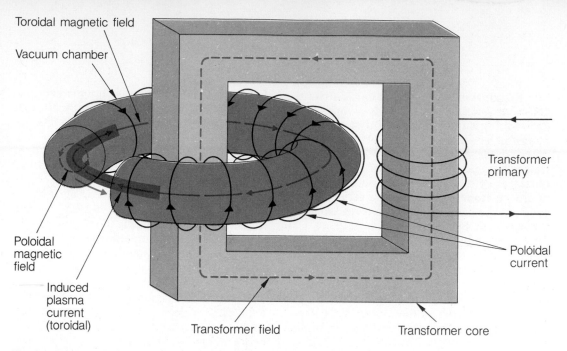

Toroidal magnetic field

Vacuum chamber

Poloidal magnetic field

Induced plasma current (toroidal)

Transformer field

Transformer primary

Poloidal current

Transformer core

The deuterium-tritium plasma inside the torus is confined by two magnetic fields created by: (1) DC current flowing around the torus, and (2) the transformer primary.

energy is needed to contain just one milligram of plasma for a split second in a torus—a doughnut-shape tube—90 centimeters across.

TEMPERATURE BREAKTHROUGH

This time I came to the PLT at Princeton, because physicists there had just achieved the highest temperature yet produced in this kind of fusion machine. As I talked to the people who built the PLT and are building the Tokamak, I learned that the temperature record is indeed significant. It is one more goal that fusion scientists set for themselves and reached on schedule. After many years during which disappointment was the rule, fusion researchers now routinely reach goals on schedule. "The key scientific issues of fusion energy have been resolved," says Anne Davies, who heads the U.S. Department of Energy's Tokamak research effort.

THE TOKAMAK

I did most of my learning at Princeton from Shoichi Yoshikawa, who about 10 years ago got the basic idea that made the PLT possible. Yoshikawa's idea is based on a major advance made in the Soviet Union. Researchers in both countries worked for a long time on torus-shaped fusion machines, but with frustrating results. Physicists could

not make a toroidal magnetic field to keep the plasma stable long enough.

The Russians then made an important advance. The late Lev Artsimovich used a transformer to produce a current in the plasma itself. This current produced its own magnetic field, which helped contain the plasma. They called the machine a *Tokamak*.

Yoshikawa improved the basic Tokamak. He designed a torus whose plasma-containing tube is fatter—and whose doughnut hole is smaller. Yoshikawa calculated that such a machine would have several advantages, including one that is brilliantly simple: A larger radius means particles take longer to leak out because they have a greater distance to travel.

MORE HEAT NEEDED

Early magnetic-confinement machines used only ohmic heating, the same principle that makes your toaster toast. Run an electric current through a wire or a plasma and it gets hot. But ohmic heating isn't enough to put a plasma into the fusion-temperature range.

Five years ago, researchers at Oak Ridge National laboratory in Tennessee discovered one way to increase the heat of the plasma. They did this by shooting a beam of high-energy neutral atoms into the plasma.

For this they used hydrogen atoms, which are electrically neutral. This is called "neutral-beam heating." The atoms penetrate the magnetic field because they are electrically neutral. Inside the plasma, the atoms lose their electrons in collisions and become part of the plasma, adding heat in the process.

On this visit, Yoshikawa told me that the neutral-beam scheme had indeed worked, but not without some trouble. At first, the neutral beam just wouldn't give the expected heating effect. It developed that atoms in the beam were interacting with one another, reducing the beam's effectiveness. The solution: a nozzle with dozens of tiny openings, separating the atoms just enough to prevent interactions. "With one stroke, we got a hundredfold improvement in heating," Yoshikawa said.

The PLT now has four neutral beams with a total of four megawatts of power. Neutral-beam heating allowed the PLT to set its temperature record, Yoshikawa told me. With all the neutral beams going and the machine adjusted for maximum temperature, PLT achieved several runs at 60 million degrees Celsius.

POWER-HUNGRY PLT

To reach the Lawson criterion and break-even fusion, all that is needed is greater plasma density and confinement time. The PLT won't do that. Indeed, none of the fusion machines now operating will reach the Lawson criterion. Each device is designed to investigate one or two different factors of the fusion problems.

"All this work is leading up to the Tokamak," Anne Davies told me. "We really think of the PLT as a small-scale test of the Tokamak. In the magnetic-confinement program, the Tokamak is the next generation. It is where we try to get out as much energy as we put in."

I got an idea of how difficult that might be when I stepped into the huge room housing the PLT's generating equipment. Yoshikawa explained the intricate, power-hungry sequence of events that goes into a single PLT run. First, hydrogen gas is injected into the torus, kept at near-perfect vacuum. Then the network of ohmic heating coils is pulsed rapidly to break down the gas, creating the plasma.

A huge direct-current pulse then flows into a third set of coils, which help contain the plasma by pushing it inward.

To power the coils, a 96-ton flywheel, run by a 700-hp engine, drops suddenly from 360 revolutions a second to 250 revolutions a second, putting that energy into a generator. All this is to achieve a confinement for about 60 milliseconds.

NEW TOKAMAK WILL PUT IT ALL TOGETHER

The Tokamak will put a lot of different elements together to reach break-even energy output. For one thing, it will be significantly bigger than today's tokamaks. The first Princeton tokamak contained a plasma with a cross section of 30 centimeters. The PLT's plasma has a 90-centimeter cross section. The Tokamak plasma will be 115 centimeters across. In addition, the Tokamak will also have four neutral-beam injectors but with a total power of 20 megawatts, five times that of the PLT.

Equally important, the Tokamak Fusion Test Reactor will be built to work with

Model of the Tokamak, which is being built at Princeton University.

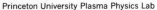

Princeton professor Melvin Gottleib, standing at left, with colleagues who operate the Large Torus and the neutral-beam heating apparatus.

Princeton University Plasma Physics Lab

the hydrogen isotopes, deuterium and tritium, which are expected to fuel the first power-producing fusion reactor. Under the same confinement conditions, this combination has 100 times the energy of deuterium alone, which is the fuel used so far for plasma-containment studies.

But tritium is tricky because it is highly radioactive (although short-lived). To make any fusion reactor safe, engineers will have to achieve near-perfect confinement of tritium. The Tokamak is expected to provide excellent working practice in tritium containment.

OPTIONS AND PROBLEMS

But what comes after the Tokamak? At this moment, no one can say for sure, although almost everyone in the field is working furiously on the subject. So many options are open that every aspect of the machine's design, from the method it uses to achieve fusion to its purpose, is open to question. For example, the machine could be used to generate electricity. Or it could be used to make hydrogen gas as a preview of the "hydrogen economy," which may result when oil and natural gas are very scarce. Or the Tokamak could be used to run a mixed fusion/fission cycle, regenerating fuel rods from current nuclear plants by irradiation.

The fusion physicists are also faced with a series of ferocious technical problems. For example, most of a fusion reactor's energy will be in the form of highly energetic neutrons. The present plan is to trap those neutrons in a "blanket," which will become heated. The heat will be used to generate electricity. Thus a big problem is to find materials that can stand intense fluxes of neu-

trons for long periods. The Tokamak will serve as a test bed where materials and components can be exposed to conditions much like those in a real reactor.

1995 OR A BETTER SOLUTION

One thing certain, in the words of Anne Davies, is that "Tokamak will achieve not just a power break-even, but will be a net power producer, in terms of heat." And that's enormously significant, because it marks a new way of talking in fusion research.

Until recently, fusion scientists talked about a moving target. In any given year, they would say that a working fusion reactor was 20 years in the future. But now the 1995 target date, which was being given five years ago for the first power-producing fusion reactor, still holds. That means the basic scientific questions about fusion have largely been answered.

It is entirely possible that all these requirements, and scores of others that apply to other parts of a fusion reactor, cannot be met at an economically competitive cost. Or it could turn out that we will not want endless supplies of power from fusion because something else—such as photovoltaic power from solar cells—is cheaper. That story will be told in the next decade or so □

📖 SELECTED READINGS

"Four new Tokamaks will each try for a finite power output" by G. B. Lubkin. *Physics Today,* January, 1978.

"Report of fusion breakthrough proves to be a media event" by William D. Metz, *Science,* September 1, 1978.

THE ACCIDENT AT
THREE MILE ISLAND

by Benedict A. Leerburger

AT 4 A.M., Wednesday, March 28, 1979 a warning buzzer went off in the control room at the Three Mile Island nuclear power plant, eleven miles south of Pennsylvania's capital, Harrisburg. The warning indicated a problem. In this case the problem was very serious. It led to the worst accident to date in America's atomic-energy program.

The accident stemmed from a series of mishaps in the reactor's cooling system. The mishaps resulted from three basic causes: human error, design failure, and mechanical failure. Initially, a pump outside the pressurized-water reactor malfunctioned. A pressurized-water reactor is the most common reactor in use today. It has two water systems. The primary system cools the fuel elements and helps control the nuclear reaction within a heavily shielded container. The secondary system cools the primary system using the heat it picks up from the primary loop to power a steam turbine.

A TWO-LOOP COOLING SYSTEM

In the primary loop, radioactive water under high pressure passes through a heat exchanger called a steam generator. Heat is transferred from the radioactive primary loop to uncontaminated water in the separate secondary loop. The water in the secondary system is quickly heated to steam that powers a steam turbine generator, thus producing electricity. Then the same water is cooled in a series of condensers and returns to cool the primary loop (see page 304).

At Three Mile Island, a pump used to push water through the secondary cooling system failed. With the loss of cool water needed to control the temperature in the reactor's primary loop, the radioactive water in the primary system began to overheat. Water pressure within the reactor began to soar. Normal operating levels are 582° F. and 1,155 p.s.i. When the internal pressure reached 2,350 p.s.i. the reactor automatically "scrammed." This caused the warning buzzer to alert the crew in the control room that there was a problem.

Boron control rods were immediately lowered into the core of the reactor to stop the fission process. Even with the reactor close to shut down, normal radioactivity in the fuel rods continue to produce about one-tenth the heat produced in a chain reaction.

McNamee/Newsweek

Radiation was frequently monitored by Geiger counters to measure human safety throughout the neighboring towns and countryside.

HUMAN ERROR AND MECHANICAL FAILURE

Next, human error played a part in the growing chain of mistakes. A valve was opened allowing superheated steam from the reactor to flow into a waste tank. Unfortunately, the water pressure was too great for the tank to contain. The plumbing ruptured, flooding the reactor's chamber with some 200,000 gallons of radioactive water. Coupled with the problem of contaminated water, a relief valve designed to prevent the water pressure from exceeding safe limits failed to close. For three hours radioactive steam was periodically vented into the atmosphere. Some radioactive water found its way into the Susquehanna River.

At 7 A.M. state authorities were notified of the accidental release of radioactive steam. An hour later the state declared a general emergency. Within 12 hours traces of radioactivity from the reactor were detected up to 20 miles away.

BUBBLE ABOVE THE FUEL RODS

Because of the lack of cool water in the primary loop the reactor itself continued to overheat. It is believed that the high temperatures broke up water molecules into hydrogen and oxygen forming a large bubble of gas in the upper part of the reactor vessel.

In addition, the gases xenon 133, iodine 131 and krypton 85—all very dangerous radioactive by-products of the nuclear process—were believed to be contained in the bubble. For a time, engineers feared that the pressure exerted by the gas bubble would force the level of the water in the reactor downward. If this occurred the tops of the fuel rods containing uranium would be exposed. A continued build-up of heat coupled with a loss of coolant can lead to one of two events—both disastrous.

EXPLOSION OR MELTDOWN

(1) Pressure caused by the extreme heat could cause the reactor itself to rupture; (2) or a meltdown could occur. If the metal fuel rods should melt, approximately 8,000,000 tiny pellets (about the size of a bean seed) would fall to the floor of the reactor. Without a coolant the pellets would form a radio-active mass, emitting an eerie robin's-egg-blue glow. Tremendous heat would be generated. The radioactive mass would either break through the containment walls of the reactor or sink deep into the ground beneath the reactor. The later event is known as the "China Syndrome"—presumably going through the earth to China.

In either case, a rupture of the reactor's wall or a meltdown, the result is a massive release of radiation. Any release of excessive radiation into the atmosphere would spread contaminants for hundreds of kilometers, depending on the direction and speed of the prevailing winds. A massive radioactive discharge into the earth could contaminate ground water thus destroying crops, wildlife, and drinking water. Destruction could spread for hundreds of miles.

At no time could a nuclear plant explode like an atomic bomb. The reactor's fuel, uranium 235, is not sufficiently enriched to create a nuclear explosion. A nuclear reactor could, of course, experience a steam explosion in which large amounts of radioactivity are spewed forth.

The gas bubble within the Three Mile Island reactor continued to cause great concern. Since it was impossible to analyze the actual composition or size of the gas bubble, scientists had to rely upon acoustical sounders to try to determine the bubble's size. A constant fear was that the hydrogen and oxygen would combine and explode. It was essential to eliminate the gas bubble. Scientists had to rely on many basic laws of physics to predict how much of a given gas can be dissolved in water at a specific temperature and pressure.

THE PEOPLE

As nuclear scientists and technicians were battling the potential disaster, about a third of the population near the reactor evacuated their homes. Governor Richard Thornburgh suggested that all children and pregnant women leave the area. By Sunday, April 1st, April Fool's day, approximately 60,000 people had left their homes. Schools were closed on Monday, and the people remaining nervously packed their belongings and awaited word on the condition of the reactor. President Jimmy Carter (a former nuclear-engineering student) toured the reactor facilities to assess the problem.

On Monday, April 2nd, the gas bubble began to be absorbed in the water contained in the reactor. The following day officials announced that the bubble no longer posed a problem and, barring further technical difficulties, the crises had passed.

Although life slowly returned to normal around Three Mile Island the problems in the power plant were far from over. Assessment of the actual damage to the reactor would take months. Actual disposal of the highly radioactive materials in the reactor presented still more problems. It was estimated that the cost to "clean" the reactor and repair the massive damage would run into millions. One estimate indicated that it would cost more to repair the damage than the actual cost of building the plant. It is conceivable that officials may decide to abandon the facility altogether.

Although the disaster at Three Mile Island is the worst commercial nuclear accident in U.S. history, it was not the only nuclear accident that occurred over the past year. In April, 1978, two workers at the Trojan nuclear-power plant near Rainer, Oregon were exposed to high doses of radiation. In March, 1978, an explosion occurred at the Vermont Yankee power plant, Vernon, Vermont—the second in four months. There were no injuries. In January, 1978, radioactive helium escaped from the Fort St. Vrain nuclear power plant near Denver, Colorado. Radiation levels were 20 to 30 times higher than normal. Some plant workers were mildly contaminated.

Many children and pregnant women left the Harrisburg area in case further damage was done in the reactor producing more radiation. However, there was no mass evacuation.

Teresa Zabala/The New York Times

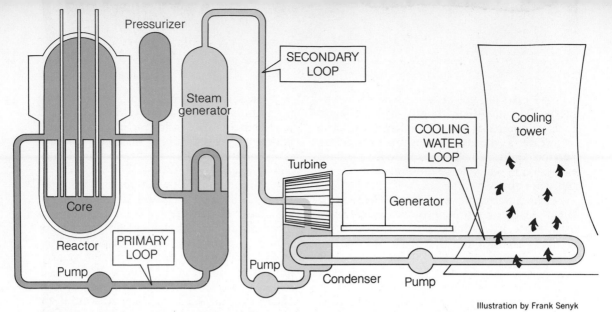

Illustration by Frank Senyk

The primary cooling system cools the nuclear reactor, and the secondary system cools the primary, using the heat to energize a turbine.

TWO TYPES OF COMMERCIAL REACTORS

There are basically two types of reactors currently in use in the United States. The pressurized-water reactor like the one at Three Mile Island and the boiling-water reactor. These reactors are designed to do the same thing: convert water to steam; the steam, in turn, propels a turbogenerator that produces electricity.

The boiling-water reactor, unlike the pressurized-water reactor, has only one water system. The same water that cools the fuel rods is allowed to boil off to produce steam to turn the turbogenerators.

Other types of reactors include the gas-cooled reactor, which uses graphite to moderate the nuclear reaction and the gas, helium, to cool the fuel rods. The breeder reactor, which converts uranium 238 to plutonium, is generally cooled by liquid sodium. Although breeders need far less fuel than water-cooled reactors their prime drawback is their by-product, plutonium. This is the element critical in the production of atomic bombs. Many people fear it would not be out of the question for individuals to steal the plutonium and manufacture a simple, but devastating, atomic bomb.

THE BIG DEBATE

A national debate over the safety of nuclear energy will continue for many years. With our shrinking supply of petroleum, energy from nuclear fission may remain an alternative for serious consideration. The current U.S. supply of uranium oxide could fuel our existing reactors for several centuries. The breeder reactor could multiply the reactor fuel supply 60 times.

As of mid-1979, there were 72 nuclear reactors licensed to operate in the United States with more than 90 others under construction. These existing reactors supply about 13 per cent of America's electrical power capacity. In 1978, nuclear energy produced nearly 300,000,000,000 kilowatt-hours of electricity. Some states are heavily dependent on atomic power for their electricity. Vermont receives more than 80 per cent of all its electric power from nuclear plants. The percentage of electricity supplied by nuclear plants for the following states is: Maine, 65%; Connecticut and Nebraska, 50%; South Carolina, 47%; Wisconsin, 32%; Illinois, 28%; New York, 24%; and New Jersey, 23%.

The potential disaster at Three Mile Island highlights the need for increased safety standards and controls over the generation of nuclear power. There are many people, however, who believe that the growing world-energy crises prevent us from abandoning our use of nuclear energy as one of several potential solutions to our demand for more energy in the future □

 SELECTED READINGS

"Nuclear Accident." *Newsweek,* April 9, 1979.
"A Nuclear Nightmare." *Time,* April 9, 1979.
"The Three-Mile Accident." *Science News,* April 1, 1979.

The results of the collisions of particles are fed into this detector called "crystal ball."

PETRA AND PEP

by Arthur L. Robinson

ELECTRON-positron colliding-beam storage rings have been by far the most successful examples of a new philosophy in accelerator design. This design involves crashing two beams of elementary particles head-on into one another rather than bombarding a fixed target. The idea has been so fruitful, in fact, that two new machines, enlarged versions of the storage rings that ushered in the era of the "new physics" of quarks and leptons are, or soon will be, open for business. Quarks are, you may remember, the supposed constituents of particles such as the proton, neutron, and pi meson. And leptons include the electron, the muon, and the neutrinos.

The apparent winner in a "friendly" race to explore higher energies than heretofore available in storage rings is a 98-million-deutschmark ($52-million) machine named PETRA. It started operation in July 1978 at the Deutsches Elektronen-Synchrotron (DESY) laboratory in Hamburg. DESY physicists then debugged the new machine, a process common to big new accelerators, and it did not operate at maximum performance until somewhat later. The second machine, named PEP, is a joint project of the Stanford Linear Accelerator Center (SLAC) and the Lawrence Berkeley Laboratory (LBL) in California. It is being built at Stanford and is planned to be operating by October 1979.

WHY HEAD-ON COLLISIONS?

The obvious way to find out what makes something tick is to break it apart into its constituent pieces. In the barest of terms, this is what high-energy physicists do when they slam protons and electrons into nuclei in accelerators. However, most of the bombarding particle's energy is not effective in the collision but simply goes to accelerating the stationary target. To curb this inefficiency, physicists have increasingly gone to a new type of machine—the colliding-beam storage ring. When two particles of equal mass and velocity crash head-on, all their energy is available for breaking them apart.

CREATING NEW PARTICLES

Electron-positron storage rings have an additional advantage over other accelerators in this endeavor. Because the electron and positron are antiparticles of each other, they are annihilated in the collision. This creates, as physicists graphically describe it, a miniature fireball of pure energy. In the now conventional wisdom, after the shortest of instants, the fireball materializes into either a pair of quarks or a pair of leptons. The pair must consist of a particle and its antiparticle, such as a negatively and a positively charged muon. The wisdom further dictates that "free" quarks do not exist. Therefore, if a pair of quarks forms from the fireball, after another exceptionally brief moment, they transform into protons, neutrons, pi mesons, and other particles of the same class called hadrons.

In every case, Einstein's famous $E = mc^2$ is obeyed, so that the sum of the rest masses of all particles created must not exceed the sum of the electron and positron energies in the storage ring. Electron-positron storage rings are thus an efficient way of creating new elementary particles from high-energy collisions. And because of the simple quark-antiquark starting state, the particles are not embedded in the confusing array of debris that accompanies events in other types of accelerators.

RESONANCE

New particles manifest themselves in two ways. The first is called a resonance and occurs when the electron and positron energies exactly match the mass of the new entity. When this match is achieved, the probability of the fireball materializing into the new particle in preference to any other combination of particles dramatically increases. The signal that the new particle was produced is a much increased rate of production of lower mass particles that form when the new entity decays. It was in this way that the J/psi particle, massive and long-lived meson, was found at SLAC and simultaneously at Brookhaven National Laboratory, though in a different type of experiment.

THRESHOLD PROCESS

The second method of producing new particles is called a threshold process. If a resonance is somewhat analogous to the transition induced between two quantum states of an atom by the absorption of light, then a threshold corresponds to ionizing the atom. At any energy above the threshold, new particles appear in pairs, and these can carry away, as kinetic energy, the energy beyond that needed to create them. The signal for a threshold process is an increase in the number of ordinary particles detected when the new ones decay, but the effect is generally less dramatic than a resonance.

TUNING THE ENERGY

Physicists can precisely tune the energy of the storage ring and in this way study in detail the properties of the new particles created. A disadvantage is that electrons and positrons, being pointlike particles with no spatial extent, do not collide very often, and it is a slow, painstaking business to scan the energy range of the storage ring. These machines are thus most useful when experimenters have some notion of which energies to tune to, a point well illustrated by the J/psi particle. SLAC's electron-positron storage ring, called SPEAR, was completed in April 1972, but the particle discovery came in November 1974.

COMPETITION

SPEAR was the brainchild of Burton Richter of SLAC, who first proposed, in 1965, that such a machine be built. Funding was not immediately forthcoming, however, and only after several years was a scaled-down version built in the remarkably short time of 21 months and at the low cost of $5.3 million.

European physicists had previously caught on to the virtues of colliding-beam storage rings. The first large electron-positron machine was, in fact, built in Italy. Jumping into the game somewhat later were German physicists from DESY, who were able to construct and put into operation by mid-1974 an electron-positron storage ring similar in complexity to the one Richter had originally proposed. In this way, what has become one of the great rivalries in physics came into being. Officials at both accelerator centers emphasize, however, that competition does not preclude cooperation. Thus, there is constant sharing of technical information concerning machine operation, although naturally not detailed plans for experiments.

Burton Richter (right) of Stanford watches an oscilloscope showing interaction of particles. (See upper figure on page 308.)

SLAC

The group at Brookhaven under Samuel Ting of the Massachusetts Institute of Technology (MIT) found the J/psi particle at the same time as the SLAC group, (which included physicists from LBL and a second Stanford group in addition to Richter's team). The majority of further studies of the J/psi and the many subsequently found particles related to it depended on two positron-electron storage rings: SPEAR and the German machine DORIS. The two new storage rings, PEP and PETRA, will continue the competition, but this time it will be DESY that has the head start.

NEARLY IDENTICAL

Both PEP and PETRA will have nearly identical performance specifications, and both are more like the U.S. SPEAR than the German DORIS. A storage ring consists of a circular tube evacuated to an ultrahigh vacuum through which electrically-charged particles travel at high velocities approaching the speed of light. Magnets surrounding the

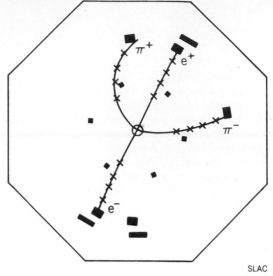

SLAC

Particle interaction (photo on page 307) producing e^-, e^+, π^-, π^+ particles.

tube confine the particles to a circular path. Radio-frequency power sources replenish energy lost by the particles as they move during each cycle.

Since electrons and positrons have identical masses but opposite electrical charges,

Here is PETRA, located at the Deutches Electronen-Synchrotron (DESY) laboratory in Hamburg, Germany.

German Information Center

they can be stored simultaneously in the same ring as counterrotating electron and positron beams. By confining the electrons and positrons to small "bunches" that travel around the ring, physicists can control where collisions take place in the ring. With one electron and one positron bunch, for example, collisions occur twice during each revolution, on opposite sides of the ring.

DORIS consists of two separate rings that intersect in two places. PETRA and PEP are single-ring machines.

SUPER-HIGH ENERGIES

The two new storage rings are improvements on SPEAR and DORIS because they will store electron and positron beams at much higher energies, thus permitting the creation of much more massive particles than heretofore possible. The high energies will also allow scientists to study the forces by which elementary particles interact. Whereas the older storage rings could reach energies of 4 and 5 GeV per beam, respectively, the new rings will be able to stretch to 18 and 19 GeV per beam. A GeV is a giga-electron volt. An electron volt is a unit of energy equal to the energy acquired by an electron falling through a potential difference of one volt. One giga-electron volt is 1,000,000,000 electron volts.

Among other details, PETRA is octagonal in shape with a circumference of 2.3 kilometers. Although there are eight possible beam-intersection regions, only four will be used at first, and two others will be activated if the "physics" looks interesting enough.

PEP is hexagonal, with a slightly smaller circumference of 2.2 kilometers. Five of its six intersection regions are scheduled for major experiments. If either machine ever is operated at the maximum possible beam energy, the total electrical power consumed will be about 15 to 20 megawatts, which is about that needed for a town of 20,000 inhabitants.

Both machines will receive electrons and positrons from accelerators already existing on site, but there is a significant difference in how this is accomplished in the two rings. SLAC has the advantage of its more than 3-kilometer-long linear electron accelerator, which is capable of injecting both electrons and positrons into PEP at any energy that the storage ring can handle. DESY has a 7.5-GeV electron synchrotron that, in combination with other machines also located at the laboratory, squirts these particles into PETRA. Thus PETRA must be able to accelerate both electrons and positrons to the operating energy, as well as to store the particles.

A sketch of PETRA to show how electrons and positrons are fed into a colliding-beam storage ring.

German Information Center

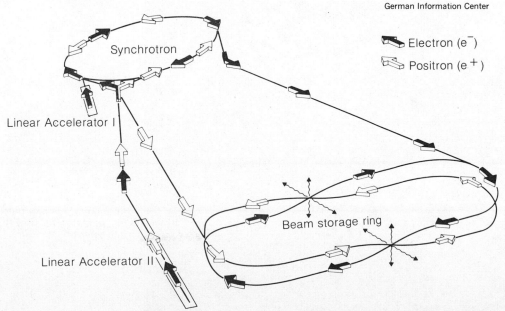

Electron (e⁻)

Positron (e⁺)

LARGE RESEARCH TEAMS

Members of the experimental teams at PETRA and PEP will be drawn from many universities and research laboratories. DESY collaborations, for example, are truly international, being made up of other Europeans, Japanese, Chinese, Israelis, and U.S. scientists in addition to the host Germans.

These large research teams will design and build the detectors that identify and measure the properties of the particles emanating from high-energy collisions. These instruments are mighty beasts in themselves, costing in some cases $10,000,000 or more, and weighing, if much use is made of iron, several hundred to a few thousand tons. More than half of the $30,000,000 million that will be spent on the five detectors planned or already built for PETRA is coming from outside Germany.

At PETRA and PEP collision energies, perhaps 150 collisions per hour will result in the production of hadrons, and only a few of these may be of interest for a given experiment. Thus, because electron-positron collisions are so rare, the detectors are designed to collect as much information as possible for later analysis by computer. In this way, one group's experiment can consist of computer-searching the data gathered by others for events of interest. Alternatively, it may take an experimental team months or years to search completely for new phenomena in data that was gathered in a short time.

DETECTORS

Although the rate of interesting events is relatively low, the peculiarities of those selected for measurement place severe constraints on the design of detectors. At PETRA and PEP energies, physicists estimate, an average of 15 particles will be produced per electron-positron collision. Half of these particles will be electrically charged and half will be neutral. Moreover, these will be distributed mainly in two "jets" that move away from the collision region in opposite directions (except at resonances). Any detector will, therefore, have to be able to sort out many closely spaced, rapidly moving particles. Unfortunately, the direction of the jets is different for each event in which particles are produced, so the detector must also be sensitive to as much of the total area as possible.

PETRA and PEP most clearly diverge in the designs of their detectors. Although none of the detectors at DESY, for example, are identical, four of the five are large, powerful detectors that are expected to do a creditable job of identifying and measuring the properties of all particles produced in the storage ring. This overlap in function may be one result of the very rapid construction pace in Hamburg, which pressured physicists to stick with all-inclusive designs.

The detectors at SLAC tend to be more complementary. One detector is a general purpose instrument; a second is exception-

SLAC

The Mark II under construction. This is a particle detector for SPEAR and possibly for PEP.

Aerial view of SPEAR. Dashed circle indicates location of tunnel for PEP.

ally good at distinguishing between electrons and charged pi mesons (a perennial problem); a third will track muons, which are difficult to tag because they penetrate through solid material easily; and a fourth will be able to measure particle momenta and masses with a high resolution.

PETRA has just started operating with three detectors in place. The first, called PLUTO, is a thoroughly tested instrument, having been one of two detectors used on the DORIS storage ring. The two others will need several weeks or possibly months of debugging before being ready for full-time data taking. The fourth and fifth detectors are under construction and are expected to be in place by the coming spring.

PEP, coming on line a year behind PETRA, may get scooped on some major new discoveries. Researchers at SLAC will have two already proven detectors (Mark II and DELCO) in place by the October 1979 opening date in addition to one all-new instrument, which will need to be broken in. Three other new detectors will be ready about six months later.

SEARCH FOR NEW PARTICLES

A search for new elementary particles containing heavier quarks could be one of the earliest findings of these new devices. With the experience of the J/psi in hand, physicists now believe that an increased probability of producing hadrons over the probability of producing muon pairs is a signal of a new quark. Since an increase in this ratio is a threshold process, even if the resonance should be missed, observation of such

an increase would tell experimenters to remeasure at lower energies. But, points out Wolfgang Panofsky, director of SLAC, other effects also can contribute to an increase in this ratio, thus requiring precision measurements. Even when a storage ring is operating at full performance, it takes hundreds of hours to gather data for one point on a high-precision energy scan.

Thus, given the necessity of breaking in PETRA and of debugging its new detectors, it could be some time, say observers, before results of experiments requiring such high-precision scans are forthcoming. One problem DESY physicists have experienced is in packing large numbers of electrons and positrons into their respective bunches, a problem that goes under the general heading of beam instability. Since beam instabilities are a fact of life in storage rings, physicists operating PEP may well run into similar difficulties. If they are lucky and avoid such problems, or if they are able to incorporate directly the solutions that their German counterparts come up with, experimenters using PEP may not find themselves so far behind after all. In any case, all observers agree that there is more than enough "physics" for both machines to lead long and productive lives □

SELECTED READINGS

"Experts build detectors for PEP turn-on in 1979" by G. B. Lubkin. *Physics Today,* June 1978.

"Head-on at 100 billion volts" by D. E. Thomsen. *Science News,* May 13, 1978.

"Head-on physics: electron-positron storage rings." *Scientific American,* March 1978.

Peter Kapitsa receiving the 1978 Nobel Prize in Physics from King Carl Gustaf of Sweden.

THE 1978 NOBEL PRIZES IN PHYSICS AND CHEMISTRY

by Barbara McDowell

RESEARCH shedding light on nothing less than the origin of the universe earned U.S. radio astronomers Arno A. Penzias and Robert W. Wilson one half of the 1979 Nobel Prize in Physics from the Swedish Royal Academy of Sciences. They shared the award with Soviet physicist Peter L Kapitsa, who is best known for his work in low-temperature physics.

The 1978 Nobel Prize in Chemistry went to Peter D. Mitchell, a British biochemist who helped explain how living organisms convert nourishment into energy.

THE PRIZE IN PHYSICS

Penzias and Wilson, who work at the Bell Telephone Laboratories in Holmdel, New Jersey, were honored by the Academy for their "fundamental" discovery of residual radiation that helped confirm the "big bang" theory of the universe's origin. "It made it possible to obtain information about cosmic processes that took place a very long time ago, at the time of the creation of the universe," noted the Academy.

The "big bang" theory, proposed in the 1940's by astronomers Ralph Alpher and George Gamow, holds that the universe began with a gigantic explosion more than 15,000,000,000 years ago and has since continued to grow and expand. The explosion dispersed a great deal of heat throughout space, some of which still remains. It is this fossil heat from the initial fireball that Penzias and Wilson succeeded in measuring.

Their discovery was made largely by accident. In 1963 Penzias and Wilson were involved in trying to design antennas to communicate with artificial satellites. Using a seven-meter horn-shaped antenna, they launched an investigation of the radiation bombarding the earth from space. Try as they might, they could not rid the antenna of some background radiation. They ruled out a large number of possible sources for this radiation ranging from the sun to the Milky Way to ill-fitting antenna joints to the droppings of pigeons that had taken up residence in the instrument.

In discussing the background radiation with their colleagues, Penzias and Wilson learned that the temperature they had recorded was close to that predicted by Princeton University researchers as the temperature of residual heat from the "big bang." Penzias and Wilson published their measurements in the July 1965 issue of the *Astrophysics Journal.* In the same issue appeared a paper by the Princeton team—Robert Dicke, James Peebles, Peter Roll, and David Wilkinson—theorizing that the radiation observed and measured by Penzias and Wilson was proof of the "big bang."

Penzias and Wilson have continued joint research, investigating intergalactic hydrogen, galactic radiation, and interstellar matter. The abundance of deuterium (heavy hydrogen) in the galaxy—an important factor in "big bang" cosmology—has been the topic of some of their most recent research.

Arno A. Penzias was born in Munich in 1933. He fled Hitler's Germany for the United States with his family five years later. He earned his bachelor of science degree from the City College of New York in 1954 and his Ph.D. from Columbia University in 1962. He joined Bell Laboratories in 1961 and now heads its Radio Research Laboratory.

Robert W. Wilson was born in Houston, Texas, in 1936. He received his B.A. in physics from Rice University in 1957 and his Ph.D. from the California Institute of Technology (Caltech) in 1962. After a postdoctoral year at Caltech's Owens Valley Radio Observatory, he began work at Bell Laboratories. He now heads Bell's Radio Physics Research Department.

LOW-TEMPERATURE PHYSICS

In addition to recognizing Peter Kapitsa's "basic inventions and discoveries in the area of low-temperature physics," the Nobel committee also took note of his "amazing capacity to organize and lead work" as the long-time director of Moscow's S. I. Vavilov Institute of Physical Problems. Kapitsa's prize may also reflect the reputation he earned beyond the scientific community for his willingness to stand up to his government. His most notable such act was his refusal in 1946 to work on atomic weapons. The refusal resulted in his being confined for seven years on orders of Soviet leader Josef Stalin.

"He will be remembered for many things," noted acquaintance R. V. Pound of Harvard University, "But most of all he will be remembered as an independent thinker in a country where independent thinking is not that easy."

One of Kapitsa's major contributions to low-temperature physics was his 1934 design of a device to simplify the liquefication of large quantities of helium. Then, studying the resulting He II, the phase of liquid helium that exists at temperatures below 2.17 degrees Kelvin, Kapitsa was among the first to identify the superfluidity that causes it to penetrate minute openings in solid containers and to defy gravity by flowing upward over the sides of containers. Kapitsa's observations, along with those of Cambridge University's Jack Allen and A. Donald Misener, were published in *Nature* in 1938.

Arno A. Penzias (right) and Robert W. Wilson, co-winners of the 1978 Nobel Prize in Physics. Their work helped confirm the "big-bang" theory.

Bell Labs

Peter Mitchell of England receiving the 1978 Nobel Prize in Chemistry.

Peter L. Kapitsa was born in 1894 in the Russian town of Kronstadt and educated at the Petrograd (now Leningrad) Polytechnical Institute. He fled in 1921 to Great Britain, where he began an apprenticeship under famed physicist Ernest Rutherford at the Cavendish Laboratory of Cambridge University. He earned his Ph.D. there in 1923.

Much of Kapitsa's early work was focused on magnetism. He designed a sophisticated apparatus to produce high-intensity magnetic fields that was not improved for three decades. In 1929 Kapitsa became the first foreigner in 200 years elected a fellow of the British Royal Society and from 1930 to 1934 served as director of the Society's Mond Laboratory.

Kapitsa returned to his homeland in 1934 for a scientific conference and was refused an exit visa. After a year during which he refused to work, he became director of the new Institute for Physical Problems, which he then proceeded to build into a highly regarded institution. Rehabilitated after Stalin's death and his seven-year confinement, Kapitsa resumed his post at the Institute and is believed to have headed the Soviet space program through the 1957 launchings of the first two Sputniks. According to his son Ser-

gei, Kapitsa continues to work "like a student" during his eight-hour days at the Institute. Among his current research subjects is the use of nuclear fusion to generate usable energy.

THE PRIZE IN CHEMISTRY

Science has long sought to understand how living organisms convert the nourishment gained through respiration and plant photo-synthesis to the substance—adenosine triphosphate (ATP)—that stores energy in the cells. Instead of joining his colleagues in their frustrating search for a strictly chemical explanation for the biological energy transfer, Peter Mitchell proposed that ATP is synthesized through an electrical process driven by positively charged protons. The controversial chemiosmotic theory that he announced in 1961 has been credited with revolutionizing the field of bioenergetics.

Mitchell holds that a voltage gradient, or difference in voltages, causes hydrogen ions—which are really protons—to move across the inner membrane of the cell mitochondria, or power plants, to provide energy for the synthesis of ATP. This proton current, has been likened to the electron current produced by a battery.

The Nobel committee acknowledged that details of the chemiosmotic process remain to be described. However, it noted that Mitchell's work may result not only in a clearer understanding of vital cell activities but also in new technologies for meeting the world's increasing energy needs.

Peter D. Mitchell was born in Mitcham, Surrey, England in 1920. Cambridge University awarded him a bachelor of arts degree in 1943 and a Ph.D. in 1950. He taught at Cambridge University and at the University of Edinburgh before leaving what he described as the "overstimulation" of academia to establish his Glynn Research Laboratory in 1964. The six-member private laboratory is located in a restored farmhouse in Cornwall, England, surrounded by 120 cows who, along with a small government grant, have financed Mitchell's work. "It is easier for people to work in small groups," he has said in defense of the site. "In a big organization people are expected to be all the same"□

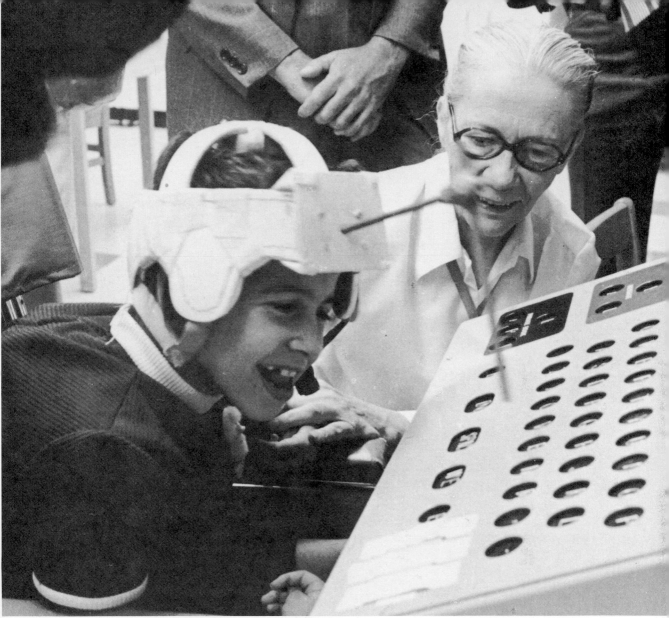

Bell Labs

Help is on the way for disabled persons who cannot speak, write, or use their hands. Here we see a cerebral-palsied child who cannot use his hands but can use a pointer fixed to a headcap to type a message. The keyboard is coupled to a microcomputer, which also is connected to a TV screen and a page printer.

TECHNOLOGY

Richard Lee

Stanford Ovshinsky holds several cheap photovoltaic cells in his hands. The cells are made of amorphous silicon—very much like glass—which is easier and less expensive than growing silicon crystals. These cells might be able to convert sunlight to electricity cheaply enough to be competitive with other forms of energy.

This Department of Energy wind turbine turns at 40 revolutions per minute (which is slow) in a wind velocity of 13 to 65 kilometers an hour. It can generate up to 200 kilowatts of electricity.

NASA

TECHNOLOGY
REVIEW OF THE YEAR

A better sunlight trap. As problems with existing energy sources continue and the search for new energy sources proves in general disappointing, more and more attention is being turned to the direct conversion of sunlight into useful energy. Most existing solar-conversion facilities on the ground use solar collectors as heat absorbers to make hot water that is then used primarily for space heating and not for the generation of electricity. Existing solar collectors that function as photovoltaics, producing an electric current when light shines on them, have a very low efficiency—only a few per cent—and are in general expensive, being made of large single crystals. Most that are used are used in spacecraft where the savings in weight outbalance the expense. There may be a promising advance, however. Late in 1978 entrepreneur Stanford R. Ovshinsky of Energy Conversion Devices, Inc., announced the development of a photovoltaic that could have a conversion efficiency of 10 per cent or higher and be made of amorphous silicon. Silicon is the earth's most abundant mineral and amorphous forms are much less expensive than crystalline forms to make. If this announcement proves true, it could make direct sunlight-to-electricity conversion a commercial possibility. The U.S. Department of Energy is guarded in its assessment of the report, in part because of Ovshinsky's somewhat controversial reputation.

Tilting toward windmills. The first U.S. government funded "commercial wind generator" in the United States went into operation at Clayton, New Mexico, on January 28, 1978. The windmill is not picturesque nor reminiscent of quaint Dutch landscapes. It looks like a giant airplane propeller on an oil derrick. Its blades span some 37 meters and turn at 40 revolutions per minute whenever the wind is blowing at a rate between 13 and 65 kilometers an hour. It generates up to 200 kilowatts of electricity, which is fed to a power grid. Thus its energy can be used when the wind is blowing, with another energy source picking up the slack when the wind is not blowing. Or the energy can be stored for later use, perhaps during peak demand. This and other types of modern windmills are being investigated by engineers looking at what is a freely available source of energy.

A rainbow under glass. For centuries technolgists have known how to give glass a specific color or make it irridescent by including particular substances in its composition. Now a glass that can exhibit all the colors of the rainbow—where you want them—is possible. Called polychromatic glass, it was developed by S. D. Stookey and J. E. Pierson of Corning Glassworks. They were working with a sodium-fluoride opal glass, which has a milky white color and contains particles of silver. Irradiation with ultraviolet light is used to give opalescent glass its proper opal tone. But when the two researchers followed the first short blast of ultraviolet with a longer shot and temperatures between 300° and 410° Celsius, they found that a full range of brilliant colors appeared. They modified the chemistry of the basic glass so that it would be transparent, and they had polychromatic glass. In a sample of polychromatic glass, progressive ultraviolet irradiation dosages affect the silver so as to cause different colors starting with blues and greens for low exposure and progressing toward yellow and red for high doses. The dosages in different parts of the glass can be regulated by using black-and-white photographic negatives, and a varicolored pattern—with the colors permanent—can thus be made. The use of polychromatic glass in museum slides, crockery, and other decorative items is foreseen.

New liquid strainer. Removing an unwanted molecule that is contaminating a batch of some liquid without chemically destroying the liquid is a frequent problem in chemical technology. Agents called molecular sieves do the job. They are crystals with open spaces in their structure, and they absorb the unwanted molecules in their openings and carry the molecules with them when they are mechanically strained from the liquid. A new molecular sieve, considered particularly important because it can remove organic molecules from water, was developed during the year by a group of researchers at Union Carbide Corporation's Tarrytown Technical Center in Tarrytown, New York. Called silicalite, it has a structure with regular openings large enough to catch many organic molecules, including molecules of methanol, propanol, butanol, phenol, pentane, and hexane. It is also the first molecular sieve to be hydrophobic—that is, to repel water. It is hoped that it will prove very useful in removing organic contaminants from water.

Union Carbide

A Union Carbide research chemist holds a model of a molecular sieve, which is a crystal with open spaces in its structure. The crystal sieve absorbs certain kinds of unwanted molecules into its openings. This function makes it useful in cleaning out contaminants from a liquid.

From microchips to microblocks? Industrial and commercial concerns always seem to want quicker and quicker electronic circuitry. A way toward that end may come from a recent development at Bell Laboratories that produced a semiconductor material in which the electrons move twice as fast as in other semiconductors. In the semiconductors now in wide use, atoms of a foreign material that can add electrons to the semiconductor's fund of conduction electrons must be added to the semiconductor for it to produce a useful electric current. This doping of the semiconductor—as it is called—often slows the current down. What four Bell researchers—Raymond Dingle, Horst L. Stormer, A. C. Gossard, and W. Wiegmann—did was to develop a sandwich-type semiconductor in which the dopant ions stay in one layer, making that layer different in energy from the other sandwich layer. This facilitates freer and faster electron movement, or, in other words, faster current. The developers foresee not only faster conventional circuitry but also, because of the layered nature of the material, possible three-dimensional circuitry. The semiconductor-laden microchip so important to today's modern electronics industry may become the microblock of tomorrow.

Bell Lab's scientist, Horst Stormer, uses an electric pulse to weld tiny gold-wire leads onto a new sandwich-type semiconductor, which lets electrons flow easier and hence faster. This new type of semiconductor crystal could lead to three-dimensional circuits.

Bell Labs

Back to steam engines. Steam locomotives once pulled most ot the world's landborne freight and passengers, and in some countries—Poland and China, for example—they still survive. Now they may make a comeback elsewhere as well—if a group of engineers at Queen Mary College of London University are successful. The steam engine's usual fuels have been wood, coal, and oil, but steam engines have been known to burn almost anything combustible, including sugar beets, corn husks, and sugar cane. Engineers M. W. Thring, J. E. Sharpe, and P. K. LeSeur think that by using fluidized combustion bed they can preserve the steam engine's omnivorousness, cut air pollution from the steam engine virtually to zero, and increase thermal efficiency to 24.5 per cent, which is competitive with diesels.

Dietrick Thomsen

A blowfly's proboscis (left) shows lobellum lobes, which secrete digestive juices on the insect's prey.

E. P. Herlihy

MICROSCOPY AS A HOBBY

by Hal Bowser

THE most exciting gift I've ever received was the microscope my parents gave me for Christmas when I was 11.

It was a tiny 'scope, hardly more than a toy, and the image you saw through its eye-piece was a bit skewed and smudgy. But no matter: that toy promptly stood my little world on its head, opening up for me a whole new realm of color, action, and ideas.

That Christmas day, the first thing I looked at under the new microscope was a drop of water dipped up from a brackish rain puddle in our backyard in Brooklyn, New York. I'd heard that long-standing puddles with a bit of rotting vegetation in them were apt to be full of strange and wonderful living things. I certainly wasn't disappointed: as the droplet sprang into focus, I saw all kinds of

odd-looking creatures tumbling and cavorting about in the bright, circular field of view.

DIRIGIBLES AND SLIPPERS

One of these creatures was a large, comparatively slow-moving fellow. It looked, I remember thinking, like a dirigible or a shrunken dinosaur (at 11, I was very big on dirigibles and dinosaurs). What puzzled me intensely was that this creature had at one end of its body what looked like two slowly turning wheels.

Then I saw another arresting sight—a long, slipper-shaped tiny organism that was darting and veering among the other creatures like a police launch cutting through crowded harbor traffic. This creature intrigued me even more than the one with "wheels" because, while I could plainly make out all its organs churning away inside it, I couldn't figure out just what it was doing to make itself zoom along so fast.

Later, I was to learn that the dirigible-shaped animal is a rotifer. The name is from the Latin for "wheelbearer." The "wheels" are actually rounded appendages covered with hairs called cilia. By lashing these cilia about, one after another, the rotifer creates currents that sweep even tinier creatures and bits of vegetation into its mouth. The rapid, one-after-the-other motion of the cilia deceives the microscopist's eye into thinking the wheels are turning, somewhat the way the lights blinking on and off on a movie marquee seem to be racing around in circles.

I also learned that the slipper-shaped creature is a paramecium, a creature so brash, active, and all-present that I think of it as the Volkswagen of the microworld. Paramecia (the plural of paramecium is paramecia) can move so fast, I found, because they, too, are covered with cilia (not visible under that first microscope of mine). These cilia beat the water like oars, or whips, and propel the creatures along smartly.

NEVER BORING

On that winter day, however, the facts about what I was looking at mattered not at all. I was too caught up in staring, agog, at the riot of movement in that droplet of water.

Hal Bowser, the author of this article, does microscopy as a hobby and collects microscopes old and new, inexpensive and costly.

Phillip A. Harrington

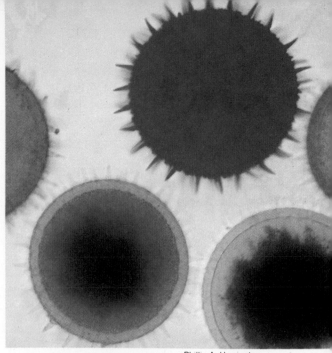

Phillip A. Harrington

Dyed grains of hollyhock pollen appear like colored golfballs under the microscope.

At the same time, on a not very conscious level, I was already beginning to take in what I now see as one of the great lessons microscopy can teach you—which is that under the piercing eye of the lens nothing, not even slimy ditchwater, is contemptible.

It took, of course, many years of devout gazing through the eyepiece at all sorts of things to bring that lesson fully home to me. During those years, like a shark in feeding frenzy, I kept thrusting under the cyclopean eye of my little 'scope anything and everything that came to hand: stamps, coins, snowflakes, houseflies, flower pollen, spiders, onion skin—even rather dim, ghostly-looking cells scraped from the wet inside lining of my cheek.

Few things are less attractive than horse urine. Yet when horse urine is evaporated until it forms crystals of hippuric acid, and is then looked at through a microscope fitted out with inexpensive polarizing filters, it blazes forth in wildly beautiful forms, and even wilder colors, that remind one of psychedelic paintings.

So when I say that the microscope transformed my view of the animal, vegetable, and mineral world around me, I mean just that. It dawned on me early that microscopy means never again having to be bored.

Phillip A. Harrington

Members of the New York Microscopical Society meet near the Museum of Natural History, New York, to discuss what they are doing.

MICRO MANIACS

A second phase of my life in microscopy began about 15 years ago, when I joined the New York Microscopical Society (NYMS) and began for the first time to meet large numbers of live "micromaniacs."

The 100-year-old Society, which alternately meets at the American Museum of Natural History and the New York Academy of Sciences, both in New York City, has about 300 amateur and professional members. Before and after the twice-monthly evening lectures I found myself talking mostly to the amateurs. These amateurs were a strangely mixed bag, ranging from happy dabblers like myself right on up to people who were doing—purely for the love of it—spare-time microscopical research on a high level.

Overnight, I found myself meeting protozoologists, mineralogists, crystallography buffs, collectors of microscopes, and diatom specialists—all of them amateurs and all of them bursting with the need to talk about their specialties.

All this was a dizzying experience for me. After several solitary decades at the microscope, here I was surrounded by like-minded amateurs. It was as if I had run into several dozen clones of myself who had already done most of the things in microscopy I'd always fantasized about, had I but space enough and time.

I'd often wished, for instance, that I could learn more about those heroic old turn-of-the-century, all-brass microscopes of

the sort one imagines Sherlock Holmes peering into. Then I met an amateur, since deceased, who knew all there was to know about old 'scopes and whose collection included hundreds.

I had also long wished I knew enough about cameras to take good, sharp photographs of my favorite specimen slides. At the meetings, talking about the latest wrinkles in technique, were amateurs whose exquisitely detailed photomicrographs are exhibited right alongside those of top professionals.

Another example: I'd often thought what fun it would be to piece together a really comprehensive collection of slides prepared by the great old-time slide makers and to learn something about the lives of these remarkable craftsmen. Suddenly, here I was talking with John Prineas, a former Australian who works all day as a clinical neurologist doing multiple sclerosis research with electron microscopes, but whose avocation is collecting information on the great slide preparers and examples of their work. Many of the slides in his collection are still perfectly usable, though they date from the late 1700's.

POND LIFE

If my years as a solitary microscopist viewing widely different things had left me with some small idea of the beauty and complexity within the microworld, I was now to learn that I didn't know the half of it. I met a lean, bearded, 36-year-old English teacher named Tom Adams who shares my excitement over protozoa. But Adams has taken things a step further. For two years he ran an intensive check on conditions among the life forms—most of them microscopic—that inhabit a two-and-one half hectare pond some 15 kilometers from his house in Lawrenceville, New Jersey. Amiable Tom Adams has the biggest protozoan-culturing aquarium any amateur could want.

"So far," he told us one night while his project was still going on, "I've charted the seasonal fluctuations among more than 700 different forms of pond life. When the pond freezes over, I walk onto it and use my pick to chop through as much as 45 centimeters of ice ... so I can get at the protozoa underneath."

Listening to him, month after month during the project, the group came to share the excitement of Adams' year-round hunt. The last time I saw him, he said, "I'll turn my findings over to the Environmental Protection Agency, or one of the other groups in-

terested in seeing serious amateurs do studies of protozoa and their role in the ecological chain."

CHALLENGING THE EXPERTS

Then there is Joseph Burke, 81-year-old past-president of the Society. He works alone from morning till night in his top-floor office at the Staten Island Museum studying an algalike species of plant called the diatom. The shining, glassy, graceful skeletons of diatoms have fascinated dedicated amateurs for many generations now, and Burke is in the classic mold.

Back in the 1920's, Burke began boning up on diatoms in his square time. Eventually, he learned so much about them that he actually began to challenge the classification system set up by earlier renowned diatomists.

Now retired and a world figure even among professional diatomists, amateur

Thomas E. Adams collects protozoa in a net that sifts residue and allows living specimens to fall into a small bottle at the end of the net.

Phillip A. Harrington

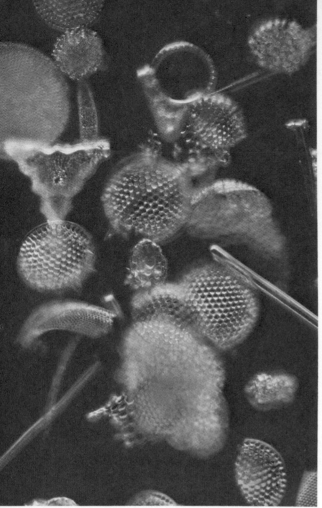

The delicate, glassy shells of diatoms are excellent subjects to study and admire under a microscope.

Microscopes come in many sizes and prices. The small one at left for about $35 is fine for beginners.

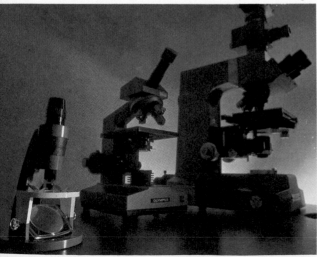

Burke works tirelessly on his thesis that given diatom species are not exactly the same the world over, but vary minutely from place to place. This research is just the sort of painstaking inquiry that seems pointless to most of us, but then suddenly turns out one day to have enormous practical implications—as when the oil companies found to their delight that some types of diatoms are highly useful as indicators of possible oil-bearing rock formations.

EQUIPMENT NUTS

Soon after joining the Society I signed up for one of its annual exhibits. A long hall was filled with microscopes set up to display members' pet projects.

There were gigantic, glistening, all-brass Victorian 'scopes, bristling with knurled adjustment wheels and looking like art objects. Then there were the formidable black-and-chrome present-day research microscopes, complete with an awesome array of accessory gadgets. For a budding equipment nut, that exhibition was heaven on earth.

My own display was a modest one I simply exhibited—through an excellent binocular 'scope I had bought second hand—a slide showing hippuric acid under polarized light. My "wrinkle" was that I had paid an optical repairman to replace my microscope's regular eyepiece with bulky telescope eyepieces. The result was an enormously wide-field "porthole" image that displayed the multihued crystals to stunning effect.

Near my table was Winston Clay, a retired businessman, showing tiny rock samples through his magnificent three-dimensional stereoscope. Such a 'scope is in effect two low-power microscopes mounted side by side and "toed in" so that each of the viewer's eyes sees the specimen from a slightly different angle. The result is something like looking at an undersea landscape of corals and other plant and animal life beneath the surface of the water.

And so it went from exhibit to exhibit: blood cells pouring through a frog's webbed foot; a horrific-looking cheese mite bristling with hairy, spiky legs; a hundred diatom skeletons carefully arranged by an old-time slide preparer in a rose-window pattern; and a late 19th-century photograph shrunk down optically by a Victorian-era slide maker till it was clearly visible only under a 100-power 'scope. (This technique foreshadowed the microdot later used by spies.)

When I burbled about the instruments and accessories to the Society's coffee-klatch gang (who'd all been there exhibiting), they nodded dourly. "Look, you don't want to get equipment-happy," one of them warned me. All of them nodded agreement, and of course they were right.

If you are willing to settle for modest magnification—say 50 or 100 power, which is plenty for the early stages of microscopy, or even for a lifetime of viewing—you can buy from one of the U.S.'s top optical "names" an excellent little beginner's microscope that costs less than $30. Add to that a $10 kit containing the paraphernalia for preparing your own slides, and you're off and winging.

TALKING WITH OTHER MICROMANIACS

In the years that followed the exhibition, I learned that there are other active microscopical societies in Philadelphia, Chicago, Los Angeles, and San Francisco. Abroad, England and Germany are the big amateur strongholds. The biggest British group is the Dickensian-sounding Quekett Microscopical Club. (The famed Royal Microscopical Society is now almost entirely professional.) In Europe there are active amateur societies in the German cities of Stuttgart, Hamburg, Mannheim, and Munich, and in Zurich, Switzerland, and Vienna, Austria. All share the facilities of the German-language journal *Mikrokosmos.*

Occasionally, someone from these overseas groups causes a stir by visiting the NYMS. E. P. Herlihy, of the Quekett Club, came over in the late 1960's and gave a charming, memorable account of his long, happy life at the microscope. He was then in his seventies. Several members, myself among them, still correspond with him occasionally, and every issue of the Quekett Club newsletter brings details of some ingenious demonstration Mr. Herlihy has given before the club in his special fields of interest—insect studies and polarizing and ultraviolet light effects. And in the NYMS newsletter,

Phillip A. Harrington

Joseph F. Burke, of New York, has been an ardent microscopist for more than half a century. His specialty is diatoms.

Imagine the patience it takes to arrange by means of a needle the many diatoms into an interesting and well balanced pattern.

Phillip A. Harrington

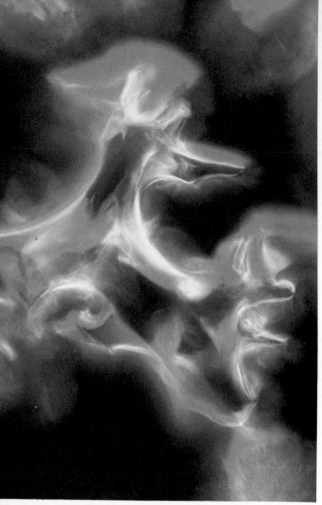

Phillip A. Harrington

The dyed spicules of the sponge skeleton make interesting subjects under the lenses of a microscope. Bath sponges do not have spicules.

which I edit, member Eric V. Gravé provides lively summary translations of articles appearing in *Mikrokosmos.*

SNOWFLAKES AND SCRATCHES

In all this talk of organized amateur activity, I don't mean to slight the "unorganized" amateur. It's just that it isn't easy to pin down details of their numbers and their interests. Many of them prefer to work alone, and others don't even know there are amateur societies. Every once in a while, though, one of these separated brethren explodes into view as when, in the early decades of the twentieth century a hermitlike Vermont farmer and amateur microscopist named Wilson Alwyn Bentley astonished scientists by doing invaluable pioneering, professional-level research on snowflakes. Bent-

ley's beautiful snowflake atlas is still a standard work.

Nowadays, Alexander Marshack, a one-time journalist and amateur, is causing a small revolution in paleontology by turning his stereomicroscopes on the dimly visible patterned scratches covering many prehistoric bones. Many of these bones—reindeer teeth, woolly mammoth tusks, and other bony remains have hitherto gathered dust in the world's museums. Paleontologists used to think the scratch markings were mere decorative patterns idly gouged and chipped out of the bones by cavemen.

But studying these bones—originally with a $15 stereomicroscope—Marshack has, since the mid-1960's, developed the startling thesis that these 30,000-year-old "scratches" were part of a complex symbol system consisting of some dozen separate notations that may be the early beginnings of the calendar, arithmetic, writing, and geometry as we know them. If he is right—and many highly regarded scholars think he is—prehistoric man was 15,000 to 30,000 years ago much more civilized and intellectually resourceful than anyone has till now suspected.

UNENDING WONDER

Original contributions or no, there will always be thousands of anonymous amateurs who, with no hope of fame or prizes, just like to sit in their garage or basement or attic workshops, gazing in wonder at the new vistas that open out constantly under the microscope. Fortunately, microscopy is an escalator that you can step onto at any age, no matter what your income, background, educational level, or previous condition of boredom. If my own experience is any sort of guide, it is an escalator you'll never want to step off □

📖 SELECTED READINGS

Adventures with a Microscope by Richard Headstrom. Dover 1977.

"Micro macabre: photography of insects using scanning electron microscope" by D. Sharf. *International Wildlife,* September 1977.

The Hidden World: The Story of Microscopic Life by Paul Villiard. School Book Service, 1975.

Guy Gillette/Photo Researchers

THE SCIENCE OF PHOTOGRAPHY

by Barbara Lobron

PHOTOGRAPHS are the threads that tie together the moments of our lives. Most of us have been posing for, gazing at, and taking them since birth. They record the personal events—the picnics and trips, holidays, birthdays, and graduations—and help tell us the news. They advertise products and reproduce legal documents. When run together in a projector to give the illusion of continuity, they entertain us as movies. When used in the study of the breakup of atoms or to capture light that has been analyzed by a spectroscope, they aid science. Via X rays, they record the interior parts of our body; at observatories, they bring us closer to the stars.

Photographs immortalize our heroes and heroines and keep fresh forever the glance of those we love. And more and more, they are used to express our personal vision, as creative photography has become a popular art form. Its technology is making this art form more accessible to everyone.

TWO SIMPLE FACTS

Any photograph is based on two simple scientific facts: 1. Light passing through a lens forms an image. 2. Light darkens certain substances.

In photography light rays reflected from the subject being photographed pass through a lens into a light-tight box, called a *camera.* These light rays affect the light-sensitive material that is on the film, which is at the other end of the camera. In this way, an image is recorded on the light-sensitive film. Later, the image is made visible and usable when it is treated with certain chemicals. The negative image that is produced is later printed on light-sensitive paper and appears as a positive image, or a *photograph.*

The first camera dates back before the tenth century—the *camera obscura* (Latin for "darkened chamber"). This camera was actually a small room with a hole in one wall. The hole allowed the light rays reflected off external objects to enter and strike the opposite wall, forming an inverted image of the object. An artist would then trace the inverted image on the wall. The modern camera works on the same principle as the *camera obscura,* but instead of the image being reflected on a wall, it is reflected and recorded on film.

BASIC PARTS

No matter how simple or sophisticated, all cameras have the same basic parts:

1. A light-tight box to keep unwanted light out and to serve as a frame to hold the other parts.

2. A lens to collect the light reflected from a subject that forms an image on the film.

3. A lens opening to control the amount of light reaching the film.

4. A shutter to control the length of time that light reaches the film. It keeps out all light until you take a picture.

5. A viewfinder, which lets you see what the camera "sees," and lets you frame your picture area.

6. A shutter release to open and close the shutter.

7. A film-advance mechanism to advance the film for the next picture.

THE SIMPLE CAMERA

The simplest kind of camera is called the viewfinder camera. It uses a small window for viewing and has a fixed-focus lens. It offers very limited focusing for close and distant pictures. In this class of cameras are the old Brownies, and most of the newer pocket-sized, instant-load cameras.

These cameras can take excellent pictures. They are not suitable for serious photography, however, because they usually lack the wide range of manual adjustments that allow for focus and exposure control. Also, such cameras do not allow for changing lenses.

The Instamatic-type camera is a simple aim-and-shoot camera with film that comes in instant-load cartridges. Such cartridges are simply dropped into the camera—no manual film threading is required. The other type of simple camera is the Polaroid, or instant-photo camera. Instead of having to

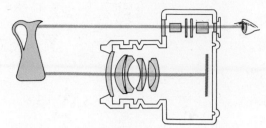

Viewfinder camera

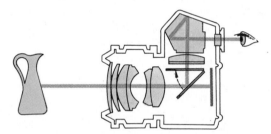

View camera

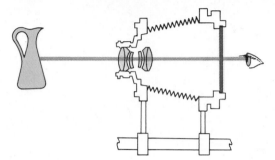

35mm single-lens reflex camera

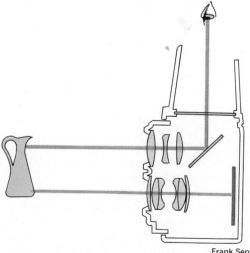

Frank Senyk

Twin-lens reflex camera

The development of a Polaroid color film takes place in the filmpack.

send film out to be processed, the picture develops *outside* the camera within seconds before your eyes. The secret of this camera is in the film, which is already packed with processing chemicals when you buy it. (Above are shown three stages in the developing process, which is automatic.)

THE VIEW CAMERA

The view camera is the pioneer camera and has hardly changed since its invention. It was originally called "view camera" because it was used to shoot "views" in the early days of photography.

It has a lens mounted in front, an accordianlike bellows in the middle, a back that holds large film, and a groundglass for viewing. The bellows is supported by two uprights that slide on a horizontal frame. One upright holds the lens, and the other holds a pane of groundglass, which can be replaced by a light-tight film holder when the exposure is to be made. The photographer composes his view on the groundglass, then he slides in the film when ready to take the picture.

The view camera is fairly heavy and must be set on a tripod. It is best used for panoramic views, architecture, and studio portraits. This kind of photography involves no motion. Another feature of the view camera is that it uses large film, which can be enlarged with better results than very small film.

THE REFLEX CAMERAS

The term "35mm SLR" refers to two factors: film size and the viewing/focusing system. A 35mm camera is one that uses film about 35 millimeters wide. SLR—which stands for "single-lens reflex"—refers to the other factor: the subject is viewed through the taking lens of the camera. This means that you see in the viewfinder almost exactly what will appear on the film.

The SLR has a mirror that reflects the image through the lens up into the viewfinder—hence the term "reflex." When you snap the picture, the mirror moves out of the way. This opens a path for the light to travel to the back of the camera and expose the film. The characteristic click you hear when you take a picture with an SLR is the sound of the mirror movement.

The 35mm SLR is sometimes called a *system* camera because it offers a system of interchangeable lenses that can be used with that camera. In this way, when you look through the viewfinder, you look through the lens of your choice.

Another type of reflex camera is the twin-lens reflex (TLR). The TLR has two external lenses and a fixed mirror. The top lens, with the aid of the mirror, is for viewing. The bottom lens is for taking the picture. Viewing a subject on the 60mm x 60mm groundglass viewer is more accurate and precise than composing through a 35mm

Short (28mm) wide-angle lens
© Judith Lucretia Wright

Medium (50mm) normal-angle lens
© Judith Lucretia Wright

Long (135mm) telephoto lens
© Judith Lucretia Wright

360° lens, or fisheye
Hidalgo, Top Realities

viewfinder. But the TLR is bulkier and slower to use.

LENSES

The lens is the eye of the camera. It is made of optical glass that bends light to form the image. It transmits just enough light during a set interval to make an image of the subject on the film.

A lens must be focused. Though your eyes automatically adjust, most camera lenses do not. For a sharp picture of an object, the lens must be moved to a certain distance from the film. To focus on distant objects, the lens is moved back closer to the film. For nearer objects, it is moved forward, away from the film.

A lens is described partly by its focal length. A lens has a certain *focal length*. This characteristic is the distance the lens must be from the film to give a sharp image of a distant object, when the lens is focused at infinity.

Lenses come in normal, short, and long focal lengths. A lens with a focal length of 50 millimeters is a normal lens for a 35mm camera. It has an angle of view of about 47 degrees. When you look through the viewfinder while using this lens, you will see about what you would with your own eyes. It is this normal lens that is most often purchased with the 35mm camera.

The focal length of a lens is related to its *angle of view*. A lens with an angle of view much greater than 47 degrees is considered *wide-angle*. It lets you get a bigger view into the frame. Such a lens shows things small within a wide field of view. It can take in whole landscapes. The lower the mm number (focal length), the broader the horizon will be.

Long lenses act like telescopes. They have a narrow angle of view—much less than 47 degrees—and they "see things large." They produce a close-up of a distant object through magnification. It is the ideal lens with which to shoot a far-off football player or the tiger in the wilds. The bigger the mm number (focal length), the bigger the image.

THE LENS AND PERSPECTIVE

In photographing, the choice of lens determines the *perspective,* or the way things look from a given viewpoint. Perspective is concerned with the changes in apparent size of objects at varying distances from each other and the observer. A psychological notion of closeness is implied by bigness, while distance is implied by smallness.

The different ways that normal, short, and long lenses show things in pictures are due largely to the different distances of the camera from the subject. If all three lenses are used at the same position from the subject, the same view with the same perspective will appear in each picture. But a subject that fills up the telephoto picture will be smaller in the normal-lens picture and tiny in the wide-angle one.

Using a normal lens to change perspective can create difficulties. For example, if you move in close to emphasize the foreground subject, you may lose a large part of the background and also distort the subject. Moving back to bring near and far objects into their proper perspective may cause you to lose touch with the subject matter in the foreground—it looks too small, too far away.

Wide-angle and telephoto lenses help with these problems. Wide angles will expand the angle of view, especially when shooting interiors. They can also make the foreground subject matter more important by letting you move in closer. The use of telephotos, on the other hand, results in a flattened perspective because the distance between foreground and background subjects appears greatly reduced. Telephotos are also used for controlling the perspective in portraiture that a normal lens would distort. For example, when you move in close with a

normal lens, undue attention is focused on the nose. But shooting further back with a telephoto reduces the prominence of the nose and restores to normal the other size relationships of the eyes and ears.

We have seen that a lens is described by its focal length and angle of view. A lens is also described by its "speed." The more light-gathering ability a lens has, the "faster" it is considered to be. A fast lens is commonly used under low-light conditions. If a lens has good light-gathering ability, a faster shutter speed can be used, which will produce a sharper image with a hand-held camera. Hence that lens is considered to be "fast." The lens speed, or light-gathering ability, depends upon its diameter and its focal length.

How fast a lens is needed depends upon the light available. During daylight hours, there is enough light so that the faster lens would make no difference. Shooting indoors, as in the subdued light in a cathedral, the faster the lens, the better.

THE LENS APERTURE

In front of the lens system is a circular opening, or *aperture,* whose size determines the amount of light that will reach the film. The size of this opening is controlled by an adjustable mask called the *diaphragm.* The numbers on the lens rim indicate the relative size of the aperture. These numbers are called *f-stops.* The lower f-stop numbers refer to larger aperture openings, which expose film to more light. The higher f-stop numbers refer to smaller aperture openings, which let in less light.

Illustration by Diana Coleman

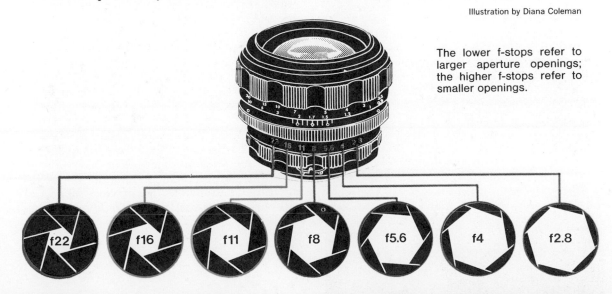

The lower f-stops refer to larger aperture openings; the higher f-stops refer to smaller openings.

Left to right: photos made with f/4, f/5.6, and f/11 openings, at same shutter speed.

Opening up means letting more light in by going from a higher f-stop to a lower f-stop. *Stopping down* means letting less light in by going from a lower f-stop to a higher one. As the aperture is opened up (higher f-stop to lower f-stop) the light that is let in doubles with each f-stop. And the reverse is true in stopping down. The following table gives the standard f-stops and relative speeds.

	f-stop	Relative speed
small opening	f/45	1X "slowest"
	f/32	2X
	f/22	4X
	f/16	8X
	f/11	16X
	f/8	32X
	f/5.6	64X
	f/4	128X
	f/2.8	256X
large opening	f/2	512X
	f/1.4	1024X "fastest"

(left margin: opening up; right margin of second column: stopping down)

In combination with the other exposure variable, the shutter speed, correspondingly greater exposures would have to be given. For example, if it is 1 second at f/11, it would be 2 seconds at f/16, and 4 seconds at f/22.

APERTURE AND DEPTH OF FIELD

Exposure control is not the only function of f-stops. The size of the aperture controls the *depth of field*. This is the amount of space in front of and behind the main subject that is in acceptably sharp focus. The larger the aperture (smaller-numbered f-stop) the shallower the depth of field. The smaller the aperture, the greater the depth of field.

The area in focus varies according to two other factors.

1. The camera-to-subject distance: With a particular lens set to a specific aperture, the depth of field decreases as you approach the subject. It increases as you back off to a greater distance. It also decreases if the lens is focused closer and increases as it is focused farther back.

2. The focal length: The longer the lens (telephoto), the shallower the depth of field. The shorter the lens (wide-angle lens), the greater the depth of field.

The photographer uses depth of field for certain effects. By using "selective focus," the background can be thrown out of focus to emphasize the sharply focused subject. Where both foreground and background are interesting, great depth of field would be preferred.

SHUTTER SPEED

The control of light entry by the aperture is only half the story. Not much could be done with a lens if there wasn't a *shutter* to let light into the camera for a certain amount of time. Like each f-stop, each shutter speed doubles or halves the exposure at the next shutter-speed setting. Standard speeds are as follows: 1 second, ½ sec., ¼ sec., ⅛, 1/15, 1/30, 1/60, 1/125, 1/250, 1/500, 1/1000. What you see on the shutter dial, however, is the denominator only—1, 2, 4, 8, and so on.

Like f-stops, shutter speeds also produce photographic effects besides controlling the exposure. A very low shutter speed shows motion through space, that is, the path of the motion. It does this more clearly than it shows the moving object. This means that the moving object will appear blurred if a slow shutter speed is used. For example, a ½-to-1 second shutter speed will show the path of movement of tall blowing grass or swaying branches.

The faster the shutter speed, the less blur. A very fast one "freezes" motion, while showing the moving object sharply. Action moving across your field of vision can also be stopped if you follow the moving subject with your camera as the shutter is pressed.

This technique is called *panning*. It keeps the moving subject in focus and blurs the background, which looks as though it were whizzing by. In this way a great feeling of motion is conveyed.

F-STOP AND SPEED EQUAL EXPOSURE

Exposure is the amount of light that gets to the film. It depends mainly on the light intensity and the time it is allowed to act on the film. An ideal exposure is one in which the negative film includes as much detail as possible in both the shadow and highlight areas.

In setting the exposure, the photographer must decide whether the image is to be controlled by the aperture or by the shutter. When depth of field is most important, pick the f-stop first, then find a shutter speed for the correct exposure. When motion is most important, pick the shutter speed first, then stop down or open up for the correct exposure.

An exposure is made with the aid of an *exposure,* or *light, meter.* This is either built into the camera or separate from it and hand-held. It measures the scene's brightness in terms that can be used by the camera. The light meter contains a photovoltaic cell, which converts the light that strikes it into electric current. The brighter the light, the stronger the current. The amount of current is indicated by a moving needle, or it may be expressed as a digital readout.

Nearly all 35mm SLR cameras have built-in, through-the-lens light meters. In a camera with *match-needle* (manual) exposure control, you adjust the lens aperture and/or the shutter speed until the two needles coincide. With the more advanced 35mm SLRs, the matching is done automatically by the camera, after the user sets the aperture or shutter speed. The most recent development is one where both the shutter and aperture are pre-determined by means of a program within the camera system.

FILM

Film is a light-sensitive material that records an image. The material is made of silver and potassium salts, which are held to a cellulose-acetate base by means of a gelatin emulsion. Exposure to light turns part of the light-sensitive material darker than other parts that receive less light. The more light there is, the darker the tone.

Films are made with a specific sensitiv-

Diana Coleman

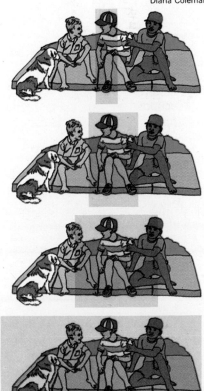

Least depth is with long lens, wide aperture, and close distance.

You get much more depth with a shorter focal length lens.

You get still more depth using a smaller lens aperture.

And you get the most depth if your subject is farther away.

ity to light, which is called *film speed*. The speed is measured on a scale originally set by the American Standards Association, hence the speeds are referred to as ASA numbers. The higher the number, the more sensitive it is to light. If a film is very sensitive, a faster shutter speed can be used with it. Therefore it is known as "fast" film. ASA ratings use an arithmetical progression—400 being twice as fast as 200 and so on.

Film speeds fall into the following groups: *slow* is ASA 32 and under; *medium* is ASA 40 to 200; *fast* is ASA 400 and over. Slow film is used when maximum sharpness and details are desired. It will highlight texture and give full contrast. Medium-speed films are excellent general purpose films, particularly when there is enough light, as in outdoor daylight conditions. High-speed films are used when there is a minimum of light.

The film's ASA number is used to key the exposure meter to existing light conditions. People who use 35mm cameras must manually set the film-speed dial on the camera to match the ASA number of the film. Those who use 110mm cameras depend on the film cartridge to automatically set the film speed of the camera.

Color-slide film comes in an ASA range of 25 to 400 and is called *transparency* film. Most color-slide film is indicated on the film box by the word "chrome" used as a suffix, as in Kodachrome.

Color prints are made with a color-negative emulsion, available in speeds ranging from ASA 80 to 400. They are indicated on the film box by the word "color" used as a suffix, as in Kodacolor.

PUSHING FILM

Both black-and-white and color films can be "pushed." This means that the film is rated and exposed at a film speed that is higher than the original ASA number set by the manufacturer. "Pushing" is usually done in order to make it possible to photograph in low-light conditions. The photographer simply sets the film-speed dial at a higher number. For example, the black-and-white film called Tri-X, which is rated by the manufacturer at ASA 400, can be pushed to a new film speed of 800 EI (EI means Exposure Index, or the film-speed rating that has been determined by the user). The photographer simply inserts the Tri-X film into the camera, and sets the film-speed dial at 800. She or he then shoots the entire role at this film-speed. When the roll of film is ready for processing, the processor must be told that the film was pushed to 800.

LIGHT AND FILTERS

In terms of natural lighting, the main source of concern to the photographer is the sun. The moving sun during the day determines the angle of the light and the types of shadow created. The early and later hours, when the sun is low on the horizon, provide a better angle of light: shadows are long, with a soft quality, and the contrasts are soft. At midday the sun is bright, shadows are black so that contrasts are strong. Subjects are then rendered in harsh, flat tones with contrasts that are unflattering.

A similar trip through the day will show the sun's effect in a color photograph. A few minutes before the sun appears over the horizon, the color has a bluish cast. As the sun rises, the color becomes reddish. But the reds disappear as the sun reaches its zenith. Because noon sunlight is bluish, skin tones are not flatteringly rendered. As the sun begins to go down, there is a shift towards the red again. The minute the sun touches the horizon, brilliant hues of reds, blues, and purples briefly fill the sky.

A knowledge of the direction from which the sun lights up a subject is very important in photography. Here are the basic variations: *Front lighting* means the light source strikes the subject from the front—the sun is at the photographer's back. This pro-

A filter is a colored, transparent material.

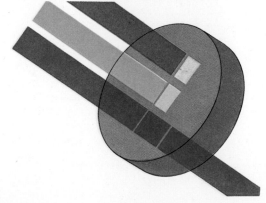

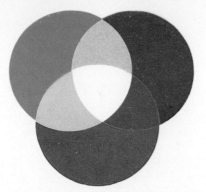

Light consists of three primary colors—red, blue, and green. When mixed, they produce white.

duces a uniformly lit picture. However, it will have few shadows, which are needed to create a feeling of depth. Front lighting picks up little detail and texture, so that the picture is flat.

Side lighting means the light strikes the subject at an angle; that is, from the left or right. Side lighting reveals texture and creates a certain amount of modeling. The highlights and the larger shadows that are produced create more depth and contrast. This makes the subjects more dimensional.

Back lighting means the light source is behind the subject. This places the subject in shadow with little frontal detail. The problem in this case is to obtain an adequate exposure for the front of the subject to avoid producing a silhouette with a halo of light around it.

Artificial light is light supplied by something other than the sun or the moon. The electronic flash gun is most ideally suited to use with a 35mm camera. Modern cameras have built-in switches to pass an electric current to the flash gun (or flash bulb) precisely when the shutter is open.

There is a factor in the use of any artificial light source called the inverse-square law. It states that as you double the distance from the subject, the light on the subject falls off in direct proportion to that distance squared. Therefore the greater the distance you are from the subject, the greater the exposure needed.

To determine proper exposure for flash, you need to know the distance to the subject, the film speed, and the *guide number* of the flash gun or bulb (a value assigned by its manufacturer). To find the correct f-stop, the guide number is divided by the distance to the subject. For example, suppose you are using 100 ASA film, the given guide number is 250, and the distance is 15 feet. You divide 250 by 15, and get 16. Therefore, the f-stop would be f/16.

Black-and-white films are sensitive to all the colors that make up sunlight. In a range of gray tones, black-and-white films reproduce the light-and-dark values of colored objects more or less as the eye sees them. If you don't want to reproduce things as they look, a *filter* will change the light that strikes the film.

A filter is a colored, transparent material. When placed over the lens, it alters the density of color of the subject by absorbing certain colors and letting others through. A filter of any color will "darken" its complementary color in the picture and "brighten" its own color as translated into the gray tones. For example, an orange filter will darken a blue sky, and a red filter will lighten skin blemishes.

Because filters work by subtracting portions of the light from the subject, they prevent the film from receiving its full exposure. Therefore, when a filter is used, the photographer must open up the lens aperture or use a slower shutter speed. Filters have a *filter factor,* which is expressed as a number. For example, a factor of 2 requires that the exposure be doubled to get a normal negative.

DEVELOPING

The "latent image" formed during the exposure of the film has to be developed to be seen. *Developing* is the process of making that image visible and capable of being used as a negative. During a chemical process, the exposed silver salts on the film are converted to metallic silver.

After the film is removed from the cam-

Necessary supplies for developing black and white film. These are easy to obtain.

Daniel Hunter

Equalizing the temperature of all chemicals.

Winding film on stainless steel reel.

Pouring chemicals into film container.

Agitation of film with chemicals.

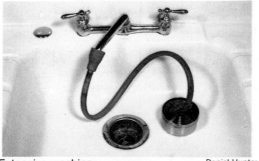

Extensive washing.

Daniel Hunter

era, it is placed in a tank, and the developer is added. It consists of one or more developing agents and other chemicals that regulate the process. The developing agents—usually a combination of Metol and hydroquinone—bring out the image. Whereas the initial light exposure determines *density,* the development process determines *contrast.* Therefore, the longer a film is left in the developer, the more contrast is built up. After it is developed, the film is rinsed in water to stop the action of the developer. It is then bathed in a fixer, called "hypo." This makes the image permanent by dissolving the unused silver salts that were not exposed. Then the film must be thoroughly washed in running water and hung up to dry.

In this way a negative is produced. It is an image in which dark stands for light and light for dark. The negative is usually not meant to be seen. It is a means to an end—the positive print.

PRINTING

The print is made by passing light through a negative onto *printing paper.* Such paper is coated with a gelatin that contains light-sensitive silver salts, similar to that used for negatives, but less sensitive.

If a print is the same size as the negative, it is called a *contact print.* The printing paper is pressed tightly against the negative in a glass frame. After being exposed to the light of an electric bulb for a few seconds, it is developed, rinsed, fixed, and washed. This process is done in a series of trays under a yellow "safelight," which does not harm the emulsion.

Prints larger than the size of the emulsion are made by *projection.* They are enlarged by an enlarger, a device that works like a turned-around camera. Strong light is thrown on the negative, and a lens projects the negative image to any desired size on the printing paper. It is then processed in the same way as a contact print.

COLOR

If you want to know what is happening in color photography, you need some knowledge of the way six colors are related. Light consists of three *primary* colors—red, blue, and green. When these are added together from separate sources, white light is created. Red, blue, and green are also described as *additive* colors because they must be added one to another to achieve an effect.

Color film is similar to a black-and-white film containing three layers of emulsion. Each emulsion layer is sensitive to only one of the primary colors. The bottom layer is sensitized to red but not to green. The middle layer is sensitized to green and slightly to blue but not to red. Next comes a yellow-dyed gelatin, which prevents blue light from reaching either of the lower levels. On top is a blue-sensitive emulsion.

During the developing process, dyes are deposited in direct proportion to the amount of exposure received by each of the three layers. Once the dye is deposited, all metallic silver and remaining silver salts are removed by bleaching and fixing. The result is a color negative.

In an enlarger, the color negative is then projected onto a sensitized color printing paper. The three primary emulsion layers of the color printing paper are in the reverse order of those of the color film. Since almost all color negatives require some kind of color correction when printed, certain filters are inserted in the enlarger's light beam to adjust the color as desired.

So far we have been referring to color-negative-to-positive print process. In the slide, or transparency, process, a positive image—not a negative—is produced at the time the film is initially developed. Kodachrome slide film consists of a piece of acetate that is coated with three emulsions sensitive respectively to blue, green, and red light. Between the blue-sensitive and green-sensitive layers is a layer of yellow dye, which acts as a filter to subtract the blue light and thus prevent it from reaching the other layers.

The three emulsion layers are developed to negatives, and are dyed. By special technique these three negatives are reversed to positives. The result is a transparency, which can be projected for viewing or from which a color print can be made.

FUTURE TRENDS

The direction of camera and lens development indicates ever smaller bodies, com-

Gloria Laposka

Side lighting produces depth and strong contrast.

pletely programmed automatic exposure, and auto-focusing lenses. Preserving color transparencies now in existence and creating new color emulsions for prints and transparencies that would prevent them from fading with age are two more challenges that seek solution in the future, as well as improvements in the present levels of technology in instant color imaging systems, both still and movie. A complete substitute for silver in film and papers is more than likely; electronic newcomers based on the principles of TV may become a viable alternative to the photographic materials and process as we know them today.

Some Tips For Taking Better Pictures

1. Keep your camera steady. If shooting slower than 1/60th of a second, you need steadying.

2. Have one center of interest and avoid cluttered backgrounds.

3. Including a second subject may make the photo more interesting.

4. Move in close. Keep the subject in the foreground. Take close-ups when possible. Photos will be more interesting if the subject fills the frame.

5. Have your subjects doing something natural instead of staring at the camera.

6. Use an interesting foreground such as a tree, arch, gate for framing your pictures.

7. Put scenes in perspective by adding people. People in the foreground increase the feeling of depth and size, when shooting distant scenes.

8. Don't always put the subject in the middle.

In this camera ultrasonic waves from the camera strike the subject and return to automatically focus the lens.

9. Test your view horizontally and vertically to see which way works best.

10. Use lines for interest and unity. Have the natural lines such as a road or fence lead the eye up to the center of interest. Vertical lines are strong; horizontal lines are placid; diagonal lines are dynamic.

11. Be aware of background. Avoid mergers of subject and background. Get subjects away from busy backgrounds. If you can't, open up the lens to blur the background.

12. Think of the angles for shooting. Shooting from a low angle provides an uncluttered sky background.

13. Consider the horizon line. Don't cut your picture in half by having the horizon in the middle. A low horizon accents spaciousness, a high one suggests closeness. Make sure the horizon is level.

14. Give a moving object plenty of visual space in the direction it is moving.

15. Make sure tonalities of subject and background contrast, especially when using black-and-white film.

16. The main subject should appear brighter than anything else because the eye is pulled toward the brightest object.

17. For portraiture use a slightly longer-than-normal focal-length lens to overcome an unpleasant distortion of the subject at a close focusing range.

18. Don't lop off arms or legs because of bad framing.

19. The closer you get to your subject, the larger any part of the body will appear. If you don't want big hands and small heads, pay attention how features appear in the viewfinder.

20. The eyes are the focus of the face, so focus on the eyes.

21. Color-negative film is better if slightly overexposed. Color-reversal film is better if slightly underexposed.

22. Avoid shiny reflections, or glare spots, by placing the camera at an angle to any shiny surfaces, such as windows or eyeglasses.

23. When using a built-in flash, keep the subject away from walls, or you will get a strong shadow on one side of the subject.

24. When the sun is bright, photograph your subject in open shade, which flatters people.

DIGITAL RECORDS

by Bernard Wysocki, Jr.

PICTURE yourself relaxing at home a few years from now. You reach into the record cabinet and pull out a small sheet of plastic about as big as a slice of toast. You then put this "record," containing millions of bits of computer data, on a playing machine that reads the computer code with a low-power laser beam. Push a button and sit back and listen.

The sensation will be so close to actually being in a concert hall that it will make your present expensive stereo or quadraphonic rig sound muffled in contrast. What's more, some computerized or "digital," records will be capable of playing uninterruptedly for two-and-a-half hours. That would be long enough for a full-length opera on one side alone.

Prototypes of this futuristic gear already exist. More than 20 manufacturers in Japan, the United States, and Europe are racing to bring the new technology to a stage suitable for the consumer market by the early or mid-1980's.

The development of digital records has been likened to such record-industry breakthroughs as the introduction of electrically made commercial records in 1925 and the switch from 78 rpm shellac records to vinyl LP disks in the 1950's.

EVEN HIGHER FI

This system of recording sound has the ability to capture extreme high and low notes with no distortion. Furthermore, there is almost complete freedom from hiss and other mechanical noises such as wow and flutter. This ability sets digital recording apart from conventional, or analog, recording.

Conventional recording gear works much like a telephone. Sound waves are transformed into corresponding electronic waveforms. Then they are later turned back into sound with the aid of amplifiers and loudspeakers.

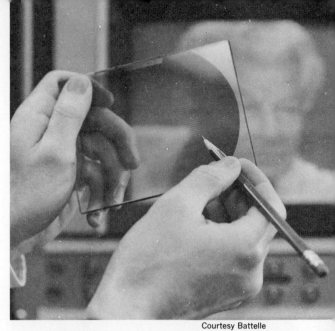

This digital record is a sequence of micron-size dots and spaces along a curved path on a photosensitive medium.

But the waveform inevitably undergoes changes, with even the finest of conventional equipment. There is difficulty making clean, realistic reproductions of sudden loud sounds, such as crashing cymbals. There is a slight "wow-wow" sound in the bass notes, and a tinny sound often colors recorded piano music. Also, hiss and other noises stemming from the recording process itself tend to obtrude.

THE DIGITAL RECORDER

Because computer-based equipment works on entirely different principles, it eliminates a lot of these deficiencies. A digital recorder measures the waveform of music thousands of times each second and assigns a numerical value to each one of these thousands of segments. Each numerical value is encoded as a stream of electronic pulses. The original sound is remembered as numerical signals on a plastic sheet, or memory bank. Then a "digital" playback machine calls back the numbers to recreate, or reassemble, the musical notes precisely as they were originally recorded.

This system is known in recording circles as "pulse-code modulation," or PCM for short. It has been used for years by the British Broadcasting Corporation (BBC) to transmit broadcasts from London to remote broadcasting centers in the British Isles.

Minnesota Mining and Manufacturing

The Cleveland Symphony Orchestra

The Cleveland Symphony Orchestra has been recorded with digital-recording equipment, which produces an extremely faithful reproduction.

Company, a pioneer in the development of digital recording, has drawn heavily upon BBC's expertise in a joint research effort to develop its PCM system. The new 3M machine is so sensitive and records so faithfully that it can detect the sound of a squeaky piano pedal amid the thunder of a rousing concerto, according to audio experts at the St. Paul-based company. In one test, the machine picked up the sound of a guitar rubbing against a musician's body as he played.

Obviously, the more often a musical waveform is measured, the more faithfully the original music is recreated. Minnesota Mining says its machine measures, or records, at a rate of 50,000 numbers a second. Each number is made up of 16 binary digits, or bits, recorded as minute magnetic points on the tape. This means there can be 800,000 separate magnetic bits in every 6.25 square centimeter of tape. The tape itself moves through the machine at a rate of 113 centimeters per second. Therefore, in a standard tape there are more data bits stored than are in the memory systems of many computers.

EDITING THE TAPE

Modern record making is a complex, many layered process. After a musical performance is recorded on tape, the tape itself is copied and recopied many times as sound engineers tinker with the original sound, editing out musicians' mistakes, dubbing in new sections, enhancing some sections and dampening others. Inevitably, there is some degeneration of the original signal. Thus there is a little less fidelity as copies are made from copies. But digital recording eliminates this problem; the hundredth generation of a tape is exactly the same quality as the original.

HYBRID DISKS

Even now, consumers are getting a partial sampling of the new sound through the medium of hybrid disks. These can be played on conventional record players but are recorded by digital methods. Several small record companies in the U.S. have turned out a handful of these high-priced, high-quality hybrids. In Japan, Nippon Columbia has been making them for more than five years, and now has more than 150 listings under its Denon label. Some of these are now being imported into the U.S.

There are some problems, however, with

Ressmayer/Sygma

A digital record is also available, with Stephen Stills playing his well-liked songs.

the present PCM hybrids. Their dynamic range is so much broader than that of conventional records that the sudden bursts of amplitude in the recording can actually damage low-powered stereo rigs. Also, to be compatible with present-day record players, the final step in making a digital hybrid is to convert it into a conventional record. If the pressing of the record isn't of the finest quality, much of the digital fidelity advantage will be lost.

Therefore, the hi-fi industry is looking

What a song looks like in a digital format, is shown below. The information-bit diameters are about 1 micron with a density of about 50,000,000 bits per square centimeter. The advantage the optical method has over the traditional magnetic method is increased density of information. The Battelle digital record is stationary with a moving scanner.

Courtesy Battelle

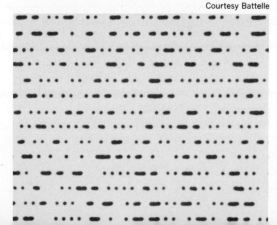

far beyond the hybrid recordings now coming on the market. The next step is to translate the computer code from computer tapes to consumer gear—records, tape, and hardware that use digital technology themselves. Only then will the fullest extent of the expanded sound be available to consumers in their homes.

The Battelle system, developed by Battelle Northwest, a unit of Battelle Memorial Institute, in Columbus, Ohio, may be typical of what's likely to come. The computer code from the digital tape recorder is translated onto a photo-sensitive plate in a Morse-code type pattern of light spots and dark spots. A laser beam then reads the spots, reassembles the digital code and turns the code back into music through conventional amplifiers and speakers. The laser never makes physical contact with the record, thereby reducing extraneous noise and eliminating wear and tear □

SELECTED READINGS

"Now, digital records." *Newsweek,* January 29, 1979.

"The digital revolution" by George Tlamsa. *Rolling Stone,* January 25, 1979.

The voice analyzer is a new kind of lie detector because it detects psychological stress. It does not evaluate stress, as one of its names implies.

Dektor

VOICE ANALYZERS

by Romaine Bamford

FOR hundreds and even thousands of years people have been interested in finding ways of determining whether someone is lying or telling the truth. One ancient Chinese test forced a subject to chew a mouthful of dry rice powder and then to spit it out. If the rice powder was still dry, the subject was pronounced guilty of lying. The idea behind the test was that lying causes physiological stress that affects the autonomic nervous system in such a way that the salivary glands do not function normally and dry food—in this case, the rice powder—is not moistened as it is chewed.

Does this Chinese method sound too simple? Well, today's methods of lie detection—some using highly sophisticated technology—are based on the same principle as the old Chinese test—namely, that lying produces stress or tension in the person lying and that this stress is manifested physiologically in a number of ways that can be measured and recorded.

NEW BREED OF LIE DETECTOR

The polygraph, invented in the 1920's, was the first of the modern line of lie-detecting devices. The polygraph works by recording a subject's blood pressure, heart and respiration rate, and skin conductivity as the subject is being questioned. As the subject's interrogation proceeds, fluctuations in the various body measurements are assumed to indicate varying degrees of stress. The trained polygraph operator then interprets the stress readings and gives an opinion as to whether the subject is lying in his or her response to certain questions. Although many question the accuracy of the polygraph, it has nonetheless become standard equipment for many police and military units.

The voice analyzer is the new breed of lie detector. It is also called a voice-stress analyzer and a psychological-stress evaluator (PSE). Like the polygraph, the voice analyzer works by recording stress. The indices of stress in the voice analyzer are not, however, heart or breathing rate, but rather are minute variations in a subject's voice pattern.

Unlike the polygraph, the voice analyzer does not need to be wired to the subject's body and can, in fact, be used without the subject's knowledge. The voice analyzer is also less bulky and simpler to use than the polygraph. Any talking a subject does—a telephone call, a job interview, a conversation—can be taped and analyzed later without the subject's knowledge.

VOICE TREMORS

When a person speaks, the sound of his or her voice is made up of many different vibrations including a particular one called a microtremor. Under conditions of stress, the frequency of microtremors increases. This is inaudible to the human ear but can be recorded mechanically. In a test situation the sound of the subject's voice is recorded on tape and fed into an electronic processor, which then separates the microtremors from the other voice vibrations. Changes in the frequency of microtremors are registered as changes in the levels of electrical energy and shown quite simply as a number on a display panel or in some models as a chart showing a stylus-traced fluctuation pattern.

The voice analyzer was invented as a result of a search, carried out by U.S. Army intelligence officers during the Vietnam War, for an alternative to the polygraph, preferably something that could be used without the subject's knowledge. It was Lt. Col. Allan Bell, an intelligence officer with a background in electronics, who established the fact that microtremors in the voice are altered by stress. With colleague Lt. Col. Charles McQuiston, a polygraph expert, he set out to design a device that was sensitive enough to record and measure the tiny vocal fluctuations that indicate stress. The result was the psychological-stress evaluator (PSE).

USES

Most voice analyzers today are bought for use in private industry and retailing. They are used to screen potential employees with the hope of weeding out thieves and others who might possibly turn out to be undesirable employees.

A number of law enforcement agencies in the United States use voice analyzers to help in criminal investigations. Although the results of voice analyzer tests cannot be accepted as evidence in a court of law, a number of authorities claim to find them effective, especially in producing confessions from suspects. It seems that when a skillful voice analyzer operator presents a suspect with apparent "proof" of his or her guilt as determined by the test, the suspect may break down and confess to the crime. Another advantage is that people seem more willing to undergo a voice analyzer test than a polygraph test.

WHAT HAPPENS

What happens in a voice analyzer test? Let's take as an example a test designed to see if job applicants have filled out their application forms truthfully and to find out if any of them have had problems with alcohol or drug addiction or a record of theft from previous employers. A typical test would contain three types of questions:

1) *Emotionally irrelevant questions.* These are questions that are not going to produce stress in the subject. They are designed to get the subject to relax, to familiarize him or her with the test procedure, and to reduce the situational stress that he or she may be experiencing because of the test itself. Such questions cover ordinary aspects of a subject's life and might include "Is you name John Doe?" ... "Do you live in Danbury, Connecticut?" ... "Is today Monday?" and so on.

2) *Control questions.* These are designed to induce a low level of stress, which the examiner can use as a basis for comparison. The type of question asked might produce a "white lie" for an answer. For instance, the examiner might ask "Do you ever lie to your husband? ... Did you ever steal anything valuable as a child? ... Have you ever had such a bad thought that you were afraid to tell anyone about it?

3) *Relevant questions.* These make up the most important part of the test because they are the questions that apply directly to the job. Thus, in our test situation, the examiner might ask "Do you have a heavy drinking problem? ... Do you ever take hard drugs? ... Have you ever been fired from a job? ... Have you ever stolen from an employer? ... Was your previous salary really as high as you have said?

If while answering the relevant questions the subject's stress level rises significantly above the base level established by asking the control questions, this supposedly indicates that the answer is not a truthful one.

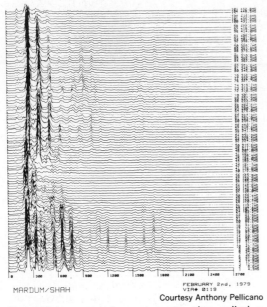

MARDUM/SHAH

FEBRUARY 2nd, 1979
VIA◆ Ø119

Courtesy Anthony Pellicano

Pictured is a sound spectogram, also called a voice print. It is a recording of the former Shah of Iran saying the word *mardum*, which means "people's" in English.

At the end of the test the examiner goes through it with the subject and gives him or her a chance to explain why answers to certain questions indicated a high level of stress. Especially in cases of employee theft, it is at this point that the guilty person often confesses the action, particularly if the examiner can handle the situation skillfully.

HOW ACCURATE?

Just how accurate and reliable are voice analyzers as lie-detecting devices? Compared with the polygraph, whose accuracy is by no means well established, studies have shown that voice analyzers are accurate in only about 50 to 60 per cent of cases involving actual criminal suspects whose guilt or innocence was finally established by confession or trial. In other words, as far as accuracy in predicting guilt or innocence, the voice analyzers scored little better than chance.

There seems little doubt that a voice analyzer can pick out a guilty suspect among a number of suspects. But it does appear that the machine has a disturbing tendency to pick out innocent suspects as well and to identify them as being guilty when, in fact, they are not. Bearing this in mind, it is easy to understand the critics of analyzers who are quick to point out its potential for abuse.

INVASION OF PRIVACY

Each year thousands of employees and job applicants are submitted to lie-detecting sweeps by voice analyzers. Failure to cooperate in taking the tests, let alone producing unsatisfactory answers to the questions asked, can be punished by dismissal or transferal to a different job. Since the sweeps are not always the result of a specific incident, they are seen by some as undesirable and unfair and as an intrusion of the so-called truth machine into the everyday lives of U.S. citizens. The U.S. Congress is considering legislation that would effectively ban the use of these devices by employers.

THE SHAPE OF THINGS TO COME

In spite of the controversy over the use of voice analyzers and other lie-detecting equipment, there are even more ideas for lie-detecting devices in the pipeline. It is already possible to buy for about $1,500 a cigarette-pack-sized voice analyzer that fits easily into a desk drawer or attache case or can be attached to a telephone. Its inventor, Rick Bennett, has plans to produce a pocket-sized and even wristwatch model.

Research is also being done into using the pitch of the voice, eye movements, and variations in face temperature as means of measuring stress. And the Israelis have a remote-control device, already in use at border crossings and airports, which indicates stress by measuring stomach palpitations caused by stress-induced rapid breathing.

But no matter how technologically sophisticated these gadgets become, they all depend on measuring levels of physiological stress and all need a trained operator to interpret the findings and give a judgment. And that is where there is room for serious error □

📖 SELECTED READINGS

"Detecting consumers' fibs; voice-pitch research," research by Consumers Response Corp. *Human Behavior,* April 1978.

"The new truth machines" by Berkeley Rice. *Psychology Today,* June 1978.

MAINTENANCE-FREE BATTERIES

by Robert Gorman

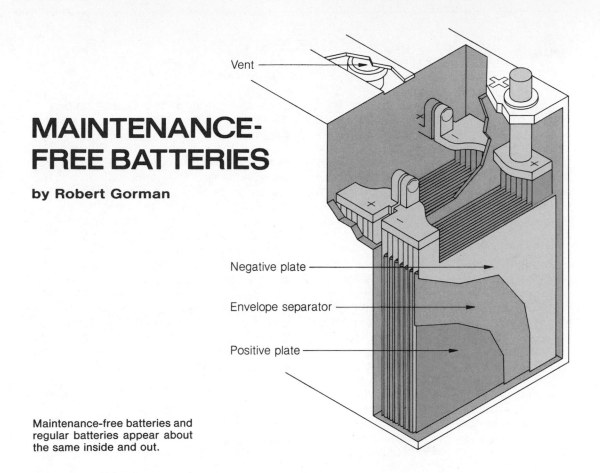

Maintenance-free batteries and regular batteries appear about the same inside and out.

BY now, you've heard of the automobile batteries that never need maintenance—not even an occasional check of the water level. Some don't even have filler caps, so you can't check the electrolyte if you want to. The new no-maintenance batteries—with or without filler caps—are called different names, and may be made differently inside. But they all share one thing: a claim by the seller that once you've installed one, you never have to do anything to maintain it.

How do these batteries differ from the old ones that need periodic attention? There is no simple answer, because some very different types of batteries are being sold under the no-maintenance label. One type is completely new—at least to the automotive field. Another is just an improvement in the same old technology that's riding under the hood of your car now.

Needless to say, each manufacturer claims that its approach is best. Which point of view will eventually prevail is, at this time, anybody's guess. But to understand what the controversy is about and what you can and can't expect from the new batteries, take a look at what goes on inside the molded case.

As explained on page 344, a battery—either lead-antimony or lead-calcium—generates electricity by an electrochemical reaction between its plates and the electrolyte. Batteries have traditionally needed maintenance because some of the water in the electrolyte is broken down by electrolysis during recharging and converted into hydrogen and oxygen. These gases escape through the battery's vent. If the water level falls enough so that part of the plate is exposed to air, the plate can be damaged. If the level falls even lower, the battery can be destroyed.

STOPPING THE WATER LOSS

Making the new batteries involves a single principle: Some way must be found to stop the loss of water caused by electrolysis, or slow it sufficiently so the battery can go through its entire normal life span without needing a refill. The new batteries do this in two ways. (To page 345.)

How Batteries Work

Lead-Calcium and Conventional Lead-Antimony

Both types of batteries use lead plates and electrolyte (sulfuric acid and water) to make electricity. Battery plates start life as lead grids. To give the grids rigidity, a hardener is added. Traditionally, that hardener has been antimony. But the new generation of batteries uses calcium to harden the grids. After the grids are formed, a lead paste is applied. The grids are then called plates.

To make positive plates, the paste added is in the form of lead peroxide. For negative plates, the paste is in the form of spongy lead. When a cell is discharged by the closing of an external circuit, as in switching on the lights, the sulfuric acid in the electrolyte solution acts on both the positive and negative plates. This forms a new chemical compound, lead sulfate.

As the sulfate forms, the chemical reaction releases electrons. The electrons flow in the external circuit from the negative to the positive plates, thus making your lights go on. As the discharge continues, the sulfuric-acid concentration of electrolyte becomes weaker.

When the acid in the electrolyte is partially used up, the battery can no longer deliver electricity at a useful voltage, and the battery is said to be discharged. To recharge it, current is passed through the battery in a direction opposite to that of discharge—from positive to negative. For the current to pass in reverse through the battery, it must be at a higher voltage than the normal battery voltage. (That is why the charging system of an automobile with a 12-volt battery is set to deliver from 13.8 to 15 volts to the battery.)

As the current passes through the battery in the direction opposite to that of the discharge, the lead sulfate on the plates is decomposed. Expelled from the plates, it returns to the electrolyte, reforming sulfuric acid, and gradually restoring the electrolyte to original strength. The plates are restored to their original condition, ready to deliver electricity. The process is called a cycle.

Hydrogen and oxygen gases are given off at the negative and positive plates during recharging. The reason for this is that water is changed into its two elements, hydrogen and oxygen, by an excess of charging current not used by the plates. This highly explosive combination of gases is vented to the outside and through the top of the battery.

Construction of lead-calcium (LC) and lead-antimony (LA) batteries is similar. Each battery has six cells, with negative and positive plates in each cell. The number of plates and amount of exposed surface area determine how much energy can be stored.

Both batteries use separators between plates to keep plates from touching and short-circuiting. Separators in an LC battery, however, are envelopes that cover positive plates. With an LA battery, separators are just flat sheets. Both separators are microporous, allowing electrolyte to flow through.

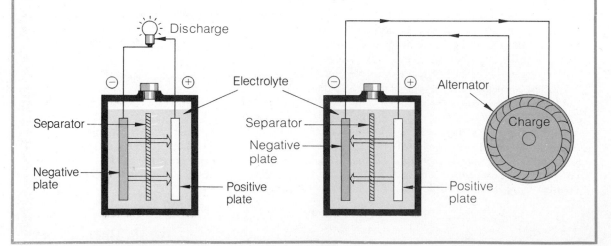

First, they use "envelopes" (described in the box) to keep the plates electrically separated. This means that the flaking of the electrodes that normally occurs is contained within the envelopes. Traditionally, manufacturers have put the plates well above the bottom of the case so the flakes would fall to the bottom, well away from the plates and thus unable to short them out.

With the plates lower in the battery, the water level can be considerably above the top of the plates. Thus far more water can be lost without exposing the plates.

Second, the new batteries are designed to reduce the amount of water lost by electrolysis to a small fraction of what it has traditionally been. This improvement involves the metal alloyed with the lead plates.

Battery engineers have always wished that they didn't have to use any other metal to give the plates the necessary mechanical stiffness, because any alloying of the lead grid can have undesirable effects. Chemical, physical, and electrical alterations can interfere with adhesion between grids and reactive coatings. Alterations from pure lead can also lead to faster oxidation, which would shorten effective life. Furthermore, an alloy can increase electrical resistance through the conducting pathways. Higher resistance increases heating and gassing of the electrolyte and causes more power to be dissipated inside a battery instead of getting outside where it's wanted.

Why, then, are the lead grids alloyed with other materials? Because otherwise, says one battery designer, "plates would have some of the characteristics of a wet noodle."

ANTIMONY—HELPFUL AND HARMFUL

So for workability and survivability, lead grids must be hardened. Virtually from the beginning of car-battery manufacture, antimony—a brittle white metal—has been the hardener of choice for reasons of economy and production convenience.

But also from the beginning it has been known that antimony is an important cause of a battery's perishability. As soon a a battery is activated, antimony begins to leach out of the grids and deposit on negative plates. This changes their chemical and electrical characteristics and lowers the voltage,

which increases the charge current. This causes gassing, which is the disassociation of the electrolyte solution into hydrogen and oxygen. In other words, antimony promotes gassing and speeds water loss. As a side effect, its gaseous discharge causes terminal corrosion.

Antimony also decreases a battery's resistance to overcharge. It does this by reducing the countervoltage inside a battery that serves to limit the amount of current a fully charged battery will accept. As you can see in the graph below, this is really the heart of the controversy.

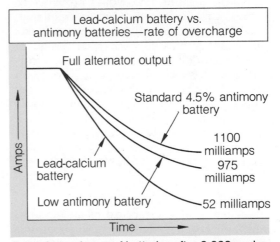

Lead-calcium battery vs. antimony batteries—rate of overcharge

Full alternator output

Standard 4.5% antimony battery

1100 milliamps

975 milliamps

Lead-calcium battery

Low antimony battery

52 milliamps

Amps

Time

Rate of overcharge of batteries after 3,000 cycles at 18 months of service. The standard battery with a charging current above one amp loses more water.

At a given time in the recharge cycle, the countervoltage in the lead-calcium "maintenance-free" battery has reduced the charging current to 52 milliamperes. The conventional battery, made with 4.5-per cent antimony, on the other hand, has a charging current of 1,100 milliamperes, which means it would lose water from the electrolyte many times faster than the lead-calcium battery.

You'll notice that the above comparisons were made between a lead-calcium battery and one made with 4.5-per cent antimony. That was standard in the 1960's. Actually, the percentage of antimony had been coming down—from about 11 per cent in the 1930's to 7 per cent in the late 1940's, and then later to 4.5 per cent.

THE HEAT PROBLEM

Meeting recent environmental and energy concerns has put a lot of new strains on battery performance. Pollution-control hardware, for one thing, has been steadily raising underhood temperatures. It's harder to keep batteries alive in this environment. And the job has often added to car weight by requiring more insulation and cooling equipment.

For some years now, battery designers have been aware that they had to do something to improve their product's resistance to heat, overcharge, water loss, and neglect. And, if possible, to move a battery to a more hospitable location that would probably be less accessible than its present up-front spot.

So the engineers developed both better alloys and improved mechanical design of grids, eventually developing thinner grids able to pack more power into a case of given size and weight. At the same time, they brought the level of antimony down to about 2.5 per cent, which meant that batteries lost water at a much slower rate. These batteries were a big improvement, able to give four or five years of relatively trouble-free life.

CALCIUM INSTEAD OF ANTIMONY

They wanted to get rid of all the antimony. There was nothing new about this idea. Many companies have been building batteries with antimony-free grids for the last 30 or 40 years. The grids, hardened with calcium, are widely used in batteries made for telephone exchanges and other stationary or standby applications.

Adapting lead-calcium technology to high-volume car-battery production, however, has not been easy. Car-battery grids are much thinner (commonly about 1.75 millimeters compared to 6.25 millimeters in a stationary battery). Also they have to be made much more resistant to vibration.

Like any alloying material, calcium also changes lead's electrical and chemical characteristics. But one thing it has going for it is that it can be used more sparingly for equal hardening effect. A typical survivable grid has about 0.07-per cent calcium (plus traces of tin). This leaves the lead much nearer to its pure state than does the 2.5 per cent alloy of a low-antimony grid.

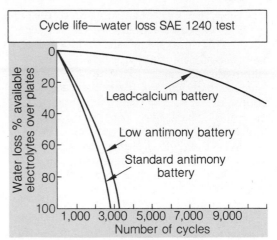

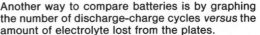

Another way to compare batteries is by graphing the number of discharge-charge cycles *versus* the amount of electrolyte lost from the plates.

CALCIUM ALSO HAS PROBLEMS

Critics point out that calcium is not without problems of its own. It reacts with oxygen to form calcium oxide, which could interfere with adhesion of active plate materials. Lead-calcium also exhibits a tendency to flake, causing particles to separate from positive plates and grow on negatives. This is one of the reasons lead-calcium plates have to be packaged in microporous envelope separators. Since these loosened particles are contained in their envelopes, they can't form a short circuit between positive and negative plates. But if enough of the live material becomes inert it could shorten battery life for reasons other than water loss.

Characteristics like these are cited by some battery specialists as a reason why lead-calcium batteries are somewhat less likely than other types to recover fully from deep discharge. Auto batteries, to be sure, aren't intended for deep-discharge service as in boats or recreational vehicles. But it can happen if you leave your lights on overnight.

ALL BATTERIES HAVE IMPROVED

Makers of lead-calcium batteries say that this type is the only one that's truly maintenance-free. But manufacturers who make the new low-antimony batteries say that they too have a maintenance-free battery.

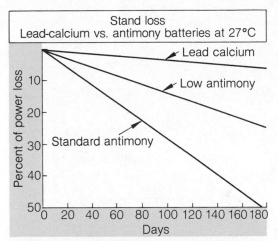

Stand loss means the amount of energy lost while a battery is unused. You could probably start a car after a year of disuse with a lead-calcium battery.

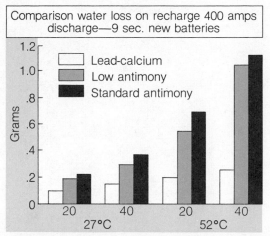
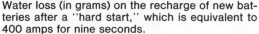

Water loss (in grams) on the recharge of new batteries after a "hard start," which is equivalent to 400 amps for nine seconds.

Who is right? That's hard to say. There are no industry standards governing the use of the term "maintenance-free." And millions of the new batteries that contain no calcium are being marketed as "maintenance-free." Some have fill holes. Some do not.

Like the lead-calcium types—most of which do not have fill holes—many of these lead-antimony batteries incorporate a range of significant design improvements. For example, grid profiles have been improved. Internal circuitry has been shortened. Better separator materials are in use. Modern space-age plastics give the molded containers stronger physical characteristics.

And the extremely low levels of antimony slow water loss significantly. In fact, say makers, water loss will not normally be the first cause of failure. And if it isn't, then further improvement in this direction is really of no importance.

To sum up, lead-calcium batteries clearly produce less gas than lead-antimony batteries. But those who have stuck with lead-antimony say their new batteries have cut water losses enough, and that further cutting isn't necessary. In addition they say, production difficulties make it difficult, if not impossible, to mass-produce lead-calcium batteries so that most of them perform adequately. So makers of lead-calcium batteries say they have solved production problems.

ONE MORE PROBLEM

How do you tell which battery type you are getting? The truth is that you may not be able to tell.

If the literature on the label is not specific or comprehensive, your best clue is to look for filler caps. But that is not a certain guide. Some lead-calcium batteries can be uncapped for testing and the addition of water. But a sealed top does give a clue that the battery is lead-calcium.

Don't get confused, in this examination, between filler caps and vent plugs. Antimony-free batteries all have little openings through which gases can escape. In other respects, however, you shouldn't see much that's different. Lead-calcium batteries all have standard top or side terminals by which they can be connected—and charged or jumped—just like the conventional ones.

You don't have to go back to school to learn how to love or live with a maintenance-free battery. Aside from the fact that you can't—or shouldn't have to—add water, you select and use it just like any other battery □

📖 SELECTED READINGS

"Big Breakthrough in Batteries ... Almost." *Mechanix Illustrated,* March 1978.

"Which battery type is best?" by A. F. Burr. *Radio Electronics,* July 1978.

A floppy disk is being inserted into the disk player of this computer, which is a visual-display text-editing system.

FLOPPY DISKS

by Jerry Willis

MOST microcomputer systems allow the user to store programs and data at wholesale prices in mass storage devices. The typical microcomputer user has several different applications for his or her system. It may play games all day Saturday, help balance the checkbook on Sunday, and serve as a word processor three or four evenings a week. Each of these applications of the microcomputer requires a different program that tells the computer what to do.

Since the microcomputer will generally be used for one application at a time, it is not necessary to tie up large amounts of memory as permanent storage for all the programs you plan to run. In the average system, programs can be stored on an ordinary audio cassette. To play chess, for example, the cassette with the chess program is put into the computer.

Audio cassettes are cheap, available everywhere, and easy to maintain. These characteristics account, in part, for their popularity. Most micro systems offer the ability to read and record tape as a standard or optional feature. Cassettes are also a popular means of packaging programs for sale or exchange. If you create a new or improved version of a game, it is easy to give the computer a command and watch it record or save your creation on a cassette. In a few minutes several copies can be produced for friends as well.

Buying programs on cassettes is convenient. If, however, you buy the printed copy of a program and want to use it, you must first type into the computer every line in the program. Before the computer will run it, every line, and in fact, just about every character and space, must be correct. The computer is not tolerant of errors. Buying the program on tape saves all the time required to type in a program and correct the errors that inevitably occur.

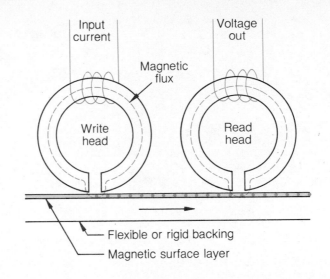

The magnetic-oxide surface of the disk can store information in the form of magnetized spots. The "write head" produces these spots, which represent binary digits. The "read head" passes over the spots, which produce electric pulses, like the ones made by the "write head."

ACCESS TO A PROGRAM

It may appear at this point that mass storage and cassette tape storage are synonymous. Cassettes do, however, have their competitors. Today the types of memory storage used with computers can be placed in two major categories, sequential access and random access. Cassette storage is sequential access. It is like the 8-track tape cartridge you may have in your car. To hear a particular song that is at the end of the tape you must run through all the songs to get to it. There is no way to get at or "access" a particular spot on the cartridge without running some of the rest of the tape by the head. Sequential memories are slow because they have to process so much irrelevant data to get to the information you want. They have one advantage, though: they're very cheap.

Random access means that any part of the information stored in the memory can be accessed, or reached, just as quickly as any other. The "mini floppy disk" is the most popular member of this family. A disk system operates much like an automatic record player. The disk is a flexible, round platter enclosed in a protective cardboard covering. It is coated with a magnetic oxide much like that used on audio tape.

A typical disk system is illustrated in Figure 1. The record/playback head can be moved across the disk. The disk itself spins around like a phonograph record while the head positions itself to read or record data on it. Compared to cassettes, disk systems are hundreds, even thousands, of times faster. Speed, in fact, is the primary advantage. Cost is its most serious drawback. It is when the cassette is compared to disk storage that the cassette's appeal begins to fade.

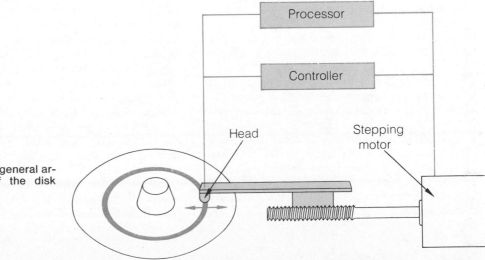

Figure 1. The general arrangement of the disk system.

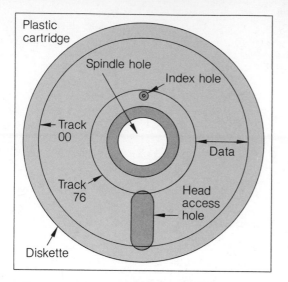

Figure 2. The general make-up of a floppy disk. The large hole in the middle is for the spindle of the disk player.

THE NEED FOR RANDOM ACCESS

The major drawback of a cassette shows up when you need to manipulate data files and programs on tape. Suppose, for example, that you are the secretary of a local computing club and thus have the job of maintaining the mailing list that is stored on cassette. You will quickly discover that changing an address or adding a new name is a somewhat time consuming process with tape.

Let's look at an analogy. How long would it take to arrive at a destination in downtown Chicago if the cab driver starts at O'Hare and must go by every house between the airport and downtown? That, essentially, is what happens with tape storage. Of course, the taxi driver has a better method. He or she will use one of the major suburban arteries to get to the general vicinity of the fare. Once in the area a major boulevard or street may be used to get even closer. Finally the correct street and correct address are found.

That is a much more efficient search routine, and one similar to that used in floppy disk systems. As a result it takes a fraction of a second to find and load a program on a disk that would take 15 minutes just to find on a cassette.

For a person who uses mass storage only to warehouse programs that will simply be loaded into the computer and run, there may be little advantage, other than the speed, to disk systems. If, however, a home or business application calls for maintaining files that are changed and modified regularly (such as your club mailing list, inventory, payroll, or accounts receivable) then a disk is almost mandatory.

THE DISK

Figure 2 shows the basic configuration of a "floppy" disk. The large hole in the middle is for the spindle, which will spin the disk when it is inserted into the transport. An index hole assures that the disk is in the same relative location on the spindle each time it is inserted. A photosensor tells the control program where the hole is. The long oval hole in the protective covering allows the read/write head access to the surface of the disk.

Microcomputers use flexible disks with a tough oxide coating bonded to them. This "floppy" disk spins at exactly 360 revolutions per minute. As shown in Figure 3 the read/write head on a floppy-disk drive actually touches the disk. In fact, it exerts a gentle pressure on it. This eliminates the need for some of the precision in manufacturing required for floating-head drives, but it also creates a wear problem.

A typical floppy disk or "diskette" will wear out after the head passes over a track a million or so times, and the head will last for approximately 20,000 hours of contact. These ratings are much lower than those for hard-disk systems but should be of little concern to micro users unless the disk will be in constant use day in and day out.

Figure 3 also shows how the head is moved from one section of the disk to another. A small stepping motor turns a screw drive that holds the head. The motor will turn a precise number of degrees each time it receives a pulse. This rotation is converted, by means of the threads on the screw, into a linear motion across the disk. To move the head from one part of the disk to another, the

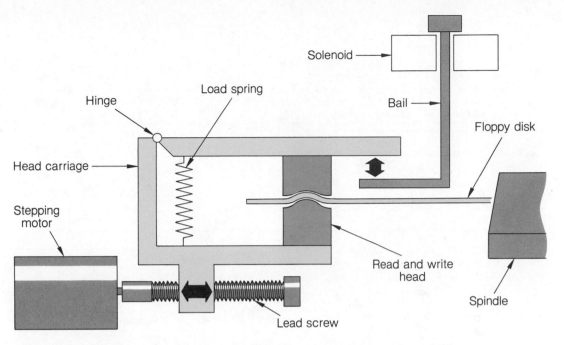

Figure 3. The head drive. How the head is moved from one section of the disk to another is important. This is done by vertical and horizontal movements, controlled by a solenoid.

disk-operating system provides the correct signals to the drive to lift up (B) the disk by releasing the solenoid. Then the head-position motor would rotate the exact number of degrees needed to move the head across (A) to the desired location. Finally, the solenoid would be actuated (B) to place the head against the disk again. Then the computer would be able to read or write on that location.

SECTORS OF INFORMATION

Just as an LP phonograph record will have different "bands" that contain separate songs, the disk has "sectors" that contain data. If you want to play a particular song that is on a record, it is first necessary to look on the record label to determine which band contains the song. Then you place the needle at the beginning of that band. With a disk this is done automatically when the operator tells the computer which file or program is needed.

A standard floppy disk is 20 centimeters in diameter with 77 concentric tracks, each of which has 26 sectors. "Concentric" means the tracks do not spiral inward the way grooves on a phonograph record do. If the

head is placed at the beginning of track 34, for example, it will read the information on that track over and over rather than spiralling inward until it reaches the innermost edge of the disk. Each of the 26 sectors in a track can store 128 bytes of data. A little arithmetic will show that this should provide a total capacity of 256,000 per disk. Actually, the disk is really capable of storing 400,000. The reason for this is that this system requires 144,000 bytes just for housekeeping.

Figure 4 illustrates the components of a track. There is one index hole on the disk, which tells the computer where each track begins. The rest of the job of finding a particular piece of data is accomplished by using a special format for data entry. If we select a particular track and pictorially display the format used, as in Figure 4, it is easy to see where the extra capacity is used. Each track has some space at the beginning and end that acts as a sort of buffer. It allows the head to be slightly out of place and still work properly.

Several other "gaps" in a track also give some additional margin for error and provide the head with some breathing space to change from read to write mode, if necessary,

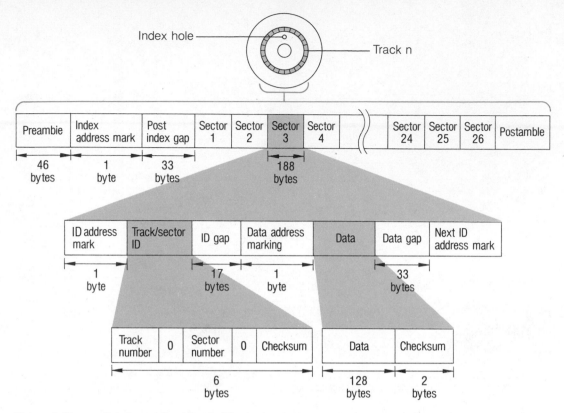

Figure 4. Floppy disk format for a track. The format is the positioning of the information on the disk. The operator tells the computer what information to find.

before it reaches the data area. The "index-address-mark" lets the computer know it can expect to receive some data that will identify which sector is being read. Each of the 26 sectors, which follow, contain 128 bytes of data plus labels that identify which track and sector they belong to. This format is repeated in every track and sector on the disk. The 144,000 bytes of housekeeping information contributes to the low error rates of these disk systems.

RENTING A LARGER MEMORY

Many people do not realize that it is possible to rent storage space for computer data. Most major cities have a number of time-sharing companies and educational institutions that allow a business or individual to rent time and space on their computer. Using a device called a "modem" it is possible to use ordinary telephone lines to connect your microcomputer to the big computer at the time-sharing company.

The micro then becomes an "intelligence terminal," which sends and receives data from the host computer. In my own work I sometimes need to store large amounts of data that would take up too much space in my micro. With a modem I can dial a number at the university and connect the IBM 360 there to my micro. The data is then stored in the university computer.

The cost of time-sharing and the method used to compute minimum monthly charges varies from company to company as does the type of services provided. Most personal computer users, however, will not find it necessary to rent memory □

📖 SELECTED READINGS

"For your home computer: pro-level disc and computer" by W. Hawkins. *Popular Science,* September 1978.

"Mass-storage systems" by H. Chamberlin. *Popular Electronics,* November 1976.

"In's and out's of computers for beginners" by E. Mitchell. *Popular Electronics,* June 1976.

Rick Kline

A young male prairie falcon perches near its nesting ledge, which is high above the Carson River in western Nevada. Falcons are able to seize their prey in the air as well as on the ground.

WILDLIFE

WILDLIFE
REVIEW OF THE YEAR

To survive in the long run, wildlife depends on the goodwill of people. It is no longer a matter of "letting nature take its course." People have altered the natural world too much for that. And because people have used the natural ecosystems to meet their own needs, they must now assume responsibility for seeing that the needs of wildlife—food, water, and cover—are met. That people of many nations, including the United States, have put more emphasis on wildlife in the past decade or so has raised the odds for wildlife.

Refuge from Habitat Loss. The Alaska habitat of many species of wildlife ranging from herds of majestic caribou to arctic foxes to ground squirrels is in possible danger. In 1978, after the U.S. Congress did not act on legislation concerning which lands in Alaska would be reserved for wildlife, President Carter designated more than 22,500,000 hectares national monument lands, thus protecting them and the wildlife on them until a permanent settlement is made. If Congress should act to declare an expected 40,000,000 hectares of Alaska to various government agencies for protection and management, it will add greatly to the already nearly 14,000,000 hectares in the U.S. National Wildlife Refuge System. ■ Most habitat threat does not, however, involve such large areas; nor does it come from well-publicized developments such as airports and dams. Rather it results from everyday building on lands surrounding cities. Each year some 400,000 hectares are lost to wildlife this way. Add to that some 325,000 hectares strip-mined each year and some 55,000 hectares of wetlands drained annually and you have a steady loss of wildlife habitat.

Endangered Species Update. The Endangered Species Act, which forbids actions that threaten the survival of endangered species, was weakened, but not crippled, by Congress in 1978. Faced with problems arising when multi-million-dollar government projects such as dams threaten the habitat of an endangered species, Congress set up a two-step process to evaluate construction projects for possible exemption from the law.

The Endangered Species list now stands at 192 species in the United States. The list changes frequently. Some species are taken off as populations build up to the point where they are no longer threatened with extinction. Others, more unfortunate, are taken off because they disappear entirely. That is what happened to the Tecopa pupfish during 1978. It was not able to survive changes in its environment caused by builders of a bathhouse . . . which is now abandoned. ■ In better bathhouse news, one endangered species, the Socorro isopod, lives only in a 3-meter iron drain pipe leading from an abandoned bathhouse in New Mexico. This creature may be the key to understanding how land creatures evolved from ancient marine isopods. ■ Special efforts to save endangered species are being made by 64 recovery teams coordinated by the U.S. Department of the Interior. Big news for one team: an endangered Florida panther was killed in 1977. This indicates that there are probably still some truly wild panthers in Florida.

Some species are thought to be better off now than ever before. The wild turkey, once feared near extinction, is now ranging in 47 states. ■ Atlantic salmon have returned to several cleaned-up rivers in the northeastern United States. ■ Populations are also up for deer, alligators, whooping cranes, brown pelicans, ospreys, bighorn sheep, ducks, and songbirds.

Alyeska Pipeline Service Company

Caribou in Alaska. Sections of the Alyeska oil pipeline have been raised so that it will not be a total barrier to migrating and foraging animals.

Even the lowly Socorro isopod is endangered in its tiny environment. It is a relative of the common sow bug, which school children are now using in their science classes.

Steve Northup/The New York Times

From Laboratory to the Field. Information gleaned in the laboratory looms larger as a key to saving wildlife. In what may have been the first instance of science arresting the death process, a Brandeis University psychologist removed two glands that control the production of reproductive hormones from female octopuses almost ready to die—the normal occurrence for them after their eggs hatch—and found that the octopuses continued to live—for a period equal to another normal life—and doubled their weight.

In an effort to reduce dependence on pesticides that can poison wildlife as well as the target pest, the U.S. federal government is funding a program to develop integrated biological controls on pests. To try to reduce the population of screwworm, a cattle pest in the southern United States, scientists sterilized adult males by irradiation and then released them to compete with fertile males in the field.

Some birds are getting housing help. As prairie-dog populations decline, there is a resulting shortage of natural burrows suitable for burrowing owls. Some California Audubon Society members designed plywood burrows and buried them in prime nesting areas. Within two days the owls began moving in. ■ Similarly, two pairs of bald eagles used platforms put up by the Michigan Audubon Society to build nests and raise eaglets. Only one surprise: the platforms had been put up for ospreys.

Plants and other "lower" life forms. Plants and other "lower" forms of life lag behind birds and mammals in protection under the law in the United States, but they are beginning to receive more attention. The first need is inventory. Two staff members of the National Museum of Natural History in Washington, D.C. are now compiling a list of all plants in the United States. The current count of 20,000 species is still growing. With this and other information scientists will be able to begin to take concerted steps to safeguard what are now thought to be a growing number of seriously endangered plants. Already one of the most famous U.S. plants—the Venus flytrap—is threatened with extinction. Opportunists are seizing and trying to sell through the mail these fragile plants that grow only on the coastal plains of North and South Carolina. ■ While nongame wildlife frequently benefit from programs aimed at game animals, many conservation groups favor legislation aimed specifically at helping nongame wildlife by, for example, providing funds for population surveys and for habitat purchase and protection. Although Congress declined to fund such programs in 1978, success is expected shortly.

And still more problems. A decade ago no one worried about bobcats, but in recent years bobcat pelts have greatly increased in price as bobcat becomes a substitute for large spotted cats whose fur cannot be marketed internationally. Bobcats are not yet endangered, but no one knows how many can be taken before population levels become critical. ■ The age-old problem of poaching still exists too. In early 1979 Michigan police broke up the biggest poaching ring in U.S. history—a business which had sold 300 deer, 1,700 squirrels, 4,400 ducks, and more than 11,000 rabbits. ■ New Mexico, where 34,000 deer are killed illegally each year, has also embarked on an intensive antipoaching campaign.

Bob Strohm

Animals Animals

Slowly but surely wild turkeys are making a comeback. Now you can find them in 47 states.

U.S. Fish and Wildlife

An endangered-species-recovery team looks on while Kristine Tollestrup records information on the blunt-nosed leopard lizard.

The fascinating, fly-eating Venus flytrap is now threatened with extinction. If you know where some grow, don't pick them.

Hugh Spencer/NAS

Left: striped skunk (*Mephitis mephitis*); right: hooded skunk (*Mephitis macoura*)

SKUNKS

by Constance Colby

IT comes ambling out of the shadows, looking like a portly little shadow itself, midnight black, streaked with a V marking of white moonlight.

The skunk's attention, as usual, is focused on food. Sniffing its way along, searching for the insects that make up most of its diet, it asks only to be let alone. Usually its wish is respected. Even giant grizzlies have been observed to give way at the approach of a single small skunk. The skunk itself, however, seldom gives way when menaced.

Its sturdy self-assurance is backed by one of nature's most potent defenses, as indicated by the skunk's scientific name *Mephitis mephitis,* which means "poisonous or offensive odor." It is doubled, understandably, for emphasis. The more common name, skunk, is derived from a word that meant "to urinate" in Indian languages spoken in southeastern New England.

BAD PRESS

The skunk has received an exceedingly bad press for centuries, but actually, the average skunk is not a bad fellow. Naturalist Ernest Thompson Seton called him "the gentlest and least aggressive creature in the woods." True, if you confront a skunk face to face, it may stop short and bristle, stamping sharply with its front feet, spreading its bushy tail up and out, peacock-style. But this is merely fair warning. Once it is sure that you are not threatening, the tail will droop back to its normal curve, and the skunk will return to its chief interest in life—the eternal search for food.

BADGER FAMILY

The skunk is not, as many people believe, a member of the cat family. It belongs to the family Mustelidae, which includes badgers, otters, weasels, minks, and wolverines. (Look at the skunk's head and you will see the family resemblance.) And although the skunk is often called a polecat, that name really belongs to a certain type of European weasel. Neither is the skunk a civet cat, an African and Asian animal with which it is sometimes confused.

SEVERAL SPECIES

Skunks are native only to the Western Hemisphere, with a range from southern Canada all the way down to Patagonia, at the southern end of South America. Within the

United States, several kinds can be found.

The smallest species found in the United States is the little spotted skunk (*Spilogale putorius*). It is not actually spotted but has thin, broken stripes running down its neck and back. Some of the stripes begin near the face, giving it a somewhat spotted appearance. It weighs about 0.7 kilogram, and averages about 30 centimeters in length, with a tail from 10 to 23 centimeters long. It is exceptionally agile. It can climb trees, perform handstands, and even dance on its forepaws like a trained circus dog. Its range is extensive—from the West and Southwest across the Gulf States to Florida.

The hog-nosed skunk (*Conepatus mesoleucus*) is not so numerous as the spotted skunk. Found in the southwestern United States and northern Mexico, the hog-nosed skunk is fairly large as skunks go, but has a shorter tail and much coarser fur than other varieties and a single, broad white stripe with no V. This animal takes its name from its distinctive nose—a bare snout, somewhat like a pig's—which is used for rooting out grubs and bugs. Another common name for this species is rooter skunk.

The skunk you are most likely to meet in the United States is the ordinary *Mephitis mephitis,* the broadstriped or common skunk. It is found everywhere, with many local subspecies. The common skunk varies more than the other species, both in size and marking. Some individuals are only 33 centimeters long, with an 18-centimeter tail, while others are 46 centimeters, with a 25-centimeter tail. The average is usually described as being about "as big as a house cat."

The hooded skunk (*Mephitis macroura*) is the same size and belongs to the same genus as the common skunk, but inhabits only parts of Arizona and New Mexico. It differs from its better-known cousin in having an unusually large area of white on the back of the neck—hence the descriptive term "hooded."

Most common skunks are marked with the familiar white V along the back, and many also have an elegant brushstroke of white running down the nose and perhaps a snowy spot on the tip. Trappers classify common skunks as half-stripers, thin stripers, broad stripers, and stars (having a white spot on the head but no stripes).

ALWAYS FORAGING

The wild skunk you may meet is likely to be either a thin striper or a broad striper, since these are the most common, but whatever the coloration, it will almost certainly be busily engaged in foraging. To a skunk, mealtime extends throughout its waking hours.

The skunk is not fussy about the menu: it will swallow bees, dig up an entire yellow-jacket nest (probably not bothered too much by stings since it works at night when the cool temperature makes the wasps inactive), and sample the leftover dog food in your back yard or even a dead sparrow fallen from its nest.

Given a choice, a skunk would probably choose a diet made up exclusively of insects. They provide the exceptionally high amounts of vitamin A and protein the skunk requires, and besides, they are relatively easy to locate. A skunk always prefers the easiest way in everything, and with insects there is no need to wear itself out digging or climbing or galloping about. Moreover, if you have ever heard the excited sniffing of a skunk closing in on a beetle, it is obvious that such tidbits are gastronomic treats. Studies have confirmed this preference: when researchers at the U.S. Department of Agriculture examined the stomach contents of 1,700 skunks, more than half of the bulk was found to consist of insects. The rest consisted mainly of mice, earthworms, turtle eggs, fruit and grain, with sometimes a ground-nesting bird.

Hog-nosed skunk (*Conepatus mesoleucus*).

New York Zoological Society Photo

Lynwood M. Chace-NAS/Photo Researchers

A newly born litter of striped skunks.

GARDENER'S FRIEND

Skunks are sometimes accused of raiding the hen house, and while an occasional renegade may possibly be guilty, in most cases, the real poultry killers are the skunk's cousins, weasels and minks. Why should any sensible skunk undertake a noisy and perhaps dangerous foray when it could dine in quiet and comfort by working its way through a nice patch of underbrush? Or somebody's vegetable garden, where it prefers beetles to beets? Ernest Thompson Seton once commented that "every skunk is the guardian angel of a garden acre." Angelic may not be the exact adjective to apply to the average skunk, but if you have ever watched one gobbling a mouthful of Japanese beetles or heaving its fat little body up on tiptoe to lick gypsy-moth caterpillars from a tree trunk, you will certainly agree that the skunk is the gardener's friend.

NIGHT HUNTER

Night is the skunk's favorite time and, like all nocturnal animals, it is superbly equipped for roaming after dark. The skunk's eyes are weak, but its nose is extraordinarily sensitive. Its ears—surprisingly small and inconspicuous—can detect the faintest rustle of a bug in the dry grass or the soft sounds that might signal the attack of its

natural enemies, the great horned owl and the gray fox.

By day, a skunk may bed down in any number of places—inside a hollow log, beneath the floor of a garage, in a crevice under a rock, or in an abandoned rabbit burrow that it has enlarged with its strong, blunt claws.

Skunks tend to be solitary animals, but a family may sometimes be seen moseying along together, and as many as a dozen skunks may den up in the same burrow during the winter for warmth.

SLEEPS DURING WINTER

A skunk's normally steady rhythm of eating speeds up with the approach of fall, when it must accumulate the protective layer of fat that will carry it through the cold months ahead. By mid-October, the adult skunk—who is, at any season, a rather pudgy figure—has become positively obese and looks even heavier with its thick winter coat.

During sub-zero weather, the skunk sleeps, but it does not undergo a true hibernation. It may sleep for several weeks at a stretch during the worst of the winter, but it will rouse itself from this temporary dormancy on the first warm day and venture sleepily out in the snow to poke about for a snack.

SPRING MOODINESS

By the time the spring thaw begins, the skunk has fully shaken off its winter lethargy and now, briefly, turns its attention to something other than food. The mating season begins in early February and lasts until the end of March. This is a time when you should be wary of any skunk you happen to encounter. The females tend to be restless and snappish, while the males may have periods of great irritability. The males have an

San Diego Zoological Society Photo

Striped skunks can make cute pets, but you should realize that it is a nocturnal animal and will try to be very active at night. They must be checked for rabies.

extra reason, apart from seasonal moodiness. At the start of the mating period, the testicles descend from the abdominal cavity into the scrotum to enable the sperm to be stored at below body temperature and so be kept fertile. Apparently, the process often causes considerable pain.

FAMILY LIFE

Mating takes place inside the den, and the pair apparently continue to share the same quarters until the first week in April, when the female makes it clear to her spouse that he must clear out. She then cleans the nest and relines it with fresh grass.

Gestation lasts for nine weeks, which means that most mother skunks give birth around the middle of June. There are from four to ten babies in a litter—blind, toothless infants about the size of a mouse and weighing only 28 grams.

The newborn skunk is hairless but the pigmentation of its skin reveals just how its fur will be marked. By the time it is three weeks old, its eyes are open and it has become a shining ball of black-and-white fluff. At seven weeks, a skunk is old enough to be weaned, and by mid-July is ready to venture out into the meadow for lessons in beetle catching. This is the season when you are most likely to see the typical skunk family procession, that solemn file of mother and babies moving through the grass. The little ones nearsightedly keep a nose-to-tail line and chirp desperately for help if they chance to stray from the trail.

Late summer is also the time when you may come upon a family of skunks at play. They wrestle, pounce on one another, make mock spray attacks, and hiss excitedly as they play tug of war with a piece of vine or a small branch. They may even splash in shallow water along a brook. Not ordinarily considered aquatic animals, skunks are strong swimmers and the babies seem to enjoy water play. But their childhood is brief. By six months, skunks are fully mature and have settled down to the serious business of life—eating.

CLEAN AND HEALTHY

The average life span of a wild skunk is believed by some naturalists to be about five years; others claim it is longer—from eight to ten years. Everyone agrees that skunks are extremely healthy animals and are remarkably disease-free. The one exception is rabies. Since skunks do not run from other creatures, they are easy targets for the bite of a rabid animal. Skunks are also clean animals. They groom their fur regularly, keep their dens neat, carefully defecate in a remote corner, and are seldom plagued with vermin or skin infections.

GOOD NEIGHBOR

A skunk's main enemy is man. Skunks often suffocate because they have gotten their heads stuck in discarded cans or jars. They are shot by nervous householders, who mistakenly consider them as troublesome or even dangerous pests; and most frequently of all, they are run over by speeding cars. In spite of all this, many skunks seem to prefer living near people—and near people's garbage scraps.

If you find that a skunk has taken up residence on your own property, there is no need to panic. If left alone and permitted to mind its own business, the chances are that the skunk will turn out to be a very good neighbor. Certainly your garden will benefit from its appetite for insects.

WARNING SIGNALS

In view of all its sterling qualities, it seems unfair that the skunk has acquired

A striped skunk splashes playfully in a brook.

Hal Harrison/Grant Heilman

Spotted skunk (*Spilogale putoris*).

such a bad reputation. Yet whenever most people think of a skunk, they immediately think of its spray. It is, to be sure, one of the most formidable weapons in the entire animal world. Yet the average skunk sprays only as a last resort, after a series of warnings had been given and ignored.

When a skunk first feels menaced, it places its front feet together and stomps sharply. If this fails to scare off whatever danger it is facing, the skunk will raise its tail and spread it out into its full magnificent fan, but with the tip hanging down. If this warning, too, is disregarded, the skunk raises the tip and flares it out as a further—and final—signal. Only if all else fails does the skunk present its backside to its attacker and fire.

SPRAY

When it does spray, the skunk's aim is accurate up to three meters. The amber fluid, with its overpoweringly obnoxious smell, is

Tomato juice is an antidote to skunk spray.

Ed Cesar-NAS/Photo Researchers

known scientifically as *butylmercaptan*. The odor is strong enough to carry nearly one kilometer and it makes most animals—and people—sick. The liquid stings the skin and burns the eyes, often causing temporary blindness.

The fluid is produced in two anal glands located beneath the skin at either side of the rectum, under the tail. It is expelled through retractable ducts that can shoot out through the sides of the anus with lightning speed. A skunk can fire a single stream or discharge both glands at once in a powerful spray, repeating it again and again if necessary. Multiple doses are seldom required. Most other animals learn at an early age to avoid the small black-and-white fellow with the big plumy tail.

Many remedies have been suggested as antidotes to skunk spray. Among the most common are repeated washing with tomato juice or vinegar, scrubbing with one of the stronger household detergents, or one of the items included on the rather grim list offered by Charles Hume and other experts, gasoline, bleach, chloride of lime, ammonia, a diluted solution of sodium hypochlorite, or a mix of equal parts of citronella and oil of bergamot. The best remedy is also the oldest and the easiest: avoid being sprayed.

As a house pet, the skunk is becoming increasingly popular, at least in states where skunk owning is not illegal. Orphaned wild skunks rescued from the roadside do not make good pets, but skunks bought from a reputable breeder and introduced to a household of humans at an early age often develop into very interesting members of the family.

SOLID CITIZEN

Wild or tame—in the forest, back yard, or kitchen—the skunk is a solid citizen, part of the naturally balanced environment, beautiful and interesting to watch. Like many solitary creatures, the skunk can be grumpy at times and set in its ways, yet generally it is willing to live and let live—a peaceful individualist deserving our respect but not our fear □

SELECTED READINGS

Skunks by B. Hunt, Prentice-Hall, 1973.

Lauros-Giraudon

THE TUNA/PORPOISE PROBLEM

by Karen Pryor and Kenneth S. Norris

PORPOISES dying in the nets of U.S. tuna fishermen has become a widely publicized environmental issue over the last few years. The issue, which has progressed toward a resolution, has aroused considerable public emotion, based not only on human misunderstandings, but on misconceptions regarding the behavior of the animals involved. In order to solve the problem, however, there must be a greater understanding of both tuna and porpoise behavior. This article will deal with aspects of porpoise behavior.

FISHING HISTORY

Fishermen have long known that large yellowfin tuna travel beneath schools of porpoise in the tropical eastern Pacific. At first bait boats, equipped with hook and line, were used. Tuna were sometimes located far offshore by spotting porpoises in the waters where the association was known to occur. After large purse seines came into use for catching small "school-fish" tuna, fishermen discovered that porpoises could be herded into nets, and that the vaulable adult yellowfin tuna, remaining beneath the porpoises, could be caught far more efficiently.

Unlike the familiar bottlenose porpoise, the pelagic spotted and spinner porpoises (genus *Stenella*) involved in the tuna fishery are not good at avoiding barriers, and easily become entangled in nets. At first, many of the encircled porpoises were entangled or suffocated when the nets were drawn in. By

the early 1960's, however, the fishermen had devised a method for releasing porpoises from the nets. This was a maneuver called "backing down." With smaller meshed nets in the backdown area, a porpoise had less of a chance of getting a flipper or a snout caught in the netting as it left.

EFFORTS TO SAVE PORPOISES

By 1971, U.S. government data compiled from a small sample of boats showed that nearly one third of the encircled porpoises were killed. An average of 3.8 porpoises were killed for each ton of tuna landed. Extrapolated across the entire fleet, these data gave a mortality estimate for 1971 of 310,000 animals. Through federal regulation and increased efforts on the part of individual captains and crews, and research into net design and deployment systems, a considerable reduction in mortality has been effected in recent years.

By 1976, the percentage of mortality in all porpoises encircled had dropped from 31.9 per cent to less than 2 per cent, and the rate of kill per ton of tuna landed was a quarter of what it had been. But given the number of boats fishing and the average number of sets made during each voyage involving porpoises, the National Marine Fisheries Service (NMFS) estimated that the total mortality for the animal in the U.S. tuna fishery for 1976 may have been 104,000 individuals.

Foreground: yellowfin tuna, background: spinner porpoise. These tuna weigh up to 700 kilograms, and the porpoises weigh between 100 and 150 kilograms.

Bill High

Population studies showed that neither of the principal species of porpoise involved were actually endangered, since both are abundant in many other areas of the Pacific. It was deemed vital, however, that the populations involved be protected from further depletion. Although it is extremely difficult to obtain an adequate population count, attempts were made to evaluate the separate breeding populations of the species involved, and then to set quotas that would permit the stocks to multiply rather than decline.

The 1977 quota was 56,000 individuals. But, thanks to a culmination of events, including new net modifications, increased motivation and communication within the fleet, and research on porpoise behavior at sea, the total 1977 porpoise mortality was 28,000 individuals. This figure was much more accurate than those of previous years, since it was based to a large extent on an actual count taken by government observers aboard almost every boat in the tuna fleet, rather than an estimate extrapolated from observations of 15 per cent of the fleet. Though the fleet remained in port part of the year due to legal and political conflicts, the lowered mortality rate was not due primarily to a reduction in fishing—85 per cent of the usual catch was brought in. In 1978 the mortality rate dropped to approximately 17,000.

There are estimated to be a total of 8,000,000 porpoises in the affected population. A mortality of 28,000, divided among various stocks according to government regulations, meets the "disadvantage test," since all stocks are assumed to be able to increase their numbers despite this fishing pressure. The government quotas for 1978 is 51,945; for 1979, 41,610; and for 1980, 31,150. These figures allow for an estimated take above the quotas by the ever-growing foreign fleet, without reaching disadvantageous levels. Yet it is apparent to all concerned that further reductions are desirable, and for political

and moral reasons even necessary. The law, in fact, requires that the porpoise kill be reduced to "insignificant levels approaching zero."

FOOD AND PROTECTION

As previously mentioned, adult yellowfin tuna, *Thunnus albicares,* often swim in close association with the Pacific spotted porpoise, *Stenella attenuata* (called "spotters") and the spinner porpoise, *Stenella longirostris,* and sometimes ·with the rather similar common dolphin, *Delphinus delphis.* The association occurs in the eastern Pacific over an area of hundreds of millions of hectares, some fifteen hundred kilometers or more west of Central and South America. It is a vast, shallow habitat. Though the water is deep, the yellowfin tuna generally stay within about 20 meters of the surface, where the temperature is to their liking.

Food is concentrated in scattered schools. Generally, spotters feed during the day on squid and small fish that are located in surface waters. They prefer prey measuring about 50 centimeters in length. Spinners feed on squid, and fishes found in deeper waters. They prefer much smaller prey and usually feed at night.

The yellowfin tuna eat crabs and other organisms unpalatable to porpoises, as well as what porpoises eat. It seems probable that the tuna seek out and associate with the porpoises to take advantage of their superior food-finding ability.

The tuna are much swifter swimmers than porpoises, perhaps achieving speeds of more than 40 knots, as compared to 21.5 knots for spotters. The porpoises probably could not evade the tuna even if they wanted to. It may be that tuna offer porpoises some protection, in that predators, primarily sharks, coming from below would have to pass through the tuna before reaching the porpoises.

DAYTIME COMPANIONS

The tuna/porpoise association is not continuous. The tuna may leave or lose sight of the porpoises at night, and rejoin them when and if they find a school of porpoises during daylight hours. The tuna usually travel below the porpoises, sometimes ahead, sometimes behind.

Spinner and spotter schools can range from 50 animals to several hundred (the usual amount) and schools may aggregate into groups of many thousands. Spotters and spinners sometimes travel together, accompanied not only by tuna but also by pilot whales, bottlenose porpoises, marlin, sharks, and several species of seabirds.

EASY-TO-SPOT PORPOISES

It is the tuna's fidelity to the porpoise that enables the fishermen to use porpoises to catch tunas. Porpoises can be easily spotted, since they are almost always near the surface. The porpoise's top speed can only be maintained for brief sprints, and a reasonably fast boat can keep up with them. And, although the porpoises can sound, or dive out of sight, they cannot stay down for more than about five minutes, nor run far enough to be out of sight when they surface again. A fishing skipper can then, using small speedboats, turn the school, herd it into a milling group with the tuna still below, and set his net around both tuna and porpoises.

BACKING DOWN

The net on a modern tuna vessel may be nearly one-and-one-half kilometers long and 200 meters deep. Once it is set, the porpoises generally remain more or less stationary in the middle, while the tuna constantly move back and forth and up and down, but rarely go deep enough to pass beneath the net. The next step is to "purse" the seine, by rapidly tightening a steel cable that runs through rings on the lower edge of the net.

The animals are now enclosed in a bowl-shaped net. Some of the net is then winched aboard so that the size of the bowl is reduced to manageable proportions. The vessel is then backed through the water, drawing the net into a long oval—the backing-down maneuver. Finally, the float-provided top edge of the net, or corkline, is pulled beneath the water at the far end of the oval. This provides an open passage over the top of the net into the ocean.

Most of the porpoises leave the net at this point. Those who are confused or fail to go out tend to "raft" or gather together, floating vertically at the surface. The net is then pulled out from under these animals. The tuna meanwhile tend to patrol back and forth in the net. When they swim to the backdown area before all the porpoises are released, the boat temporarily stops to allow the corkline to pop to the surface until the tuna turn around. Unlike the porpoises, the tuna will instantly take advantage of the opening provided by the backdown maneuver, and many tons may be lost in a matter of minutes.

When all the porpoises have been released, the ship stops, again allowing the corkline to pop to the surface, and the rest of the net is brought aboard. Then the tuna are lifted from the net sack, and transferred to the refrigerated hold.

BEHAVIORAL CAUSES OF PORPOISE MORTALITY

A set of the net as just described, in which nothing untoward occurs and no porpoises are injured or killed, was once a rarity. Now it constitutes the norm. Even on a well-run set, however, some porpoises may drown (or more accurately, suffocate, since they rarely open their blowholes underwater) after becoming entangled in the net. Entanglement is often a by-product of the behavior of the porpoises themselves.

The buoyed top edge of the net is visible, and a porpoise appears to be diving over it.

Bill High

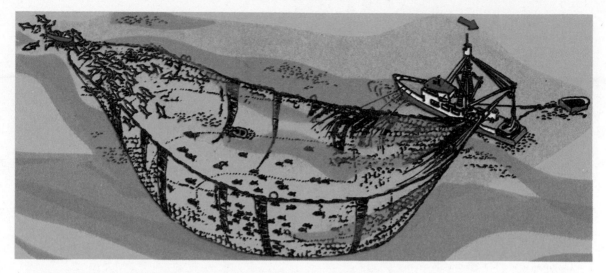

In backing down, the trailing edge of the net dips, and the porpoises swim over it. The arrow above the vessel shows the direction of the vessel during backdown.

There is a public mystique about the intelligence of porpoises. This notion holds that the familiar Atlantic bottlenose porpoises are remarkably intelligent and all other porpoise species are assumed to be so, too. In fact, the open-ocean spinner and spotter which are approximately half the size of the bottlenose, are behaviorally very different.

High-strung, active, and nervous, spinner and spotter porpoises have difficulty adapting to captivity, in contrast to the bottlenose. Faced with danger or the unfamiliar, forward flight is their immediate and principal response. Coastal bottlenose porpoises can wriggle their way safely through mangrove swamps and tidal flats. Spotters and spinners cannot maneuver in tight quarters. To turn, they must use their whole bodies.

For spinners and spotters, backing up is physically difficult and psychologically inconceivable. Thus a spotter who pokes its snout into a mesh hole in the net is doomed, unless hand-rescued or accidentally jostled free. It cannot back up the necessary 15 centimeters to save itself, nor does it comprehend enough of its situation to try. It can only continue to swim forward.

Spotters and spinners that find themselves in an area where the net has formed a roof of netting at the water surface also are likely to be lost. There may be plenty of swimming room and turning space under the canopy, but these porpoises do not turn around and look for open water surface, but rather tend to fight upward against the netting to air until exhausted.

Death may also occur if the animals become entangled in vertical folds of loose webbing. The netting sometimes buckles at the stern of the vessel during pursing. Occasionally, a group of animals may head into bulging netting at the stern (called a "stern bend") as if it were open water. They may be joined by other portions of the school, leading to a "disaster set" in which more than 20 animals are lost. Skippers now usually keep one speedboat actively circling in the stern area to help the porpoises.

Sometimes a few animals remain hidden in the net after the rest of the school has been safely released. Once the net is brought on board, releasing porpoises by hand is extremely difficult.

SOME WORKABLE AND UNWORKABLE SOLUTIONS

Some ideas for reducing porpoise mortality crop up again and again, put forth by members of the public unaware of the nature of spinner and spotter porpoises. People ask, for example, why not train them to leap over the net? Training, of course, is not feasible while fishing. In any case, spotter and spinner porpoises show a strong disinclination to leap barriers.

Why not drive the porpoises out of the net with killer whale sounds? As we have seen, the porpoises already have adequate motivation to leave the net, and they will go out quietly when they find an opening. Increasing their fear is hardly desirable. When researchers tried broadcasting killer whale sounds underwater, many porpoises panicked and blundered into worse positions.

How about using porpoise sounds to lure animals out of the net? So far, spinner and spotter porpoises in the net have shown no reaction to taped porpoise sounds of any sort. And, finally—how about using trained porpoises to show the wild ones how to get out of the net? As we have seen, finding the way out of the net is not the problem. In any case (aside from the practically insuperable logistic problems) porpoises do not follow leaders, and all porpoises and spotters especially, may ignore, avoid, or be openly hostile to strangers, even of their own species.

However, there have been many practical research contributions to the problem. The most important has been the joint effort on gear research over the years by the NMFS and the tuna fishery. This has resulted in a series of improvements in the backdown area of the net, and in an understanding of why some nets work and others do not. The present net design—required by U.S. federal regulations and in use also on some foreign boats—includes a panel of fine-meshed (31-millimeter) webbing, that spills out at the backdown area like the lip of a pitcher, forming a channel over which the porpoises pass to be released. The depth and width of the fine-mesh area has been extended on many boats, to prevent porpoises on the fringes of the school from blundering into the layer mesh parts of the net where they can get entangled.

Technicians have also learned that the net must be hung correctly from the corkline, so that folds and canopies in the backdown area do not occur. Getting the net to set correctly is called "fine-tuning." A fine-tuned net in the hands of a skilled captain and crew may be set around school after school of porpoise and tuna without the loss of a single porpoise.

HELP FROM CREW MEMBER

The safety records of some vessels that lost animals before backdown—when the porpoises panicked and became entangled in large webbing—has been greatly improved by increasing the depth of the net, thus increasing both the volume and the surface area available to the porpoises after pursing.

To further reduce mortality, a crew member equipped with a face mask is stationed on a raft in the backdown area. When backdown seems to have been completed, he looks and listens underwater for passive animals, alerting the skipper to continue the procedure until all porpoises come up for air and can be released.

THE EDUCATED AND UNTOUCHABLE

We also should not overlook the contribution the porpoises themselves have made to reducing their numbers killed. Spinners and spotters are quite capable of learning from experience. To the behaviorist watching animals in a set, it is evident that they have been through the experience before, and have learned what to do. They rest more or less in the center of the net with apparent calmness during pursing. As the backdown procedure continues, they crowd up against the net, as if waiting for the corkline to sink. Some animals may even slither or scramble over the corkline before it is totally under the surface. Fishermen call these educated animals "Sea World Porpoises."

Other learned behavior may be noticed during the chase. The authors have observed groups of porpoises "hiding,"—that is, hanging motionless just under the surface of the water, exposing only their blowhole in order

In the backdown area a member of the crew checks for and helps trapped porpoises.

Bill High

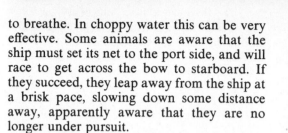

Spotted porpoise.

Bill High

to breathe. In choppy water this can be very effective. Some animals are aware that the ship must set its net to the port side, and will race to get across the bow to starboard. If they succeed, they leap away from the ship at a brisk pace, slowing down some distance away, apparently aware that they are no longer under pursuit.

Others have learned to go under the noisy speedboats, or the bubbling wake of the ship, instead of turning away from these obstacles. In coastal areas, spotter porpoises have become so skilled at avoiding pursuit that they have been nicknamed "the untouchables."

WHAT NEXT?

National Marine Fisheries Service figures for 1978 indicated that the fleet is continuing to show improvement. The kill per ton was down again, from 1977's 0.26 to a new low of 0.15. Is this enough? Is it ever going to be enough? That depends on who is asking the question.

Let us suppose that by achieving nearly perfect records on every set, the fleet was able to reduce its kill to 10,000 animals a year. To the population dynamicist, and perhaps even to the environmentalist, this is permissable. Apparently, even two or three times that number would not harm the populations of spotted and spinner porpoises, but in fact would allow them to increase back to approximately their original levels. To an animal protectionist, however, whose concern is primarily for the survival of individuals of particular species, 10,000 is too many. Ten may be too many, and there may be no possible solution—except to discontinue the tuna fishery.

FRINGE BENEFITS

Throughout 1978, the tuna processing and fishing industries provided funds and a vessel, in cooperation with government agencies, for at-sea research. Means to corral and release porpoises before backdown were tested. Behavioral observations, school composition studies, population and distribution studies, gear-improvement research and other programs were also undertaken. Thousands of porpoise specimens have been measured, dissected, computerized, and compared, so that we now probably know more about *Stenella* biology, physiology, and systematics than about any other small whale or whale relative. A massive air-sea survey undertaken in 1977 provided more information about porpoise distribution than we ever had before for any species. A trained cadre of more than 80 government observers are recording sightings, giving scientists an unprecedented look at populations and distribution of all whalelike fauna, including a number of nearly unknown species, over a large area.

New fishing grounds are being investigated and canneries are being established in the western Pacific, where the tuna do not associate with porpoises. Finally, experiments are underway seeking alternative methods of attracting and holding adult yellowfin tuna. While this work is at best speculative, promising approaches—such as scent attractants and floating aggregating devices—are under study. As long as tuna fishing continues, there is an opportunity for research to devise fishing methods without using porpoises □

SELECTED READINGS

"Fishing the seven seas: tuna fishing" by S. Solon. *Forbes,* April 3, 1978.

"Hunt for tuna" by A. Kessler. *Oceans,* July 1976.

"Murder of the porpoise: closing in on a solution" by V. Cox. *Science Digest,* July 1977.

"Tuna/dolphin problem: five years of progress" by W. W. Fox. *Oceans,* May 1978.

WILDLIFE IN CHINA

by Norman Myers

FOR centuries, the winds of exploitation have blown hard across China. And of all the country's hard-used natural resources, few have bent before the gale more dramatically than wildlife. But beginning in the late 1960's, something significant began to happen in the People's Republic of China. Instead of continuing to encourage peasants to wipe out the fabled Chinese tiger, the government started planning a system of reserves to save it. In other ways, as well, the Chinese began to show an unprecedented concern for wildlife.

During a two-and-a-half-week stay in China, I attempted to assess the depth of this commitment. I concluded that a genuine conservation ethic has indeed permeated the nation of 800 million people. There seems to be a new environmental consciousness, which is almost as revolutionary as the People's Republic itself.

The country's zoos are well patronized, from what I could gather in Canton and Peking. And the Chinese press covers such broad environmental issues as anti-pollution measures, water conservancy, tree planting, and similar activities more often than the western media.

The growing awareness throughout China of the need for efficient land use and conservation bodes well for habitat restoration. And that approach offers far more hope for all of China's wildlife than mere protection of certain endangered species. If China were still committed to developing the western mountains and forests, many wild species—most of them already reduced to mere fragments of their former populations—would be doomed. But, instead, attention has turned to increasing the yield of cropland already in use, making fertilizers, irrigation, and manpower turn bigger dividends.

What this means for wildlife is breathing space and time to rebuild certain dwindling populations. Reserves and sanctuaries similar to those of western nations already embrace several significant areas of China's 9.5 million square kilometers. According to government spokesmen, additional reserves are on the planning boards.

The Chinese commitment to preserving wildlife goes beyond habitat preservation. At least 32 species and subspecies, including all the remaining deer species, receive protection. The Chinese are also going to include several more species.

GIANT PANDA

Most publicized of all China's wildlife is the giant panda. Its formerly vast range, now largely covered by farms and villages or merely deforested, has shrunk to ribbons of bamboo and forest encircling the mountains of central China at elevations from 3,500 to 4,500 meters. Today, a strategic sector of this rugged, almost impenetrable country is set aside for the several hundred rigidly protected pandas still surviving.

The creature's main stronghold, Szechuan Province's Wang-Lang Reserve, covers about 200 square kilometers of ravines and thick forest in the Min Shan Mountains. A few pandas are reportedly holding out in a range of the Chuing-lai Mountains stretching nearly 320 kilometers from north to south in western Szechuan.

Several factors tip the scales in favor of the panda's recovery. Preferring the most inaccessible terrain, the giant panda is almost never seen, and it poses no threat to livestock or people. Its pelt has no commercial value. Furthermore, a sweeping public-relations campaign has made it such an object of national pride and international affection that hardly any Chinese would dream of killing one. Its remaining habitat is so lush that thousands of pandas could grow fat on it, supposing the panda's social systems allowed its numbers to grow. Its only real enemy, in fact, is the leopard, which shares its range in moderate numbers.

In recent years, the panda has become a genuine *cause célèbre* for the Chinese. Schoolchildren, government officials, and scientists alike boast of its protected status. Perhaps the real significance of the panda craze will turn out to be its role in raising the value of all threatened wildlife in China.

DEER

Among the mammals that might benefit from the panda's good public relations are China's deer. Nine species or sub-species appear in the International Union for Conservation of Natural Resources (IUCN) Red Data Book. All are threatened to some degree. Others, such as Hende's and Swinhoe's sika deer, are already extinct. Habitat loss and overkilling have taken a heavy toll. For centuries, the Chinese have delighted in wild meat, including venison. But they have sought out deer even more intensively to obtain the antlers, which are said to have aphrodisiac properties.

Like rhinoceros horns, deer antlers have been discounted by scientists on this score. But superstition is hard to shake. Fifty years ago, a pair of sika antlers in velvet would sell for $150 to $280, a considerable sum then. However, the Chinese government has succeeded in debunking the myth. Today, aphrodisiacs are almost invariably scorned by the modern young Chinese.

Unfortunately, the forests in which most of China's deer live had been steadily cut down over the centuries for firewood, build-

China's new interest in forest and wildlife conservation should preserve the Sika deer.

Bruce Coleman

Bruce Coleman

The Przewalski's horse reminds one of the horses painted by prehistoric peoples in their caves. At one time they ranged over central Asia.

ing materials, and to create cropland. In fact, it is surprising that deer have survived at all in the eastern half of the country, where most of the people live.

Père David's deer disappeared from its swampy habitat in eastern China more than 2,000 years ago, thereafter surviving only in the Emperor's park and, in the nineteenth century, in a few European zoos. Even those in the Emperor's park were destroyed during the Boxer Rebellion, so that Père David's deer existed only outside of its native country until the 1950's, when a few zoo animals were returned to China.

Elsewhere, deer maintain a tenuous foothold in scattered forest pockets. All four surviving races of sika deer are near extinction in the few wild eastern forest tracts that escaped felling before 1950. A few herds on deer farms, however, have fared better. In Chekiang Province, the black muntjac is hard pressed, and the white-lipped deer of eastern Tibet and neighboring regions is very rare. The same is true for M'Neill's deer in Tibet and parts of Sinkiang and Turkestan. Until 1960, the musk deer was sought relentlessly. Though it has no antlers, the aggressive, tusked males were sought for the pasty secretions of their musk glands, used in perfume.

All the surviving species are now protected. Having discovered a way to remove the valuable musk from musk deer without killing the animals, the Chinese now hope to see the species thrive. Since 1960, in fact, its numbers have climbed to the point where limited hunting is permitted. Exportation of musk is subject to an annual quota to ensure that the practice is not abused. Hunting is forbidden for China's remaining deer species, and specific sanctuaries are set aside for each.

PRZEWALSKI'S HORSE

Like China's deer, Przewalski's horse has suffered from drastic habitat loss. An "endangered species" in the IUCN's Red Data Book, less than 100 remain in the wild, most or all of these in Outer Mongolia. Once, this creature of the arid plains ranged from Outer Mongolia far into the northern sector of Sinkiang. In the past, both Mongolians and Chinese hunted the brush-maned horse. But this practice has been stringently suppressed by the Chinese authorities.

Domestic livestock has posed a far more significant threat. Until the 1960s, nomads pushed their livestock farther and farther into unoccupied territories, seeking new grazing and new sources of water. Several herdsmen in the vicinity of a water hole for just a few weeks can effectively deny access to a timid creature such as Przewalski's horse.

During the past 15 years, however, nomads have been encouraged to settle near artificial watering points in semi-desert tracts. This means less competition for wildlife. Now, herds of Przewalski's horse reportedly cross from Outer Mongolia southward into China during the winter. This trend may grow if the Chinese leave extensive areas in Sinkiang undeveloped for the time being. Such a possibility was confirmed by officials who worked in western China during the late 1960's and early 1970's.

ASSES AND CAMELS

A similar situation exists for the kiang, an Asiatic wild ass, though it is not considered in danger of extinction. For at least 2,000 years it has competed with domestic herds for grazing and water. But the ass is steadily giving way. The kiang cannot last more than two or three days without drinking, and, like the horse, is readily deterred by livestock from visiting watering points. Confined now to parts of Tibet, the kiang is no longer losing numbers and may even be recovering under complete protection.

The kulan, or Mongolian wild ass, is rarer than the kiang, in part because the Chinese once relished its meat. The Chinese say they are trying to build up the population of kulans that stray over the border from Outer Mongolia. They can do this through better management of domestic livestock herds and through strict protection of the kulans.

The wild two-humped bactrian camel, found mostly in Outer Mongolia and Sinkiang, is restricted to about 30,000 square kilometers between Lakes Lop Nor and Bagrach Kol in China. This area is near China's atomic testing ground, and no government official would discuss the region. Few people encroach upon its habitat.

TIGERS AND LEOPARDS

Almost insurmountable odds have pushed the tiger toward extinction. The so-called Chinese race once roamed across a broad belt of central and southern China, and along river valleys into mountainous parts of western China. As huge tracts of this range were converted to human use, prey species disappeared, and the cat turned to domestic herds. Thus it became the enemy of every human. Moreover, tiger bones and blood were once thought to have medicinal properties.

So persistent were the tiger's livestock depredations, that, until the mid-1960's, the Chinese government took a formal stand on eliminating the tiger in most areas. This policy has been partially reversed. Tigers persist in mountain zones of southeastern, southwestern, and southern provinces, generally in forests and brush country. Details of a refuge system are still being worked out by Peking.

In the south of China, Bengal tigers are scattered among the mountains and against the borders with Burma, Laos, and North Vietnam. Like the Chinese tiger, they receive partial protection.

In the northeast, in the Changpai Mountains and lesser Hsingan Mountains of

Frederic-Jacana

The two-humped wild camel of the vast Gobi desert region, between China and the Soviet Union are an endangered species. Camels can lose one fourth of their weight from evaporation while losing only one tenth of the water content of their blood.

G. Schaller/Bruce Coleman

The yellow-gray coat of the snow leopard, of southwestern China, becomes white in the winter.

Kirin and Heilungkiang provinces, a few remaining individuals of the long-haired Siberian are totally protected. These are the largest of all tigers. Forests of various tree species are being planted in the northeast that will create habitats for the deer, boar, and other game or fur-bearing animals that Siberian tigers prey upon.

Leopards are somewhat better off than tigers, for they can live off small prey and are less inclined to take domestic animals. Their stealthy, secretive nature enables them to live near human communities without being noticed. The leopard is also fairly common in China's northern, western, and southern frontiers.

Unfortunately, leopard pelts are highly valued by Hong Kong dealers. All but three of the dozen or more traders I interviewed admitted to buying many leopard skins from China each year. I asked if they could supply 50 per month as a regular order, and they seemed to think it would not be difficult. Unconfirmed reports suggest that the Chinese engage in regulated cropping of leopards to supply the Hong Kong trade. This produces as many as 3,000 skins each year from just a few provinces of central China. But on the other hand, all the dealers I spoke to insisted they had been able to obtain al-most no tiger skins from China since the late 1960's, supporting China's policy switch to tiger protection.

Two much rarer forms of leopard are also found in China. The clouded leopard occurs in southern areas, and the snow leopard is found in mountainous parts of Sinkiang and across parts of the Tibetan Plateau. Chinese authorities say that both receive protection, subject to occasional need to eliminate individual animals that take livestock. Though Hong Kong dealers readily produced skins of both species for sale (one merchant offered 50 clouded leopard skins at $150 each) they claimed none came from China.

EGRETS, PHEASANTS, AND RAPTORS

If information about mammals is hard to obtain, the status of birds is even more obscure. I had expected, however, to see a variety of bird species, since they are usually visible in towns and in the countryside even when mammals are not. But wherever I went, I saw fewer birds than in any country I've visited.

The Chinese egret was reduced to a tiny population by the feather trade in the first half of this century. Fortunately, it may still be breeding in coastal wetlands of Kwangtung Province. But this means it is close to the traders of Hong Kong, who will—according to dealers I spoke with on the spot—offer considerable sums for egret plumes.

The Chinese ring-necked pheasant was brought to America by Benjamin Franklin's son-in-law.

J. Van Wormer/Bruce Coleman

There may be more Bengal tigers in captivity than in the wild. They are now strongly protected.

A number of pheasant species are rare and some are still declining, but all are totally protected. In the past, they, too, were hunted for their ornamental feathers. Favoring forest-edge environments, they suffered from the same pre-1950 forest clearing that mammals did. While Chinese ring-necked pheasants seem to be numerous, Cabot's trapagon is said to hang on only in upland forests of Fukien and Kwangtung provinces, too near Hong Kong for comfort.

The white-eared and brown-eared pheasants, Elliot's pheasant, Hume's bartailed pheasant, and both Sclater's monal and the Chinese monal pheasant are extremely rare, living in isolated forest patches in central, southern and southwestern China. Inquiries in Hong Kong revealed that the trade in pheasant feathers from China declined rapidly after 1950, and more or less dried up since 1960.

I managed to spot only three raptors throughout the whole trip. Birds of prey are considered a delicacy in Hong Kong, so large numbers are shipped from Kwangchow (Canton) along the two-hour rail route to Hong Kong. Predatory birds have been shown time and time again to render many ecological benefits, and the Chinese could help themselves by stopping this traffic. The total trade brings in only about $150,000 per year to China, less than the country earns in one day from the sale of pigs to Hong Kong.

DISRUPTING ECOLOGICAL SYSTEMS

In the mid-1950's, the new government decided to get rid of four pests: rats, mosquitoes, houseflies, and sparrows (the sparrows because of their alleged seed-eating habits). Later, the Chinese realized they were succeeding too well. The decimation of sparrows and other bird species was leading to plagues of insects in many areas.

Gradually, the Chinese have become sensitive to the damage heavy-handed management can do to ecological systems. They are still only vaguely aware of the ecological benefits to be gained from a diversity of bird species. However, they want to cover their bets by rehabilitating bird communities. So, in the list of four pests, sparrows are replaced by bedbugs.

THE HUMAN POPULATION PICTURE

In the long run, of course, the main factor determining the fate of China's wildlife is the rate of human increase. In population planning, the Chinese have accomplished near miracles. The annual growth rate has fallen from over three per cent in the 1950's to about one-and-a-half per cent. If present trends continue, China may be the first developing country to lower its population growth rate to one per cent, within the next 10 years.

But despite the best efforts of her population campaign, China will eventually have more than 1,000,000,000 people. With an economic growth rate of more than ten per cent, these multitudes are going to make increasingly greater demands upon the country's natural environment. Eighty per cent of the Chinese are still engaged in agriculture, and they've hardly begun their "green revolution."

Whether the mounting pressures of development will ultimately dampen China's burgeoning concern for wildlife is a difficult question □

SELECTED READINGS

A Closer Look at Bears and Pandas by S. Cook. Watts, 1977.

"Giant pandas in the wild" by S. Wang. *Natural History,* December 1973.

"Giant panda is a bear, maybe." *Science News,* October 13, 1973.

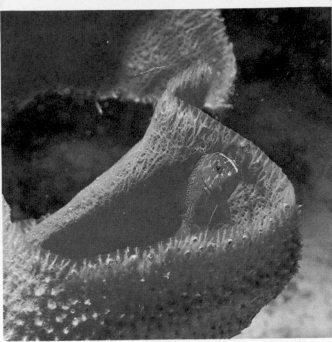

Peter D. Capen

Peter D. Capen

Above: a young Nassau grouper takes refuge in a vase sponge. Right: a scuba diver investigates a huge barrel sponge.

SPONGES

by Shirley A. Pomponi

SPONGES are just barely animals. In fact, they are such a borderline case that until the nineteenth century they were called zoophytes, the animal-plants. Sponges are among the most primitive forms of multicellular animal life. They have no muscles or nerves, no mouth or digestive cavity, no heart, no brain, nothing in the way of organs. But they have been around a long time and must be doing something right. More than 5,000 species inhabit this planet, living in fresh water and throughout the sea down to depths of more than 7,500 meters.

Often strikingly beautiful, sponges grow in a kaleidoscope of colors, sizes, and shapes. Used for thousands of years, they are now seen as an important source of pharmacolog-ical compounds, including one being tested against certain cancers.

Their water-holding capabilities have made the word sponge a part of our language. And the pores that give the sponge phylum its name—*Porifera,* meaning pore bearer—are the key to their existence.

FILTERING MACHINES

Sponges consist of several types of cells, loosely organized into external and internal areas of the body. What distinguishes sponges from every other group of animals are chambers formed by groups of choanocytes, or collar cells. This type of cell is named for its collar of minute cellular projections, in the center of which is a single,

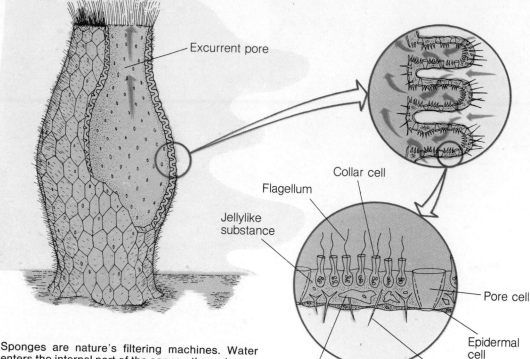

Excurrent pore

Collar cell

Flagellum

Jellylike
substance

Pore cell

Epidermal
cell

Amebocyte

Spicule

Sponges are nature's filtering machines. Water enters the internal part of the sponge through pore cells, and the collar cells remove oxygen and food from the water. The flagella of these cells sweep the water toward an excurrent pore of the sponge.

A large coral-reef sponge reproduces by releasing its mucuslike sheets of eggs into the water.

Peter D. Capen

long, whiplike flagellum. The flagella beat actively to direct water through the canals that extend throughout the body of the sponge.

The water, of course, brings with it oxygen and food. The choanocytes ingest bacteria, small algae, and organic debris and then pass them on in food bags, or vacuoles, to cells called amoebocytes. Amoebocytes are highly motile cells that digest the food and pass the nutrients on to other cells. All the cells seem able to exchange oxygen and carbon dioxide.

A sponge ten centimeters tall and less than two centimeters across has more than 2,-000,000 choanocyte chambers and can pump more than 110 liters of water through its canals each day. A living sponge is simply a very efficient filtering machine.

SEVERAL WAYS TO REPRODUCE

Most sponges are hermaphroditic, producing both egg and sperm cells, although a few species have separate sexes. An individual sponge releases its egg and sperm cells at different times. This prevents sperm from fertilizing eggs from the same individual and ensures cross-fertilization, with the sperm of

A sponge (orange color) and a large white sea anemone compete for space in the crowded environment of a coral reef.

one individual fertilizing the egg of another sponge. In some species the release is highly visible: sperm cells in clouds of milky fluid and in egg cells.

When a sperm cell enters another sponge through its canal system, it is engulfed by a collar cell and transported to the egg. Fertilization occurs when the sperm-bearing collar cell fuses with an egg. In some species the fertilized eggs are released directly into the water, but in most the eggs are retained until they develop into larvae. The larvae are then released and swim around for a few hours to a few days before settling down on some suitable surface to begin their own lives as sponges.

Sponges can also reproduce asexually by simply budding off new individuals. And some species, threatened by temperature extremes, dryness, pollution, or food scarcity, find an alternate solution to ensure reproduction. They release gemmules, cystlike masses of cells. The gemmules themselves are resistant to harsh environmental conditions. The cells remain encysted until conditions become favorable for growing into new sponges. Gemmules are common among freshwater sponges, but are evident in some saltwater species as well.

Perhaps the most remarkable thing about sponges is their ability to regenerate after being pulled apart. In a classic experiment, a sponge is forced through layers of gauze or heavy silk into a bowl of seawater. The cells settle on the bottom of the bowl and within hours or days reaggregate into a tiny but functional sponge.

BEAUTIFUL AND SUCCESSFUL

Sponge skeletons are formed either by elastic collagen fibers or tiny elements called spicules, or both. Scientists classify sponges primarily by their spicules, which in most cases are either siliceous (glassy) or calcareous (limy).

As a group, sponges first appeared about 550,000,000 years ago. They probably evolved from single-celled protozoans, and have changed very little since. As individuals

These sponge spicules have been dyed and photographed under a microscope.

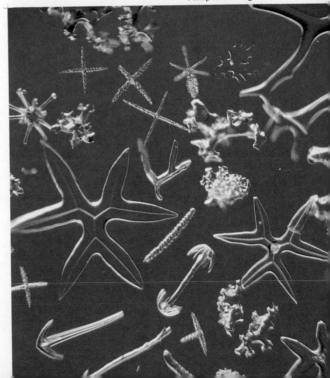

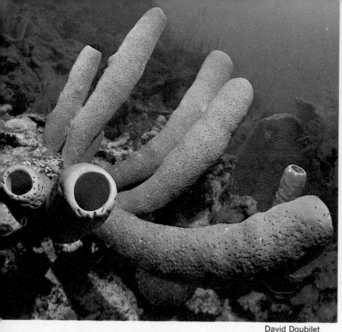

These tube sponges of the Caribbean show how firmly they attach to the underlying coral.

The colorful nudibranch is a marine mollusk without a shell, searches for food around a sponge.

they have life-spans from just a few years to 20 years or more. One recently discovered class, the sclerosponges, are thought to live several hundred years.

By far the most beautiful and diverse species of sponges are found on coral reefs. They range in color from the deepest reds and brightest yellows to iridescent pinks, blues, and purples. Some of the reddish tones come from carotenoid pigments in the various cells. Sponges also contain pigments such as chlorophyll and melanin, which come from microscopic algae living inside the sponge or from algal cells the sponge has ingested.

DIFFERENT NICHES

On coral reefs where competition for space is intense, sponges have evolved forms that allow them to occupy three different niches. The common and most visible sponges are the massive varieties, which can be amorphous in shape, long and branching, tubular, or vase-shaped. These sponges may require only a small surface area for attachment for successful growth.

A second group forms thin encrustations on the undersides of corals and other hard substrates. Some, like the orange encrusting sponge, *Mycale laevis,* actually protect corals by preventing other organisms from settling and boring into the coral.

The third group of sponges themselves tunnel into the coral or other limestone substrates. They secrete an acid or an enzyme that removes microscopic chips of the substrate. The chips are carried through the loosely packed cells of the sponge body and out through the canals. Eventually the sponge fills numerous cavities and tunnels, weakening the coral skeletons and making the coral vulnerable to strong currents and storm waves.

Most of the body of the excavating sponge is inside the substrate, with only the sponge's intake and outflow openings showing, often on chimneylike papillae. And even then, the papillae of most boring sponges are so small that they are barely visible. However some species that excavate extensive tunnels need so many papillae that they form an encrustation over the reef.

MANY FRIENDS, FEW ENEMIES

Sponges in turn provide shelter to other reef dwellers. The loggerhead variety of sponge houses thousands of shrimps in its canals. Brittlestars are often seen draped across tubular and branching sponges, and crabs, fish, and even sea urchins hide in the bottom of vase-shaped sponges.

Not all sponges lead a stationary life. Larvae of the sponge *Suberites domuncula* may settle on a snail shell occupied by a hermit crab. As the sponge grows, it completely covers the snail shell. Eventually the shell dissolves and the hermit crab lives within the cavity in the sponge.

Then there's the crab *Dromia vulgaris,* which has a broad, hairy shell and a last pair of legs that bend upward. After breaking off a piece of sponge with its claws, the crab uses these legs to hold the fragment against its hairy back. The sponge grows and soon covers the shell like a cap, camouflaging the crab. In both cases the crabs are protected from predators because most fish do not eat sponges, and the sponge is moved from place to place by the crab, enabling it to feed in different places.

An interesting Japanese custom stems from the relationship between the shrimp *Spongicola* ("sponge dweller") and the glass sponge *Euplectella,* also known as Venus' flower basket. The shrimp live in pairs and enter the sponge while still small. Eventually they grow too large to leave the sponge. They survive because, like the sponge, they filter food from the water. The sponge, with the entrapped shrimp, is given by the Japanese as a wedding present, a symbol of lifelong faithfulness.

Sponges have very few enemies. In polar and temperate seas, sea stars and nudibranchs are the major predators. In the tropics, certain fishes and sea urchins nibble or scrape off pieces of sponge, and sea turtles are known to take some sizable bites. But the needlelike spicules, as well as poisonous compounds in some sponges, deter many would-be attackers.

USEFUL TOO

Appealing in their own right, sponges offer the added virtue of usefulness. Even with synthetic sponges widely available, a market for natural sponges persists. Natural sponges hold more water without dripping, are easier to clean, and last longer, even under heavy use. Painters, window washers, and ceramic workers frequently prefer the real thing. And now, after centuries in the bathtub and decades on the Saturday morning driveway, sponges are finding their way into the laboratories of pharmacologists and cell biologists. As do so many marine invertebrates that have limited defenses in the usual sense (they are capable of neither fight nor flight), sponges produce some extremely powerful chemical compounds, toxic and otherwise, that hold great promise as drugs for the treatment of human disorders.

At the same time, sponges are getting more and more attention from those trying to advance our understanding of life at the cellular level. Knowledge of how sponge cells move about, recognize each other, and link up could have enormous implications for the study of life further up the evolutionary scale, including our own.

We can learn a lot from this "primitive" animal. But even if we do isolate a marvelous drug or achieve a better grasp of how cells do what they do, we can hardly lose sight of the infinitely varying forms, the flamboyant colors, and the intriguing adaptations of the sponges themselves □

SELECTED READINGS

Aspects of Sponge Biology edited by Frederick Harrison and Ronald R. Cowden. Academic Press, 1976.

"Consider the sponge" by M. E. Long. *National Geographic,* March 1977.

Wonders of Sponges by Morris Jacobson and Rosemary Pang. Dodd Mead, 1976.

An inspector checks the quality and size of bath sponges in Tarpon Springs, Florida.

David Doubilet

Because angelfish are noted for their brilliant colors, they are popular as aquarium fish.

The white-spotted filefish flashes its white spots as a warning to ward off attack.

WHY ARE FISH SO COLORFUL?

by Peter D. Capen

VISITING the clear underwater world of a coral reef is always a memorable experience. The scuba diver is greeted by a great variety of colorful animal life. Everywhere there are different kinds of sponges sporting nearly every conceivable hue. There are delicate, brightly colored tube worms; feather stars with long, slender oranges or black arms; pretty sea anemones with their subtle shades; and a host of tiny beautiful shrimps, crabs, snails, and other creatures.

But the colorful appearance of all these animals seems to pale next to a group whose beauty has set them apart in the coral community—the tropical fishes. Their delicate, tantalizing shapes and frequently bold coloration have made them much sought after by divers and aquarists alike.

DRESS CHANGES

Not only are the colors themselves fascinating, but so too is the ingenious way in which a great many true fishes, or teleosts, change their colors for display or better camouflage. Situated in the under layers of the skin of these fishes are great numbers of color cells, known as chromatophores. These color cells have saclike shapes with numerous branches. Each chromatophore contains a pigment, such as black, brown, or gray melanin pigment, yellow, orange, or red carotenoid, or the white granules of guanin.

Alteration of a certain color is brought about by the movement of the appropriate pigment within its chromatophores. The pigment may become concentrated into the cell centers, having the overall effect of decreasing that particular color. Or it may become spread out into the cell branches, increasing the color. These changes are often nothing short of spectacular. Watching an elongated trumpetfish move across the reef, for example, you can hardly believe the rapid series of color changes and modifications that it goes through.

A fish's ability to alter its dress is not only limited to the action of chromatophore pigments. A wide variety of fishes have an additional group of color cells known as iridocytes. These, with their crystals of guanin, produce an iridescent sheen that can complement the other color changes.

EYES AS TRIGGER

Together, the chromatophores and iridocytes enable a fish to change its overall shade and color, and to modify particular patterns. The whole color-adaptive process may occur slowly, or may be accomplished in minutes or even seconds. It has been shown experimentally to be triggered via the fish's eyes. The eyes record any changes in situation or background color, and the fish's body colors are adjusted accordingly.

COUNTERSHADING

Tropical teleosts have evolved widely differing techniques of coloration and color adaptation to meet specific needs. One of the simplest but most successful means of fish concealment, for example, is countershading. Early one afternoon on a dive off the Caribbean island of Cozumel, Mexico, I witnessed a startling illustration of just how good a countershading type of camouflage can become. Seemingly out of nowhere, a large barracuda materialized a short distance in front of me.

After regaining my composure, I slowly swam toward it. With little more than a slight flick of its tail, it disappeared into the blue void, as ghostlike as it had first appeared. I had been unaware of the barracuda's comings and goings because of its contrasting shading.

In countershading, a fish has a relatively dark back and light underside so that, seen from any direction, its body will be less conspicuous. When you are above the fish, its darker back tends to merge with the increasing darkness of the water as the sun's rays are absorbed and scattered. But when you are below the fish its light underside causes it to blend into the light streaming down from the surface. Even when viewed from the side a countershaded fish seems to be obscured, because the light catching its back is counteracted by the darker coloring. This makes the fish appear flat and inconsequential against its watery background.

MASTERS OF DISGUISE

While open-water fishes are often countershaded to make them less obvious, some reef species have other concealing techniques. In the shy, nocturnal squirrelfishes, individuals that live on shallow water reefs, particularly around large stretches of sand, often seem to exhibit a much lighter color phase than their deep water counterparts of the main reefs. The smooth trunkfish also lightens in color when it moves from darker to brighter areas in its submarine home.

Such voracious carnivores as the trumpetfish, the scorpionfish, and the grotesque-looking toadfishes are all masters of disguise. The trumpetfish, with its elongated body, is rarely detected as it hangs head downwards in among the branches of the sea whips. There, nearly motionless, it patiently waits for some small fish to venture too close. Then, lightning fast, it strikes, engulfing its victim so quickly that it appears to vanish from a point well in front of the trumpetfish's mouth. More than once I have also stared, quite fascinated, while this harmless looking fish has stalked its quarry. With its special camouflage, shape, and behavioral trait of drifting head downwards like a stick, it very slowly maneuvers towards its unsuspecting prey until, drawing close enough, it can strike.

The trumpet fish has a tubelike mouth and grows to about 60 centimeters long.

This camouflaged toadfish inhabits the tropical coastal waters of the Americas. It is dangerous.

WAITING FOR DINNER

Just as adept at concealment are the venomous scorpionfish and the toadfish. Quietly resting on sand, rock, or coral, the scorpionfish's rough textured skin and extraordinary camouflage perfectly mask its presence. Its ability to escape detection is so successful that on several occasions divers have paused to look at something, and nearly put their hands down on its poisonous spines. To eat, the scorpionfish only has to lie motionless and wait for its meal to come wandering by.

The toadfish has a broad, flattened head with many branching whiskerlike appendages on the lower jaw. These appendages together with its coloration makes the overall camouflage excellent. Using its concealment in much the same way as the scorpionfish, it also lies silently in wait. But, unlike the scorpionfish, this predator seems to hunt primarily at night.

Quite unexpectedly I came across one large toadfish completely out in the open on a night dive. At first my light passed over without my noticing it was there. But the light blinded some tiny, electric blue, nocturnal fishes. They frantically darted back and forth and suddenly, like a springing trap, the toadfish gulped down two or three of these hapless little fishes. Apart from gobbling its midnight meal, the toadfish showed no other movement. Sweeping my light backwards one last time, I saw it still quietly lying there waiting, almost invisible against its outcrop of coral.

BREAKING UP SHAPE

Characteristically active reef fishes often have striking but disruptive patterns that tend to break up their distinctive body shape. When seen against the backdrop of the variegated reef landscape, the camouflaging effectiveness of such disruptive coloration can be well appreciated. Pronounced bands or deeply contrasting patterns of color create an optical illusion of multiple objects, rather than one simple distinguishable form. Juvenile queen and French angelfishes even have bright vertical stripes over their already bold color patterns, although they lose the stripes as they become mature.

In some species, the disruptive colors and patterns extend into the fins, particularly the dorsal fins, and so break up even further the fish's general body shape. This situation

The stripes on the four-eyed butterflyfish break up its visible shape.

is seen perhaps best of all in one beautiful member of the Sciaenidae family. The tiny, juvenile spotted drum has a magnificent long flowing dorsal fin. One of the fish's several prominent black stripes cuts diagonally across its white body and runs not only to the end of its tail, but also stretches out to the very tip of the dorsal fin, disguising the fish's true contours in a remarkably successful way.

HIDING THE EYES

The overall effect of much disruptive coloration would be considerably diminished if fishes did not also conceal their eyes. When it is completely exposed, a large, rounded black pupil quickly attracts the predator's attention. Consequently, many fishes use disruptive eye masks in conjunction with their other markings. The essential feature of these eye masks is a highly complex bar structure, or ocular band, that runs across the fish's face and almost completely hides the staring pupil. This band blends into one unit the several distinct pigmented areas around the pupil as well as the pupil itself. Not only is the fish's eye well concealed, but so too is the movement of the eye within the orbit.

In addition to hiding its real eyes, the foureye butterflyfish also has a pair of false eyes, large black spots located on either side of its body near the base of the tail. It has been suggested that an attacker would be more likely to strike at the prominent false eyes than at the concealed true eyes, and in so doing would give the butterflyfish a chance of escape.

SIGNAL FOR CLEANING

Numerous tropical fishes use colors as signals. One of the most fascinating examples is the tiger grouper found in the waters around the Caribbean island of Bonaire. This large, handsome fish is regularly plagued by certain parasitic crustaceans. To rid itself of its unwanted guests, it has developed mutually beneficial relationships with tiny, brightly colored cleaner fishes.

One or more individuals of a cleaner species, whose colors may themselves act as attracting signals, set up residence on a particular coral head. There they wait until their services are needed. When a grouper requires the removal of either parasites or injured tissue, it simply swims over to its cleaning station and indicates that it is ready to be cleaned. For most groupers the "go ahead" signal to the cleaners is quite specific. It often takes the form of distinct body movements in which the body is inclined in the water and the gill structures are spread out.

Bonaire's tiger groups have gone a step further, adding a color change to the signalling process. In addition to their body move-

Left: saddle butterflyfish. Right: masked butterflyfish. Note how the eyes are hidden.

RESTING POSE

Fishes displaying disruptive coloration may alter their seemingly fixed patterns. For example, when twilight comes to the reef, the banded butterflyfish becomes marked with darkish blotches over the light areas of its body. In the spotfin butterflyfish, the large dusky spot on the soft dorsal fin becomes black, while broad but diffuse dark bands appear on its sides. Perhaps such changes are necessary to give these generally active fishes a different kind of camouflage when lying still on the bottom at night.

ments, they spontaneously flash an opaque whitish covering over their normally rich patterns. They keep this covering throughout the cleaning, but lose it when it is time for the cleaning procedure to end. I have observed this strange behavior on frequent occasions, and it always seems as though the cleaners do not start their work until their client has first changed to its whitish hue. Then, they just as rapidly leave when the color has switched back to normal.

Two aspects of a smooth trunkfish as it changes its background color, for protection or warning, by means of its chromatophores.

WARNING AND FRIGHT

Just as intriguing as the tiger grouper's color signal is that used by another Caribbean species, the whitespotted filefish, which has the ability to flash white spots all across its orange or brown patterned body. It can retain these markings for some time, or simply fade them out. I could not understand this puzzling behavior until one afternoon when, while exploring the reefs of Klein Bonaire, I found at least part of the answer.

Coming upon a large whitespotted filefish showing no spots, I patiently followed it around the reef. As we passed a large coral head, a pugnacious dusky damselfish darted out. The filefish instantaneously flashed its white spots, which stood out strikingly on its body. Quickly moving on, its spots slowly faded. The filefish's unusual reaction may well have been a warning signal, or a response to fright. I suspect it was actually a little of both.

MATING SIGNALS

Of all the animal kingdom's color signals, perhaps none are more basic to a species' survival than those relating to mating. Except for the parrotfishes, few Caribbean reef fishes show distinct sex differences.

Probably the most familiar of all the reef fishes, parrotfishes are frequently seen and heard crunching loudly on the coral with their beaklike teeth, or glimpsed as they swim past and suddenly vent an enormous cloud of sandy fecal matter. Considerable confusion has long surrounded parrotfish identification, as some species have not just one or two, but as many as three distinct color phases.

The confusion arises because various species are represented by a drab-colored female, a drab-colored male, and yet another male whose hues are strikingly vivid. For a long time the two dissimilar males were given separate identities, instead of being placed together in the same species. Interestingly, the marked difference in coloration between the males reflects different breeding patterns.

The drab male typically spawns in aggregations with other males, which together fertilize the eggs of a single female. The brilliantly colored male, sometimes referred to as the terminal or supermale, is territorial and individually spawns with a female.

It is believed the terminal male phase is actually the result of a sex reversal from the female. Experiments have shown that a female injected with male hormones will change color to the much more vibrant hues of the supermale. Undoubtedly, there would be little real advantage to the terminal male to assume such singular resplendence if it did not serve as a definite signalling device, attracting the females and, at the same time, warning off any competing males □

 SELECTED READINGS

"Color control; multihued fishes" by C. Roessler. *Oceans*, September 1977.

The Healing Sea: A Voyage into the Alien World Offshore by George Ruggieri S.J. and Norman David Rosenberg. Dodd Mead, 1978.

INDEX

ACKNOWLEDGMENTS. Sources of articles appear below, indicating those reprinted with the kind permission of publications and organizations.

A BIG DOUBT ON SOLAR THEORIES, Page 11: Copyright 1978 Smithsonian Institution, from *Smithsonian* magazine March 1978.

THE SPACE SHUTTLE, Page 19: Reprinted from *American Scientist,* November/December 1978.

PLUTO, Page 27: *Astronomy,* December 1978. Reproduced by permission of publisher. Copyright © 1978 by AstroMedia Corp., Milwaukee, WI. All rights reserved.

IS ANYBODY OUT THERE? Page 32: Copyright ©, American Chemical Society, reprinted by permission of the author.

A SURPRISE IN THE SOLAR SYSTEM, Page 37: *The Sciences,* April 1978 © 1978 by The New York Academy of Sciences.

HYPERACTIVE CHILDREN, Page 44: Adapted from U.S. Department of Health, Education, and Welfare publication.

SLEEP AND THE ELDERLY, Page 49: Reprinted from *Science News,* the weekly news magazine of science, copyright 1978 by Science Service, Inc.

FIRST BORNS MAY BE BRIGHTER, Page 54: Adapted from U.S. Department of Health, Education, and Welfare publication.

COLD HANDS, WARM HEART, Page 59: Reprinted from *Psychology Today* Magazine, copyright © 1978 Ziff-Davis Publishing Company.

THE ECOLOGY OF DEAD TREES, Page 71: Copyright 1978 by the National Wildlife Federation. Reprinted from the June-July issue of *National Wildlife* Magazine.

THE DUTCH ELM DISEASE, Page 75: Reprinted from the January 1979 issue of *American Forests* Magazine by permission of the author.

BIOLOGICAL CONTROL OF INSECTS, Page 85: This article first appeared in *Horticulture* which was published by the Massachusetts Horticultural Society in January 1978.

NEW COMPUTER MEMORIES, Page 99: This article originally appeared in the June 5, 1978 issue of *Fortune* Magazine under the title ''New Technology Scrambles the Memory Market.''

COMPUTER LOGIC, Page 105: Reprinted from the August 1978 issue of *Science Digest* by permission of the author.

MATH ANXIETY, Page 110: Adapted from U.S. Department of Health, Education, and Welfare publication.

HURRICANES, Page 118: Reprinted by permission from *THE CHRISTIAN SCIENCE MONITOR* © 1978 The Christian Science Publishing Society. All rights reserved.

TSUNAMI! Page 121: Reprinted from *Science* Volume 200, pages 521–522, 5 May 1978. Copyright 1978 by the American Association for the Advancement of Science.

CAN ANIMALS ANTICIPATE EARTHQUAKES? Page 125: Reprinted with permission from *Natural History* Magazine, November 1977. Copyright © The American Museum of Natural History, 1977.

YOU AND THE WEATHER, Page 131: Reprinted with permission of the author from *NOAA* Magazine, October 1976.

BIOMASS, Page 140: Reprinted from *Science News,* the weekly news magazine of science, copyright 1978 by Science Service, Inc.

THE ENERGY PICTURE: 1985 TO 2000, Page 145: Reprinted from *Science* Volume 203, pages 233–239, 19 January 1979. Copyright 1979 by the American Association for the Advancement of Science.

HOMEMADE HEAT, Page 157: Reprinted from the September 1978 issue of *American Forests,* magazine of the American Forestry Association, 1319 18th Street, N.W., Washington, D.C. 20036.

ACID RAIN UPDATE, Page 170: Reprinted by permission from *National Parks & Conservation Magazine,* October 1978. Copyright © 1978 by National Parks and Conservation Association.

WHAT HAPPENED TO THE ENDANGERED SPECIES? Page 178: © 1978/79 by The New York Times Company. Reprinted by permission.

LOVE CANAL, U.S.A., Page 185: Copyright © 1979 by Michael H. Brown. All rights reserved. From the forthcoming book on chemical landfills by Michael H. Brown to be published by Pantheon, a division of Random House, Inc.

PAIN, Page 198: Reprinted by permission of the author from the February 1979 issue of *OMNI.*

FOODS THAT BLOCK CANCER, Page 203: © 1979 by The New York Times Company. Reprinted by permission.

OBESITY, Page 206: © 1979 by The New York Times Company. Reprinted by permission.

ALCOHOL AND BIRTH DEFECTS, Page 210: Reprinted from the May 1978 issue of *FDA Consumer,* the official magazine of the U.S. Food and Drug Administration.